To
Gertrude

Preface

Recent years have brought amazing changes in statistics. New theory and new practice continually have come into being. Demands for new experimental designs never cease. To serve the needs of users of statistics in biology, I have included in this 5th edition a selection of the newer devices which promise to be most useful to the experimenter.

As in earlier editions, two groups of readers are envisioned—beginners and research workers in biology. For the first group, the earlier parts of all chapters are kept simple, with somewhat elaborate explanations. The guideposts are retained in the text to direct them into the more elementary parts of the subject. Also there is the short course outlined on the page preceding the Table of Contents. To meet the needs of the second group, I have collected the methods which have been found most useful in my practice as consultant in experimental statistics. The meanings and limitations of the designs are stressed. Computations are explained so that they may be done by a clerk. References are given as guides to more advanced reading. Some of this material, occupying the latter portions of the chapters, is of necessity treated concisely.

The most notable change in this edition is the presentation of factorial experiments in chapter 12. Here I have gathered and augmented the pertinent methods formerly scattered throughout the book. I believe this will be found helpful to the many research workers who are using factorial arrangements of their treatments but who are not capitalizing on all the information contained in such experiments.

Since heavy calculations tend to distract attention from the purpose of statistics, I have tried, especially in the earlier parts of the chapters, to lighten the burden of computation and to keep attention centered on the biological objectives.

Additional progress is made in diverting emphasis from tests of significance to point and interval estimates. How far this trend will continue remains to be seen. At present it is clear that the estimate is often more informative than the test.

A few of the multitudinous non-parametric tests are introduced for the information of the reader. Their various uses are discussed and their results compared with those of the more usual procedures.

It has seemed desirable to alter some of the notation and terminology in order to make it easier for the student to transfer his reading to current journals. Many of the changes serve to emphasize the distinction between population parameters and sample statistics. But always I have aimed at relieving the nonmathematical reader of the necessity of depending on algebraic symbolism. Explanations and directions for calculation can be followed without reference to the formulas.

I am happy to present the newly written chapter 17 on "Design and Analysis of Samplings," prepared by Professor William G. Cochran, a recognized authority on this rapidly developing subject. Professor Cochran has chosen illustrative material suitable to the biological orientation of this text.

For their generous permission to reprint tables, I am indebted to Sir Ronald Fisher and his publishers, Oliver and Boyd of Edinburgh; to Maxine Merrington, Catherine M. Thompson, Joyce M. May, and E. Lord whose work was published by Dr. E. S. Pearson, Editor of Biometrika; and to Bernard Ostle and his publishers, The Iowa State University Press.

Without the unfailing interest and cooperation of my colleagues, both in statistics and biology, this book could not have been written. The statisticians have been ready with advice and constructive criticism. The experimenters have contributed technical information in their fields and have allowed me free use of their data. If I have succeeded in reporting them adequately, their experiences should be helpful to others engaged in research.

GEORGE W. SNEDECOR

A SHORT COURSE IN THE ELEMENTS OF
STATISTICAL METHOD

Table of Contents

STATISTICAL METHODS

STATISTICAL METHODS

APPLIED TO EXPERIMENTS IN AGRICULTURE AND BIOLOGY

by GEORGE W. SNEDECOR

Former Professor of Statistics
and Director, Statistical Laboratory
Iowa State University

With Chapter 17 on Sampling by

WILLIAM G. COCHRAN

Professor of Statistics
Harvard University

The Iowa State University Press, *Ames*, Iowa, U.S.A.

First edition, 1937
Second edition, 1938
Third edition, 1940
Fourth edition, 1946

Second printing, 1946
Third printing, 1948
Fourth printing, 1950
Fifth printing, 1953
Sixth printing, 1955
Seventh printing, 1955

Fifth edition, 1956

Second printing, 1957
Third printing, 1959
Fourth printing, 1961
Fifth printing, 1962
Sixth printing, 1964
Seventh printing, 1965
Eighth printing, 1966
Ninth printing, 1966

Library of Congress Catalog Card Number: 56-7378

CHAPTER 1

Sampling of Attributes. Binomial Distribution

1.1—Sampling. Everybody these days is affected by sampling. Public opinion polls are reported and discussed in the newspapers. Quality control is widely used to maintain uniformity in manufactured products. Surveys of consumer needs and desires help to guide both production and marketing. Even the Census Bureau has a well-developed sampling program which may, in time, replace much of the attempted complete enumeration coming every 10 years.

Less in the public eye but no less valuable are numerous other practical samplings. A dozen rats, for example, may disclose useful facts about a population that runs into millions. A carload of coal is accepted or rejected on the evidence gained from testing only a few pounds. The physician makes inferences about the patient's blood through examination of a single drop. This practice of sampling, so widespread and on which so much depends, deserves more than passing notice.

Sampling may be far-flung, as in the effort to learn how an election will go, or it may be confined to a few experimental plots or to the field of a microscope. Most of this book, excepting a final chapter, is devoted to the experimental type of sampling, moderate in extent, where environmental conditions are more or less controlled.

1.2—The twin problems of sampling. A *sample* consists of a small collection from some larger aggregate about which we wish information. The sample is examined and the facts about it learned. Based on these facts, the problem is to make correct inferences about the aggregate or *population*. It is the sample that we observe, but it is the population which we seek to know.

This would be no problem were it not for ever-present variation. If all individuals were alike, a sample consisting of a single one would give complete information about the population. Fortunately there is endless variety among individuals as well as in their environments. A consequence is that successive samples are usually different. Clearly the facts observed in a sample cannot be taken as facts about the population. Our job then is to reach appropriate conclusions about the population despite sampling variation.

But not every sample contains information about the population sampled. Suppose the objective of an experimental sampling is to determine the growth rate in a population of young mice fed a new diet. Ten of the animals are put in a cage for the experiment. But the cage gets located in a cold draught or in a dark corner. Or it may be that an unnoticed infection spreads among the mice in the cage. If such things happen, the growth rate in the sample may give no worth-while information about that in the population of normal mice. Again, suppose an interviewer in an opinion poll picks only families among his friends whom he thinks it will be pleasant to visit. His sample may not at all represent the opinions of the population. This brings us to a second problem: to collect the sample in such wise that the sought-for information is contained in it.

So we are confronted with the twin problems of the investigator: to design and conduct his sampling so that it shall be representative of the population; then, having studied the sample, to make correct inferences about the sampled population.

1.3—A sample of farm facts. Point and interval estimates. In 1950 the U.S.D.A. Division of Cereal and Forage Insect Investigations, cooperating with the Iowa Agricultural Experiment Station, conducted an extensive sampling in Boone County, Iowa, to learn about the interrelation of factors affecting control of the European corn borer (16).* One objective of the project was to determine the extent of spraying or dusting for control of the insects. To this end a random sample of 100 farmers were interviewed; 23 of them said they applied the treatment to their corn fields. Such are the facts of the sample.

What *inferences* can be made about the population of 2,300 Boone County farmers? There are two of them. The first is described as a *point estimate*, while the second is called an *interval estimate*.

1. The *point estimate* of the fraction of farmers who sprayed is 23%, the same as the sample ratio; that is, an estimated 23% of Boone County farmers sprayed their corn fields in 1950. This may be looked upon as an average of the numbers of farmers per hundred who sprayed. From the actual count of sprayers in a single hundred farmers it is inferred that the average number of sprayers in all possible samples of 100 is 23.

This sample-to-population inference is usually taken for granted. Most people pass without a thought from the sample fact to this inference about the population. Logically, the two concepts are distinct. Indeed, the inference may not be true unless the sample has been taken competently. It is wise to examine the procedure of the sampling before attributing to the population the percentage reported in a sample.

---

* Reference 16 at the end of the chapter.

2. An *interval estimate* of the point is made by use of table 1.3.1. In the first part of the table, indicated by 95% in the heading, look across the top line to the sample size of 100, then down the left-hand column to the number (or frequency) observed, 23 farmers. At the intersection of the column and line you will find the figures 15 and 32. The meaning is this; one may be confident that the true percentage in the sampled population lies in the interval from 15% to 32%. This interval estimate is called the *confidence interval*. The nature of our confidence will be explained below.

In summary: based on a random sample, we said first that our estimate of the percentage of sprayers in Boone County was 23%, but we gave no indication of the amount by which the estimate might be in error. Next we asserted confidently that the true percentage was not farther from our point estimate, 23%, than 8 percentage points below or 9 above.

Since these concepts lie at the foundation of sampling theory, let us illustrate them in another fashion. Imagine a bin filled with beans, some white and some colored, thoroughly mixed. Dip out a scoopful of them at random, count the number of each color and calculate the percentage of white, say 40%. Now this is not only a count of the percentage of white beans in the sample but it is an estimate of the fraction of white beans in the bin. How close an estimate is it? That is where the second inference comes in. If there were 250 beans in the scoop, we look at the table and say with confidence that the percentage of white beans in the bin is between 34% and 46%.

So far we have given no measure of the amount of confidence which can be placed in the second inference. The table heading is "95% Confidence Interval," indicating a degree of confidence that can be described as follows: If the sampling is repeated indefinitely, each sample leading to a new confidence interval (that is, to a new interval estimate), then in 95% of the samples the interval will cover the true population percentage. Or it may be said that if one makes a practice of sampling and if for each sample he states that the population percentage lies within the corresponding confidence interval, about 95% of his statements will be correct. Other and briefer descriptions will be proposed later. Usually it is sufficient to say merely that you are confident that the interval estimate covers the population fraction.

If you feel unsafe in making the second inference with the chance of being wrong in 5% of your statements, you may use the second part of the table, "99% Confidence Interval." For the Boone County sampling the interval widens to 13%–35%. If one says that the population percentage lies within these limits, he will be right unless a one-in-a-hundred chance has occurred in the sampling.

If the size of the population is known, as it is in the case of Boone County farmers, the point and interval estimates can be *expanded* from percentages to numbers of individuals. Thus we estimate the number of sprayers in Boone County in 1950 as $(0.23)(2,300) = 529$ farmers. In the

TABLE 1.3.1

95% CONFIDENCE INTERVAL (PER CENT) FOR BINOMIAL DISTRIBUTION

Number Observed f	Size of Sample, n 10	15	20	30	50	100	Fraction Observed f/n	Size of Sample 250	1000
0	0 31	0 22	0 17	0 12	0 07	0 4	.00	0 1	0 0
1	0 45	0 32	0 25	0 17	0 11	0 5	.01	0 4	0 2
2	3 56	2 40	1 31	1 22	0 14	0 7	.02	1 5	1 3
3	7 65	4 48	3 38	2 27	1 17	1 8	.03	1 6	2 4
4	12 74	8 55	6 44	4 31	2 19	1 10	.04	2 7	3 5
5	19 81	12 62	9 49	6 35	3 22	2 11	.05	3 9	4 7
6	26 88	16 68	12 54	8 39	5 24	2 12	.06	3 10	5 8
7	35 93	21 73	15 59	10 43	6 27	3 14	.07	4 11	6 9
8	44 97	27 79	19 64	12 46	7 29	4 15	.08	5 12	6 10
9	55 100	32 84	23 68	15 50	9 31	4 16	.09	6 13	7 11
10	69 100	38 88	27 73	17 53	10 34	5 18	.10	7 14	8 12
11		45 92	32 77	20 56	12 36	5 19	.11	7 16	9 13
12		52 96	36 81	23 60	13 38	6 20	.12	8 17	10 14
13		60 98	41 85	25 63	15 41	7 21	.13	9 18	11 15
14		68 100	46 88	28 66	16 43	8 22	.14	10 19	12 16
15		78 100	51 91	31 69	18 44	9 24	.15	10 20	13 17
16			56 94	34 72	20 46	9 25	.16	11 21	14 18
17			62 97	37 75	21 48	10 26	.17	12 22	15 19
18			69 99	40 77	23 50	11 27	.18	13 23	16 21
19			75 100	44 80	25 53	12 28	.19	14 24	17 22
20			83 100	47 83	27 55	13 29	.20	15 26	18 23
21				50 85	28 57	14 30	.21	16 27	19 24
22				54 88	30 59	14 31	.22	17 28	19 25
23				57 90	32 61	15 32	.23	18 29	20 26
24				61 92	34 63	16 33	.24	19 30	21 27
25				65 94	36 64	17 35	.25	20 31	22 28
26				69 96	37 66	18 36	.26	20 32	23 29
27				73 98	39 68	19 37	.27	21 33	24 30
28				78 99	41 70	19 38	.28	22 34	25 31
29				83 100	43 72	20 39	.29	23 35	26 32
30				88 100	45 73	21 40	.30	24 36	27 33
31					47 75	22 41	.31	25 37	28 34
32					50 77	23 42	.32	26 38	29 35
33					52 79	24 43	.33	27 39	30 36
34					54 80	25 44	.34	28 40	31 37
35					56 82	26 45	.35	29 41	32 38
36					57 84	27 46	.36	30 42	33 39
37					59 85	28 47	.37	31 43	34 40
38					62 87	28 48	.38	32 44	35 41
39					64 88	29 49	.39	33 45	36 42
40					66 90	30 50	.40	34 46	37 43
41					69 91	31 51	.41	35 47	38 44
42					71 93	32 52	.42	36 48	39 45
43					73 94	33 53	.43	37 49	40 46
44					76 95	34 54	.44	38 50	41 47
45					78 97	35 55	.45	39 51	42 48
46					81 98	36 56	.46	40 52	43 49
47					83 99	37 57	.47	41 53	44 50
48					86 100	38 58	.48	42 54	45 51
49					89 100	39 59	.49	43 55	46 52
50					93 100	40 60	.50	44 56	47 53
					*			†	†

* If f exceeds 50, read 100 − f = number observed and subtract each confidence limit from 100.

† If f/n exceeds 0.50, read 1.00 − f/n = fraction observed and subtract each confidence limit from 100.

TABLE 1.3.1—(*Continued*)
99% CONFIDENCE INTERVAL (PER CENT) FOR BINOMIAL DISTRIBUTION

Number Observed f	10		15		20		30		50		100		Fraction Observed f/n	250		1000	
0	0	41	0	30	0	23	0	16	0	10	0	5	.00	0	2	0	1
1	0	54	0	40	0	32	0	22	0	14	0	7	.01	0	5	0	2
2	1	65	1	49	1	39	0	28	0	17	0	9	.02	1	6	1	3
3	4	74	2	56	2	45	1	32	1	20	0	10	.03	1	7	2	4
4	8	81	5	63	4	51	3	36	1	23	1	12	.04	2	9	3	6
5	13	87	8	69	6	56	4	40	2	26	1	13	.05	2	10	3	7
6	19	92	12	74	8	61	6	44	3	29	2	14	.06	3	11	4	8
7	26	96	16	79	11	66	8	48	4	31	2	16	.07	3	13	5	9
8	35	99	21	84	15	70	10	52	6	33	3	17	.08	4	14	6	10
9	46	100	26	88	18	74	12	55	7	36	3	18	.09	5	15	7	12
10	59	100	31	92	22	78	14	58	8	38	4	19	.10	6	16	8	13
11			37	95	26	82	16	62	10	40	4	20	.11	6	17	9	14
12			44	98	30	85	18	65	11	43	5	21	.12	7	18	9	15
13			51	99	34	89	21	68	12	45	6	23	.13	8	19	10	16
14			60	100	39	92	24	71	14	47	6	24	.14	9	20	11	17
15			70	100	44	94	26	74	15	49	7	26	.15	9	22	12	18
16					49	96	29	76	17	51	8	27	.16	10	23	13	19
17					55	98	32	79	18	53	9	29	.17	11	24	14	20
18					61	99	35	82	20	55	9	30	.18	12	25	15	21
19					68	100	38	84	21	57	10	31	.19	13	26	16	22
20					77	100	42	86	23	59	11	32	.20	14	27	17	23
21							45	88	24	61	12	33	.21	15	28	18	24
22							48	90	26	63	12	34	.22	16	30	19	26
23							52	92	28	65	13	35	.23	17	31	20	27
24							56	94	29	67	14	36	.24	18	32	21	28
25							60	96	31	69	15	38	.25	18	33	22	29
26							64	97	33	71	16	39	.26	19	34	22	30
27							68	99	35	72	16	40	.27	20	35	23	31
28							72	100	37	74	17	41	.28	21	36	24	32
29							78	100	39	76	18	42	.29	22	37	25	33
30							84	100	41	77	19	43	.30	23	38	26	34
31									43	79	20	44	.31	24	39	27	35
32									45	80	21	45	.32	25	40	28	36
33									47	82	21	46	.33	26	41	29	37
34									49	83	22	47	.34	26	42	30	38
35									51	85	23	48	.35	27	43	31	39
36									53	86	24	49	.36	28	44	32	40
37									55	88	25	50	.37	29	45	33	41
38									57	89	26	51	.38	30	46	34	42
39									60	90	27	52	.39	31	47	35	43
40									62	92	28	53	.40	32	48	36	44
41									64	93	29	54	.41	33	50	37	45
42									67	94	29	55	.42	34	51	38	46
43									69	96	30	56	.43	35	52	39	47
44									71	97	31	57	.44	36	53	40	48
45									74	98	32	58	.45	37	54	41	49
46									77	99	33	59	.46	38	55	42	50
47									80	99	34	60	.47	39	55	43	51
48									83	100	35	61	.48	40	56	44	52
49									86	100	36	62	.49	41	57	45	53
50									90	100	37	63	.50	42	58	46	54
												*		†		†	

* If f exceeds 50, read $100 - f$ = number observed and subtract each confidence limit from 100.

† If f/n exceeds 0.50, read $1.00 - f/n$ = fraction observed and subtract each confidence limit from 100.

same way the 95% confidence interval is from 345 to 736 farmers who spray.

In this brief prevue I have displayed a goodly portion of the wares that the statistician has to offer: the sampling of populations, examination of the facts turned up by the sample, and, based on these facts, inferences about the sampled population. Before going further, you may clarify your thinking by working a few examples.

You will find that examples form an essential part of my presentation of statistics. In each list they are graded so that you may start with the easier. It is suggested that a few in each group be worked after the first reading of the text, reserving the more difficult until experience is enlarged. It is my firmly grounded belief that statistics cannot be mastered without this or similar practice.

EXAMPLE 1.3.1—Of a sample of 100 seeds drawn at random from a bag of uniformly mixed bluegrass seeds, 92 germinated in a standard test. The seed analyst wishes to make a statement about the proportion of seeds in the bag that will germinate under similar conditions, and he is willing to run the risk of only one per hundred that his sample has misled him. What may he say? Ans. Between 83% and 97% will germinate. Hint: look in the table for $100 - 92 = 8\%$.

EXAMPLE 1.3.2—If the seed analyst in the foregoing example had tested 1,000 seeds instead of 100 and had found only 8% ungerminated, what statement might he have made with 99:1 odds? Ans. Between 90% and 94% will germinate.

EXAMPLE 1.3.3—An investigator making a nation-wide survey interviewed 115 women over 40 years of age from the lower middle economic level in rural areas of middle western states. Forty-six of them had listened to a certain radio program three or more times during the preceding month. Assuming random sampling, what statement can be made about the population fraction of such women listening, using the 99% confidence interval? Ans. Approximately, between 28.4% and 52.5% listen. You will have to interpolate these values in the table.

EXAMPLE 1.3.4—A sampler of public opinion asked 50 men to express their preferences between candidates A and B. Twenty preferred A. Assuming random sampling from a population of 5,000, the sampler stated that between 1,150 and 2,950 men of the population preferred A. What confidence interval was he using? Ans. 99%.

EXAMPLE 1.3.5—In a random sample from a farming population, 86% expressed approval of a certain agricultural program. On the basis of this sample the statistician asserted that unless a one-in-twenty chance had come off the percentage of those favorable in the sampled population was between 81% and 90%. What was the size of the sample? Ans. 250.

EXAMPLE 1.3.6—If you guess that in a certain population between 25% and 75% of the housewives own a specified appliance, and if you wish to draw a sample that will, at the 95% confidence level, yield an estimate differing by not more than 6 from the correct percentage, about how large a sample must you take? Ans. 250.

EXAMPLE 1.3.7—If you draw a sample properly, then make a statement about the population ratio, the statement will be either right or wrong but you will not know which. Do you see clearly how chance enters into the making of the statement?

EXAMPLE 1.3.8—After the survey of a certain underprivileged community it was reported (12) that among 978 children less than age 16, 54.4% were girls. Does the 95% confidence interval include a reasonable sex ratio for this group?

EXAMPLE 1.3.9—If in the sample of 100 Boone County farmers none had sprayed, what 95% confidence statement would you make about the farmers in the county? Ans. Between none and 4% sprayed. But suppose all the farmers in the sample were sprayers, what is the 99% confidence interval? Ans. 95% – 100%.

1.4—Definitions and discussions. Size of sample. I have rushed you along through the first three sections, thinking you might enjoy a quick glimpse into the ideas and utility of statistics. Some points need considerable clarification. A few of them will be discussed in this section; others will come up later.

Part of the heading of this chapter is "Sampling of Attributes." So far we have considered such diverse attributes as spraying of corn fields, germination of seed, approval of an agricultural program, and interest in a radio program. The possession or lack of an attribute distinguishes the two classes of individuals making up the populations we have been studying. The record of the sampling consists of the numbers of individuals found to have or lack the attribute under investigation. I call these records *enumeration data* in distinction from records of measurements of such variables as height or age. The theory and methods for *measurement data* will be developed later, beginning with Chapter 2.

For a sample to contain reliable information about the population each member of the sample must be selected at *random*. Random selection implies that every individual in the population has a known probability of appearing in the sample. This cannot be left to the judgment of the sampler; if he exercises any choice, then the probability of his selection is unknown and the theory flies out the window.

The statement about randomness leads to a more specific definition of the word *population*. It may now be said that the population is that aggregate of which every member has a known probability of appearing in the sample.

There are two common devices used to attain randomness: the population itself may be thoroughly mixed, or else the choice of the sample may be left to some mechanical process beyond the control of the sampler. A uniformly mixed population is illustrated by the mascerating and blending of food or other chemical products before the sample is taken, or by a naturally mixed aggregate such as the blood stream. The second device is the more common. In the Boone County sampling a township plat book was available; it showed the location of every farm in the county. Each was numbered so that a random sample could have been drawn by mixing the numbers in a box, then having a hundred of them drawn by a blindfolded person. Actually, the samplers used a scheme known as *stratified random sampling*. From the farms in each township they drew a random sample whose size was proportional to the number of farms in that area. The chief advantage of this was to spread the sample rather uniformly over the county, retaining the principle of randomness within each township. The statistical methods for stratified samples are presented in Chapter 17. The conclusions are only slightly altered by considering the sample completely random.

Randomness in sampling is perhaps never quite attained in practice. It is nevertheless the mathematical model on which much statistical theory rests, and since the theory must be used in drawing conclusions from work-a-day samplings, it is to the interest of the investigator to approximate, as closely as feasible, the ideal conditions. The better the approximation, the more nearly correct will be the inferences drawn.

The question most often asked by experimenters and other designers of samplings is, "How large a sample must I take?" The answers that may be given in various situations are not easy and always involve the element of chance. However, at appropriate places in this text (see Index) attempts will be made to clarify the problems involved. You doubtless noticed the method of attack proposed in example 1.3.6, where the confidence interval and a guess about the population percentage were proposed as data. Perhaps you noticed, also, that the method doesn't work so well in the upper and left-hand portions of the table; not only do the confidence limits change rapidly with the unknown f, but they are not equally spaced above and below this fraction. Despite these shortcomings of the table, approximations can usually be got from it close enough for practical purposes. It is futile to attempt exact estimates of sample size because unpredictable sampling variation will upset the best-laid plans. At the present stage my advice is to read the table as accurately as you may, then take a somewhat larger sample if you can afford it. If you cannot afford so large a sample and if you cannot tolerate a larger confidence interval, you should refrain from the sampling and so avoid wasting time and money.

Concerning the interval estimate, two points need emphasis. First, the confidence statement is a statement about the population ratio, *not about the ratio in other samples that might be drawn.* Second, the uncertainty involved is associated with the sampling process itself. Each sample specifies an interval estimate. Whether or not the interval happens to include the fixed population ratio, this is a hazard of the process. Theoretically, the 0.95 confidence intervals are determined so that 95% of them will cover the true value.

It is helpful to observe this: before a sample is drawn, one can specify the *probability* of the truth of his prospective confidence statement. He can say, "I expect to take a random sample and to make an interval estimate from it. The probability is 0.95 that the interval will cover the population fraction." After the sample is drawn, when the truth or falsity of the confidence statement is fixed, an assertion about probability is meaningless.

More than two kinds of individuals are often present in populations. An illustration is found in sampling opinions or preferences where three categories instead of two are usually encountered: "yes," "no," and "don't know." Again, in populations segregating according to inherited characteristics, more than two kinds of progeny may be expected. In such situations, a confidence statement about every class requires the multinomial distribution which is not presented in this book. But a complete set of statements is not often needed. For example, it may be only one reply for which a confidence interval is desired, "yes," perhaps. In that case, the correct interval is estimated by separating "yes" from all other answers, making the two categories, "yes" and "not yes." The interval estimate is based on the total sample size and the number of answers, "yes".

1.5—An exercise in sampling. Whenever I draw samples from a known population, I am amazed at the capricious way in which the items turn up. It is a salutary discipline for an experimenter or enumerator occasionally to observe the laws of chance in action lest he become too confident of his professional samplings. Drawing marbles from an urn or cards from a pack, tossing coins, and throwing dice are the classical methods of obtaining samples. Formerly I asked my students to collect their samples by drawing marked or numbered beans from a bag, but the more modern method is to use a table of random numbers such as table 1.5.1. This table contains 10,000 digits jumbled together presumably in random fashion, the 5 x 5 blocks serving merely to facilitate reading. There are 100 rows and 100 columns, each numbered from 00 to 99. Instead of examining peas to learn if they are wrinkled or smooth, or instead of asking people to vote "Yes" or "No," you can draw a random sample of digits from this table and observe whether each is odd or even. Since the digits are supposed to be thoroughly mixed, with no particular order or groupings, any sequence of them may be considered random; so, begin at any point in the table and count the number of odd digits in a sample of some predetermined size. For example, suppose you decide on 50 digits as the sample size, and elect to start at row 31, column 17. You find

752   54450   19031   . . .

Read on to the end of this row, then return to the beginning of row 32 and continue till 50 digits have been surveyed, ending with

33851   44

In this particular sample you will count 23 odd digits; that is, 46% of the sample of 50 are odd.

Three ways of introducing elements of chance into your sampling will decrease the likelihood of duplicating the drawings of others. (i) Start at a randomly selected point for each sample. A good way to do this is to place your pencil aimlessly on some digit in the table, then use this and the subsequent three digits to fix the initial point of your first sample. As an example, suppose your pencil point picks out 2 in row 80, column 84. Let this with the three digits following, 2061, specify row 20, column 61 as the point to begin sample number one. For the second sample, start at a point fixed by the first four (or last four or any other convenient four)

TABLE 1.5.1
TEN THOUSAND RANDOMLY ASSORTED DIGITS

	00–04	05–09	10–14	15–19	20–24	25–29	30–34	35–39	40–44	45–49
00	54463	22662	65905	70639	79365	67382	29085	69831	47058	08186
01	15389	85205	18850	39226	42249	90669	96325	23248	60933	26927
02	85941	40756	82414	02015	13858	78030	16269	65978	01385	15345
03	61149	69440	11286	88218	58925	03638	52862	62733	33451	77455
04	05219	81619	10651	67079	92511	59888	84502	72095	83463	75577
05	41417	98326	87719	92294	46614	50948	64886	20002	97365	30976
06	28357	94070	20652	35774	16249	75019	21145	05217	47286	76305
07	17783	00015	10806	83091	91530	36466	39981	62481	49177	75779
08	40950	84820	29881	85966	62800	70326	84740	62660	77379	90279
09	82995	64157	66164	41180	10089	41757	78258	96488	88629	37231
10	96754	17676	55659	44105	47361	34833	86679	23930	53249	27083
11	34357	88040	53364	71726	45690	66334	60332	22554	90600	71113
12	06318	37403	49927	57715	50423	67372	63116	48888	21505	80182
13	62111	52820	07243	79931	89292	84767	85693	73947	22278	11551
14	47534	09243	67879	00544	23410	12740	02540	54440	32949	13491
15	98614	75993	84460	62846	59844	14922	48730	73443	48167	34770
16	24856	03648	44898	09351	98795	18644	39765	71058	90368	44104
17	96887	12479	80621	66223	86085	78285	02432	53342	42846	94771
18	90801	21472	42815	77408	37390	76766	52615	32141	30268	18106
19	55165	77312	83666	36028	28420	70219	81369	41943	47366	41067
20	75884	12952	84318	95108	72305	64620	91318	89872	45375	85436
21	16777	37116	58550	42958	21460	43910	01175	87894	81378	10620
22	46230	43877	80207	88877	89380	32992	91380	03164	98656	59337
23	42902	66892	46134	01432	94710	23474	20423	60137	60609	13119
24	81007	00333	39693	28039	10154	95425	39220	19774	31782	49037
25	68089	01122	51111	72373	06902	74373	96199	97017	41273	21546
26	20411	67081	89950	16944	93054	87687	96693	87236	77054	33848
27	58212	13160	06468	15718	82627	76999	05999	58680	96739	63700
28	70577	42866	24969	61210	76046	67699	42054	12696	93758	03283
29	94522	74358	71659	62038	79643	79169	44741	05437	39038	13163
30	42626	86819	85651	88678	17401	03252	99547	32404	17918	62880
31	16051	33763	57194	16752	54450	19031	58580	47629	54132	60631
32	08244	27647	33851	44705	94211	46716	11738	55784	95374	72655
33	59497	04392	09419	89964	51211	04894	72882	17805	21896	83864
34	97155	13428	40293	09985	58434	01412	69124	82171	59058	82859
35	98409	66162	95763	47420	20792	61527	20441	39435	11859	41567
36	45476	84882	65109	96597	25930	66790	65706	61203	53634	22557
37	89300	69700	50741	30329	11658	23166	05400	66669	48708	03887
38	50051	95137	91631	66315	91428	12275	24816	68091	71710	33258
39	31753	85178	31310	89642	98364	02306	24617	09609	83942	22716
40	79152	53829	77250	20190	56535	18760	69942	77448	33278	48805
41	44560	38750	83635	56540	64900	42912	13953	79149	18710	68618
42	68328	83378	63369	71381	39564	05615	42451	64559	97501	65747
43	46939	38689	58625	08342	30459	85863	20781	09284	26333	91777
44	83544	86141	15707	96256	23068	13782	08467	89469	93842	55349
45	91621	00881	04900	54224	46177	55309	17852	27491	89415	23466
46	91896	67126	04151	03795	59077	11848	12630	98375	52068	60142
47	55751	62515	21108	80830	02263	29303	37204	96926	30506	09808
48	85156	87689	95493	88842	00664	55017	55539	17771	69448	87530
49	07521	56898	12236	60277	39102	62315	12239	07105	11844	01117

TABLE 1.5.1—(*Continued*)

	50–54	55–59	60–64	65–69	70–74	75–79	80–84	85–89	90–94	95–99
00	59391	58030	52098	82718	87024	82848	04190	96574	90464	29065
01	99567	76364	77204	04615	27062	96621	43918	01896	83991	51141
02	10363	97518	51400	25670	98342	61891	27101	37855	06235	33316
03	86859	19558	64432	16706	99612	59798	32803	67708	15297	28612
04	11258	24591	36863	55368	31721	94335	34936	02566	80972	08188
05	95068	88628	35911	14530	33020	80428	39936	31855	34334	64865
06	54463	47237	73800	91017	36239	71824	83671	39892	60518	37092
07	16874	62677	57412	13215	31389	62233	80827	73917	82802	84420
08	92494	63157	76593	91316	03505	72389	96363	52887	01087	66091
09	15669	56689	35682	40844	53256	81872	35213	09840	34471	74441
10	99116	75486	84989	23476	52967	67104	39495	39100	17217	74073
11	15696	10703	65178	90637	63110	17622	53988	71087	84148	11670
12	97720	15369	51269	69620	03388	13699	33423	67453	43269	56720
13	11666	13841	71681	98000	35979	39719	81899	07449	47985	46967
14	71628	73130	78783	75691	41632	09847	61547	18707	85489	69944
15	40501	51089	99943	91843	41995	88931	73631	69361	05375	15417
16	22518	55576	98215	82068	10798	86211	36584	67466	69373	40054
17	75112	30485	62173	02132	14878	92879	22281	16783	86352	00077
18	80327	02671	98191	84342	90813	49268	95441	15496	20168	09271
19	60251	45548	02146	05597	48228	81366	34598	72856	66762	17002
20	57430	82270	10421	05540	43648	75888	66049	21511	47676	33444
21	73528	39559	34434	88596	54086	71693	43132	14414	79949	85193
22	25991	65959	70769	64721	86413	33475	42740	06175	82758	66248
23	78388	16638	09134	59880	63806	48472	39318	35434	24057	74739
24	12477	09965	96657	57994	59439	76330	24596	77515	09577	91871
25	83266	32883	42451	15579	38155	29793	40914	65990	16255	17777
26	76970	80876	10237	39515	79152	74798	39357	09054	73579	92359
27	37074	65198	44785	68624	98336	84481	97610	78735	46703	98265
28	83712	06514	30101	78295	54656	85417	43189	60048	72781	72606
29	20287	56862	69727	94443	64936	08366	27227	05158	50326	59566
30	74261	32592	86538	27041	65172	85532	07571	80609	39285	65340
31	64081	49863	08478	96001	18888	14810	70545	89755	59064	07210
32	05617	75818	47750	67814	29575	10526	66192	44464	27058	40467
33	26793	74951	95466	74307	13330	42664	85515	20632	05497	33625
34	65988	72850	48737	54719	52056	01596	03845	35067	03134	70322
35	27366	42271	44300	73399	21105	03280	73457	43093	05192	48657
36	56760	10909	98147	34736	33863	95256	12731	66598	50771	83665
37	72880	43338	93643	58904	59543	23943	11231	83268	65938	81581
38	77888	38100	03062	58103	47961	83841	25878	23746	55903	44115
39	28440	07819	21580	51459	47971	29882	13990	29226	23608	15873
40	63525	94441	77033	12147	51054	49955	58312	76923	96071	05813
41	47606	93410	16359	89033	89696	47231	64498	31776	05383	39902
42	52669	45030	96279	14709	52372	87832	02735	50803	72744	88208
43	16738	60159	07425	62369	07515	82721	37875	71153	21315	00132
44	59348	11695	45751	15865	74739	05572	32688	20271	65128	14551
45	12900	71775	29845	60774	94924	21810	38636	33717	67598	82521
46	75086	23537	49939	33595	13484	97588	28617	17979	70749	35234
47	99495	51434	29181	09993	38190	42553	68922	52125	91077	40197
48	26075	31671	45386	36583	93459	48599	52022	41330	60651	91321
49	13636	93596	23377	51133	95126	61496	42474	45141	46660	42338

TABLE 1.5.1—(*Continued*)

	00–04	05–09	10–14	15–19	20–24	25–29	30–34	35–39	40–44	45–49
50	64249	63664	39652	40646	97306	31741	07294	84149	46797	82487
51	26538	44249	04050	48174	65570	44072	40192	51153	11397	58212
52	05845	00512	78630	55328	18116	69296	91705	86224	29503	57071
53	74897	68373	67359	51014	33510	83048	17056	72506	82949	54600
54	20872	54570	35017	88132	25730	22626	86723	91691	13191	77212
55	31432	96156	89177	75541	81355	24480	77243	76690	42507	84362
56	66890	61505	01240	00660	05873	13568	76082	79172	57913	93448
57	48194	57790	79970	33106	86904	48119	52503	24130	72824	21627
58	11303	87118	81471	52936	08555	28420	49416	44448	04269	27029
59	54374	57325	16947	45356	78371	10563	97191	53798	12693	27928
60	64852	34421	61046	90849	13966	39810	42699	21753	76192	10508
61	16309	20384	09491	91588	97720	89846	30376	76970	23063	35894
62	42587	37065	24526	72602	57589	98131	37292	05967	26002	51945
63	40177	98590	97161	41682	84533	67588	62036	49967	01990	72308
64	82309	76128	93965	26743	24141	04838	40254	26065	07938	76236
65	79788	68243	59732	04257	27084	14743	17520	95401	55811	76099
66	40538	79000	89559	25026	42274	23489	34502	75508	06059	86682
67	64016	73598	18609	73150	62463	33102	45205	87440	96767	67042
68	49767	12691	17903	93871	99721	79109	09425	26904	07419	76013
69	76974	55108	29795	08404	82684	00497	51126	79935	57450	55671
70	23854	08480	85983	96025	50117	64610	99425	62291	86943	21541
71	68973	70551	25098	78033	98573	79848	31778	29555	61446	23037
72	36444	93600	65350	14971	25325	00427	52073	64280	18847	24768
73	03003	87800	07391	11594	21196	00781	32550	57158	58887	73041
74	17540	26188	³6647	78386	04558	61463	57842	90382	77019	24210
75	38916	55809	47982	41968	69760	79422	80154	91486	19180	15100
76	64288	19843	69122	42502	48508	28820	59933	72998	99942	10515
77	86809	51564	38040	39418	49915	19000	58050	16899	79952	57849
78	99800	99566	14742	05028	30033	94889	53381	23656	75787	59223
79	92345	31890	95712	08279	91794	94068	49337	88674	35355	12267
80	90363	65162	32245	82279	79256	80834	06088	99462	56705	06118
81	64437	32242	48431	04835	39070	59702	31508	60935	22390	52246
82	91714	53662	28373	34333	55791	74758	51144	18827	10704	76803
83	20902	17646	31391	31459	33315	03444	55743	74701	58851	27427
84	12217	86007	70371	52281	14510	76094	96579	54853	78339	20839
85	45177	02863	42307	53571	22532	74921	17735	42201	80540	54721
86	28325	90814	08804	52746	47913	54577	47525	77705	95330	21866
87	29019	28776	56116	54791	64604	08815	46049	71186	34650	14994
88	84979	81353	56219	67062	26146	82567	33122	14124	46240	92973
89	50371	26347	48513	63915	11158	25563	91915	18431	92978	11591
90	53422	06825	69711	67950	64716	18003	49581	45378	99878	61130
91	67453	35651	89316	41620	32048	70225	47597	33137	31443	51445
92	07294	85353	74819	23445	68237	07202	99515	62282	53809	26685
93	79544	00302	45338	16015	66613	88968	14595	63836	77716	79596
94	64144	85442	82060	46471	24162	39500	87351	36637	42833	71875
95	90919	11883	58318	00042	52402	28210	34075	33272	00840	73268
96	06670	57353	86275	92276	77591	46924	60839	55437	03183	13191
97	36634	93976	52062	83678	41256	60948	18685	48992	19462	96062
98	75101	72891	85745	67106	26010	62107	60885	37503	55461	71213
99	05112	71222	72654	51583	05228	62056	57390	42746	39272	96659

TABLE 1.5.1—(*Continued*)

	50–54	55–59	60–64	65–69	70–74	75–79	80–84	85–89	90–94	95–99
50	32847	31282	03345	89593	69214	70381	78285	20054	91018	16742
51	16916	00041	30236	55023	14253	76582	12092	86533	92426	37655
52	66176	34047	21005	27137	03191	48970	64625	22394	39622	79085
53	46299	13335	12180	16861	38043	59292	62675	63631	37020	78195
54	22847	47839	45385	23289	47526	54098	45683	55849	51575	64689
55	41851	54160	92320	69936	34803	92479	33399	71160	64777	83378
56	28444	59497	91586	95917	68553	28639	06455	34174	11130	91994
57	47520	62378	98855	83174	13088	16561	68559	26679	06238	51254
58	34978	63271	13142	82681	05271	08822	06490	44984	49307	62717
59	37404	80416	69035	92980	49486	74378	75610	74976	70056	15478
60	32400	65482	52099	53676	74648	94148	65095	69597	52771	71551
61	89262	86332	51718	70663	11623	29834	79820	73002	84886	03591
62	86866	09127	98021	03871	27789	58444	44832	36505	40672	30180
63	90814	14833	08759	74645	05046	94056	99094	65091	32663	73040
64	19192	82756	20553	58446	55376	88914	75096	26119	83898	43816
65	77585	52593	56612	95766	10019	29531	73064	20953	53523	58136
66	23757	16364	05096	03192	62386	45389	85332	18877	55710	96459
67	45989	96257	23850	26216	23309	21526	07425	50254	19455	29315
68	92970	94243	07316	41467	64837	52406	25225	51553	31220	14032
69	74346	59596	40088	98176	17896	86900	20249	77753	19099	48885
70	87646	41309	27636	45153	29988	94770	07255	70908	05340	99751
71	50099	71038	45146	06146	55211	99429	43169	66259	97786	59180
72	10127	46900	64984	75348	04115	33624	68774	60013	35515	62556
73	67995	81977	18984	64091	02785	27762	42529	97144	80407	64524
74	26304	80217	84934	82657	69291	35397	98714	35104	08187	48109
75	81994	41070	56642	64091	31229	02595	13513	45148	78722	30144
76	59537	34662	79631	89403	65212	09975	06118	86197	58208	16162
77	51228	10937	62396	81460	47331	91403	95007	06047	16846	64809
78	31089	37995	29577	07828	42272	54016	21950	86192	99046	84864
79	38207	97938	93459	75174	79460	55436	57206	87644	21296	43395
80	88666	31142	09474	89712	63153	62333	42212	06140	42594	43671
81	53365	56134	67582	92557	89520	33452	05134	70628	27612	33738
82	89807	74530	38004	90102	11693	90257	05500	79920	62700	43325
83	18682	81038	85662	90915	91631	22223	91588	80774	07716	12548
84	63571	32579	63942	25371	09234	94592	98475	76884	37635	33608
85	68927	56492	67799	95398	77642	54913	91853	08424	81450	76229
86	56401	63186	39389	88798	31356	89235	97036	32341	33292	73757
87	24333	95603	02359	72942	46287	95382	08452	62862	97869	71775
88	17025	84202	95199	62272	06366	16175	97577	99304	41587	03686
89	02804	08253	52133	20224	68034	50865	57868	22343	55111	03607
90	08298	03879	20995	19850	73090	13191	18963	82244	78479	99121
91	59883	01785	82403	96062	03785	03488	12970	64896	38336	30030
92	46982	06682	62864	91837	74021	89094	39952	64158	79614	78235
93	31121	47266	07661	02051	67599	24471	69843	83696	71402	76287
94	97867	56641	63416	17577	30161	87320	37752	73276	48969	41915
95	57364	86746	08415	14621	49430	22311	15836	72492	49372	44103
96	09559	26263	69511	28064	75999	44540	13337	10918	79846	54809
97	53873	55571	00608	42661	91332	63956	74087	59008	47493	99581
98	35531	19162	86406	05299	77511	24311	57257	22826	77555	05941
99	28229	88629	25695	94932	30721	16197	78742	34974	97528	45447

digits of the first one, and so on. (ii) Vary the direction in which you traverse the table; to the right or left, up or down, or diagonally. (iii) Vary the sample size, choosing in some random manner the various sizes, 10, 15, . . . 250, heading table 1.3.1 (1,000 is unnecessarily large).

For each sample make a record of the following facts: (i) initial point, (ii) direction taken in counting, (iii) sample size, and (iv) frequency of odd digits. If you can spare the time, draw 100 or more samples, carefully preserving the records, in the order made, for future use.

You have now done experimentally what the mathematical statistician does theoretically when he studies the distribution of samples drawn at random from a specified population, and you can verify the results which he derives from his equations. Let us look at these results in some detail.

1.6—The frequency distribution and its graphical representation. One group of students in statistics drew 200 samples of $n = 10$. The results are summarized in the *frequency distribution* of table 1.6.1. Each

TABLE 1.6.1
FREQUENCY DISTRIBUTION OF NUMBERS OF ODD DIGITS IN 200 SAMPLES OF $n = 10$

Class (Number of Odd Digits)	Class Frequency	Theoretical Class Frequency
0	1	0.2
1	1	1.8
2	8	8.2
3	25	22.3
4	39	40.0
5	45	49.2
6	36	42.0
7	25	24.6
8	16	9.4
9	4	2.1
10	0	0.2
Total Frequency	200	200.0

number of odd digits is known as a *class*. The number of samples falling into a class is the *class frequency*, the sum of the class frequencies being the total number of samples drawn. There is an extensive lore about the structure of statistical tables. For detailed information, see reference (13). I find that most students read frequency distributions quite freely with little or no instruction.

One striking feature of the sampling distribution is the concentration of frequencies near the middle of the table. The greatest frequency is in the class of 5 odd digits; that is, half odd and half even. The three middle classes, 4, 5, 6, contain $39 + 45 + 36 = 120$ samples, more than half of the total frequency. This central tendency is the characteristic that gives us confidence in sampling—most samples furnish close estimates of the population fraction of odds. This should counterbalance the perhaps discouraging fact that some of the samples are notably divergent.

Another interesting feature is the symmetry of the distribution, the greatest frequency at the center with a trailing away at each end. This is because the population fraction is near 50%; if the percentage were nearer zero or 100, the frequencies would pile up at or near one end.

The regularity that has appeared in the distribution shows that chance events follow a definite law. The turning up of odd digits as you counted them may have seemed wholly erratic: whether an odd or an even would come next was a purely chance event. But the summary of many such events reveals a pattern which may be predicted (aside from sampling variation). The theoretical pattern, shown in the last column, is a *binomial distribution*; it is the shape of the population from which we are sampling and its form is known exactly. For the fraction of odds, 0.506 (there are 5,060 odd digits in the table), and for sample size, $n = 10$, the theoretical distribution of odds was calculated by a method which will be

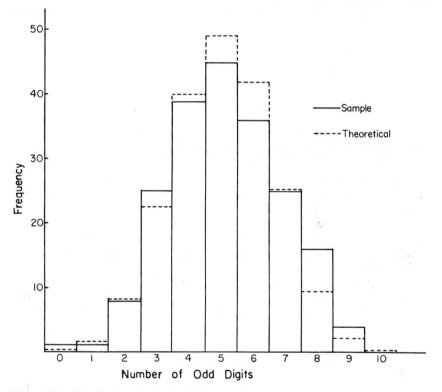

FIG. 1.6.1—Distribution of odd digits in 200 samples of ten. The dotted lines represent the theoretical binomial distribution from which the samples were drawn.

explained in chapter 16. I think you will be pleased with the agreement between actual and theoretical frequencies.

The *graphical representation*, figure 1.6.1, brings out vividly the features of the binomial distribution. On the horizontal axis are marked off intervals corresponding to the classes of the frequency distribution. Upon each is constructed a rectangle with altitude proportional to the corresponding class frequency, the scale of frequencies being indicated at the left. This kind of graphical representation of the frequency distribution is known as a *histogram*. Many chapters and books have been written about the making of statistical graphs. Reference (1) contains an adequate description of the technique.

1.7—Confidence interval; verification of theory. The samples you have drawn may be used to verify the theory of the confidence interval. From table 1.3.1 write down the 95% interval for each of your samples, then observe whether it covers the known population fraction of odds. Thus, for the sample of 50 discussed above, 23 of the digits were odd. This leads to the statement that the population percentage lies between 32% and 61%, a correct conclusion because we know that 50.6% of the digits in the table are odd. But suppose one of your samples of 250 had started at row 85, column 23, you would have counted, moving down the successive columns, only 101 or 40.4% odd, and would have asserted that the true value is between 34% and 46%. You would have been wrong despite the fact that this sample is randomly drawn from the same population as the others. This sample merely happens to be unusually divergent. You should find about five samples in a hundred leading you to incorrect statements, but there will be no occasion for surprise if only three, or as many as seven, turn up. If you had examined the intervals for $P = 0.99$, you would have expected (allowing as usual for sampling variation) about 99 per 100 of these to include the true ratio of 50.6%. I hope your results may be sufficiently concordant with theory to give you confidence in it. Of one thing I am sure—you are more aware of the vagaries of sampling then you were before, and that is one of the objects of the experiment. Another lesson to be learned is that only broad confidence intervals can be based on small samples, and that even so the inference can be wrong.

Finally it is to be observed that the interval narrows but slowly with increasing sample size. This fact is made vivid by considering the entire 2,000 observed digits as a single random sample. The number of odd digits is

$$1(1) + 2(8) + 3(25) + \ldots + 9(4) = 1,028$$

From this large sample the estimated population fraction of odd digits is $1,028/2,000 = 0.5056$. Using methods explained in Chapter 16, the 0.95 confidence interval is set from 0.4837 to 0.5275. Compare this with the interval for $n = 1,000$.

Let me emphasize the point that failure to make correct inferences in a small portion of samples is not a fault that can be remedied but is inevitably bound up in the sampling procedure. Fallibility is the very nature of such evidence. The sampler can only take available precautions, then prepare himself for his share of mistakes. In this he is not alone. The journalist, the judge, the banker, the weather forecaster— these along with the rest of us are subject to the laws of chance, and each makes his own quota of wrong guesses. The statistician has this advantage—he can, in favorable circumstances, know exactly his likelihood of error.

EXAMPLE 1.7.1—If you wish to learn by sampling what portion of radio owners in a selected region listen to a certain program, would you get an accurate sample if you conducted the interviews by telephone? Would all radio owners have a chance of being interviewed?

EXAMPLE 1.7.2—A sampler of public opinion estimates from a sample the number of voters in a state favoring a certain candidate for governor. Assuming that his estimate was very close to the population value at the time the survey was made, might the ballot on election day be quite different?

EXAMPLE 1.7.3—Why does a mailed questionnaire often result in an inaccurate estimate?

EXAMPLE 1.7.4—Combine all your samples of digits, irrespective of size, into one. The correct percentage of odd digits can be got in two ways: (i) add all the counts of odd digits and divide by the total digits counted; (ii) compute the weighted average of the percentages of the various sized samples, using the formula,

$$\text{weighted average} = \frac{W_1 p_1 + W_2 p_2 + W_3 p_3 + \ldots}{W_1 + W_2 + W_3 + \ldots}$$

where p_1 is the percentage of odds in the samples of 10 and W_1 is the total number of digits counted in these samples. p_2 and W_2 are defined in the same way for samples of 15, etc.

EXAMPLE 1.7.5—Based on the combined sample of the preceding example, set the 99% confidence interval. Does it cover the known population ratio?

EXAMPLE 1.7.6—In a 1951 sample of Iowa open-country householders within operating range of WOI-TV, 106 of the 425 respondents had television sets in operation. Calculate the 95% interval estimate of the percentage of television-owning householders in the region surveyed. Ans. 21 – 30%.

EXAMPLE 1.7.7—It was estimated that there were 31,025 householders in the open country within operating range of the station. Make point and interval estimates of the number of television sets in the region. Ans. 7,750 sets. Between 6,500 and 9,300.

EXAMPLE 1.7.8—Five dice were tossed 100 times with these results:

Number Deuces per Toss	Frequency of Occurrence	Theoretical Frequency
5	2	0.013
4	3	0.322
3	3	3.214
2	18	16.075
1	42	40.188
0	32	40.188
Total	100	100 000

Draw the histogram showing the sample distribution of deuces together with the theoretical binomial distribution. Do you think the dice were balanced and fairly tossed? See example 1.14.2.

1.8—Hypotheses about populations. In contrast with the foregoing, the investigator often has in mind a definite *hypothesis* about the population ratio, the purpose of the sampling being to get evidence concerning his hypothesis. Thus, a geneticist studying heredity in the tomato had reason to believe that, in the F_1 generation, segregation of fruits with red flesh and yellow flesh would be in the ratio, 3:1. Counting the number of fruits with red flesh in a sample of 400 he found 310 instead of the hypothetical 300. With your experience of sampling variation, would you accept this as verification or refutation of the hypothesis? Again, the sampler of public opinion foresees a close election in some critical state. He sets up the hypothesis of an equal number of votes for the two dominant parties, then asks 10,000 voters their preferences, the resulting division being 5,100 to 4,900. Shall he say that this is or is not convincing evidence about his hypothesis of a tie vote?

To answer such questions two data are needed, a measure of the deviation of the sample from the hypothetical population ratio, and a means of judging whether or not this measure is an amount commonly experienced in sampling or, on the contrary, is so great as to throw doubt upon the hypothesis. Both data were furnished by Karl Pearson in 1899 (8). He devised an index of dispersion denoted by χ^2 (*chi-square*), and provided a table of its probable occurrence in sampling.* Let us first examine the index.

1.9—Chi-square, an index of dispersion. Naturally, the deviations of the observed numbers from those specified by the hypothesis form the basis of the index. In the election sampling of the previous section, the numbers expected on the hypothesis of an equally divided vote are each 5,000. The deviations, then, are

$$5,100 - 5,000 = 100$$

and

$$4,900 - 5,000 = -100,$$

the sum of the two being zero. The value of chi-square is given by,

$$\chi^2 = \frac{(100)^2}{5,000} + \frac{(-100)^2}{5,000} = 4$$

Each deviation is squared, each square is divided by the hypothetical number, and the results are added. The hypothetical numbers appear in the denominators in order to introduce sample size into the quantity—it is the *relative* size of the deviation which is important. The squaring may puzzle you. You will find this a very common practice in statistics. Incidentally, it makes the sign of the deviation unimportant since the

---

* G. U. Yule and R. A. Fisher discovered an error in certain uses of the table and corrected it in 1922 (15, 2).

square of a negative number is the same as that of the corresponding positive. It is plain that chi-square would be zero if the sample frequencies were the same as the hypothetical and that it will increase with increasing deviation from hypothetical. In that respect, it is a reasonable measure of variation. But it is not at all plain whether the chi-square value of 4 is to be considered large, medium, or small. To furnish you a basis for comparison is our next aim. Pearson founded his judgment on the solution and tabulation of a somewhat elaborate equation, but for non-mathematicians the customary way of going about the matter is to set up an experiment. Before doing that, a couple of formulas will be given, together with a few examples to help fix them in mind.

1.10—Symbolic statement of chi-square. It is convenient to represent by f_1 and f_2 the sample counts of individuals who do and do not possess the attribute being investigated, the corresponding hypothetical frequencies being F_1 and F_2. The two deviations, then, are $f_1 - F_1$ and $f_2 - F_2$, so that chi-square is given by the formula,

$$\chi^2 = (f_1 - F_1)^2/F_1 + (f_2 - F_2)^2/F_2$$

The formula may be condensed to the more easily remembered as well as more general one,

$$\chi^2 = \Sigma \ (f - F)^2/F,$$

where Σ denotes summation. In words, "Chi-square is the sum of such ratios as

(deviation square)/(hypothetical number)"

As will appear later, there may be more than two of these ratios in the summation.

Let us apply the formula to the counts of red and yellow tomatoes in section 1.8. There, $f_1 = 310, f_2 = 400 - 310 = 90, F_1 = \frac{3}{4}$ of $400 = 300$, and $F_2 = \frac{1}{4}$ of $400 = 100$. Whence,

$$\chi^2 = \frac{(310 - 300)^2}{300} + \frac{(90 - 100)^2}{100} = 1.33$$

It is apparent that the hypothesis set up about the population is the sole criterion for dividing the sample into hypothetical numbers. Only if the investigator wishes to test some hypothesis will he be interested in calculating chi-square.

EXAMPLE 1.10.1—In a certain cross of two varieties of peas genetic theory led the investigator to expect half wrinkled seeds and half smooth. In a sample of 800 seeds examined he found 440 wrinkled. What is the value of chi-square? Ans. 8.

EXAMPLE 1.10.2—If the count in the foregoing example had been 220 wrinkled in a total of 400, would chi-square also be half its original value?

EXAMPLE 1.10.3—In the text example about tomatoes the deviation from expected was 10. If this same deviation had occurred in a sample of twice the size (that is, in a sample of 800), what would have been the value of chi-square? Ans. 0.67, half the original value.

EXAMPLE 1.10.4—In a political campaign a candidate claimed that 60% of the electorate would vote for him. A sampler of public opinion asked 1,000 registered voters if they expected to vote for this candidate and 55% of them said, "Yes." Calculate the value of chi-square on the assumption that the candidate's claim was correct. Ans. 10.42.

EXAMPLE 1.10.5—In the foregoing example, what statement about the electorate may the sampler make based on the 99% confidence interval? Ans. Between 51% and 59% will vote for the candidate

1.11—An experiment in sampling chi-square; the sampling distribution. You have now had some practice in the calculation of chi-square. It is to be hoped that it appeals to you as a reasonable and informative measure of the deviation of the observed sample numbers from those expected under the hypothesis set up. But it has another function— it enables us to judge whether the sample ratio itself departs much or little from the hypothetical population value. To use it for that purpose we must answer the question already proposed: what values of chi-square are to be considered as indicating unusual deviation, and what as ordinary sampling variation? Our experimental method of answering the question will be to calculate chi-square for each of the samples drawn from the table of random numbers, then to observe what values of chi-square spring from the more unusual samples. If a large number of samples of various sizes have been drawn and if the value of chi-square is computed from each, the distribution of chi-square may be mapped.

To illustrate the calculation of chi-square for one of your samples, suppose the sample size is $n = 100$; then, since 50.6% of the tabular digits are odd, $F_1 = (0.506)(100) = 50.6$ and $F_2 = 49.4$. If you counted $f_1 = 44$ odd digits in this sample, the value of chi-square is

$$\chi^2 = \frac{(44 - 50.6)^2}{50.6} + \frac{(56 - 49.4)^2}{49.4} = 1.74$$

In case there are several samples of this same size, calculating time can be saved by rearranging the formula. Remembering that the two deviations are the same in absolute value (that is, disregarding sign), this absolute value being 6.6 for each deviation, chi-square can be written

$$\begin{aligned}\chi^2 &= (f_1 - F_1)^2 \, (1/F_1 + 1/F_2) \\ &= (6.6)^2(1/50.6 + 1/49.4) \\ &= (43.56)(0.019763 + 0.020243) \\ &= (43.56)(0.040006) = 1.74\end{aligned}$$

as before. The advantage is that once the sum of the reciprocals of the expected numbers has been calculated, it can be used again and again so long as the sample size and the population ratio are unchanged: just square the deviation from expected and multiply by 0.040006. Of course, an appropriate factor must be calculated for each sample size.

Those who do not have adequate computing facilities (table of squares, slide rule, calculating machine) may prefer to sacrifice some accuracy to save a good deal in the time required for the experiment just outlined. If they assume 50% of the tabular digits to be odd, then $F_1 = F_2 = n/2$, an integer in most of the samples. For $n = 100$, the formula above then becomes

$$\chi^2 = (0.04)(f - 50)^2$$

The effect on the frequency distribution is striking, but the broad outline is unchanged.

Proceed now to calculate chi-square for each of your samples. The results may be summarized conveniently, especially if there are a hundred or more of them, in a sampling distribution like that of table 1.11.1.

TABLE 1.11.1

SAMPLING DISTRIBUTION OF 230 VALUES OF CHI-SQUARE CALCULATED FROM SAMPLES
DRAWN FROM TABLE 1.5.1
Sample sizes—10, 15, 20, 30, 50, 100, and 250

Class Interval	Frequency	Class Interval	Frequency
0.00–0.49	116	6.00– 6.49	0
0.50–0.99	39	6.50– 6.99	1
1.00–1.49	18	7.00– 7.49	0
1.50–1.99	22	7.50– 7.99	0
2.00–2.49	12	8.00– 8.49	0
2.50–2.99	5	8.50– 8.99	1
3.00–3.49	5	9.00– 9.49	0
3.50–3.99	6	9.50– 9.99	0
4.00–4.49	1	10.00–10.49	1
4.50–4.99	2	10.50–10.99	0
5.00–5.49	0	11.00–11.49	1
5.50–5.99	0		

Observe the concentration of sample chi-squares in the smallest class (the class or *class interval* here contains not one but a group of values of the variable), practically half of them being less than 0.5. Attention has already been called to the fact that, in the process of sampling, small deviations (with small chi-squares) are predominant, this being the foundation of our faith in sampling. But taking a less optimistic view, one must not overlook the samples with large deviations and chi-squares. The possibility of getting such as these makes for caution in drawing conclusions. In this sampling exercise we know the population ratio and are not led astray by discrepant samples; but in actual investigations, where the hypothesis set up is not known to be the right one, a large value of chi-square constitutes a dilemma. Shall we say that it denotes only an unusual sample from the hypothetical population, or shall we conclude that the hypothesis misrepresents the true population ratio? Statistical theory contains no certain answer. Instead, it furnishes an *evaluation of the probability of possible sample deviations from the hypothetical population.* If chi-square is large, the investigator is warned that the sample is an improbable one under his hypothesis. This is evidence to be added to that which he already possesses, all of it being the basis for his decisions. A more exact determination of probability will be explained in the second section to follow.

The graphical representation of the distribution of our chi-squares

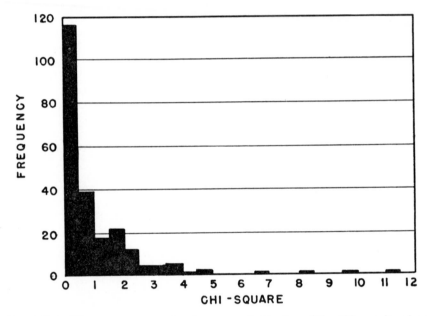

Fig. 1.11.1—Histogram representing frequency distribution of the 230 sample values of chi-square in table 1.11.1.

appears in figure 1.11.1. The graph serves to emphasize both the concentration of small chi-squares at the left and the comparatively large size of the few at the right. It is now evident that, for the election sampling of section 1.9, $\chi^2 = 4$ does not lie far out on the scale but is nevertheless larger than a great majority of the chi-squares in this distribution. If the electorate were really divided equally, this would be an unusually large value of chi-square.

1.12—Frequency distribution with unequal class intervals. Two features of our chi-square distribution are yet to be examined: (i) how does it compare with the theoretical distribution, and (ii) how may we evaluate more exactly the probabilities of various chi-square sizes? Both features become evident if the class intervals are rearranged as in table 1.12.1, column 1. Very narrow at the start, these theoretically determined intervals increase in width so as to make the chi-square distribution symmetrical as in column 4. Furthermore, they are adjusted so that each contains a convenient percentage of chi-square values; in other words, so that the probabilities of specific values are easily read. As an example, the last line of column 4 indicates the probability of 0.01 that, in random sampling from the hypothetical population, chi-square will be larger than 6.635.

The distribution of our sample of 230 chi-squares in columns 2 and 3 is readily compared with the theoretical distribution of column 4. Clearly

TABLE 1.12.1

SAMPLING DISTRIBUTION OF CHI-SQUARE WITH UNEQUAL CLASS INTERVALS

Class Interval	Discontinuous Variable		Continuous Variable	
	Distribution of 230 Sample Values	Percentage Distribution	Theoretical Percentage Distribution	Cumulative Percentage Distribution
1	2	3	4	5
0. −0.000157	0	0.00	1	100
0.000157−0.00393	11	4.78	4	99
0.00393 −0.0158	20	8.70	5	95
0.0158 −0.1015	26	11.31	15	90
0.1015 −0.455	59	25.65	25	75
0.455 −1.323	62	26.96	25	50
1.323 −2.706	32	13.91	15	25
2.706 −3.841	14	6.09	5	10
3.841 −6.635	3	1.30	4	5
6.635 − ∞	3	1.30	1	1
Total	230	100.00	100	

the two do not differ greatly. The discrepancies are due partly to sampling variation, but mainly to this fact: the theoretical distributions in columns 4 and 5 are based on a "continuous" variable, one capable of taking all numerical values, while those in columns 2 and 3 arise from counting a "discontinuous" or "discrete" variable which jumps from one integral number to the next, leaving out intermediate values (fractions and irrationals). You may have observed, for example, that no sample of sizes which you have drawn can yield a chi-square in the first class interval, but if samples of 500 or more were counted, an occasional one would have so small a value.

Column 5 contains a *cumulative frequency distribution* of the percentages in column 4. Beginning at the foot of this column 5, each entry is the sum of all the preceding ones in column 4, hence the name. The column is read this way: the third to the last entry means that 10% of all samples in the theoretical distribution have chi-squares greater than the 2.706. Again, 50% of them exceed 0.455; this may be looked upon as an average value, exceeded as often as not in the sampling. Finally, chi-squares greater than 6.635 are rare, occurring only once per 100 samples. So in this sampling distribution of chi-square we find a measure in terms of probability, the measure we have been seeking to enable us to say exactly which chi-squares are to be considered small and which large. We are now to learn how this measure can be made use of.

1.13—The test of a null hypothesis or test of significance. As indicated in section 1.8, the investigator's objective usually can be translated into a hypothesis about his experimental material. The geneticist, you remember, knowing that a certain simple pattern of inheritance produced a 3:1 ratio, set up the hypothesis that the tomato population had this ratio of red to yellow fruits. This is called a *null hypothesis*, meaning that there is no difference between the hypothetical ratio and that in the population of tomato fruits. If this null hypothesis is true, then random samples of n will have ratios distributed binomially, and chi-squares calculated from the samples will be distributed as in table 1.12.1. Now, to *test the hypothesis*, a sample is taken and its chi-square calculated; in the illustration the value was 1.33. Reference to the table shows that, if the null hypothesis is true, 1.33 is not an uncommon chi-square, the probability of a greater one being about 0.25. As the result of this test, the geneticist would not likely reject the null hypothesis. He knows, of course, that he may be in error, that the population ratio among the tomato fruits may not be 3:1. But the discrepancy, if any, is so small that the sample has given no convincing evidence of it.

Contrasting with the genetic experiment, the election sampling turned up $\chi^2 = 4$. If the null hypothesis (an equally divided electorate) is true, a larger chi-square has a probability of only about 0.05. This suggests that the null hypothesis is false, so the sampler would likely reject it. As before, he may be in error because this might be one of those 5 samples per 100 that are expected to have chi-squares greater than 3.841 even when the sampling is from an equally divided population. In rejecting the null hypothesis, the sampler faces the possibility that he is wrong. Such is the kind of risk always run by those who test hypotheses and rest decisions on the tests.

The illustrations show that in testing hypotheses one is liable to *two kinds of error*. If his sample leads him to reject the null hypothesis when it is true, he is said to have committed an *error of the first kind*, or a Type I error. If, on the contrary, he is led to accept the hypothesis when it is false, his *error is of the second kind*, a Type II error. The Neyman-Pearson theory of testing hypotheses emphasizes the relations between these types. For recent accounts of this theory see references (7, 6, 14).

In biological research it is customary to reject the null hypothesis where chi-square exceeds 3.841; that is, chi-square greater than 3.841 constitutes the *region of rejection*. A sample value lying in this region is called *significant* because it signifies rejection. As shown by the last column of the table, this practice makes the probability of a Type I error only 0.05 when the null hypothesis is true. This probability was not too badly verified by the experimental sampling which turned up $3 + 3 = 6$ chi-squares greater than 3.841; that is, $6/230 = 0.026$ instead of 0.05.

It should be said that, in case the null hypothesis, H_0, is rejected, there must be some alternative hypothesis, H_A, to be accepted. In the situations we have been discussing the alternative has been rather obvious; if the hypothesis of *no difference* is rejected then the alternative of *some difference* is accepted. Later we shall encounter circumstances in which the outcome of the test may depend upon the selection of the alternative.

It is understood that a biologist seldom if ever rests his decisions wholly on a test of hypothesis. Knowing that a sample furnishes evidence but not proof, he adds this evidence to that already accumulated from experience and reports of other research. Too, there is collateral information which has accrued during the progress of the experiment. Finally, if the experiment is of any great value, it leads to new hypotheses which, before conclusions are reached, must be tested either by new experiments or by their agreement with the known structure of the science. It is the investigator's responsibility to integrate all this evidence and to make a decision. He cannot evade this responsibility by citing a value of chi-square. The probability that he will reach a false conclusion is presumably much less than that of his errors of the first kind.

EXAMPLE 1.13.1—For the pea seeds of example 1.10.1, $\chi^2 = 8$. Presumably the investigator would reject the null hypothesis of equal numbers of wrinkled and smooth in the population, accepting the alternative hypothesis of unequal numbers. If so, what is the probability of an error of Type I? Ans. $P < 0.01$ (more accurately, $P = 0.0046$. For a method of evaluating probabilities not in the table, see section 8.8, 3.)

EXAMPLE 1.13.2—In some experiments on heredity in the tomato, MacArthur (5) counted 3,629 fruits with red flesh and 1,176 with yellow. This was in the F_2 generation where the theoretical ratio was 3:1. Compute $\chi^2 = 0.71$. MacArthur concluded that "the discrepancies between the observed and expected ratios are not significant."

EXAMPLE 1.13.3—In the same series of experiments, MacArthur counted 671 plants with green foliage and 569 with yellow. This was a backcross in which the theoretical ratio was 1:1. Chi-square = 8.39 is strong evidence against the 1:1 hypothesis, "resulting without doubt from a lower viability in the recessive class."

EXAMPLE 1.13.4—In a South Dakota farm labor survey of 1943, 480 of the 1,000 reporting farmers were classed as owners (or part owners), the remaining 520 being renters. It is known that, of nearly 7,000 farms in the region, 47% are owners. Assuming this to be the population percentage, calculate chi-square for the sample of 1,000. Ans. $\chi^2 = 0.41$. Does this increase your confidence in the randomness of the sampling? Such collateral evidence is often cited. The assumption is that if the sample is shown to be representative for one attribute it is probably representative also of the attribute under investigation, provided the two are related.

EXAMPLE 1.13.5—James Snedecor (10) tried the effect of injecting poultry eggs with female sex hormones. In one series 2 normal males were hatched together with 19 chicks which were classified as either normal females or individuals with pronounced female characteristics. What is the probability of the ratio 2:19, or one more extreme, in sampling from a population with equal numbers of the sexes? Ans. $\chi^2 = 13.76$, $P = 0.0002$ (see example 8.8.12).

EXAMPLE 1.13.6—In table 1.12.1, $62 + 32 + 14 + 3 + 3 = 114$ samples have chi-squares greater than 0.455, whereas 50% of 230 were expected. What is the probability of drawing a more discrepant sample if the sampling is truly random? Ans. $\chi^2 = 0.0174$, $P = 0.90$. What is the probability of greater deviation from half-and-half than the deviation in your samples drawn in accord with section 1.11?

1.14—More than two kinds of individuals in the population. Attention has been called to the fact (section 1.4) that more than two kinds of individuals often inhabit a population. If the investigator has some hypothesis about the population fractions of these kinds he may use chi-square to test it. But now the sampling distribution of chi-square is different from that in table 1.12.1. The form of the distribution depends on the number of *degrees of freedom* associated with the sampling. Heretofore, we have learned to test a null hypothesis about only two kinds of individuals, and there has been only a single degree of freedom (though nothing has been said about it). To see this, consider a sample whose size has been fixed at 100 individuals. If 30 of them are found to possess the attribute under investigation, this fixes the value of chi-square. The number having the opposite attribute is got by subtraction, $100 - 30$. The single degree of freedom is associated with the random occurrence of the individuals of a specified kind appearing in the sample. Their number might be anywhere from zero to 100; but once this number has been counted, there is no further freedom about the number in the alternative category.

If there are more than two kinds of individuals, the degrees of freedom increase. At present we shall deal with situations in which the number of degrees of freedom is one less than the number of kinds, the argument being parallel to that for two kinds.

As an example, Lindstrom (4) crossed two recessive types of maize, golden and green-striped. "In the F_2 generation four distinct types of plants were produced. Two were like the parents (one green-striped and one golden), one was like the F_1 hybrid (green), and one was entirely new, being a combination of the two recessive types, namely, a golden-green-striped type." Of the 1,301 plants, there were

$$\begin{aligned} f_1 &= 773 \text{ green} \\ f_2 &= 231 \text{ golden} \\ f_3 &= 238 \text{ green-striped} \\ f_4 &= 59 \text{ golden-green-striped} \\ \hline & 1,301 \end{aligned}$$

According to a simple type of Mendelian inheritance, segregation would follow 9:3:3:1 ratios. We select this as the null hypothesis. According to it the hypothetical numbers are

$$
\begin{aligned}
F_1 &= (9/16)(1{,}301) = 731.9 \\
F_2 &= (3/16)(1{,}301) = 243.9 \\
F_3 &= (3/16)(1{,}301) = 243.9 \\
F_4 &= (1/16)(1{,}301) = \underline{\ \ 81.3} \\
&\qquad\qquad\qquad\quad\ 1{,}301.0
\end{aligned}
$$

Substituting in the formula for chi-square (section 1.10),

$$
\chi^2 = \Sigma\ (f - F)^2/F,
$$

$$
\chi^2 = \frac{(773 - 731.9)^2}{731.9} + \frac{(231 - 243.9)^2}{243.9} + \frac{(238 - 243.9)^2}{243.9} + \frac{(59 - 81.3)^2}{81.3}
$$

$$
= \frac{(41.1)^2}{731.9} + \frac{(-12.9)^2}{243.9} + \frac{(-5.9)^2}{243.9} + \frac{(-22.3)^2}{81.3}
$$

$$
= 2.31 + 0.68 + 0.14 + 6.12
$$

$$
= 9.25,
$$

with $4 - 1 = 3$ degrees of freedom. Note: The sum of the four deviations, $41.1 - 12.9 - 5.9 - 22.3$, is zero. This serves as a check on the preceding calculations. But it also verifies the fact that there are 3 degrees of freedom; only three of the deviations can be chosen at will, the fourth being fixed as zero minus the sum of the first three.

Is $\chi^2 = 9.25$, with $d.f. = 3$, a common event in sampling from the population specified by the null hypothesis, 9:3:3:1, or is it a rare one? For the answer refer to table 1.14.1, in the line for 3 $d.f.$ You will find that 9.25 is beyond the 5% point, near the 2.5% point. On the basis of the statistical evidence alone the null hypothesis would be rejected. Yet Lindstrom concluded: "The data do not fit the 9:3:3:1 ratio very closely, but the deviations therefrom are largely explained by a physiological cause, which is the weakened condition of the last three classes due to their chlorophyll abnormality. The last class (golden-green-striped) is not very vigorous." It is this last kind that contributed nearly two-thirds to the total chi-square. So, the null hypothesis was not rejected despite the large value of chi-square.

EXAMPLE 1.14.1—In table 1.14.1 identify the probabilities in the upper border with those in column 5 of table 1.12.1.

EXAMPLE 1.14.2—In example 1.7.8 there was a frequency distribution of deuces turning up in tosses of 5 dice. The theoretical distribution of fairly tossed, balanced dice is given in the right-hand column. In testing hypotheses by means of chi-square,

TABLE 1.14.1
ACCUMULATIVE DISTRIBUTION OF CHI-SQUARE*

Degrees of Freedom	Probability of a Greater Value												
	0.995	0.990	0.975	0.950	0.900	0.750	0.500	0.250	0.100	0.050	0.025	0.010	0.005
1	...	...	...	...	0.02	0.10	0.45	1.32	2.71	3.84	5.02	6.63	7.88
2	0.01	0.02	0.05	0.10	0.21	0.58	1.39	2.77	4.61	5.99	7.38	9.21	10.60
3	0.07	0.11	0.22	0.35	0.58	1.21	2.37	4.11	6.25	7.81	9.35	11.34	12.84
4	0.21	0.30	0.48	0.71	1.06	1.92	3.36	5.39	7.78	9.49	11.14	13.28	14.86
5	0.41	0.55	0.83	1.15	1.61	2.67	4.35	6.63	9.24	11.07	12.83	15.09	16.75
6	0.68	0.87	1.24	1.64	2.20	3.45	5.35	7.84	10.64	12.59	14.45	16.81	18.55
7	0.99	1.24	1.69	2.17	2.83	4.25	6.35	9.04	12.02	14.07	16.01	18.48	20.28
8	1.34	1.65	2.18	2.73	3.49	5.07	7.34	10.22	13.36	15.51	17.53	20.09	21.96
9	1.73	2.09	2.70	3.33	4.17	5.90	8.34	11.39	14.68	16.92	19.02	21.67	23.59
10	2.16	2.56	3.25	3.94	4.87	6.74	9.34	12.55	15.99	18.31	20.48	23.21	25.19
11	2.60	3.05	3.82	4.57	5.58	7.58	10.34	13.70	17.28	19.68	21.92	24.72	26.76
12	3.07	3.57	4.40	5.23	6.30	8.44	11.34	14.85	18.55	21.03	23.34	26.22	28.30
13	3.57	4.11	5.01	5.89	7.04	9.30	12.34	15.98	19.81	22.36	24.74	27.69	29.82
14	4.07	4.66	5.63	6.57	7.79	10.17	13.34	17.12	21.06	23.68	26.12	29.14	31.32
15	4.60	5.23	6.27	7.26	8.55	11.04	14.34	18.25	22.31	25.00	27.49	30.58	32.80
16	5.14	5.81	6.91	7.96	9.31	11.91	15.34	19.37	23.54	26.30	28.85	32.00	34.27
17	5.70	6.41	7.56	8.67	10.09	12.79	16.34	20.49	24.77	27.59	30.19	33.41	35.72
18	6.26	7.01	8.23	9.39	10.86	13.68	17.34	21.60	25.99	28.87	31.53	34.81	37.16
19	6.84	7.63	8.91	10.12	11.65	14.56	18.34	22.72	27.20	30.14	32.85	36.19	38.58
20	7.43	8.26	9.59	10.85	12.44	15.45	19.34	23.83	28.41	31.41	34.17	37.57	40.00

TABLE 1.14.1—(*Continued*)

ACCUMULATIVE DISTRIBUTION OF CHI-SQUARE*

Degrees of Freedom	Probability of a Greater Value												
	0.995	0.990	0.975	0.950	0.900	0.750	0.500	0.250	0.100	0.050	0.025	0.010	0.005
21	8.03	8.90	10.28	11.59	13.24	16.34	20.34	24.93	29.62	32.67	35.48	38.93	41.40
22	8.64	9.54	10.98	12.34	14.04	17.24	21.34	26.04	30.81	33.92	36.78	40.29	42.80
23	9.26	10.20	11.69	13.09	14.85	18.14	22.34	27.14	32.01	35.17	38.08	41.64	44.18
24	9.89	10.86	12.40	13.85	15.66	19.04	23.34	28.24	33.20	36.42	39.36	42.98	45.56
25	10.52	11.52	13.12	14.61	16.47	19.94	24.34	29.34	34.38	37.65	40.65	44.31	46.93
26	11.16	12.20	13.84	15.38	17.29	20.84	25.34	30.43	35.56	38.89	41.92	45.64	48.29
27	11.81	12.88	14.57	16.15	18.11	21.75	26.34	31.53	36.74	40.11	43.19	46.96	49.64
28	12.46	13.56	15.31	16.93	18.94	22.66	27.34	32.62	37.92	41.34	44.46	48.28	50.99
29	13.12	14.26	16.05	17.71	19.77	23.57	28.34	33.71	39.09	42.56	45.72	49.59	52.34
30	13.79	14.95	16.79	18.49	20.60	24.48	29.34	34.80	40.26	43.77	46.98	50.89	53.67
40	20.71	22.16	24.43	26.51	29.05	33.66	39.34	45.62	51.80	55.76	59.34	63.69	66.77
50	27.99	29.71	32.36	34.76	37.69	42.94	49.33	56.33	63.17	67.50	71.42	76.15	79.49
60	35.53	37.48	40.48	43.19	46.46	52.29	59.33	66.98	74.40	79.08	83.30	88.38	91.95
70	43.28	45.44	48.76	51.74	55.33	61.70	69.33	77.58	85.53	90.53	95.02	100.42	104.22
80	51.17	53.54	57.15	60.39	64.28	71.14	79.33	88.13	96.58	101.88	106.63	112.33	116.32
90	59.20	61.75	65.65	69.13	73.29	80.62	89.33	98.64	107.56	113.14	118.14	124.12	128.30
100	67.33	70.06	74.22	77.93	82.36	90.13	99.33	109.14	118.50	124.34	129.56	135.81	140.17

* Condensed from table with 6 significant figures by Catherine M. Thompson, by permission of the Editor of *Biometrika* (11).

it is a recommended precaution that every class have a theoretical frequency of at least 5. So, combine the first 3 classes like this, rounding to one decimal:

Deuces	f	F
5,4,3	8	3.5
2	18	16.1
1	42	40.2
0	32	40.2

Calculate chi-square. Ans. 7.76, *d.f.* = 3. The hypothesis of random sampling from the theoretical distribution might not be rejected, but one would look with suspicion on the large number of deuces in the first three classes.

EXAMPLE 1.14.3—The samples in table 1.6.1 are known to be randomly drawn from the theoretical distribution. For practice, calculate chi-square after combining the first 3 classes and also the last 3 classes. Ans. 7.47, *d.f.* = 6. In sampling from the theoretical population, the probability of a larger chi-square is about 0.28. But one suspects that in some of the samples of class 8 the digits may not have been counted correctly.

In this opening chapter the reader has been introduced to the broad principles of scientific statistics. He has encountered the problems of learning about a population through means of a sample drawn from it. He knows that inferences about the population are valid only if information has been built into the sample data by proper design and skillful conduct of the sampling. He has learned to make point and interval estimates as well as to test hypotheses. And he has experienced the uncertainties involved in drawing conclusions from the results of a sampling. The remainder of the book is occupied with more and more elaborate designs for collecting data, together with appropriate statistical methods for extracting information from them.

Those who are primarily interested in measurements, rather than counts, may wish to turn forward to chapter 2, omitting the remainder of this one. The necessary preparation has been made. Others, who prefer to continue the study of enumeration statistics, will find the subject of chapter 1 continued in chapter 9.

1.15—Chi-square and sample size. From the formula,

$$\chi^2 = \Sigma(f - F)^2/F,$$

it is clear that if the deviation, $f - F$, is unchanged, chi-square decreases as the size of sample increases, because, for any particular hypothesis, F varies directly as sample size. This is illustrated by the first example in table 1.15.1. Multiplying sample size, n, by four reduces chi-square to one-fourth its former value. The meaning is that, while a deviation of 10 is unusual in a sample of 100, it is rather common in the larger sample—the larger the sample, the more latitude there is for sampling variation.

In the second example the deviation is increased fourfold along with sample size, the effect being to multiply the original chi-square by four. The deviation, 40, in the larger sample is much less likely than is 10 in the original. This shows that the latitude for sampling variation does not increase directly with sample size.

The deviation in example three is only doubled as the original sample size is quadrupled, chi-square remaining unchanged; that is, the deviation, 20, in a sample of 400 has the same expectation as the deviation, 10, in the sample one-fourth as large. Thus, for equal likelihood of occurrence the deviation must vary directly as the square root of n.

Clear understanding of the illustrated principles is necessary if one is to appreciate the meaning of chi-square. Here is one application: results are often reported not in numbers originally counted but as percentages of individuals having the attribute; that is, as so many *per hundred* enumerated. It is clear that such percentages cannot be used directly in the calculation of chi-square except in the case where the sample size is an even hundred. In all other samples, before chi-square is computed, the percentage must be converted to the actual number of individuals found

TABLE 1.15.1

THREE EXAMPLES ILLUSTRATING CHANGES IN UNADJUSTED CHI-SQUARE RESULTING FROM QUADRUPLING THE ORIGINAL SAMPLE SIZE

	Original Random Sample	Example 1. Deviation Unchanged	Example 2. Deviation Increased Directly as n	Example 3. Deviation Increased as $\sqrt{n}$
Sample size, n	100	400	400	400
Number having attribute	60	210	240	220
Expected on basis of 1:1 hypothesis	50	200	200	200
Deviation	10	10	40	20
Chi-square	4	1	16	4

with the attribute, or else some appropriate device must be employed for accomplishing the same end.

Another application of the principles of this section is made in planning the size of a sampling. Consider a circumstance like this: A geneticist studying heredity in the tomato has examined 100 seedlings and found 46 with yellow foliage. Theoretically the plants are expected to segregate half green and half yellow, but he suspects lower viability in the seeds having the recessive yellow gene. The deviation of yellow seedlings from the 50 which was expected is 4% of the number examined, but chi-square is only 0.64, so the statistical evidence against the 1:1 ratio is slight. Nevertheless, the suspicion of lower viability must be tested, and the question is asked, "In the event that the 4% deviation is found in a larger sample, how many plants should be examined to make chi-square 10 times its present sample value?" The appropriate example in table 1.15.1 is the second because, the deviation being assumed to be 4% of the plants counted, its size is to increase directly as n. If so, chi-square will increase in the same way, and a sample of 10 times 100 should have the required value, 6.4. MacArthur's data presented in example 1.13.3 might have been the outcome of some such reasoning, verifying the suspected character of the gene. On the other hand, the suspicion might have proved unfounded, the larger sample turning up with no more than ordinary deviation from the 1:1 ratio. In either event the investigator has acquired the desired information.

1.16—Another formula for chi-square. This formula gives the same result as the more general one and often makes computation easier:

$$\chi^2 = \frac{(a - rb)^2}{r(a + b)},$$

where a and b are the numbers in the two classes and r is the hypothetical ratio of the corresponding numbers in the population. Applying this to the tomato problem of section 1.8:

$$a = \text{number of red-fleshed fruits} = 310$$
$$b = \text{number of yellow-fleshed fruits} = 90$$
$$a + b = 400$$
$$r = 3/1 = 3$$
$$\chi^2 = \frac{(310 - 3 \times 90)^2}{3(400)} = 1.33, \text{ as before.}$$

EXAMPLE 1.16.1—Jenkins and Bell (3) reported a gene producing yellow seedlings in maize, a simple recessive to the normal green. Among 9,717 counted, the ratio of green to yellow seedlings was 78.95% to 21.05%, whereas the hypothetical ratio was 3:1. Does the sample evidence support the hypothetical ratio? Ans. $\chi^2 = 81.04$. The investigators showed by means of further experiments that the gene was "linked with lethal or semi-lethal factors which caused a deficiency in the yellow seedling class. Satisfactory 3:1 ratios were not obtained until these cultures had been outcrossed and the disturbing factors eliminated."

1.17—Ratios, rates, and percentages. These fractions are very popular in the presentation of statistics because, being usually reduced to some common denominator, their numerators are readily compared. Examples are given in table 1.17.1. The percentages of males all have the denominator, 100 guinea pigs. The two sets of ratios are numerators, respectively, of *one* and *one hundred* females. Other denominators are sometimes used. Death rates, for example, are usually expressed as so many per thousand people, or per 100,000 for some rare diseases.

Ease of comparison in a set of these fractions is gained at the expense of information. The original denominators are set aside, even sometimes lost sight of, a fault to be deplored. Many computations require return

TABLE 1.17.1
AVERAGE NUMBERS OF MALES AND FEMALES LITTERED IN A COLONY OF GUINEA PIGS,
BY MONTH. FROM SCHOTT AND LAMBERT (9)
VARIOUS SEX RATIOS

	Jan.	Feb.	Mar.	Apr.	May	June
Males	65	64	65	41	72	80
Females	49	58	81	48	62	80
Total	114	122	146	89	134	160
Percentage males	57.0	52.5	44.5	46.1	53.7	50.0
Ratio, males to females	1.327	1.103	0.802	0.854	1.161	1.000
Ratio, males per 100 females	132.7	110.3	80.2	85.4	116.1	100.0

	July	Aug.	Sept.	Oct.	Nov.	Dec.	Total
Males	88	114	80	129	112	86	996
Females	95	118	94	104	144	85	1,018
Total	183	232	174	233	256	171	2,014
Percentage males	48.1	49.1	46.0	55.4	43.8	50.3	49.45
Ratio, males to females	0.926	0.966	0.851	1.240	0.778	1.012	0.9784
Ratio, males per 100 females	92.6	96.6	85.1	124.0	77.8	101.2	97.84

to the original data, as for example the fractions in the column of totals
where

$$49.45\% = (100)(996)/2{,}014, \text{ etc.}$$

Attention has already been called to the fact (section 1.15) that percentages cannot be used in the calculation of chi-square unless some method is provided for recovery of the original base, thus giving due weight to sample size.

In many instances the bases of comparable percentages are not very different so that the percentages themselves can be averaged with no great inaccuracy. Even the guinea pig percentages of males have an average,

$$\frac{57.0 + 52.5 + \ldots + 50.3}{12} = \frac{596.5}{12} = 49.71\%,$$

which is not greatly divergent from the correct 49.45%. However, if one wishes an accurate average of percentages that have different bases he must go back to the original fractions, add their numerators and denominators separately, then divide.

EXAMPLE 1.17.1—Three dairy herds of a certain community showed the following reaction to a test for tuberculosis:

Number cows in herd	40	100	10
Percentage reactors	5	2	60

Calculate the average, 6.7%. Do you think this is a better average than $(5 + 2 + 60)/3 = 22.3\%$?

EXAMPLE 1.17.2—The percentages of noxious weed seeds in two samples of timothy are 0.01% and 0.05%. If each sample consisted of 10,000 seeds, what is the average percentage in the two? Ans. 0.03%.

EXAMPLE 1.17.3—If the samples in the foregoing example were 80,000 and 20,000 seeds, respectively, what would be the average? Ans. 0.018%, quite properly nearer the percentage of the larger sample.

EXAMPLE 1.17.4—Schott and Lambert reported that the numbers in table 1.17.1 are averages for 7 years so that the total number of males was 6,972 and of females, 7,126, the sex ratio being 97.84 males per 100 females. Test the hypothesis that the population sex ratio is 100. Ans. $\chi^2 = 1.68$. NOTE: If the averages were used, chi-square would be 0.24, only one-seventh the correct value.

REFERENCES

1. HERBERT ARKIN and RAYMOND R. COLTON. Graphs: How To Make and Use Them. Harper and Brothers, New York. Revised Edition (1940).

2. R. A. FISHER. Journal of the Royal Statistical Society, 85:87(1922).

3. MERLE T. JENKINS and MARTIN A. BELL. Genetics, 15:253 (1930).

4. E. W. LINDSTROM. Cornell University Agricultural Experiment Station Memoir 13 (1918).

5. JOHN W. MACARTHUR. Transactions of the Royal Canadian Institute, 18:1 (1931).

6. ALEXANDER MCFARLANE MOOD. Introduction to the Theory of Statistics. Mc-Graw-Hill Book Company, Inc., New York (1950).

7. J. NEYMAN. First Course in Probability and Statistics. Henry Holt and Company, New York (1950).

8. KARL PEARSON. Philosophical Magazine, Series 5, 50:157 (1899).

9. R. G. SCHOTT and W. V. LAMBERT. Iowa State Journal of Science, 4:343 (1930).

10. J. G. SNEDECOR. Journal of Experimental Zoology, 110:205 (1949).

11. CATHERINE M. THOMPSON. Biometrika, 32:187 (1941).

12. RAY E. WAKELEY. Iowa State University Research Bulletin 249 (1938).

13. HELEN M. WALKER and N. DUROST. Statistical Tables; Their Structure and Use. Teachers College, Columbia University, New York (1936).

14. S. S. WILKS. Mathematical Statistics. Princeton University Press, Princeton, New Jersey (1946).

15. G. U. YULE. Journal of the Royal Statistical Society, 85:95 (1922).

16. These data were furnished by courtesy of Dr. T. A. Brindley, leader of the cooperative project.

CHAPTER 2

Sampling From a Normally Distributed Population

2.1—Normally distributed population. In the first chapter, sampling was mostly from a population with only two kinds of individuals; odd or even, alive or dead, infested or free. Random samples of n from such a population made up a *binomial distribution*. The variable, an enumeration of successes, was discrete. Now we turn to another kind of population whose individuals are measured for some characteristic such as height or yield or income. The variable flows without a break from one individual to the next—a continuous variable with no limit to the number of individuals with different measurements. Such variables are distributed in many ways, but we shall be occupied mainly with the *normal distribution*.

Next to the binomial, the normal distribution was the earliest to be developed. De Moivre published its equation in 1733, 20 years after Bernoulli had given a comprehensive account of the binomial. That the two are not unrelated is clear from figure 2.1.1. On the left is the graph of a symmetrical binomial distribution similar to that in figure 1.6.1. In this new figure the sample size is 48 and the population sampled has equal numbers of the two kinds of individuals. An indefinitely great

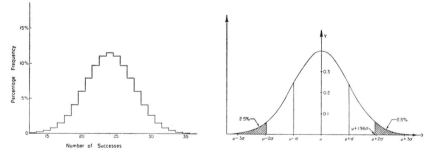

Fig. 2.1.1—At left: Binomial Distribution of successes in samples of 48 from 1:1 population. At right: Normal Distribution with mean μ and standard deviation σ (see table 8.7.1); the shaded areas comprise 5% of the total.

[35]

number of samples were drawn so that the frequencies are expressed as percentages of the total. Successes less than 13 and more than 35 do occur, but their frequencies are so small that they cannot be shown on the graph.

Imagine now that the size of the sample is increased without limit, the width of the intervals on the horizontal axis being decreased correspondingly. The steps of the histogram would soon become so small as to look like the continuous curve at the right. Indeed, the normal distribution is related to the binomial in some such manner as that described. The discrete variable has become *continuous* and the frequencies have merged into each other without a break.

This normal distribution is completely determined by two constants or *parameters*. First, there is the *mean*, μ, which locates the center of the distribution. Second, the *standard deviation*, σ, measures the spread or variation of the individual measurements; in fact, σ is the *scale* (unit of measurement) of the variable which is normally distributed.

From the figure you see that during one sigma on either side of μ the frequency is decreasing ever more rapidly but beyond that point it decreases at a continuously lesser rate. By the time the variable, X, has reached $\pm 3\sigma$ the percentage frequencies are negligibly small. Theoretically, the frequency of occurrence never vanishes entirely, but it approaches zero as X increases indefinitely. The concentration of the measurements close to μ is emphasized by the facts that over $2/3$ of the observations lie in the interval $\mu \pm \sigma$ while some 95% of them are in the interval $\mu \pm 2\sigma$. Beyond $\pm 3\sigma$ lies only 0.26% of the total frequency.

You are doubtless wondering why such a model is being presented since it obviously cannot describe any real population. It is astonishing that this normal distribution has dominated statistical practice as well as theory. Some of the reasons will be noted at suitable places (sections 3.4, 5.6, and 5.7), but three of them can be indicated here. First, there are many biological variables whose distributions are approximately normal, such as heights of men, for example, or lengths of ears of corn, or dressing percentages of swine. Second, it has been learned from both theory and experience that the inferences we shall make from sampling experimental populations are little affected by ordinary deviations from normality. Third, the mathematical treatment of the equation of the normal distribution is surprisingly easy and has been productive of a large body of theory with practical applications. Further discussion of the normal distribution will be found in chapter 8.

2.2—Estimators of μ and σ. While μ and σ are seldom known, they may be estimated from random samples. To illustrate the estimation of the parameters, we turn to the data reported in table 2.2.1. In 1936 the Council on Foods of the American Medical Association sampled the vitamin C content of commercially canned tomato juice by analyzing a specimen from each of the brands that displayed the seal of the Council (3). The data are shown in the second column of the table.

TABLE 2.2.1

VITAMIN C CONCENTRATION OF 17 SPECIMENS OF COMMERCIALLY CANNED
TOMATO JUICE, 1936*

Observation Number	Vitamin C Concentration Mg. Per 100 g.	Deviation From Mean	Deviation Squared
n	X	$x = X - \bar{x}$	x^2
1	16	− 4	16
2	22	+ 2	4
3	21	+ 1	1
4	20	0	0
5	23	+ 3	9
6	21	+ 1	1
7	19	− 1	1
8	15	− 5	25
9	13	− 7	49
10	23	+ 3	9
11	17	− 3	9
12	20	0	0
13	29	+ 9	81
14	18	− 2	4
15	22	+ 2	4
16	16	− 4	16
17	25	+ 5	25
Totals	340	−26 +26	254

$$\bar{x} = 340/17 = 20 \text{ mg. per 100 grams}$$
$$s^2 = \Sigma x^2/(n-1) = 254/16 = 15.88 \quad s = 3.98 \text{ mg.}/100 \text{ g.}$$
$$s_{\bar{x}}^2 = s^2/n = 15.88/17 = 0.934 \quad s_{\bar{x}} = s/\sqrt{17} = 0.965 \text{ mg.}/100 \text{ g.}$$

* Slightly modified, as is our custom, to make calculation easy. The conclusions are unaltered. For the original data see example 2.12.1.

Assuming random sampling from a normal population, μ is estimated by an average called the *mean of the sample* or, more briefly, the *sample mean*. This is calculated by the familiar process of dividing the sum of the observations, X, by their number. Representing the sample mean by $\bar{x}$,

$$\bar{x} = 340/17 = 20 \text{ mg. per 100 grams of juice}$$

The symbol, $\bar{x}$, is often called "bar-x" or "x-bar." We say that this sample mean is an estimator of μ or that μ is estimated by it.

As for the standard deviation, the simplest estimator of it is based on the *range* of the sample observations, that is, the difference between the largest and smallest measurements. For the vitamin C data,

$$\text{range} = 29 - 13 = 16 \text{ mg.}/100 \text{ g.}$$

From the range, sigma is estimated by means of a fraction which depends on the sample size; see table 2.2.2 (13, 18). For $n = 17$, halfway between 16 and 18, the fraction is 0.279, so that

$$\sigma \text{ is estimated by } (0.279)(16) = 4.46 \text{ mg.}/100 \text{ g.}$$

TABLE 2.2.2

RATIO OF σ TO RANGE IN SAMPLES OF *n* FROM THE NORMAL DISTRIBUTION.
EFFICIENCY OF RANGE AS ESTIMATOR OF σ. NUMBER OF OBSERVATIONS WITH
RANGE TO EQUAL 100 WITH *s*

n	$\frac{\sigma}{\text{Range}}$	Relative Efficiency	Number per 100	*n*	$\frac{\sigma}{\text{Range}}$	Relative Efficiency	Number per 100
2	0.886	1.000	100	12	0.307	0.815	123
3	.591	0.992	101	14	.294	.783	128
4	.486	.975	103	16	.283	.753	133
5	.430	.955	105	18	.275	.726	138
6	.395	.933	107	20	.268	.700	143
7	.370	.912	110	30	.245	.604	166
8	.351	.890	112	40	.231	.536	186
9	.337	.869	115	50	.222	.49	204
10	.325	.850	118				

Quite easily, then, we have made a *point estimate* of each parameter of a normal population; these estimators constitute a summary of the information contained in the sample. The sample mean cannot be improved upon as an estimator of μ, but we shall learn to estimate σ more efficiently. Also we shall learn about interval estimates and tests of hypotheses. Before doing so, it is worth while to examine our sample in greater detail.

The first point to be clarified is this: What population was represented by the sample of 17 determinations of vitamin C? I have raised this question tardily; it is the first one to be considered in designing any sampling. The report makes it clear that not all brands were sampled, only the seventeen that were allowed to display the seal of the Council. The dates of the packs were mostly August and September of 1936, about a year before the analyses were made. The Council report states that the vitamin concentration ". . . may be expected to vary according to the variety of the fruit, the conditions under which the crop has been grown, the degree of ripeness and other factors." About all that can be said, then, is that the sampled population consisted of those year-old containers still available to the 17 selected packers.

Other details are discussed in the following sections.

2.3—The array and its graphical representation. Some of the more intimate features of a sample are shown by arranging the observations in order of size, from low to high, in an *array*. The array of vitamin contents is like this:

13, 15, 16, 16, 17, 18, 19, 20, 20, 21, 21, 22, 22, 23, 23, 25, 29

For a small sample the array serves some of the same purposes as the frequency distribution of a large one.

The range, from 13 to 29, is now obvious. Also, attention is attracted to the concentration of the measures near the center of the array and to their thinning out at the extremes. In this way the sample may reflect the distribution of the normal population from which it was drawn. But the smaller the sample, the more erratic its reflection may be.

In looking through the vitamin C contents of the several brands, one is struck by their variation. What are the causes of this variation? Different processes of manufacture, perhaps, and different sources of the fruit. Doubtless, also, the specimens examined, being themselves samples of their brands, differed from the brand means. Finally, the laboratory technique of evaluation is never perfectly accurate. Variation is the very essence of statistical data.

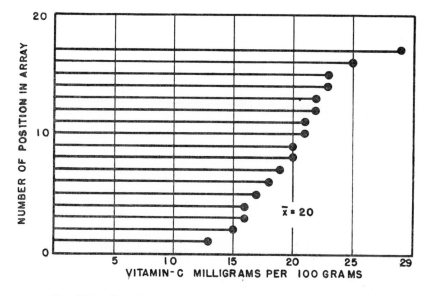

FIG. 2.3.1—Graphical representation of an array. Vitamin C data.

Figure 2.3.1 is a graphical representation of the foregoing array of 17 vitamin determinations. A dot represents each item. The distance of the dot from the vertical line at the left, proportional to the concentration of ascorbic acid in a brand specimen, is read in milligrams per 100 grams on the horizontal scale.

The diagram brings out vividly not only the variation and the concentration in the sample, but also two other characteristics: (i) the rather symmetrical occurrence of the values above and below the mean, and (ii) the scarcity of both extremely small and extremely large vitamin C contents, the bulk of the items being near the middle of the set. These features recur with notable persistence in samples from normal distributions. For many variables associated with living organisms there are averages and ranges peculiar to each, reflecting the manner in which each seems to express itself most successfully. These norms persist despite the fact that individuals enjoy a considerable freedom in development. A large part of our thinking is built around ideas corresponding to such statistics. The words, pig, daisy, man, each raises an image which is quantitatively described by summary numbers. It is difficult to conceive of any progress in thought until memories of individuals are collected into concepts like averages and ranges of distributions.

2.4—Symbolical representation. The items in any set may be represented by

$$X_1, X_2, X_3, \ldots X_n,$$

where the subscripts 1, 2, . . . n, may specify position in the set of n items (not necessarily an array). The three dots accompanying these symbols are read "*and so on.*" Matching the symbols with the values in column 2 of table 2.2.1,

$$X_1 = 16, X_2 = 22, \ldots X_{17} = 25 \text{ mg./100 g.}$$

The sample mean is represented by $\bar{x}$, so that

$$\bar{x} = (X_1 + X_2 + \ldots X_n)/n$$

This is condensed into the form,

$$\bar{x} = (\Sigma X)/n,$$

where X stands for every item successively. The symbol, ΣX, is read, "summation X" or "sum of the X." Applying this formula to the values of X in table 2.2.1,

$$\Sigma X = 340, \text{ and } \bar{x} = 340/17 = 20 \text{ mg./100 g.}$$

2.5—Deviations from sample mean. The individual variations of the items in a set of data may be well expressed by the *deviations* of these items from some centrally located number such as the sample mean. For example, the deviation-from-mean of the first X-value in table 2.2.1 is $16 - 20 = -4$ mg. per 100 g.; that is, this specimen falls short of $\bar{x}$ by 4 mg./100 g. Of special interest is the whole set of deviations calculated from the array in section 2.3:

$$-7, -5, -4, -4, -3, -2, -1, 0, 0, 1, 1, 2, 2, 3, 3, 5, 9$$

These deviations are represented graphically in figure 2.3.1 by the distances of the dots from the vertical line drawn through the sample mean.

Deviations are almost as fundamental in our thinking as are averages themselves. "What a whale of a pig" is a metaphor expressing astonishment at the deviation of an individual's size from the speaker's concept of the normal. Gossip and news are concerned chiefly with deviations from accepted standards of behavior. Curiously, interest is wont to center in departures from norm, rather than in that background of averages against which the departures achieve prominence. Statistically, freaks are freaks only because of their large deviations.

Deviations are represented symbolically by lower case letters. That is:

$$x_1 = X_1 - \bar{x}$$
$$x_2 = X_2 - \bar{x}$$
$$\cdot \qquad \cdot \qquad \cdot$$
$$\cdot \qquad \cdot \qquad \cdot$$
$$x_n = X_n - \bar{x}$$

Just as X may represent any of the items in a set, or all of them in succession, so x represents deviations from sample mean. In general,

$$x = X - \bar{x}$$

It is easy to verify the theorem that the sum of a set of deviations-from-mean is zero; that is $\Sigma x = 0$. The set listed in table 2.2.1 adds to zero, the sum of the positive deviations being equal to the sum of the negatives. This theorem about deviations-from-mean is useful for verifying the calculation of a set of deviations—be sure that the sum is zero. As a consequence of the theorem, it follows that the *mean* of the deviations is zero. This is a theorem about which you will be reminded later.

EXAMPLE 2.5.1—The weights of 12 staminate hemp plants in early April at College Station, Texas, (16), were approximately:

13, 11, 16, 5, 3, 18, 9, 9, 8, 6, 27, and 7 grams

Array the weights and represent them graphically. Calculate the sample mean, 11 grams, and the deviations therefrom. Verify the fact that $\Sigma x = 0$. Show that σ is estimated by 7.4 grams.

EXAMPLE 2.5.2—The heights of 11 men are 64, 70, 65, 69, 68, 67, 68, 67, 66, 72, and 61 inches. Compute the sample mean and verify it by summing the deviations. Are the numbers of positive and negative deviations equal, or only their sums?

EXAMPLE 2.5.3—The yields of alfalfa from 10 plots were 0.8, 1.3, 1.5, 1.7, 1.7, 1.8, 2.0, 2.0, 2.0, and 2.2 tons per acre. How many deviations are positive and how many negative? Is their sum zero? Estimate σ. Ans. 0.46 ton per acre.

EXAMPLE 2.5.4—The weights of 11 forty-year-old men were 148, 154, 158, 160, 161, 162, 166, 170, 182, 195, and 236 pounds. Contrast the graphical representation of this array with that of the preceding example. Notice the fact that only three of the weights exceed the sample mean. Would you expect weights of men to be normally distributed? A test of symmetry will be given in section 8.5.

EXAMPLE 2.5.5—The following were the yields of two varieties of oats in five successive years (bushels per acre):

Variety	\multicolumn{5}{c}{Year}
	1	2	3	4	5
A	34	30	41	25	45
B	30	17	33	25	25

Calculate the 5 differences, $A - B$. Might these differences be a sample from a normal population of differences? Assuming that they are, estimate μ and σ. Ans. 9.0 and 8.6 bushels per acre.

EXAMPLE 2.5.6—The following data are adapted from Reddy's (14) investigations of the differences in yield attributable to the disinfection of Diplodia infected seeds of maize.   The figures represent bushels per acre.

Treatment	Pairs of Plots in 1933					
	1	2	3	4	5	6
Treated	68.1	74.6	64.4	69.2	61.8	57.9
Untreated	64.7	62.5	66.8	69.2	53.9	58.5
Differences	3.4	12.1	−2.4	0.0	7.9	−0.6

Pairs of Plots in 1934									
1	2	3	4	5	6	7	8	9	10
18.0	24.0	18.8	17.8	18.5	27.2	23.6	23.9	20.3	11.9
10.9	24.4	15.1	16.8	13.2	21.6	13.7	17.5	16.3	15.5
7.1	−0.4	3.7	1.0	5.3	5.6	9.9	6.4	4.0	−3.6

Clearly the yields in the two years are not samples from the same population, but the differences may be.   Represent graphically the array of differences.   Estimate μ and σ in the population of differences.   Ans. 3.7 and 4.4 bushels per acre.

EXAMPLE 2.5.7—If you sum the deviations from 3.7 bushels per acre in the foregoing example you will not get zero.   Why?   If you compute the sample mean of the deviations and add it to 3.7, will you get the exact sample mean of the differences?

EXAMPLE 2.5.8—If you should calculate the sample mean of the yields of the 16 untreated plots in example 2.5.6, would it estimate the parameter of any population that you can describe?

EXAMPLE 2.5.9—Suppose you wish to estimate the yield of a field of 300 rows of corn.   You actually harvest 10 rows, chosen at random, and determine the sample mean yield, 5 bushels per row.   Would you hesitate to fix the field yield at 1,500 bushels?   You would be assuming that the field mean is the same as that of the 10 harvested rows, and would be using the theorem, $\Sigma X = n\bar{x}$.

EXAMPLE 2.5.10—If you have some skill in algebra, prove the theorem that $\Sigma x = 0$.   Starting with the relation, $x = X - \bar{x}$, sum both members, then substitute $\Sigma X = n\bar{x}$.

EXAMPLE 2.5.11—If you have two sets of data which are paired as in example 2.5.5, and if you have calculated the resulting set of differences, prove that the sample mean of the differences is equal to the difference between the sample means of the two sets.   Verify this theorem by use of the data in example 2.5.5.

2.6—Another estimator of σ; the sample standard deviation. The range, dependent as it is on only the two extremes in a sample, has a more variable sampling distribution than an estimator based on the whole set of deviations-from-mean in a sample, not just the largest and smallest. Such a set, with 17 deviations, was shown in table 2.2.1 and again as an array in section 2.5. What kind of average is appropriate to summarize these deviations, and to estimate σ with the least sampling variation?

Clearly, the sample mean of the deviations is useless as an estimator because it is always zero. But a natural suggestion is to ignore the signs, calculating the sample mean of the absolute values of the deviations. The resulting measure of variation, the *mean absolute deviation*, had a considerable vogue in times past. Now, however, we have other estimators, more efficient and more easily calculated.

One of the more efficient estimators is the *sample standard deviation* which we shall denote by *s*. Its calculation is set out in the right-hand part of table 2.2.1. First, each deviation is squared. Next, the *sum of squares*, Σx^2, is divided by the number of *degrees of freedom*, one less than the sample size. The result is the *mean square*, s^2. Finally, the extraction of the square root recovers the original unit of measurement (in this example, mg. per 100 g.). Before further discussion of this average, its calculation should be fixed in mind by the working of a few examples.

EXAMPLE 2.6.1—The five differences, $A-B$, in example 2.5.5 were 4, 13, 8, 0, and 20 bushels per acre. Calculate *s*. Ans. 7.8 bu./acre. Compare this with the estimate based on the range.

EXAMPLE 2.6.2—In example 2.5.1, calculate the sample standard deviation. Ans. 6.7 grams. Compare this with your first estimate of σ.

EXAMPLE 2.6.3—Calculate *s* for the alfalfa yields of example 2.5.3. Ans. 0.41 ton per acre.

It may be a little surprising to have the divisor, $n - 1$, proposed for computing an average; you have always calculated the sample mean by using the divisor, *n*. In computing s^2, it is necessary to divide by the degrees of freedom if you wish to avoid a bias in estimating σ^2. Division by *n* does produce an estimate of σ^2 but it is a *biased estimate*. In the problems we shall consider there is no occasion to use any but the *unbiased estimate*.

You now have two estimators of σ, one of them easier to calculate than the other, but *less efficient*. You need to know what is meant by "less efficient" and what governs the choice of which to use. Both pieces of information are supplied by the fourth columns of table 2.2.2. As an example, if $n = 10$, the estimate from the range is only 85% as efficient as that from *s*; meaning that, for the same precision, a sample of 10 with *s* as estimator is equivalent to a sample of $10/0.85 = 12$ using range. The argument will become clearer as you proceed, but the table indicates right away that, other things being equal, you have to weigh the cost of calculating *s* against the cost of more observations; in this instance, 12 instead of 10. Now there are some operations where observations are taken for other purposes and are then available to the statistician at no extra cost. For estimating σ he could have a few extra just by copying them. His cue would be to use the range. But consider the alfalfa experiment of example 2.6.3. How much would it cost the investigator to provide 2 extra plots? There is the cost of land and equipment to be considered, together with their availability for use, there are salaries and wages, and finally there there is the sale price of the alfalfa. The net cost of the 2 extra plots is to be balanced against the few cents or the few minutes it would take to calculate *s*. I suggest that, if you value the information to be obtained from the experiment, you should proceed with the calculation of s. This will give you the maximum information to be obtained from the data. The advantage of the range is that it provides a quick preliminary estimate. Also, since computers sometimes make mistakes, the estimate from the range is an easy approximate check on the calculation of s. For this purpose, it is well to fix in mind a few of the fractions, σ/range. Remember:

If n Is Near This Number	Then σ Is Roughly Estimated From Dividing Range by
5	2
10	3
25	4
100	5

In statistical practice, this rough-and-ready estimator of σ proves itself a most useful device. But for the usual run of experimental data it pays to calculate s.

If you study mathematical statistics, you may hear a good deal about the Principle of Least Squares. The sample mean and deviations therefrom are related to that principle in this manner: if deviations are measured from the sample mean, then the sum of their squares is a minimum. In particular (and reversing the statement) if deviations in table 2.2.1 are measured from some number different from the sample mean, 20, the sum of their squares will be greater than 254. Verify this by trying deviations from, say, 19 then 22.

It seems rather characteristic that large things vary much and small things little. For this reason it is often convenient to express the sample standard deviation as a fraction of the sample mean, the resulting statistic being called *relative standard deviation* or *coefficient of variation*, C. As an example, it is reported (1) that the average statures of one-year and eighteen-year girls are 74.4 and 161.0 cm. respectively, with sample standard deviations 2.64 and 6.12 cm. The two coefficients of variation are

$$C_1 = 2.64/74.4 = 0.036$$
$$C_{18} = 6.12/161.0 = 0.038,$$

almost the same. Usually C is expressed as a percentage, C_1 for example, being 3.6%. Discussion of this characteristic of the sample standard deviation is resumed in section 2.16.

EXAMPLE 2.6.4—The birth weights of 20 guinea pigs, borne in litters of two, were: 30, 30, 26, 32, 30, 23, 29, 31, 36, 30, 25, 34, 32, 24, 28, 27, 38, 31, 34, 30 grams. Estimate σ in 3 ways: (i) by the rough approximation, one-fourth of the range (Ans. 3.8 g.); (ii) by use of the fraction, 0.268, in table 2.2.2 (Ans. 4.0 g.); (iii) by calculating s (Ans. 3.85 g.). N B.: Observe the time required to calculate s.

EXAMPLE 2.6.5—In the preceding example, how many birth weights would be required to yield the same precision if the range were used instead of s? Ans. 29 weights.

EXAMPLE 2.6.6—If it takes 5 minutes to weigh a guinea pig (removing and returning to cage, weighing and recording) and 2 minutes to estimate σ using the range, would you have saved or lost time by calculating s?

EXAMPLE 2.6.7—Suppose you lined up according to height the 16 men in 2 squads of 18-year-old freshmen, then measured the height of the shortest, 64 inches, and of the tallest, 72 inches. Would you accept the midpoint of the range, $(64 + 72)/2 = 68$ inches as a rough estimate of μ, and $8/3 = 2.7$ inches as a quick-and-easy estimate of σ?

EXAMPLE 2.6.8—The mean yield of hay from 15 plots of alfalfa was 2.2 tons per acre, with $s = 0.35$ ton per acre. Using table 2.2.2, approximate the range on the assumption that $\sigma = 0.35$ ton per acre. Ans. 1.2 tons per acre. Would this suggest that the highest yielding plot bore about 2.8 tons per acre?

2.7—"Student's" t**-distribution.** We now have adequate point estimators for μ and σ. Next to be considered are *interval estimates* and *tests of hypotheses*.

First we require a sampling distribution analogous to that of chi-square. Known as *"Student's" t-distribution*, it was discovered by W. S. Gosset in 1908 (15) and perfected by R. A. Fisher in 1924 (6). This distribution has revolutionized the statistics of small samples. In the next chapter you will be asked to verify the distribution by the same kind of sampling process as you used for chi-square; indeed it was by such sampling that Gosset first learned about it.

The quantity t is given by the equation,

$$ t = \frac{\bar{x} - \mu}{s/\sqrt{n}} $$

That is, t is the deviation of the estimated mean from that of the population, measured in terms of $s/\sqrt{n}$ as the unit. Both $\bar{x}$ and s are calculated from a sample of n observations, assumed to be a random sample from a normal population. We do not know μ though we may have some hypothesis about it. Without μ, t cannot be calculated; but its sampling distribution has been worked out.

The denominator, $s/\sqrt{n}$, is a useful quantity estimating $\sigma/\sqrt{n}$, the *standard error*. We shall call $s/\sqrt{n}$ the *sample standard error* and symbolize it by $s_{\bar{x}}$. Further explanation will be given in chapter 3. For vitamin C, table 2.2.1, $s_{\bar{x}} = 3.98/\sqrt{17} = 0.965$ mg./100 g.

The distribution of t is laid out in table 2.7.1. In large samples it is practically normal with $\mu = 0$ and $\sigma = 1$. It is only for samples of less than 30 that the distinction becomes obvious.

Like the normal, the t-distribution is symmetrical about the mean. This allows the probability in the table to be stated as that of a larger absolute value, sign ignored. As an example, look at the value, $t = 1.96$, for infinite (∞) degrees of freedom, the normal distribution. The probability indicated is 0.05. This means that among samples of great size, drawn at random from a normal population, 5% of them are expected to have either $t > 1.96$ or $t < -1.96$. Figure 2.7.1 shows such values of t

TABLE 2.7.1

THE DISTRIBUTION OF t*

Degrees of Freedom	Probability of a Larger Value, Sign Ignored								
	0.500	0.400	0.200	0.100	0.050	0.025	0.010	0.005	0.001
1	1.000	1.376	3.078	6.314	12.706	25.452	63.657		
2	.816	1.061	1.886	2.920	4.303	6.205	9.925	14.089	31.598
3	.765	.978	1.638	2.353	3.182	4.176	5.841	7.453	12.941
4	.741	.941	1.533	2.132	2.776	3.495	4.604	5.598	8.610
5	.727	.920	1.476	2.015	2.571	3.163	4.032	4.773	6.859
6	.718	.906	1.440	1.943	2.447	2.969	3.707	4.317	5.959
7	.711	.896	1.415	1.895	2.365	2.841	3.499	4.029	5.405
8	.706	.889	1.397	1.860	2.306	2.752	3.355	3.832	5.041
9	.703	.883	1.383	1.833	2.262	2.685	3.250	3.690	4.781
10	.700	.879	1.372	1.812	2.228	2.634	3.169	3.581	4.587
11	.697	.876	1.363	1.796	2.201	2.593	3.106	3.497	4.437
12	.695	.873	1.356	1.782	2.179	2.560	3.055	3.428	4.318
13	.694	.870	1.350	1.771	2.160	2.533	3.012	3.372	4.221
14	.692	.868	1.345	1.761	2.145	2.510	2.977	3.326	4.140
15	.691	.866	1.341	1.753	2.131	2.490	2.947	3.286	4.073
16	.690	.865	1.337	1.746	2.120	2.473	2.921	3.252	4.015
17	.689	.863	1.333	1.740	2.110	2.458	2.898	3.222	3.965
18	.688	.862	1.330	1.734	2.101	2.445	2.878	3.197	3.922
19	.688	.861	1.328	1.729	2.093	2.433	2.861	3.174	3.883
20	.687	.860	1.325	1.725	2.086	2.423	2.845	3.153	3.850
21	.686	.859	1.323	1.721	2.080	2.414	2.831	3.135	3.819
22	.686	.858	1.321	1.717	2.074	2.406	2.819	3.119	3.792
23	.685	.858	1.319	1.714	2.069	2.398	2.807	3.104	3.767
24	.685	.857	1.318	1.711	2.064	2.391	2.797	3.090	3.745
25	.684	.856	1.316	1.708	2.060	2.385	2.787	3.078	3.725
26	.684	.856	1.315	1.706	2.056	2.379	2.779	3.067	3.707
27	.684	.855	1.314	1.703	2.052	2.373	2.771	3.056	3.690
28	.683	.855	1.313	1.701	2.048	2.368	2.763	3.047	3.674
29	.683	.854	1.311	1.699	2.045	2.364	2.756	3.038	3.659
30	.683	.854	1.310	1.697	2.042	2.360	2.750	3.030	3.646
35	.682	.852	1.306	1.690	2.030	2.342	2.724	2.996	3.591
40	.681	.851	1.303	1.684	2.021	2.329	2.704	2.971	3.551
45	.680	.850	1.301	1.680	2.014	2.319	2.690	2.952	3.520
50	.680	.849	1.299	1.676	2.008	2.310	2.678	2.937	3.496
55	.679	.849	1.297	1.673	2.004	2.304	2.669	2.925	3.476
60	.679	.848	1.296	1.671	2.000	2.299	2.660	2.915	3.460
70	.678	.847	1.294	1.667	1.994	2.290	2.648	2.899	3.435
80	.678	.847	1.293	1.665	1.989	2.284	2.638	2.887	3.416
90	.678	.846	1.291	1.662	1.986	2.279	2.631	2.878	3.402
100	.677	.846	1.290	1.661	1.982	2.276	2.625	2.871	3.390
120	.677	.845	1.289	1.658	1.980	2.270	2.617	2.860	3.373
∞	.6745	.8416	1.2816	1.6448	1.9600	2.2414	2.5758	2.8070	3.2905

* Parts of this table are reprinted by permission from R. A. Fisher's *Statistical Methods for Research Workers*, published by Oliver and Boyd, Edinburgh (1925–1950); from Maxine Merrington's "Table of Percentage Points of the *t*-Distribution," Biometrika, 32:300 (1942); and from Bernard Ostle's *Statistics in Research*, Iowa State University Press (1954).

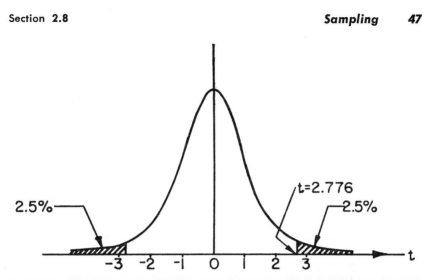

Fig. 2.7.1—Distribution of t with 4 degrees of freedom. The shaded areas comprise 5% of the total area. The distribution is more peaked in the center and has higher tails than the normal.

in the shaded areas; 2.5% of them are in one tail and 2.5% in the other. Effectively, the table shows the two halves of the figure superimposed, giving the sum of the shaded areas (probabilities) in both. So, the probability in the two tails of the t-distribution corresponds to that in one tail of chi-square, table 1.14.1. The reason for making the table this way will shortly appear.

EXAMPLE 2.7.1—In the vitamin C sampling of table 2.2.1, set up the hypothesis that $\mu = 17.954$ mg./100 g. Calculate t. Ans. 2.12.

EXAMPLE 2.7.2—For the vitamin C sample, degrees of freedom $= 17 - 1 = 16$, the denominator of the fraction giving s^2. From table 2.7.1, find the probability of a value of t larger in absolute value than 2.12. Ans. 0.05. This means that, among random samples of $n = 17$ from normal populations, 5% of them are expected to have t-values below -2.12 or above 2.12.

EXAMPLE 2.7.3—If samples of $n = 17$ are randomly drawn from a normal population and have t calculated for each, what is the probability that t will fall between -2.12 and $+2.12$? Ans. 0.95.

EXAMPLE 2.7.4—If random samples of $n = 17$ are drawn from a normal population, what is the probability of t greater than 2.12? Ans. 0.025.

EXAMPLE 2.7.5—What size of sample would have $t > |2|$ in 5% of all random samples from normal populations? Ans. 61. (Note the symbol for "absolute value," that is, ignoring signs.)

EXAMPLE 2.7.6—Among very large samples ($d.f. = \infty$), what value of t would be exceeded in 2.5% of them? Ans. 1.96.

2.8—The interval estimate of μ; the confidence interval. The argument about the *interval estimate* for μ is a bit complicated so I am going to tell you how to set the interval before explaining why. As illustration, recall the vitamin C determinations in table 2.2.1; $n = 17$, $\bar{x} = 20$ and

$s_{\bar{x}} = 0.965$ mg./100 g. To get the 95% confidence interval (interval estimate):

1. Enter the table with $d.f. = 17 - 1 = 16$ and in the column headed .05 take the entry, $t_{.05} = 2.12$

2. Calculate the quantity,

$$t_{.05}s_{\bar{x}} = (2.12)(0.965) = 2.05 \text{ mg./100 g.}$$

3. The confidence interval is from

$$20 - 2.05 = 17.95 \text{ to } 20 + 2.05 = 22.05 \text{ mg./100 g.}$$

If you say that μ is covered by the interval from 17.95 to 22.05 mg./100 g., you will be right unless a 1-in-20 chance has occurred in the sampling.

The point and 95% interval estimate of μ may be summarized this way: 20 ± 2.05 mg./100 g. (The formula is $\bar{x} \pm t_{.05}s_{\bar{x}}$.)

The explanation of these rules rests on the selection of a particular value for t in the table. If for $d.f. = n - 1$ the value $t_{.05}$ is chosen, it may be said that this value of t is expected to be exceeded in absolute value in 5% of all samples drawn at random from normal populations. Or the statement may be changed to this: t will lie between $-t_{.05}$ and $+ t_{.05}$ in 95% of such samples. That is, the probability is 0.95 that $-t_{.05} \leq t \leq t_{.05}$. Substituting the expression for t, the probability is 0.95 that

$$- t_{.05} \leq \frac{\bar{x} - \mu}{s_{\bar{x}}} \leq t_{.05}$$

Multiplying both sides of each inequality by $s_{\bar{x}}$, the probability is 0.95 that

$$- t_{.05}s_{\bar{x}} \leq \bar{x} - \mu \leq t_{.05}s_{\bar{x}}$$

Transposing $\bar{x}$, changing signs, and reversing the terms, the probability is 0.95 that

$$\bar{x} - t_{.05}s_{\bar{x}} \leq \mu \leq \bar{x} + t_{.05}s_{\bar{x}}$$

The interpretation is: Before the sample is drawn, the probability is 0.95 that the interval indicated will include μ. After the sample is drawn and the values of $\bar{x}$, s, and n are substituted, it may be said with confidence that the interval includes μ and the statement will be correct unless a 1-in-20 chance has occurred in the sampling.

An interval estimate for σ will be presented in section 2.14.

EXAMPLE 2.8.1—For the yields of alfalfa in examples 2.5.3 and 2.6.3, $n = 10$, $\bar{x} = 1.70$ and $s = 0.41$ ton/acre. Set 95% confidence limits on the mean of the population from which this is a random sample. Ans. 1.41 and 1.99 tons/acre.

EXAMPLE 2.8.2—In examples 2.5.5 and 2.6.1, the 5 differences had $\bar{d} = 9.0$ and $s_D = 7.8$ bu./acre. Set the 99% interval estimate on μ. Ans. From -7.0 to 25.0 bu./acre. Might the population difference be zero?

EXAMPLE 2.8.3—In an investigation of growth in school children of 8 private schools (7), the sample mean height of 265 boys of age 13.5 to 14.5 years was 63.84 inches with standard deviation, 3.08 inches. What is the 95% confidence interval for μ? Ans. 63.5 to 64.2 inches. Calculate $C = 4.8\%$.

2.9—Estimates and tests of differences. Experiments are most often designed to discover and evaluate *differences* between effects rather than the effects themselves. It is differences between yields produced by fertilizers or differences between gains produced by feeds that are wanted. One of the simplest of such experiments is designed to contrast the effects of two treatments. Pairs of similar individuals are selected, one of the treatments being applied to each. The individuals in the pairs may be field plots or pigs or colonies of bees. If there were only a single pair it would be impossible to say whether the difference in behavior is to be attributed to the two treatments imposed or to the natural variability of the individuals or partly to each. Hence, there must be two or more pairs, or *replications*, one member of every pair being chosen at random to receive the first treatment, the other member the second. The differences between the measurements of the two pairs constitute the sample data upon which inferences are to be based. If there were no individual variation the differences would presumably be all alike. Always there is variation.

In many experiments it may be assumed that the differences make up a random sample from a normal population. Commonly the objective is to learn the size of the mean of this population and particularly if it is different from zero. Let us examine such an experiment.

Youden and Beale (19) wished to find out if two preparations of the mosiac virus would produce different effects on tobacco leaves. The method employed was to rub half a leaf of a tobacco plant with a piece of cheesecloth soaked in one preparation of the virus extract, then to rub the other half similarly with the second preparation. The measurement of potency was the number of local lesions appearing on the half leaf; the measurement is assumed to be a continuous variable. The data reported in table 2.9.1 are taken from leaf number 2 on each of 8 plants. The differences, $D = X_1 - X_2$ in the fourth column make up the random sample in which the experimenter is interested. The question posed by the experiment is this: Does the preparation of the virus affect the number of lesions? In statistical terms, is the mean of the sampled population equal to zero or is it different from zero?

One way to answer the question is to set confidence limits on the population mean difference, μ_D. With $\bar{d} = 4$ lesions, $s_{\bar{d}} = 1.52$ lesions and $t_{.05} = 2.365$, it may be said that, unless a 1-in-20 chance has occurred,

$$4 - (2.365)(1.52) \leq \mu_D \leq 4 + (2.365)(1.52)$$

That is, μ_D is expected to be greater than $4 - (2.365)(1.52) = 0.4$ lesions and less than 7.6. Since zero is not included in the confidence interval,

TABLE 2.9.1

NUMBERS OF LESIONS ON HALVES OF 8 TOBACCO LEAVES, EACH BEING LEAF NO. 2
ON ONE OF 8 PLANTS. THE LESIONS MEASURE THE EFFECTS OF TWO PREPARATIONS
OF THE MOSIAC VIRUS*

Plant No.	Preparation 1 X_1	Preparation 2 X_2	Difference $D = X_1 - X_2$	Deviation $d = D - \bar{d}$	Squared Deviation d^2
1	9	10	−1	−5	25
2	17	11	6	2	4
3	31	18	13	9	81
4	18	14	4	0	0
5	7	6	1	−3	9
6	8	7	1	−3	9
7	20	17	3	−1	1
8	10	5	5	1	1
Total	120	88	32	0	130
Mean	15	11	$\bar{d}$ = 4 lesions		$s_D^2 = 18.57$

$s_D = \sqrt{18.57} = 4.31$ lesions. $s_{\bar{d}}^2 = 18.57/8 = 2.32.$ $s_{\bar{d}} = 1.52$ lesions.

* Slightly changed to make calculation easier.

we conclude that μ_D is positive; that in the population the second preparation produces fewer lesions than the first.

If the confidence interval had included zero, the inference would have been that μ_D might be zero, that the preparations may be equally potent.

The reader may be startled by the fractional number of lesions at the confidence limit. We are treating these discrete data as though they were from a continuous population. Is the present method appropriate for counts as well as for measurements, and may a normal distribution be assumed? Neither question can be categorically answered, "yes." Counts may fall into an approximately normal distribution so that the methods of this section are appropriate, but the evidence from this sample is not encouraging. On the other hand, since there are no hypothetical frequencies, the methods of chapter 1 are not available. For the moment, the normal theory is assumed because it works fairly well even with samples from distributions far from normal. Later some alternatives will be examined (example 11.14.1), but conclusions will not be changed.

A second method of making an inference about μ_D, the classical method, is by a *test of significance*. If necessary, review section 1.13. The usual null hypothesis is $\mu_D = 0$. For samples from normal populations the distribution of t furnishes the test. For substitution in the equation for t we have, for the tobacco virus data, H_0: $\mu_D = 0$, and the sample statistics, $\bar{d} = 4$ lesions, $s_{\bar{d}} = 1.52$ lesions; so,

$$t = \frac{\bar{d} - \mu_D}{s_{\bar{d}}} = \frac{4 - 0}{1.52} = 2.63, \, d.f. = n - 1 = 7$$

Is this an ordinary value of t in sampling from a normal population with $\mu_D = 0$, or is it so unusual as to cause rejection of the null hypothesis? Table 2.7.1 shows that for $d.f. = 7$ the probability of a larger value in sampling from $\mu_D = 0$ is beyond 0.05, about 0.04; the sample evidence points to rejection of H_0. The difference, $\bar{d} = 4$ lesions, is said to be *significant*. The conclusion is that the two preparations are capable of producing different numbers of lesions on tobacco leaves number 2.

It is evident that the two methods of making an inference about μ_D lead to the same conclusion. The confidence interval gives an estimate of the distance that μ_D lies beyond (or within) the interval. The test of significance yields a probability of drawing a larger t in sampling from $\mu_D = 0$. One may take his choice or use both of them.

In a paired experiment like that on the half leaves, s_D^2 (or sometimes s_D) is referred to as *experimental error*. It is an estimate of σ_D^2, the measure of variation in the sampled population of differences. One objective of experimental design is to insure an appropriate estimate of the real error involved. As you proceed you will hear much more about the evaluation of experimental error.

EXAMPLE 2.9.1—L. C. Grove (8) determined the sample mean numbers of florets produced by seven pairs of plots of Excellence gladiolus, one plot of each pair planted with high (first-year) corms, the other with low (second-year or older) corms. The plot means were as follows:

Corm	Florets						
High	11.2	13.3	12.8	13.7	12.2	11.9	12.1
Low	14.6	12.6	15.0	15.6	12.7	12.0	13.1

Calculate the sample mean difference. Ans. 1.2 florets. About the population of such differences, test $H_0: \mu_D = 0$. Ans. $P = 0.06$, approximately; strictly speaking, H_0 is not rejected, but recall the last paragraph of section 1.13

EXAMPLE 2.9.2—Mitchell, Burroughs, and Beadles (10) computed the biological values of proteins from raw peanuts (P) and roasted peanuts (R) as determined in an experiment with 10 pairs of rats. The pairs of data P, R are as follows: 61, 55; 60, 54; 56, 47; 63, 59; 56, 51; 63, 61; 59, 57; 56, 54; 44, 63; 61, 58. Compute the sample mean difference, 2.0, and the sample standard deviation of the differences. 7.72 units. Since $t = 0.82$, almost half of similar samples from a population with $\mu_D = 0$ would be expected to have larger t-values.

Note: 9 of the 10 differences, $P - R$, are positive. One would like some information about the next-to-the-last pair 44, 62. The first member, especially, seems abnormal. While unusual individuals like this do occur in the most carefully conducted trials, their appearance demands immediate investigation. Doubtless an error in recording or computation was searched for but not found. What should be done about such aberrant observations is a moot question; their occurrence detracts from one's confidence in the experiment. Further discussion will be found in section 2.15.

EXAMPLE 2.9.3—Crampton (4) reports the gains in weight per 100 pounds of feed eaten by 10 pairs of swine constituting lots I and III of MacDonald College hog feeding trial 33B. The pigs were paired on the basis of being litter mates of as nearly the same initial weight as feasible. The pairs of gains are as follows, the datum for the member of lot I in each pair being set down first: 17, 20; 22, 21; 22, 21; 15, 24; 24, 24; 22, 22; 21, 23; 21, 21; 17, 22; 21, 23 pounds gain per 100 pounds feed. Compute the sample mean of the differences. Ans. 2.0 lbs./100 lbs. feed. Test the hypothesis that the rations produce the same gain. Ans. $P = 0.07$ approximately   Presumably H_0 would not be rejected.   Calculate the 95% confidence interval for μ_D.   Ans. From -0.2 to 4.2 lbs./100 lbs. feed.

EXAMPLE 2.9.4—Prof. H. H. Love of Cornell University took a leading part in introducing "Student's" small sample theory in America. In one of his illustrations (9) he compared the yields of Great Northern (G) and Big Four (B) oats in the nine years 1912–1920. The differences, $G - B$, were 16.3, 13.4, 3.8, 7.9, 2.6, 2.5, 9.6, 7.2, and 3.3 bushels per acre. Compute $\bar{x} = 7.4$ bushels per acre. Test the null hypothesis that the two varieties have the same yield. Ans. $P = < 0.01$. Of what population can this be a random sample? Set the 95% confidence interval on the population difference in yield. Ans. From 3.6 to 11.2 bushels per acre.

2.10—Reasons and conditions for pairing. The student will observe that, to conduct successfully an experiment like Youden and Beale's, a great deal must be known already about the behavior of the experimental materials. The object of the half-leaf experiment was to demonstrate the effectiveness of the pairing of the half leaves. It was realized that different leaves reacted to the virus with great variation, especially leaves at different heights on the stem. If a random selection even of leaves No. 2 had been used, the differences, $D = X_1 - X_2$, would have been much greater than those in the table. Some idea of this greater variation can be got by looking at the data in the second and third columns; if these numbers were paired at random, the range of differences might have been as great as from $7 - 18 = -11$ to $31 - 5 = 26$, or 37. This would estimate σ as about $37/3 = 12$ lesions instead of the experimental estimate, $s = 4.3$ lesions. Of course, the occurrence of this extreme pairing is an unlikely event, but you will learn later that random pairing would be almost as inefficient, requiring about 40 pairs to reach the same precision as Youden and Beale got with 8; this experiment would have been about 5 times as costly if whole leaves No. 2 had been used.

What kind of information is required in order to pair successfully? Whether one pairs or not, it must be known that the individuals will behave alike (aside from random variation) if treated alike. Otherwise the experiment is ambiguous—it cannot be known whether differences in behavior are attributable to the treatments or to other causes. Pairing is indicated if twos can be found that differ between themselves less than from other twos. Identical twins, for example, are natural pairs, and litter mates of the same sex are often paired successfully. If treated alike, they usually behave more nearly alike than do animals less closely related. Again, two observations on the same individual would always be paired: such would be weights before and after a football game, or blood sugar concentration before and after an injection of insulin. As a final illustration, environmental variation often calls for pairing. Two treatments should be laid down side by side in the field or on the greenhouse bench in order to avoid the effects of unnecessary differences in soil, moisture, temperature, etc. Two plots or pots next to each other respond more nearly alike than do those at a distance. Animals receiving the two treatments should be either in the same enclosure or in adjacent ones.

This scheme of pairing should be utilized whenever it is available. If you wish to learn about differences in treatment effects, the economical way is to try them on pairs of individuals who would otherwise behave as nearly alike as possible.

If it could be known that two individuals were exactly alike, the difference between treatments could be evaluated by trying them on a single pair. The more the individuals differ, the more pairs will be required to balance out the random differences, leaving in the clear the effect of treatments. The balancing out is insured by randomizing the treatments on the members of each pair. Economy is attained by pairing similar individuals.

For conditions in which there is no known basis for pairing, suitable statistical methods will be presented in chapter 4.

Before passing to some less fundamental topics, let us pause for a summary. First, we have become acquainted with the normal distribution whose two parameters are the mean, μ, and the standard deviation, σ (or the variance, σ^2). Next we learned some estimators derived from a random sample:

1. The sample mean, $\bar{x}$, an estimate of μ.

2. The sample standard deviation, s, and a multiplier times range, estimates of σ.

3. The mean square, s^2, an estimate of σ^2.

After introducing the sampling distribution of the test criterion, t, we made an interval estimate of μ and tested the null hypothesis, $\mu = 0$, with $H_A: \mu \neq 0$. The experiment with replicated pairs of closely related individuals yielded a random sample of differences for estimating and testing the differential effects of treatments.

Later in the chapter we shall consider other null hypotheses and another alternative hypothesis about μ, as well as interval estimates and tests of hypotheses for σ^2. But immediately it is well to enlarge our powers of calculation.

2.11—Calculation of s without machine. So far, you have been provided with examples in which ΣX was exactly divisible by n. This has made easy the squaring of the deviations. In practice $\bar{x}$ is carried to one or two extra digits so that the calculation and squaring of the deviations become laborious. The work is lightened by taking deviations from some arbitrarily chosen number, G, usually guessed to be near the sample mean. The sum of the deviations from G is not zero, but it provides a correction which yields $\bar{x}$ as exactly as desired. The sum of the squares of the deviations from G is greater than $\Sigma x^2 = \Sigma(X - \bar{x})^2$, the latter being the *least* sum of squares; but again $\Sigma(X - G)$ gives a correction which produces Σx^2 as accurately as may be needed.

For illustration, take the birth weights of 20 guinea pigs as listed in the left-hand column of table 2.11.1 (compare example 2.6.4). Instead of calculating $\bar{x}$, just glance at the weights and choose an arbitrary origin, say $G = 30$ grams, near the middle of the array. It will soon appear that 29 grams or 40 grams or any other arbitrarily selected number leads to exactly the same result after the corresponding corrections are made. But the calculations are slightly easier if G is chosen close to $\bar{x}$.

The sum of the deviations from G is not zero, proving that 30 grams is not $\bar{x}$. However, the average deviation, 0.25 gram, is the necessary correction for mean, the amount that must be added to G to arrive at the correct value of $\bar{x}$, 30.25 grams.

In the last column of the table are the squares of the deviations from G, together with their sum, 247. What we require is Σx^2, the sum of the squares of the deviations from the sample mean, usually abbreviated to *sum of squares*. The correction for sum of squares is always subtracted

TABLE 2.11.1

COMPUTATION OF SAMPLE STANDARD DEVIATION BY THE USE OF AN ARBITRARILY CHOSEN ORIGIN OF MEASUREMENT

Birth weights of 20 guinea pigs in litters of two

Birth Weights (grams)	Deviations From 30 Grams		Squares of Deviations
X	$X - G$		$(X - G)^2$
30	0		0
30	0		0
26	−4		16
32		2	4
30	0		0
23	−7		49
29	−1		1
31		1	1
36		6	36
30	0		0
25	−5		25
34		4	16
32		2	4
29	−1		1
28	−2		4
27	−3		9
38		8	64
31		1	1
34		4	16
30	0		0
Total	−23	28	247

$$\Sigma(X - G) = 28 - 23 = 5 \qquad\qquad \Sigma(X - G)^2 = 247$$
$$[\Sigma(X - G)]/n = 5/20 = 0.25 \qquad [\Sigma(X - G)]^2/n = 5^2/20 = \underline{1.25}$$
$$\bar{x} = G + [\Sigma(X - G)]/n \qquad\qquad \Sigma x^2 = \overline{245.75}$$
$$= 30 + 0.25 \qquad\qquad s^2 = 245.75/19 = 12.93$$
$$= 30.25 \text{ grams} \qquad\qquad s = 3.60 \text{ grams}$$

from $\Sigma(X - G)^2$ to get Σx^2. The resulting value, 245.75, may be verified by computing the 20 deviations from $\bar{x}$, $30 - 30.25 = -0.25$, etc., then adding the resulting squares. A less tedious exercise will be provided in example 2.11.1.

Some people, unaccustomed to computation, confuse two of the quantities required in the foregoing calculations. First, there is the sum of the squares of deviations from G, $\Sigma(X - G)^2 = 247$. Second, there is the square of the sum of the same deviations, $[\Sigma(X - G)]^2 = 25$. In the first the squaring is done before the addition, while in the second the order of the operations is reversed. The objectives and results are so different that it is only necessary to direct attention to the speciousness of the analogy.

EXAMPLE 2.11.1—Here is a set of numbers chosen for easy computation:

15, 12, 10, 10, 10, 8, 7, 7, 4, 4, 1

In the manner of table 2.2.1, calculate $\bar{x} = 8$ and $s = 4$. Then try various arbitrary origins, such as 5, 10, and 1. Continue until you convince yourself that the answers, $\bar{x} = 8$ and $s = 4$, can be reached regardless of the value chosen for G, and until you can carry through the process without hesitancy. Finally, try $G = 0$.

EXAMPLE 2.11.2—In table 2.11.1, if you use $G = 23$, or more conveniently 20, you will have no negative deviations. Is there any advantage in computing with deviations which are all positive?

EXAMPLE 2.11.3—Those who enjoy algebraic manipulations will wish to derive the formula, $\Sigma x^2 = \Sigma(X - G)^2 - [\Sigma(X - G)]^2/n$. Start with the relation, $x = X - \bar{x} = (X - G) - (\bar{x} - G) = (X - G) - \Sigma(X - G)/n$. Either transpose the term, $\Sigma(X - G)/n$, then square and sum; or square and sum the equation as it stands.

2.12—Computation of s with calculating machine. The methods which have been described were devised to confine the computations, so far as possible, to small integers. If a calculating machine is available, large integers can be manipulated almost as easily as small ones. Other objectives, therefore, may be set up. One is the avoidance of negative numbers. Another is the elimination of most of the subtractions. Both of these objectives are easily attained, the resulting method being especially adapted to machine calculation. Here it is.

Returning to the weights in the first column of table 2.11.1, their sum, $\Sigma X = 605$, and the sum of their squares, $\Sigma X^2 = 18,547$, are readily calculated with any machine. The details of the operations differ with the style of machine used. Usually the two sums are run up simultaneously, the appropriate method being described in the manual of instructions issued by each manufacturer. With any machine it is unnecessary to copy down the squares of the individual weights; the sum is accumulated in the machine as the operation proceeds. At the end, it is only necessary to copy the results from the dials into a table like 2.12.1. The sample mean, of course, is $(\Sigma X)/n = 605/20 = 30.25$ grams. The correction for sum of squares is $(\Sigma X)^2/n = (605)^2/20 = 18,301.25$. Deducting this from ΣX^2, the corrected sum of squares is 245.75 as before.

TABLE 2.12.1

METHOD OF COMPUTING THE SAMPLE MEAN AND SUM OF SQUARES IF A
CALCULATING MACHINE IS USED

Birth weights of 20 guinea pigs as recorded in table 2.11.1

$n = 20$	$\Sigma X^2 = 18{,}547$
$\Sigma X = 605$	$(\Sigma X)^2/n = 18{,}301.25$
$\bar{x} = 30.25$ grams	$\Sigma x^2 = \quad 245.75$

This method of machine calculation may be thought of as a special case of the general method described in section 2.11. Now, $G = 0$, the arbitrary origin being the same as the zero point on the scale of weights. The deviations, $X - G = X - 0 = X$, are the same as the observed values. The correction necessary to obtain the sum of squares is $[\Sigma(X - G)]^2/n = [\Sigma(X - 0)]^2/n = (\Sigma X)^2/n$. Not only is the machine method a timesaver, but, obviating as it does the subtractions associated with deviations, it affords less chances for error.

At first reading, the remainder of this chapter, together with chapter 3, may be omitted. In chapter 4, the comparison of two treatments is extended to the situation where there is no known basis for pairing.

EXAMPLE 2.12.1—The original determinations of vitamin C, simplified for table 2.2.1, were

16, 22, 21, 20, 23, 22, 17, 15, 13, 22, 17, 18, 29, 17, 22, 16, 23

Using the machine method, calculate $\Sigma X = 333$, $\Sigma X^2 = 6{,}773$, and from them, $\bar{x} = 19.6$ and $s = 3.95$ mg./100 g.

EXAMPLE 2.12.2—From the results of the preceding example, set the 0.95 confidence interval on μ. Ans. 17.6 — 21.6 mg./100 g. Compare these limits with those of section 2.8

EXAMPLE 2.12.3—In example 2.5.6, calculate $\bar{d} = 3.71$ and $s_D = 4.46$ bu./acre. Compare these with the earlier estimates. The negative differences may cause trouble if you accumulate ΣX and ΣX^2 simultaneously. One easy way is to record separately the results for positives and negatives:

	ΣX	ΣX^2
Positives	66.4	499.90
Negatives	− 7.0	19.24
Total	59.4	519.14

EXAMPLE 2.12.4—Set 99% confidence limits on the population mean difference of the corn yields of examples 2.5.6 and 2.12.3. Ans. 0.42 to 7.00 bu./acre. Note: Since the confidence interval does not include zero, a test of H_0: $\mu_D = 0$ would result in rejection at the 1% level. Try it.

EXAMPLE 2.12.5—It is easy to derive the formula, $\Sigma x^2 = \Sigma X^2 - (\Sigma X)^2/n$. Start with the relation, $x + \bar{x} = X$. Also show that $\Sigma x^2 = \Sigma X^2 - \bar{x}\Sigma X = \Sigma X^2 - n\bar{x}^2$.

2.13—Tests of other null hypotheses about μ. The null hypothesis, $\mu_D = 0$, is not the only one that is useful, and the *alternative*, $\mu_D \neq 0$, may be unrealistic. Illustrations are found in the Boone County survey of corn borer effects (section 1.3). On 14 farms, the effect of spraying was evaluated by measuring the corn yield from both sprayed and unsprayed strips in each field. The data are recorded in table 2.13.1. The sample

TABLE 2.13.1

Yields of Corn (Bushels Per Acre) in Sprayed and Unsprayed Strips of 14 Fields
Boone County, Iowa, 1950

Sprayed	64.3	78.1	93.0	80.7	89.0	79.9	90.6	102.4
Unsprayed	70.0	74.4	86.6	79.2	84.7	75.1	87.3	98.8
Difference	− 5.7	3.7	6.4	1.5	4.3	4.8	3.3	3.6
			70.7	106.1	107.4	74.0	72.6	69.5
			70.2	101.1	83.4	65.2	68.1	68.4
			0.5	5.0	24.0	8.8	4.5	1.1

mean difference is 4.7 bu./acre with s_D = 6.48 bu./acre and $s_{\bar{d}}$ = 6.48/$\sqrt{14}$ = 1.73 bu./acre.

First case: $H_A : \mu_D > 0$. It had already been established that the spray, at the concentration used, could not decrease yield. If there is a decrease, as in the first field, it must be attributed to causes other than the spray, or to sampling variation. Consequently, if μ_D is not zero then it must be greater than zero. The objective of this experiment was to test $H_0 : \mu_D = 0$ with $H_A : \mu_D > 0$. As before,

$$t = \frac{4.7 - 0}{1.73} = 2.72, \; d.f. = 13$$

A test with this kind of alternative hypothesis is known as a *one-tailed* or *one-sided* test. The left half of the *t*-distribution is excluded. In table 2.7.1, half of the indicated probability is ruled out so that the column headed 0.05 now corresponds to the remaining half, 0.025. Looking at the matter from the operational viewpoint, here is the rule: *To make a one-tailed test with table 2.7.1, locate the sample value of* t *and use half of the probability indicated.*

Applying this rule to the $t = 2.72$ above, P is slightly less than 0.02/2; the null hypothesis is rejected at $P < 0.01$. Evidently spraying did decrease corn borer damage, resulting in increased yields in Boone County in 1950.

Second case: $\mu_D \neq 0$. This same Boone County experiment may be cited to illustrate the use of a null hypothesis different from $\mu_D = 0$. This experiment might have had as its objective the test of the null hypothesis, "The cost of spraying is equal to the gain from increased yield." To evaluate costs, it is known that the fee of commercial sprayers was $3 per acre and that the 1950 crop was sold at about $1.50 per bushel. So, 2 bushels per acre would pay for the spraying. The test would have been $H_0: \mu_D = 2$ bu./acre, $H_A: \mu_D \neq 2$ bu./acre, resulting in

$$t = \frac{4.7 - 2.0}{1.73} = 1.56, \ d.f. = 13$$

The corresponding probability is about $P = 0.15$, so the null hypothesis would presumably not be rejected; Boone County farmers could be assured that, under similar conditions, they would on the average break even by spraying, provided, of course, that all of them sprayed. This would scarcely induce them to spray, unless spraying could be shown to decrease the attack of borers next year.

Third case: $H_A: \mu_D > \mu_0$. It is possible that $H_0: \mu_D = 2$ bu./acre might be tested with $H_A: \mu_D > 2$ bu./acre; that is, the alternative hypothesis might be put in the form of a slogan, "It pays to spray." If this were done, $t = 1.56$ would be associated with $P = 0.15/2 = 0.075$, not significant. But the implication of this one-sided test is that H_0 would be accepted no matter how far the sample mean might fall short of 2 bu./acre. This, I think, would not be realistic. Nobody would be content to accept $\mu_D = 2$ if the sample mean were -2 or -3 bu./acre. Rather, he would reject $\mu_D = 2$ and conclude that spraying does not pay, that $\mu_D < 2$ bu./ acre. That is, it is the two-tailed test which is appropriate here.

This point is stressed for the reason that at present there seems to be a tendency to use the one-sided test because, as a man said, "I am not interested in the other alternative." If interest is the criterion, then the test becomes subjective; the experimental results will be interpreted in different ways by different people. Or else the investigator is in effect choosing $P < 0.1$ for rejection instead of $P < 0.05$. The correct criterion for the one-sided test is this: H_0 will be accepted for every sample outcome except those significantly greater than μ_D. A similar statement applies if the proposed alternative is $\mu_D < \mu_0$.

EXAMPLE 2.13.1—In an investigation of the effect of feeding 10 mcg. of vitamin B_{12} per pound of ration to growing swine (2), eight lots (each with 6 pigs) were fed in pairs. The pairs were distinguished by being fed different levels of aureomycin, an antibiotic which did not interact with the vitamin; that is, the differences were not affected by the aureomycin. The average daily gains (to about 200 lbs. live weight) are summarized as follows:

Ration	Pairs of Lots							
	1	2	3	4	5	6	7	8
With B_{12}	1.60	1.68	1.75	1.64	1.75	1.79	1.78	1.77
Without B_{12}	1.56	1.52	1.52	1.49	1.59	1.56	1.60	1.56
Difference, D	0.04	0.16	0.23	0.15	0.16	0.23	0.18	0.21

For the differences, calculate the statistics, $\bar{d} = 0.170$ lb./day and $s_{\bar{d}} = 0.0217$ lb./day.

EXAMPLE 2.13.2—It is known that the addition of small amounts of the vitamin cannot decrease the rate of growth. While it is fairly obvious that $\bar{d}$ will be found significantly different from zero, the differences being all positive and, with one exception, fairly consistent (see section 5.8), you may be interested in evaluating t. Ans. 7.83, far beyond the 0.01 level in the table. The appropriate alternative hypothesis is $\mu > 0$.

EXAMPLE 2.13.3—The effect of B_{12} seems to be a stimulation of the metabolic processes including appetite. The pigs eat more and grow faster. In the experiment above, the cost of the additional amount of feed eaten, including that of the vitamin, corresponded to about 0.130 lb./day of gain. Test the hypothesis that the profit derived from feeding B_{12} is zero. Ans. $t = 1.84$, $P = 0.11$ (two-sided alternative).

EXAMPLE 2.13.4—Manufacturing of foods and drugs is often controlled by regulations specifying limiting quantities of some essential constituent; for example, there must be at least 80% of fat in butter. The butter from one creamery was tested 25 times with the resulting statistics, $\bar{x} = 80.16\%$ and $s = 0.316\%$ fat. From the viewpoint of the enforcement officers, $\mu_0 = 80\%$ would not be rejected at any percentage above 80% but only for percentages below. If the law were scientifically written, which it is not, the enforcement agency would test the hypothesis, $\mu = 80\%$, with $H_A: \mu < 80\%$. Calculate t and evaluate the probability of a larger value if $\mu = 80\%$. Ans. $P = 0.01$.

2.14—Interval estimate and tests of σ^2. Samples from normal populations afford interval estimates of σ^2 (11). For example, the 95% confidence interval is found approximately from the relation,

$$\frac{\Sigma x^2}{\chi^2_{0.025}} \leq \sigma^2 \leq \frac{\Sigma x^2}{\chi^2_{0.975}}$$

As an illustration we shall set 95% confidence limits on σ^2 of the normal population of vitamin C sampled in section 2.2. From table 2.2.1, $\Sigma x^2 = 254$, $d.f. = 16$; while from table 1.14.1, $\chi^2_{0.975} = 6.91$ and $\chi^2_{0.025} = 28.8$. Substituting,

$$\frac{254}{28.8} \leq \sigma^2 \leq \frac{254}{6.91},$$

that is,

$$8.82 \leq \sigma^2 \leq 36.76$$

fixes the confidence interval on σ^2. From this it may be said that, unless a 1-in-20 chance has occurred in the sampling, σ lies between 2.97 and 6.06 mg./100 g. Note: Like s^2, $s = 3.98$ is not in the middle of its confidence interval; the distributions of s^2 and s are not symmetrical (see section 3.5).

The null hypothesis that the variance of a normal population has some specified value, σ_0^2, may be tested by a sample of size n randomly drawn from it. The alternative hypothesis may either be $\sigma^2 \neq \sigma_0^2$ or $\sigma^2 > \sigma_0^2$ (or $\sigma^2 < \sigma_0^2$). One merely computes

$$\chi^2 = \frac{\Sigma x^2}{\sigma_0^2},$$

then compares it with the χ^2 distribution having $n - 1$ degrees of freedom. To illustrate the process, suppose that, in a well-established colony, the standard deviation of weights of male rats (between ages of 56 and 84 days) is $\sigma_0 = 26$ grams. It was suspected that a new ration would increase the standard deviation but could not decrease it. An experiment on 20 rats resulted in $\Sigma x^2 = 23{,}000$. From this,

$$\chi^2 = \frac{23{,}000}{(26)^2} = 34.02, \; d.f. = 19$$

In table 1.14.1 it is seen that $\chi^2 > \chi^2_{0.05}$, so the null hypothesis, $\sigma_0^2 = 676$, is rejected.

If H_A were $\sigma^2 \neq \sigma_0^2$, the region of rejection would be $\chi^2 < \chi^2_{0.975}$ and $\chi^2 > \chi^2_{0.025}$. For $H_A : \sigma^2 < \sigma_0^2$, reject if $\chi^2 < \chi^2_{0.975}$.

If you wish to test the hypothesis that two mean squares are samples from a common σ^2, turn forward to section 4.8.

2.15—Size of sample. The number of replications to be used is a critical problem. Too small an experiment may fail to detect a difference that is important; one that is unnecessarily large is wasteful of time and money.

Solution of the problem requires two pieces of information. The first is an estimate of σ in the populations to be sampled. This is normally got from a previous experiment or from a knowledge of the range to be encountered. The second is a specification of the largest confidence interval to be tolerated or the smallest mean difference worth knowing.

Equations for sample size are a bit troublesome to handle, so let us consider first an easier problem. Suppose the number of replications has been tentatively fixed; for example, there may be no more than n pairs available. The experimenter needs to know how small a population difference the proposed experiment may be expected to detect, which means to show significance at, say, the 5% level. The formula is

$$\delta = \frac{s_D \, t_{.05}}{\sqrt{n}}.$$

where δ is the population difference, s_D is the sample standard deviation *of differences*, and n is the proposed number of replications.

As an illustration, refer to example 2.9.2 about the biological value of peanuts. There it was shown that $s_D = 7.72$ units in a sample of $n = 10$ pairs. Since, for $d.f. = 9$, $t_{.05} = 2.262$,

$$\delta = \frac{(7.72)(2.262)}{\sqrt{10}} = 5.52 \text{ units}$$

If the population difference had been as great as 5.52 units, this experiment would have been expected to show the difference as significant at the 5% level. Put in another way, this experiment was large enough to detect a difference of 5.52 or larger if it had existed.

This statement must be made more specific. One can never be certain that an experiment will perform as expected. The present formula gives only modest assurance. The more exact statement is that if the population difference had been as great as 5.52 units, the probability is about 0.5 that this experiment would have detected it at the 5% level of significance.

If stronger assurance is desired, or if the experimenter wishes to detect a smaller difference, then a larger sample will be necessary (section 10.18).

As indicated before, one pair of observations in this experiment was suspect. If the next-to-the-last pair (44, 63) had proved to be erroneous and had therefore been omitted, the statistics would have been $n = 9$, $\bar{d} = 4.3$, $s_D = 2.40$ units, $t_{.05} = 2.306$. With these hypothetical data, the difference which the experiment would stand a 50–50 chance of detecting would be

$$\delta = \frac{(2.40)(2.306)}{\sqrt{9}} = 1.84 \text{ units}$$

This difference is only $1.84/57.3 = 3.2\%$ of the mean of the 18 biological values reported, indicating a sensitive experiment compared to the original where one could detect a difference of no less than $5.52/56.9 = 9.7\%$.

Should the calculated δ be too large to be worth an experiment, the question would be "How many replications will be required to detect a worthwhile difference?" For the 9 pairs of biological values, it might be required to learn if there is a population difference as large as 2% of the mean, that is, $(0.02)(57.3) = 1.15$ units. To get the answer, we use the same equation as before but in a different way. One cannot solve directly for n because $t_{.05}$ changes with n. Some corresponding values must be tried until δ takes the size specified. First, guess $n = 16$; then for $d.f. = 15$, $t_{.05} = 2.131$, and with $s_D = 2.40$,

$$\delta = \frac{(2.40)(2.131)}{\sqrt{16}} = 1.28$$

Since this is larger than the designated 1.15 units, try a larger value of n, say $n = 20$. Then

$$\delta = \frac{(2.40)(2.093)}{\sqrt{20}} = 1.12$$

Now δ is slightly smaller than necessary, so try a smaller n. It will be found that $n = 19$ is about right. In making these trials it helps to know that, except for very small samples, $t = 2$ approximately.

Again, the odds are about 1:1 that an experiment with 19 pairs will detect, at the 5% level, a difference so large as 1.15 if it exists. If you wish greater assurance of detecting the selected δ, a method will be provided in section 10.18. You will find that if the odds are placed at 3:1 (that is, $p = 0.75$) then 28 replications instead of 19 will be required.

If it is a confidence interval on a difference that is to be examined, the same formula is used, δ now being the half length—the quantity to be added to or subtracted from $\bar{d}$.

It is often convenient to express δ as a percentage of the mean. The formula becomes

$$\frac{\delta}{d} = \frac{C_D \, t_{.05}}{\sqrt{n}},$$

where C_D is the coefficient of variation of the difference (section 2.6).

EXAMPLE 2.15.1—If you use the original statistic of example 2.9.2, $s_D = 7.72$, and wish to detect $\delta = 1.15$ units at the 5% level with probability 0.5, what sample size would be required? Ans. 176 pairs.

EXAMPLE 2.15.2—Omit the suspected pair (44, 63); then calculate the size of sample that would detect $\delta = 1.15$ units at the 1% level with probability 0.5. Ans. 33 pairs.

EXAMPLE 2.15.3—In the vitamin C data of table 2.2.1, $s = 3.98$ mg./100 g., so $s_D = \sqrt{2} \,(3.98) = 5.63$ (section 3.9). Design an experiment to discover the loss in vitamin C due to stewing the tomatoes. The vitamin concentration in each can would be determined immediately, then again after the cooking. It is desired to detect, at the 5% level, the loss in vitamin C if it is as much as 10% of the mean, that is, 2 mg./100 g. Calculate n. Ans. 33 cans.

EXAMPLE 2.15.4—In table 2.11.1, the random sample of birth weights of guinea pigs in litters of two had $\bar{x} = 30.25$ g. and $s = 3.60$ g. It is required to draw a sample which will estimate μ within 3%. Assume $\delta = (0.03)(30.25) = 0.91$ g. and calculate n. Ans. 63. Hint: Use s, not s_D.

2.16—Relative variation. Coefficient of variation. In section 2.6, C was defined as $s/\bar{x}$. As was indicated, its utility lies mainly in the fact that in many series the mean and standard deviation tend to change together. This is illustrated by the mean stature and corresponding standard deviation of girls from 1 to 18 years of age shown graphically in figure 2.16.1. Until the twelfth year the standard deviation increases at a somewhat greater rate, relative to its mean, than does stature, causing the coefficient of variation to rise, but by the seventeenth year and thereafter C is back to where it started. Without serious discrepancy one may fix in mind the figure, $C = 3.75\%$, as the relative standard deviation of human stature, male as well as female. More precisely, the coefficient rises rather steadily from infancy through puberty, falls sharply during a brief period of uniformity, then takes on its permanent value near 3.75%.

A knowledge of relative variation is valuable in planning and in evaluating experiments. In the preceding section was an indication of the use of C in estimating sample size. After the statistics of an experiment are summarized, one may judge of its success partly by looking at C. In corn variety trials, for example, although mean yield and standard deviation vary with location and season, yet the coefficient of variation is often between 5% and 15%. Values outside of this interval cause the investigator to wonder if an error has been made in calculation, or if some unusual circumstances throw doubt on the validity of the experiment. Similarly, each sampler knows what values of C may be expected in his own data, and is suspicious of any great deviation.

Other uses of the coefficient of variation are numerous but less prevalent. Since C is the ratio of two averages having the same unit of measurement it is itself independent of the unit employed. Thus, it is the same

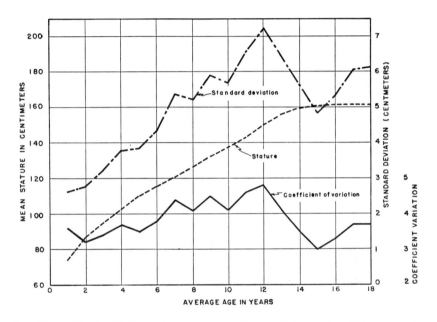

Fɪɢ. 2.16.1—Graph of 3 time series; stature, standard deviation and coefficient of variation of girls from 1 to 18 years of age. See reference (1).

whether inches, feet, or centimeters are used to measure height. Also, the coefficient of variation of the yield of hay is comparable to that of the yield of corn.

Experimental animals have characteristic coefficients of variation, and these may be compared despite the diversity of the variables measured. The body weight of male albino rats between 90 and 243 days of age has an average C of about 14% (5), while that for annual egg production of Barred Plymouth Rock hens is close to 32% (12). Such information is essential to those planning experiments.

Like many other ratios, the coefficient of variation is so convenient to use that some people overlook the information contained in the original data. Try to imagine how limited you would be in interpreting the stature-of-girls coefficients if they were not accompanied by $\bar{x}$ and s. You would not know whether an increase in C is due to a rising s or a falling $\bar{x}$, nor whether the saw-tooth appearance of the C-curve results from irregularities in one or both of the others, unless indeed you could supply the facts from your own fund of knowledge. The coefficient is informative and useful in the presence of $\bar{x}$ and s, but abstracted from them it may be misleading

EXAMPLE 2.16.1—In experiments involving chlorophyll determinations in pineapple plants (17), the question was raised as to the method that would give the most consistent results. Three bases of measurement were tried, each involving 12-leaf samples, with the statistics reported below. From the coefficients of variation, it was decided that the methods were equally reliable, and that the most convenient one could be chosen with no sacrifice of precision.

STATISTICS OF CHLOROPHYLL DETERMINATIONS OF 12-LEAF SAMPLES FROM PINEAPPLE PLANTS, USING THREE BASES OF MEASUREMENT

Statistic	100-gram Wet Basis	100-gram Dry Basis	100-sq. cm. Basis
Sample Mean (milligrams)	61.4	337	13.71
Sample Standard Deviation (milligrams)	5.22	31.2	1.20
Coefficient of Variation (per cent)	8.5	9.3	8.8

EXAMPLE 2.16.2—In well-conducted experiments with properly developed and adequately fed growing swine, the sample standard deviation of gains in weight may be taken as 10% of the sample mean. If you are told that a lot of pigs gained 150 pounds during a certain period, would you expect the sample standard deviation of the gains to be about 15 pounds? Would it be equally true that an average daily gain of 1.5 pounds per day should be accompanied by a sample standard deviation of approximately 0.15 pound per day?

EXAMPLE 2.16.3—In a certain laboratory there is a colony of rats in which the coefficient of variation of the weights of males between 56 and 84 days of age is close to 13%. Estimate the sample standard deviation of the weights of a lot of these rats whose sample mean weight is 200 grams. Ans. 26 grams.

EXAMPLE 2.16.4—Assuming that the coefficient of variation of yields in field plot tests with wheat is usually near 5%, would you be surprised if told that in an experiment where the yield was 25 bushels per acre, the sample standard deviation of plot yields was 0.5 bushel per acre?

REFERENCES

1 BERNICE BOYNTON. University of Iowa Studies in Child Welfare, Vol. 12, No. 4 (1936).

2 D. V. CATRON, H. M. MADDOCK, V. C. SPEER, and R. L. VOHS. Antibiotics and Chemotherapy, 1:31 (1951).

3. COUNCIL ON FOODS. Journal of the American Medical Association, 110:651 (1938).

4. EARL WILCOX CRAMPTON. Journal of Nutrition, 7:305 (1934).

5. HENRY H. DONALDSON. The Rat. The Wistar Institute of Anatomy and Biology, No. 6. Philadelphia (1924).

6 R. A. FISHER. Proceedings of the International Mathematical Congress, Toronto, 805 (1924).

7. HORACE GRAY and J. C. AYRES. Growth in Private School Children. The University of Chicago Press (1931).

8. L. C. GROVE. Iowa Agricultural Experiment Station Bulletin 253 (1939).

9. H. H. LOVE. Journal of the American Society of Agronomy, 16:64 (1924)

10 H. H. MITCHELL, WISE BURROUGHS, and JESSE R. BEADLES. Journal of Nutrition, 11:257 (1936).

11 ALEXANDER McFARLANE MOOD. Introduction to the Theory of Statistics. McGraw-Hill Book Company, Inc., New York (1950).

12 RAYMOND PEARL and F. M. SURFACE, U.S.D.A., Bureau of Animal Industry Bulletin No. 110, Part I (1909).

13. E. S. PEARSON. Biometrika, 24:416 (1932)

14. CHAS. S. REDDY. Iowa State Journal of Science, 9:530 (1935).

15. "STUDENT." Biometrika, 6:1 (1908).

16. PAUL J. TALLEY. Plant Physiology, 9:737 (1934).

17. R. K. TAM and O. C. MAGISTAD. Plant Physiology, 10:161 (1935)

18. L. H. C. TIPPETT. Biometrika, 17:386 (1925).

19. W. J. YOUDEN and HELEN PURDY BEALE. Contributions from Boyce Thompson Institute, 6:437 (1934).

CHAPTER 3

Sampling From a Normally Distributed
Population: Sampling Distributions

3.1—Introduction. In chapter 1 the facts about confidence intervals were verified through sampling, and this same device outlined the chi-square distribution which led to desired probabilities of occurence. But in chapter 2 you were asked to accept $s_{\bar{x}}$ and t with almost no justification. Now we are ready to examine their distributions along with those of $\bar{x}$, s^2, and s, in the expectation of learning the reasons for the statements already made about them.

There are two devices for studying the sampling properties of statistics. The first is that employed by the mathematician who arrives at the results through use of his symbolical logic. He furnishes the formulas and tables that make statistical methods accurate and convenient. The second device is the actual drawing of samples. This requires no mathematical training but makes it possible to verify many findings of probability theory. More important, the layman is enabled by his experience in sampling to appreciate the foundations upon which the mathematical logic is built.

Both the mathematician and the experimenter have been eager to draw samples from actual populations which depart more or less from the mathematical models. The data may come from harvesting a crop in small plots, with perhaps a thousand measurements of some such character as yield (1) (5) (7). The *geographical distribution* of the variable is then known as well as the *frequency distribution*. The latter may be compared with the normal distribution, often assumed to be the source of samples, while the former is the basis for studying the effectiveness of various experimental designs.

For our purposes, we shall, as before, set up a particular kind of distribution and draw samples from it with the help of the table of random digits. But now, instead of the binomial distribution, we shall sample the normal distribution, described in section 2.1 and in chapter 8. In this model distribution there is no limit to the number of different weights, but practically the scale for measuring can be read no closer than a certain *least count*.   Hence, the population that we have devised to simulate a normal population departs from the model in two respects; it is limited in size and range instead of being infinite, and has a *discontinuous* variate in lieu of the continuous one implied in the theory.   The effects of these departures will scarcely be noticed because they are small in comparison with sampling variation.

3.2—A finite population simulating the normal.   In table 3.2.1 are the weight gains of a hundred swine, slightly modified from experimental data so as to form a distribution which is approximately normal. The items are numbered from 00 to 99 in order that they may be identified easily with corresponding numbers taken from the table of random digits.   The salient features of this kind of distribution may be discerned in figure 3.2.1.   The gains, clustering at the midpoint of the array, thin out symmetrically, slowly at first, then more and more rapidly: two-thirds of the gains lie in the interval 30 ± 10 pounds, that is, in an interval of two standard deviations centered on the mean.   In a real population,

TABLE 3.2.1

ARRAY OF GAINS IN WEIGHT (POUNDS) OF 100 SWINE DURING A PERIOD OF 20 DAYS

The gains approximate a normal distribution with
$\mu = 30$ pounds and $\sigma = 10$ pounds

Item Number	Gain	Item Number	Gain	Item Number	Gain	Item Number	Gain
00	3	25	24	50	30	75	37
01	7	26	24	51	30	76	37
02	11	27	24	52	30	77	38
03	12	28	25	53	30	78	38
04	13	29	25	54	30	79	39
05	14	30	25	55	31	80	39
06	15	31	26	56	31	81	39
07	16	32	26	57	31	82	40
08	17	33	26	58	31	83	40
09	17	34	26	59	32	84	41
10	18	35	27	60	32	85	41
11	18	36	27	61	33	86	41
12	18	37	27	62	33	87	42
13	19	38	28	63	33	88	42
14	19	39	28	64	33	89	42
15	19	40	28	65	33	90	43
16	20	41	29	66	34	91	43
17	20	42	29	67	34	92	44
18	21	43	29	68	34	93	45
19	21	44	29	69	35	94	46
20	21	45	30	70	35	95	47
21	22	46	30	71	35	96	48
22	22	47	30	72	36	97	49
23	23	48	30	73	36	98	53
24	23	49	30	74	36	99	57

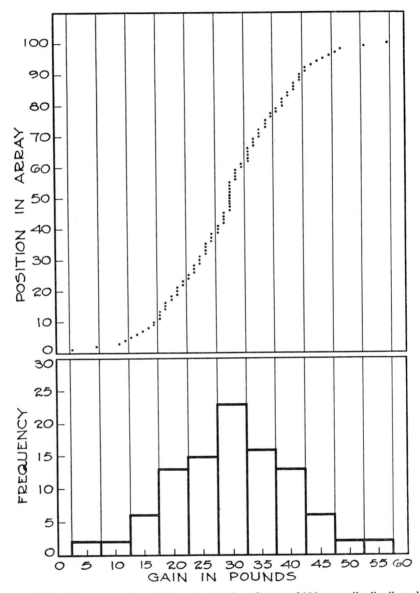

FIG. 3.2.1—Upper part: Graphical representation of array of 100 normally distributed gains in weight. Lower part: Histogram of same gains. The altitude of a rectangle in the histogram is proportional to the number of dots in the array which lie between the vertical sides.

indefinitely great in number of individuals, greater extremes doubtless would exist, but that need cause us little concern.

The relation of the histogram to the array is clear. After the class bounds are decided upon, it is necessary merely to count the dots lying between the vertical lines, then make the height of the rectangle proportional to their number. The central value, or *class mark*, of each interval is indicated on the horizontal scale of gains.

In table 3.2.2 is the frequency distribution which is graphically represented in figure 3.2.1. Only the class marks are entered in the first row. The class intervals are from 2.5 to 7.5, etc. This is a notably concise method of presenting data from large samples.

TABLE 3.2.2

Frequency Distribution of Gains in Weight of 100 Swine

A finite population approximating the normal

Class mark (pounds)	5	10	15	20	25	30	35	40	45	50	55
Frequency	2	2	6	13	15	23	16	13	6	2	2

3.3—Random samples from a normal distribution. An easy way to draw random samples from the table of pig gains is to take numbers consecutively from the table of random numbers, table 1.5.1, then match them with the gains by means of the integers, 00 to 99, in table 3.2.1. To avoid duplicating the samples of others, start at some randomly selected point in the table of random numbers instead of at the beginning, then proceed upwards, downwards, or crosswise. Suppose, using the device described in section 1.5, you have hit upon the digit, 8, in row 71, column 29. This with the following digit, 3, specifies pig number 83 in table 3.2.1, a pig whose gain is 40 pounds. Hence, 40 pounds is the first number of the sample. Moving upwards among the random numbers you read the integers 09, 75, 90, etc., and record the corresponding gains from the table, 17, 37, and 43 pounds. Continuing, you get as many gains and as many samples as you wish.

Samples of 10 are suggested. Unlike the procedure in chapter 1, for our present purposes the samples must all be of the same size because the distributions of their statistics change with n. It is well to record the items in columns, leaving a half dozen lines below each for subsequent computations. For your guidance, four samples are listed in table 3.3.1. The computations below them will be explained as we go along. Draw as many of the samples as you think you can process with the time at your command. It is fortunate if several are working together so that the results of each can be made available to all. Keep the records carefully because you will need them again and again.

It will be noted that each pig gain may be drawn as often as its number appears in the table of random digits—it is not withdrawn from circula-

TABLE 3.3.1

FOUR SAMPLES OF 10 ITEMS DRAWN AT RANDOM FROM THE PIG GAINS OF TABLE 3.2.1,
EACH FOLLOWED BY STATISTICS TO BE EXPLAINED IN SECTION 3.4–3.8

Item Number and Formulas	Sample Number			
	1	2	3	4
1	33	32	39	17
2	53	31	34	22
3	34	11	33	20
4	29	30	33	19
5	39	19	33	3
6	57	24	39	21
7	12	53	36	3
8	24	44	32	25
9	39	19	32	40
10	36	30	30	21
$\bar{x}$	35.6	29.3	34.1	19.1
s^2	169.8	151.6	9.0	112.3
s	13.0	12.31	3.00	10.6
$s_{\bar{x}}$	4.11	3.89	0.95	3.35
t	1.36	−0.18	4.32	−3.25
$t_{.05}s_{\bar{x}}$	9.3	8.8	2.2	7.6
$\bar{x} \pm t_{.05}s_{\bar{x}}$	26.3–44.9	20.5–38.1	31.9–36.3	11.5–26.7

tion after being taken once. Thus, the sampling is always from the same population, and the probability of drawing any particular item is constant throughout the process.

EXAMPLE 3.3.1—Determine the range in each of your samples of $n = 10$ The mean of the ranges estimates $\sigma/0.325$ (table 2.2.2); that is, $10/0.325 = 30.8$.   How close is your estimate?

3.4—The distribution of sample means. First add the items in each sample, then put down the sample mean, $\bar{x}$ (division is by 10). While every mean is an estimator of $\mu = 30$ pounds, yet there is great variation among them. Make an array of the means of all your samples. If there are enough of them, group them into a frequency distribution like table 3.4.1.

As indicated, our laboratory means ranged from 19 to 39 pounds, perhaps to the novice a disconcerting variability. To assess the meaning of this to you, try to imagine doing an experiment resulting in one of these more divergent mean gains instead of the population value, 30 pounds. Having no information about the population except that furnished by the sample, you would be considerably misled and there is no way to overcome this hazard. One of the objects of the experimental samplings you have done is to acquaint you with the risks involved in all conclusions based on small portions of the aggregate. The investigator seldom knows the parameters of the sampled population; he knows only the sample estimates. He learns to view his experimental data in the light of his experience of sampling error. His judgments must involve not only the facts of his sample but all the related information which he and others have accumulated.

The more optimistic are prone to draw satisfaction from the large number of means near the center of the distribution. If this were not characteristic, sampling would not be so useful and popular. The improbability of getting poor estimates produces a sense of security in making inferences. This is proper. With the right balance between confidence and prudence the experienced investigator is seldom a victim of the accidents of sampling.

The distribution of sample means in table 3.4.1 brings to attention three more basic features of the sampling. First, the distribution is itself approximately normal, as you may see by comparing the actual with the theoretical normal frequencies. The theory is that the means of samples drawn from a normal population are likewise normally distributed. We may go further and say that, as sample size increases, sample means tend to be distributed normally even if the parent population is anormal, a great convenience in practical applications where the exact form of the sampled populations is usually unknown. This *Central-Limit Theorem* "is

TABLE 3.4.1

Frequency Distribution of 511 Means of Samples of 10 Items Randomly Drawn From the Pig Gains, Table 3.2.1. Theoretical Normal Frequency for Comparison

Class Mark (pounds)	Frequency	Theoretical Frequency (For computation, see examples 8.8.10 and 8.8.11)
19	1	0.20
20	1	0.41
21	0	1.18
22	7	2.71
23	5	5.62
24	10	10.78
25	19	18.60
26	30	29.02
27	41	41.14
28	48	52.07
29	66	61.63
30	72	64.23
31	56	61.63
32	46	52.07
33	45	41.14
34	22	29.02
35	24	18.60
36	12	10.78
37	5	5.62
38	0	2.71
39	1	1.84*
Total	511	511.00

* Including subsequent classes.

the most important theorem in statistics from both the theoretical and applied points of view. And it is one of the most remarkable theorems in the whole of mathematics" (6).

The second feature to be noticed is that the range of the means, great as it is, is only about one-third that of the population of gains in table 3.2.1. Means are less variable than items, as we have had occasion to remark before. Discussion of this second feature will be resumed in section 3.6 below.

The final characteristic to be noted in the distribution is its mean. This may be calculated by adding all the sample means and dividing by 511, but a shorter method will be explained in section 8.2. The value, 29.87 pounds, is an estimate of $\mu = 30$ pounds. Clearly, if one could command large samples such as this, he wouldn't bother much about sampling variation.

3.5—Sampling distributions of s^2 and s. These estimators are calculated as in table 2.12.1. In table 3.3.1 you will observe that three of the mean squares, s^2, overestimate $\sigma^2 = 100$ while the fourth is notably small. Examine any of your samples with unusual s^2 to learn what peculiarities of the arrays are indicated. This freakish sample 3 in the table has a range of only $39 - 30 = 9$ pounds with not a single item less than μ.

Did you happen to get a sample with range equal to that of the sampled population?

The distribution of s^2 in our 511 samples is displayed in table 3.5.1. Notice its *skewness*, with the clustering below the mean and a long tail above—somewhat like the chi-square distribution of chapter 1, though less extreme. Despite this, the mean of these mean squares is 101.5, closely approximating the population variance, 100, and verifying the fact that the sample mean square is an unbiased estimator of σ^2.

You may think that we are now ready to go ahead with confidence limits and tests of hypotheses based on the distribution of s or s^2. s^2 is a measure of dispersion similar to chi-square, and might be used in much the same fashion were it not that the more convenient t has been discovered. This will be discussed in section 3.7.

Our distribution of s, the square root of s^2, in table 3.5.2 conforms closely to theory. It shows a slight skewness (not so large as that of s^2)

TABLE 3.5.1

FREQUENCY DISTRIBUTION OF 511 MEAN SQUARES OF SAMPLES WITH $n = 10$ DRAWN FROM THE NORMAL DISTRIBUTION OF TABLE 3.2.1

Class mark	0	20	40	60	80	100	120	140	160	180	200	220	240	260	280	300	320	340
Frequency	1	11	47	92	93	72	73	42	29	26	11	8	2	1	0	1	1	1

TABLE 3.5.2

<small>Frequency Distribution of 511 Sample Standard Deviations Corresponding to the Mean Squares of Table 3.5.1</small>

Class mark	3	4	5	6	7	8	9	10	11	12	13	14	15	16	17	18
Frequency	1	2	9	18	58	77	80	71	79	44	41	17	8	3	1	2

as well as a small bias with mean 9.8 pounds, slightly less than $\sigma = 10$ pounds. Thus, even in samples so small as 10 the bias of the sample standard deviation is negligible in single samples. But compare section 2.14.

EXAMPLE 3.5.1—Theoretically, 50% of the means in table 3.4.1 should be smaller than 30 pounds. Assuming that half of the means in the interval with class mark 30 pounds have values less than 30, the sample number of means less than 30 pounds is 264, the remaining 247 being greater. Calculate chi-square on the hypothesis that in the population the distribution is 1:1. Ans. 0.57.

EXAMPLE 3.5.2—If half the sample standard deviations of table 3.5.2 were expected to be less than 10 pounds, calculate $\chi^2 = 4.89$ for the sample. This is evidence against a symmetrical distribution in the population.

EXAMPLE 3.5.3—The theoretical distribution of s^2 in random samples of n from a normal population with variance, σ^2, is reflected in the distribution of table 3.5.1. The theoretical distribution has the mean, $\mu_{s2} = \sigma^2$ and the variance $2\sigma^4/(n-1)$. Accordingly, the sample mean of the 511 values of s^2 in the table, $\bar{s}^2 = 101.5$, estimates $\mu_{s2} = 100$ and the mean square of the 511 values of s^2 estimates $2(100)^2/9 = 2,222$. This mean square, calculated as in table 8.3.1, is 2,424.

EXAMPLE 3.5.4—Each s^2 is the basis for an estimate of $2\sigma^4/(n-1)$. This estimate is $2s^4/(n+1)$. Examples: Sample No. 1 in table 3.3.1 has $s^2 = 169.8$, estimating 2,222 by $2(169.8)^2/11 = 5,242$. But Sample No. 4, nearer the average, estimates 2,222 by $2(112.3)^2/11 = 2,293$.

3.6—An estimator of the standard error, $\sigma/\sqrt{n}$. This estimator, one of the most useful in our kit of tools, is calculated from either

$$s_{\bar{x}} = s/\sqrt{n} \qquad \text{or} \qquad s_{\bar{x}} = \sqrt{(s^2/n)},$$

whichever is more convenient. In each of your samples of 10, $s_{\bar{x}}$ is an estimate of

$$\sigma_{\bar{x}} = \sigma/\sqrt{n} = 10/\sqrt{10} = 3.162 \text{ pounds}$$

In your drawings you will experience the usual sampling variation, but the average of your sample standard errors should approximate the theoretical 3.162 pounds. Since $s_{\bar{x}}$ is slightly biased in the same manner as s, you would get a still more biased average if you calculated the mean of your sample estimates, $s_{\bar{x}}$. To get the most accurate estimate, add your unbiased mean squares of the means,

$$s_{\bar{x}}^2 = s^2/n,$$

then extract the square root of their mean. In our 511 samples, for example, this average is easily got by taking the average of the mean squares, 101.5, dividing by 10, and extracting the root, $\sqrt{10.15} = 3.186$

pounds. This close approximation to the population value constitutes sampling evidence that $s_{\bar{x}}$ is an estimate to $\sigma_{\bar{x}}$. But what is the nature of this $\sigma_{\bar{x}}$ of which $s_{\bar{x}}$ is an estimate? As indicated in section 2.7, $\sigma_{\bar{x}}$ is the standard deviation of means of samples of n drawn at random from a normal population with standard deviation, σ. Verification of this theorem is found in the distribution of 511 sample means in table 3.4.1. Their sample standard deviation turns out to be 3.178 pounds (in section 8.2 is explained a calculating device easier than that of table 2.2.1), a satisfactory approach to the theoretical 3.162 pounds. If we now combine these two pieces of information, we are prepared for the statement that each random sample affords an estimate, $s_{\bar{x}}$, of the standard deviation of means, or standard error, $\sigma_{\bar{x}}$. Ordinarily only the single sample is drawn. You have seen from examination of your small samples that the estimate may be disconcertingly divergent, but we have now learned that it is only slightly biased in even small samples of 10.

EXAMPLE 3.6.1—Four hundred plants of a certain hybrid rye (3) produced their first flowers an average of 70.5 days after planting, the sample standard deviation being 6.9 days. Estimate the standard deviation of means of similar samples. Ans. $s_{\bar{x}} = 0.34$ day.

EXAMPLE 3.6.2—If you were to draw a sample of 40 items from the pig gains of table 3.2.1, $s_{\bar{x}}$ is an estimate of what population parameter? Ans. 1.58 pounds. You can try this conveniently by combining 4 of your samples of 10, taking them just as they came in your original drawing.

EXAMPLE 3.6.3—Provided you have 10 or more samples of 10, you can easily make a sample of 100. If you used the computational method of section 2.12, your 10 values of ΣX and ΣX^2 are quickly combined for calculation of Σx^2 in this sample of 100. $s_{\bar{x}}$, which may then be computed for this sample, is an estimate of what parameter? Ans. 1 pound.

EXAMPLE 3.6.4—It was reported that a lot of pigs gained at the rate of 1.4 pounds per day with $s_{\bar{x}} = 0.02$ pound per day. The author failed to state the number of pigs in the lot. If you wish to get an idea of this number, you can use the relation, $s_{\bar{x}} = s/\sqrt{n}$ provided you know from experience that the coefficient of variability of fattening swine is about 10%. This would lead to an approximation to s, 10% of 1.4 = 0.14 pound per day. Then $\sqrt{n} = s/s_{\bar{x}} = 0.14/0.02 = 7$; and finally, $n = 49$ pigs. This value of the coefficient of variation, 10%, is fairly small for fattening swine, but may be reduced still further by efficient experimental methods.

3.7—Distribution of t. You became acquainted with this statistic in sections 2.7, 2.8, and 2.9, but explanation had to be delayed until now. The formula is

$$t = (\bar{x} - \mu)/s_{\bar{x}}$$

In your sampling, μ is known to be 30 pounds. Contrast this with section 2.9, where the hypothesis was set up that $\mu = 0$, and where consequently t was equal to $\bar{x}/s_{\bar{x}}$, a value completely determined by the sample. A second contrast is furnished by section 2.8, where the value of μ was unknown. The two confidence limits were,

$$\bar{x} - t_{.05} s_{\bar{x}} \qquad \text{and} \qquad \bar{x} + t_{.05} s_{\bar{x}}$$

in which $t_{.05}$ was a positive number taken from the table. Clearly, we must know more about this useful quantity, t.

Since $\bar{x}$ and $s_{\bar{x}}$ have already been calculated for each of your samples of 10, the sample value of t may now be got by putting $\mu = 30$, the resulting formula being

$$t = (\bar{x} - 30)/s_{\bar{x}}$$

Here, t will be positive or negative according as $\bar{x}$ is greater or less than 30 pounds. In the present sampling the two signs are equally likely, so you may expect about half of each. On account of this symmetry the mean of all your t should be near zero.

The samples in table 3.3.1 were selected to illustrate the manner in which large, small, and intermediate values of t arise in sampling. A small deviation, $(\bar{x} - \mu)$, and/or a large sample standard error tend to make t small. Some striking combinations are put in the table, and you can doubtless find others among your samples.

The distribution of the laboratory sample of t is displayed in table 3.7.1. The class intervals in the present table are, as in table 1.12.1, unequal, adjusted so as to bring into prominence certain useful probabilities in the tails of the distribution. The theoretical percentage frequencies are recorded for comparison with those of the sample. In the last two columns are the cumulative percentage frequencies which make the table

TABLE 3.7.1
SAMPLE AND THEORETICAL DISTRIBUTIONS OF t. SAMPLES OF 10.
DEGREES OF FREEDOM, 9

Interval of t		Sample		Theoretical		
					Cumulative	
From	To	Frequency	Percentage Frequency	Percentage Frequency	One Tail	Both Tails
......	−3.250	3	0.6	0.5	100.0	
−3.250	−2.821	4	0.8	0.5	99.5	
−2.821	−2.262	5	1.0	1.5	99.0	
−2.262	−1.833	16	3.1	2.5	97.5	
−1.833	−1.383	31	6.1	5.0	95.0	
−1.383	−1.100	25	4.9	5.0	90.0	
−1.100	−0.703	52	10.2	10.0	85.0	
−0.703	0.0	132	25.8	25.0	75.0	
0.0	0.703	126	24.6	25.0	50.0	100.0
0.703	1.100	41	8.0	10.0	25.0	50.0
1.100	1.383	32	6.3	5.0	15.0	30.0
1.383	1.833	18	3.5	5.0	10.0	20.0
1.833	2.262	13	2.5	2.5	5.0	10.0
2.262	2.821	8	1.6	1.5	2.5	5.0
2.821	3.250	2	0.4	0.5	1.0	2.0
3.250	.....	3	0.6	0.5	0.5	1.0
		511	100.0	100.0		

convenient for confidence statements and tests of hypotheses. Examination of the table reveals that 2.5% of all t-values in samples of 10 theoretically fall beyond 2.262, while another 2.5% are smaller than −2.262. Combining these two tails of the distribution, as shown in the last column, 5% of all t in samples of 10 lie further from the center than $|2.262|$, which is therefore called the 5% *level* of t. The 5% *point*, you will note, beyond which 5% of each tail lies, is ± 1.833. The utility of these and similar markers is to be explained. At the moment, make a distribution of your own sample t to be compared with the theoretical distributions in the table.

Cumulative percentage distributions of t for other sample sizes have been worked out and were presented in table 2.7.1. Because of symmetry, only the positive half of the t are listed in the body of the table, that is, only those corresponding to the lower half of table 3.7.1. Along the top border may be read the cumulative percentages for the two tails combined, while on the left are degrees of freedom, $n - 1$. The boundaries of the class intervals in table 3.7.1 (0.703, 1.383, 1.833, etc.) may be found in the row specified by 9 degrees of freedom.

3.8—The interval estimate of μ; the confidence interval. The theory of the confidence interval may now be verified from your sampling. Each sample specifies an interval, $\bar{x} \pm t_{.05} s_{\bar{x}}$, said to cover μ. In each of your samples, substitute the estimators, $\bar{x}$ and $s_{\bar{x}}$, together with $t_{.05} = 2.262$, the .05 level for 9 $d.f.$ You will get results similar to those in the last line of table 3.3.1. Finally, if you say, for any particular sample, that the interval includes μ you will be either right or wrong; which it is may be determined readily because you know that $\mu = 30$ pounds. The theory will be verified if about 95% of your statements are right and about 5% wrong.

Referring again to table 3.3.1, sample 1 warrants the statement that the population mean lies between 26.3 and 44.9 pounds, and we know in the present instance that this interval does contain μ. On the contrary, samples 3 and 4 were selected to illustrate cases leading to false statements, one because of an unusually divergent sample mean, the other because of a small sample standard deviation. Of the 511 laboratory samples, 486 resulted in correct statements about μ; that is, 95.1% of the statements were true. The percentage of false statements, 4.9%, closely approximated the theoretical 5%. Always bear in mind the condition involved in every confidence statement at the 5% level—it is right unless a 1-in-20 chance has occurred in the sampling.

Practical applications of this theory are by people doing experiments and other samplings without knowledge of the population parameters. When they make confidence statements, they do not know if they are right or wrong—they know only the probability selected. It is possible, though improbable, that the first five samples you draw in your research career will lead to false statements, not because of unskillful manipulation but through an unlucky quirk of chance. Let us hope that the wise counsel of a more experienced leader would guide you around such a sampling pitfall.

I trust you now have a clear view of the nature of the 0.95 interval estimate, and that you will make use of it, with a happy combination of caution and confidence. In the following sections we shall study another inference involving certain hypotheses about populations.

EXAMPLE 3.8.1—Using the sample frequencies of table 3.7.1, test the hypothesis (known to be true) that the t-distribution is symmetrical in the sense that half of the population frequency is greater than zero. Ans. $\chi^2 = 1.22$.

EXAMPLE 3.8.2—From table 3.7.1 it is seen that $3 + 4 + 5 + 8 + 2 + 3 = 25$ samples have $|t| > 2.262$. Test the hypothesis that 5% of the population values are greater than $|2.262|$. Ans. $\chi^2 = 0.0124$.

EXAMPLE 3.8.3—In table 3.7.1, accumulate the sample frequencies in both tails and compare their percentage values with those in the last column of the table.

EXAMPLE 3.8.4—During the fall of 1943, approximately one in each 1,000 city families of Iowa (cities are defined as having 2,500 inhabitants or more) was visited to learn the number of quarts of food canned. The average for 300 families was 165 quarts with standard deviation, 153 quarts. Calculate the 95% confidence limits. Ans. 165 ± 17 quarts.

EXAMPLE 3.8.5—The 1940 census reported 312,000 dwelling units (roughly the same as families) in Iowa cities. From the statistics of the foregoing example, estimate the number of quarts of food canned in Iowa cities in 1943. Ans. 51,500,000 quarts with 95% confidence limits, 46,200,000 and 56,800,000 quarts.

EXAMPLE 3.8.6—Compute the 99% confidence limits of the mean in example 3.8.4. Ans. 165 ± 23 quarts.

3.9—Differences. Test of null hypotheses. Beginning with section 1.13 and again with section 2.9, you learned how to test useful hypotheses pertaining to sampled populations. It is time to examine the latter section in more detail, using the familiar technique of drawing samples from the hypothetical population. In practice, the null hypothesis most often set up is that there is no difference between the two populations sampled; that is, that the contrasted members of the pairs are drawn from the same source. A convenient model is a normally distributed population of differences with mean equal to zero. We can easily sample such a population by taking advantage of this theorem; if items are drawn at random from a normal population, then randomly paired, the differences between pairs are normally distributed with zero as mean. Merely copy down your samples in pairs, as in table 3.9.1, subtract each item in the second from the corresponding item in the first, and use the differences as the new samples. Naturally, the samples must be taken just as they came from the original drawing, without selection as to which shall be first and which second, and there must be no rearrangement of the items. Two of the pairs in the table were selected from our 511 samples to illustrate features to be commented on below. The third is a made-up sample illustrating a theorem that will be needed later.

These two facts will be noticed right away: (i) the differences, both in size and number, are almost equally divided between pluses and minuses, resulting in sample means falling with equal likelihood above and below zero; and (ii) the variation of the differences is much greater than that of the original population. The reason for this second fact is apparent when you observe that the possible range of differences is from $3 - 57 = -54$ pounds to $57 - 3 = 54$ pounds, a range of $54 - (-54) = 108$ pounds, twice the range of the gains in table 3.2.1. You will not be surprised, then, by these theorems: (i) the variance of random differences,

TABLE 3.9.1

Two Samples of Differences Drawn at Random From Table 3.2.1, and a Made-Up Sample

$\mu_d = 0. \quad \delta_D^2 = 200$

1. Random			2. Random			3. Selected		
Paired Items		Differences	Paired Items		Differences	Paired Items		Differences
X_1	X_2	D	X_1	X_2	D	X_1	X_2	D
39	17	22	19	33	−14	32	22	10
34	29	5	14	30	−16	31	17	14
22	30	− 8	57	41	16	28	34	− 6
27	36	− 9	34	42	− 8	24	24	0
33	41	− 8	39	33	6	44	12	32
42	30	12	34	21	13	53	29	24
36	3	33	39	36	3	9	23	−14
24	23	1	13	33	− 20	35	37	− 2
25	38	−13	39	33	6	33	21	12
29	30	− 1	23	22	1	31	11	20
$\bar{d}$		3.4			− 1.3			9
s_D^2		222.9			155.6			207.4
$s_{\bar{d}}^2$		22.29			15.56			20.74
$s_{\bar{d}}$		4.72			3.94			4.55
t		0.72			− 0.33			1.98

σ_D^2, is double that of the original population; and (ii) the mean square of the sample differences, s_D^2, is an unbiased estimate of $2\sigma^2 = 200$. So if you average the mean squares of all your samples of differences, the result should be not far from 200, twice the variance of the pig gains. I had 144 such mean squares with the average, 207.9. You are doubtless impressed, perhaps startled, by the variability of s_D^2 in your samples.

You are now prepared for another theorem: not only the differences but also the sample means of the differences are normally distributed about $\mu = 0$, the variance of the means being $\sigma_{\bar{d}}^2 = 2\sigma^2/n$. Again, the mean square, $s_{\bar{d}}^2$ of each sample mean, is an unbiased estimate of $\sigma_{\bar{d}}^2$. In verification, I found the average of my 144 sample mean differences to be 0.51 pound with mean square, 22.2, instead of the expected $\mu_{\bar{d}} = 0$ and $\sigma_{\bar{d}}^2 = 20$.

This variance of differences and of mean differences, double those in the original population, may be disconcerting to the many who expect to set up experiments for evaluating differences. Being confronted by such great variation, how can they hope to get means with confidence intervals small enough to be of practical use? Obviously, larger samples would do it, but such may not be feasible. Some devices must be found for reducing the error encountered, or else random pairing must be avoided whenever possible. Both alternatives are to be considered in the next section. At the moment we must look at the values of t in our samples of differences. Since μ is now zero, the formula is

$$t = \bar{d}/s_{\bar{d}},$$

as in section 2.9. The calculation is illustrated in table 3.9.1. Here is an interesting new feature. Since the differences have greater variability than the original gains, both $\bar{d}$ and $s_{\bar{d}}$ have wider ranges; but the ratio, t, is distributed exactly as in table 3.7.1, a fact substantiated by the distribution of table 3.9.2. Clearly, these 144 t might be added to the previous

TABLE 3.9.2

DISTRIBUTION OF 144 VALUES OF t IN SAMPLES OF DIFFERENCES
RANDOMLY DRAWN FROM TABLE 3.2.1; $n = 10$

Class Interval*		Frequency	Percentage Frequency	Theoretical Percentage Frequency
.....	−2.821	0	0.00	1
−2.821	−1.833	6	4.17	4
−1.833	−1.100	11	7.64	10
−1.100	0.000	48	33.33	35
0.000	1.100	55	38.20	35
1.100	1.833	13	9.03	10
1.833	2.821	10	6.94	4
2.821	.....	1	0.69	1
		144	100.00	100

* Because this sample is small, each pair of intervals in table 3.7.1 is here combined into one.

511, making a sample of 655 values all randomly and independently drawn from a single population of t. This justifies the use of the same table of t for samples of gains and for samples of differences. For any one size of sample the distribution of t is contingent only upon normality in the population sampled, irrespective of μ or σ. This is one reason for the utility of the statistic.

In your samples of differences, did you get any values of t larger (in absolute value) than the 5% level, 2.262? Among my 144 samples I got 10 instead of the expected 7. One was greater than 3.250, the 1% level. You are well aware by now that if these were experimental results, the null hypothesis would have been rejected in these 10 samples though it was, in fact, true.

It should be noted that if X_1 in table 3.9.1 were randomly drawn from $N(\mu_1, \sigma_1^2)$, a symbol meaning "a normal population with mean μ_1 and variance σ_1^2", and if X_2 were randomly drawn from $N(\mu_2, \sigma_2^2)$, then the differences $X_1 - X_2$ would be normally distributed with mean $\mu_1 - \mu_2$ and variance $\sigma_1^2 + \sigma_2^2$. This is a more general formula; that given above is a special case where $\mu_1 = \mu_2$ and $\sigma_1^2 = \sigma_2^2$.

EXAMPLE 3.9.1—Refer to your samples from table 3.2.1 and copy in one column the first 30 items you drew. In a parallel column copy the next 30. The differences make up a random sample from a normally distributed population with $\mu_D = 0$ and $\sigma_d^2 = 200$. From your sample of differences calculate the estimators, $\bar{d}$ and s_d^2.

If you read section 2.14 you can use the sample statistics to make an interval estimate of σ_D^2; also you can test the null hypothesis, $\sigma_D^2 = 200$. Is your sample an ordinary one or is it one of the unusual kind?

EXAMPLE 3.9.2—In section 2.10, attention was directed to the non-random pairing of the lesions produced by tobacco virus, table 2.9.1. You can now assess the effect on the variation of the differences. Suppose the observations X_1 to be randomly paired with X_2. We need to estimate the variance of the resulting population of random differences. To approach this, it is reasonable to assume that σ^2 is the same in the populations of the two preparations. Using the observed lesions, X_1 and X_2, calculate:

Preparation	Σx^2	d.f.
1	468	7
2	172	7
Total	640	14

From this, $s^2 = 640/14 = 45.71$ estimates the common population variance of lesions, irrespective of the two means. Finally, the variance of differences is estimated as $2(45.71) = 91.4$. As noted in section 2.10, this is about five times as great as the experimental estimate, $s^2 = 18.75$, in table 2.9.1. The object of the design of the virus experiment was to avoid the variability of random pairs, taking advantage of the fact that the two halves of the same leaf could be expected to react more nearly alike than would randomly selected halves.

EXAMPLE 3.9.3—Collins, Flint, and McLane (2) investigated the effect of a small electric current on the growth of corn seedlings. The seedlings were grown in pairs of boxes, one of each pair treated, the other not. The differences in elongation, treated–untreated, were as follows: 6.0, 1.3, 10.2, 23.9, 3.1, 6.8, −1.5, −14.7, −3.3, 11.1 mm. It seems obvious that the null hypothesis, $\mu = 0$. will not be rejected; but for practice test $H_0: \mu = 0$; $H_A: \mu \neq 0$. The value of t is 1.33. What conclusion do you reach about the effect of an electric current in the growth of corn seedlings?

EXAMPLE 3.9.4—For an interesting account of some of the early testing of experimental data from paired individuals, read Fisher's *Design of Experiments* (4), chapter 3. It is there shown that even Darwin and Galton were uncertain of the principles governing this type of experiment.

EXAMPLE 3.9.5—Prove that the mean square of aX is given by the formula,
$$s_{aX}^2 = a^2 s_X^2$$

EXAMPLE 3.9.6—Prove that $s_{(aX + bY)}^2 = a^2 s_X^2 + b^2 s_Y^2$.

3.10—Reducing the error involved in sampling. Having observed the large variation in random differences, we felt that something must be done to avoid such imprecision in experimentation. Extending the sampling to great numbers of pairs would decrease $s_{\bar{z}}$ to any specified value, but this process would be expensive. Furthermore, since practical samplings are often from populations restricted in size, any great expansion of n may be impossible. Therefore, samplers have sought other methods for increasing precision.

Three additional ways of reducing sampling errors are in common use: (i) selecting or developing populations in which variation is known to be small, (ii) subdividing the aggregates into sub-populations or *strata* of similar individuals, and (iii) utilizing information contained in related variables. These methods may be used in all combinations. Some details follow immediately, but most of them are distributed throughout the remainder of the book.

It is sometimes practicable to get information by sampling populations whose variation is small. For example, one might decide to restrict his inquiry about radio program listeners to women in a certain city, questioning only those who are housekeepers with one or more children and whose family income is between, say, $3,000 and $4,000. The variable being measured, such as amount spent for toilet soap, might have little range within this restricted population. Clearly, no specific information would be got about other parts of the aggregate, but the information about the population sampled should be relatively precise. Again, for certain problems in nutrition of rats it seems adequate to sample a highly inbred colony whose range in 28-day weight, for example, is half that resulting from random mating. Standard errors for means of n such animals would be half those in the randomly mated population; consequently, confidence intervals would be decreased by the same fraction while sample values of t would be doubled.

The facts just stated can be verified by sampling from the normal population represented by table 3.10.1. This population has $\sigma = 5$ pounds instead of the 10 pounds of table 3.2.1, the range also being half the previous value. Since the facts seem obvious, it will scarcely pay you to draw a lot of samples from this table—its real use will come later. It is probably sufficient to look at the distribution of 400 means of 10 items drawn in the laboratory, table 3.10.2. The range is seen to be about half that in table 3.4.1. The mean of the sample means in table 3.10.2 is 30.0 pounds, while their standard deviation is 1.57 pounds instead of the expected

$$\sigma_{\bar{z}} = \sigma/\sqrt{n} = 5/\sqrt{10} = 1.58 \text{ pounds}$$

Clearly, this scheme of reducing sampling variation by sampling from small-ranged populations is effective. Unfortunately, there are not many circumstances in which the method is available. Usually the information desired is about existent populations over whose variation the sampler

TABLE 3.10.1

ARRAY OF 100 GAINS HAVING HALF THE RANGE AND STANDARD DEVIATION AS THAT IN TABLE 3.2.1. DISTRIBUTION IS APPROXIMATELY NORMAL WITH $\mu = 30$ POUNDS AND $\sigma = 5$ POUNDS

Item No.	Gain	Item No.	Gain	Item No.	Gain	Item No.	Gain
00	17	25	27	50	30	75	33
01	19	26	27	51	30	76	34
02	20	27	27	52	30	77	34
03	21	28	27	53	30	78	34
04	22	29	27	54	31	79	34
05	22	30	27	55	31	80	34
06	22	31	28	56	31	81	34
07	23	32	28	57	31	82	35
08	23	33	28	58	31	83	35
09	23	34	28	59	31	84	35
10	23	35	28	60	31	85	35
11	24	36	28	61	31	86	35
12	24	37	29	62	32	87	36
13	24	38	29	63	32	88	36
14	25	39	29	64	32	89	36
15	25	40	29	65	32	90	36
16	25	41	29	66	32	91	37
17	25	42	29	67	32	92	37
18	26	43	29	68	33	93	37
19	26	44	29	69	33	94	38
20	26	45	30	70	33	95	38
21	26	46	30	71	33	96	39
22	26	47	30	72	33	97	40
23	26	48	30	73	33	98	41
24	27	49	30	74	33	99	44

has no control, and the less variable population may not be representative of the other.

The second method of reducing error variation, by sub-division of the aggregate into relatively homogeneous strata, has been found useful in a surprising variety of situations. Most sampling and experimental designs employ it either exclusively or in connection with other devices. The reader will be reminded of it many times as he pursues this text, and later will be referred to more specialized discussions. An instance of this second method is the sampling from pairs of half leaves described in section 2.9, where the concentration of a virus was being examined. The leaf areas to be inoculated with the two preparations were chosen adjacent because it was suspected that they would react more nearly alike than areas on different leaves. Therefore, if one half of each leaf is rubbed with preparation number 1 and the other half with number 2, the lesion differences are expected to vary less than they would if the two preparations were applied to half leaves selected by chance from different plants.

As will be emphasized again, the efficacy of this method of stratification depends on foreknowledge of the behavior of experimental material, and this can be gained only by experience. No advantage is to be expected unless the members of a pair tend to perform in a similar fashion when treated alike. If these members differ as much as the pairs differ, then the stratification is no better than random pairing.

Does stratification imply a desertion of the fundamental principle of randomness? Not at all. It is merely a device for utilizing any knowledge one may have of outcome in order to exclude from the estimate of error that variation which he can anticipate. In the virus experiment two sources of variation had been learned from experience: (i) the differences from plant to plant, and (ii) the differences among leaves on the same plant. Such variability was avoided in estimating experimental error by trying the two preparations on halves of the same leaf. Randomness was attained by allotment of the two preparations to the right and left halves by some such mechanical device as the toss of a coin or a table of random digits. The variation entering the estimate of error was only

TABLE 3.10.2

FREQUENCY DISTRIBUTION OF MEANS OF SAMPLES OF 10 ITEMS DRAWN AT RANDOM
FROM THE NORMAL DISTRIBUTION IN TABLE 3.10.1

Class mark (pounds)	26	27	28	29	30	31	32	33	34
Frequency	5	20	43	80	99	85	48	18	2

that due to random differences in the reactions of two areas of the same leaf.

The third method of controlling error variation, by use of additional information from the measurement of related variates, will be presented in chapter 6.

EXAMPLE 3.10.1—In example 2.9.2 were given the biological values of raw and roasted peanuts as determined in 10 pairs of rats. The sample standard deviation of the differences was 7.72, so that the experimental variance per rat is estimated as $(7.72)^2/2 = 29.8$. Calculate the average mean square among the rats in the two groups. Ans. 26.9. It appears then that, so far as biological values are concerned, the pairing was less efficient than random assortment.

EXAMPLE 3.10.2—If the ninth pair, 44, 63, had not turned up in example 2.9.2, computation will show that the paired sample would have had a mean square per rat less than one-fourth the average mean square in the two unpaired groups. Since such radical changes in attitude depend on one pair of rats, the investigator learns to be cautious.

EXAMPLE 3.10.3—In the first sample of differences in table 3.9.1, $s_D{}^2 = 222.9$. Estimate σ^2 in the population from which the two samples, X_1 and X_2, were drawn. Ans. σ^2 is estimated by 111.45.

EXAMPLE 3.10.4—If a random sample of n is drawn from each of two normal populations with means μ_1 and μ_2 and variances $\sigma_1{}^2$ and $\sigma_2{}^2$, and if the items are randomly paired, the differences are normally distributed with $\mu_D = \mu_1 - \mu_2$ and $\sigma_D{}^2 = \sigma_1{}^2 + \sigma_2{}^2$.

If you draw a sample of 25 weights from table 3.2.1 and a similar sample from table 3.10.1, the differences of randomly paired weights will have $\bar{d}$ estimating what parameter? Ans. $\mu_D = 0$. The sample standard deviation will estimate what parameter? Ans. $\sigma_D = \sqrt{125}$ or 11.18 lbs. (section 3.9, last paragraph). Try it.

REFERENCES

1. A.A.Bryan. Iowa Agricultural Experiment Station Research Bulletin 163 (1933).

2. G. N. Collins, L. H. Flint and J. W. McLane. Journal of Agricultural Research 38:585 (1929).

3. Pedro A. David. Iowa State University Journal of Science, 5:285 (1931).

4. R. A. Fisher. Design of Experiments. Oliver and Boyd, London (1942).

5. W. B. Mercer and A. D. Hall. Journal of Agricultural Science, 4:107 (1911).

6. Alexander McFarlane Mood. Introduction to the Theory of Statistics. Mc-Graw-Hill Book Company, Inc., New York (1950).

7. Gustav A. Wiebe. Journal of Agricultural Research, 50:331 (1935).

CHAPTER 4

The Comparison of Two Randomized Groups

4.1—Introduction. The pairing of similar individuals has been shown to be an effective experimental design. But there may not be enough knowledge of behavior in the experimental material to warrant pairing, and random pairing was found to be unprofitable. The alternative is merely to assign the individuals *at random* to two groups or lots, and then apply one of the treatments to each group. It will be only the two means that are compared, not the individual measurements. Experimental error will be determined by the average variation among the individuals within the groups.

4.2—The structure of an experiment with randomized groups or lots. This structure is shown clearly by two of the random samples drawn from the pig gains of chapter 3. Consider samples 1 and 2 of table 3.3.1. Think of the first as a group of pigs fed a ration that is capable of changing the population mean gain to μ_1 pounds. In the second group, the ration may produce μ_2 pounds of gain. For evidence we have the group means, $\bar{x}_1 = 35.6$ and $\bar{x}_2 = 29.3$ pounds. The familiar question is this: Is the difference, $\bar{x}_1 - \bar{x}_2 = 6.3$ pounds, attributable to a population difference, $\mu_1 - \mu_2$, or may it be random variation from a single population mean?

To answer this question, we set up the null hypothesis, $\mu_1 - \mu_2 = 0$. The t-distribution furnishes a test:

$$ t = \frac{(\bar{x}_1 - \bar{x}_2) - (\mu_1 - \mu_2)}{s_{\bar{x}_1 - \bar{x}_2}}, $$

which becomes, with H_0: $\mu_1 - \mu_2 = 0$,

$$ t = \frac{\bar{x}_1 - \bar{x}_2}{s_{\bar{x}_1 - \bar{x}_2}} $$

It remains only to calculate the denominator.

Each group provides an estimate of σ^2, the variance common to the two experimental populations. The estimators are $s_1^2 = 169.8$ and $s_2^2 = 151.6$,

[85]

the average being $(169.8 + 151.6)/2 = 160.7$. From this we have as an estimate of the variance of either mean,

$$s_{\bar{x}}^2 = \frac{s^2}{n} = \frac{160.7}{10} = 16.07$$

But it is the difference between the means for which we need an estimate of variance. Now in random samples from normal populations, differences between means follow the same laws as differences between observations because means also are normally distributed. We have then (section 3.9),

$$s_{\bar{x}_1 - \bar{x}_2}^2 = 2s_{\bar{x}}^2 = 2(16.07) = 32.14$$

Substituting the difference between the group means, 6.3 pounds, along with its standard deviation, $\sqrt{32.14} = 5.67$,

$$t = \frac{6.3}{5.67} = 1.11$$

As for degrees of freedom, there are $n - 1 = 9$ associated with s_1 and 9 with s_2, making $2(n - 1) = 18$ in all. Here, n is the size of each group.

Comparison of $t = 1.11$, $d.f. = 18$, with the distribution in table 2.7.1 shows that this t is of modest size. The null hypothesis is not rejected as, indeed, should be the case in this simulated experiment.

Let us now see what would have happened if the rations had really changed the population means. In group 1, add 10 pounds to each gain. This makes $\mu_1 = 40$ pounds instead of 30 and $\bar{x}_1 = 45.6$ pounds instead of 35.6. The sample standard deviation is unchanged. Substituting the new data in the equation for t, keeping the same H_0: $\mu_1 - \mu_2 = 0$,

$$t = \frac{45.6 - 29.3}{5.67} = 2.87, \, d.f. = 18$$

This would indicate rejection of H_0 and the conclusion that μ_1 and μ_2 are different.

The structure of this experiment is now plain. Two groups are randomly drawn from populations in which different treatments may have differentiated the means but not the variances. The difference between the group means estimates the population difference, $\mu_1 - \mu_2$. The difference is tested against the null hypothesis, $\mu_1 - \mu_2 = 0$; that is, $\mu_1 = \mu_2$. The error variance is σ^2, common to the two populations. From this, the variance of the difference between means, $2\sigma^2/n$, is estimated by

$$\frac{2}{n} \cdot \frac{s_1^2 + s_2^2}{2} = \frac{2}{n} \cdot \frac{\Sigma x_1^2 + \Sigma x_2^2}{2(n - 1)}$$

It is now time to look at a real experiment of this type.

4.3—An experiment for comparing two groups of equal size.
Using male chicks, Breneman (2) contrasted the 15-day mean comb
weight of two lots, one receiving sex hormone A (testosterone) and the
other C (dehydroandrosterone).   Day-old chicks, eleven in number,
were assigned at random to each of the treatments.   The two lots, caged
together, were distinguished by red and purple head-stains.   The individual comb weights are recorded in table 4.3.1.   It is plain that there

TABLE 4.3.1

WEIGHT OF COMBS* (15TH DAY) OF MALE CHICKS GIVEN HORMONES A AND C

Hormone	Number of Chicks	Weight of Comb (milligrams)	Mean
A	11	57 120 101 137 119 117 104 73 53 68 118	97
C	11	89 30 82 50 39 22 57 32 96 31 88	56

* Slight alterations of the original data have been made to simplify computations.

is no reason for comparing the comb weight of any chick receiving hormone A with that of any particular chick receiving C; it is only the means
that can be compared.

The calculations are conveniently summarized in table 4.3.2.   As
indicated above, one change is made; instead of computing and averaging
the two mean squares, the corrected sums of squares are added or pooled
and the sum divided by the total degrees of freedom.

The evidence is convincing that the two hormones differentiate comb
weights into two populations with different means; that is, the difference,
41 mg., is significant.

TABLE 4.3.2

SUMMARY OF STATISTICS FOR COMPARISON OF TWO GROUPS OF EQUAL SIZE
Chick data of table 4.3.1

Hormone	Number of Chicks	Degrees of Freedom	Mean Comb Weight (milligrams)	Sum of Squares
A	11	10	97	8,472
C	11	10	56	7,748
		Sum = 20	Diff. = $\bar{x}_1 - \bar{x}_2 = 41$	Sum = $\Sigma x^2 = 16,220$

Pooled mean square $= s^2 = \dfrac{\Sigma x^2}{2(n-1)} = 16,220/20 = 811$

$$s_{\bar{x}_1 - \bar{x}_2} = \sqrt{2s^2/n} = \sqrt{2(811)/11} = \sqrt{147.5} = 12.14 \text{ mg.}$$
$$t = (\bar{x}_1 - \bar{x}_2)/s_{\bar{x}_1 - \bar{x}_2} = 41/12.14 = 3.38. \quad P < 1\%$$

Notice that equality of variance in the two populations has been taken for granted. A glance at the sums of squares makes this appear reasonable. Ordinarily, similar treatments do not change the variance; or, if they do, the change is too small to be detected. But in some experiments the assumption may not be lightly made. If one has reason to believe that σ will be affected by the contemplated treatments he will need a different statistical method from that here presented. See section 4.9.

After the reader has mastered the argument leading to table 4.3.2 he may find it convenient to summarize the calculations by use of this formula:

$$ t = (\bar{x}_1 - \bar{x}_2) \sqrt{\frac{n(n-1)}{\Sigma x^2}} $$

in which $\bar{x}_1 - \bar{x}_2$ designates the difference between the two group means and Σx^2 is the *pooled* sum of squares. Substituting the chick data, $\bar{x}_1 - \bar{x}_2 = 97 - 56 = 41$ mg., $n = 11$, and $\Sigma x^2 = 8,472 + 7,748 = 16,220$. Then

$$ t = 41 \sqrt{\frac{(11)(10)}{16,220}} = 3.38, \text{ as before.} $$

Having reached the conclusion that there are two population means instead of one, it may be informative to set confidence limits to their difference, of which 41 mg. is an unbiased estimate. Since $t_{.05} = 2.086$ for $d.f. = 20$, the 95% limits are

$$ 41 - (2.086)(12.1) \quad \text{and} \quad 41 + (2.086)(12.1), $$

that is, 16 and 66 mg. If the experimenter states that the difference between the means of the two populations is within these limits he will be right unless a one-in-twenty chance has come off.

Note that the confidence interval may be used to reach a conclusion about $H_0: \mu_1 - \mu_2 = 0$. Since the interval does not include zero, H_0 is rejected.

EXAMPLE 4.3.1—Lots of ten bees were fed two concentrations of syrup, 20% and 65%, at a feeder half a mile from the hive (7). Upon arrival at the hive their honey sacs were removed and the concentration of the fluid measured. In every case there was a decrease from the feeder concentration. The decreases were: from the 20% syrup, 0.7, 0.5, 0.4, 0.7, 0.5, 0.4, 0.7, 0.4, 0.2, and 0.5; from the 65% syrup, 1.7, 2.8, 2.2, 1.4, 1.3, 2.1, 0.8, 3.4, 1.9, and 1.4%. Here, every observation in the second sample is larger than any in the first, so that rather obviously $\mu_1 < \mu_2$. Show that $t = 5.6$ if $\mu_1 - \mu_2 = 0$. There is little doubt that, under the experimental conditions imposed, the concentration during flight decreases more with the 65% syrup. But how about homogeneity of variance? See sections 4.8 and 4.9 for further discussion.

EXAMPLE 4.3.2—Four determinations of the pH of Shelby loam were made with each of two types of glass electrode (5). With a modified quinhydrone electrode, the readings were 5.78, 5.74, 5.84, and 5.80; while with modified $Ag/AgCl$ electrode, they were 5.82, 5.87, 5.96, and 5.89. With the hypothesis that $\mu_1 - \mu_2 = 0$, calculate $t = 2.66$.

EXAMPLE 4.3.3—Fifteen kernels of mature Iodent corn were tested for crushing resistance. Measured in pounds the resistances were: 50, 36, 34, 45, 56, 42, 53, 25, 65, 33, 40, 42, 39, 43, 42. Another batch of 15 kernels was tested after being harvested in the dough stage: 43, 44, 51, 40, 29, 49, 39, 59, 43, 48, 67, 44, 46, 54, 64. Test the significance of the difference between the two means. Ans. $t = 1.38$.

EXAMPLE 4.3.4—When yearling steers are shipped in from the range for fattening, so little is known of their previous history that estimating outcome is an uncertain process. They may be just as well placed in lots at random. Culbertson and Hammond (4) report the average daily gains of two lots of steer calves, one (I) having a supplement of linseed oil meal, and a second (V) receiving a light allowance (1 pound per steer daily) of whole soybeans. The rates of gain were: (I) 1.95, 2.17, 2.06, 2.11, 2.24, 2.52, 2.04, 1.95: (V) 1.82, 1.85, 1.87, 1.74, 2.04, 1.78, 1.76, 1.86 pounds per day. Calculate the difference of the means, 0.29 pound per day, and $t = 3.92$.

EXAMPLE 4.3.5—You may wonder why, in group experiments, the observations are not paired at random, and then handled as in section 2.9 and in table 3.9.1. This could be done. But the random pairing is an additional hazard which it is better to avoid. There are many possible pairings, all leading to different results. In a sense, the calculations of table 4.3.2 yield a kind of average of the possible pairings.

In the first two samples of table 3.3.1, try pairing the observations as they occur—they are already randomly paired. The differences are $33 - 32 = 1$, $53 - 31 = 22$, etc., some of them negative. If you test the significance of the mean difference, 6.3 pounds, you will get $t = 0.88$ instead of the value in section 4.2. Other random pairings will usually produce different values of t: occasionally one of them will appear significant, as you will see later (section 4.6).

EXAMPLE 4.3.6—In reading reports of researches it is sometimes desirable to supply a test of significance which was not considered necessary by the author. As an example, Smith (10) gave the sample mean yields and their standard errors for two crosses of maize as 8.84 ± 0.39 and 7.00 ± 0.18 grams. Each mean was the average of five replications. We wish to determine if the mean difference is significant. It is necessary to retrace the original computations till each sum of squares is reached. Starting with $s_{\bar{x}} = 0.39$, $s_{\bar{x}}^2 = 0.1521$, $s^2 = 0.7605$, and $\Sigma x^2 = 3.042$. Similarly, in the second cross, $\Sigma x^2 = 0.648$. Pooling these two sums of squares with $d.f. = 8$, the value of t may be calculated. Ans. $t = 4.29$.

EXAMPLE 4.3.7—Derive the formula, $t = (\bar{x}_1 - \bar{x}_2)\sqrt{n(n-1)/\Sigma x^2}$, starting with the rules of calculation given in connection with table 4.3.2.

4.4—Difficulties met in experiments with groups.

The foregoing test of the null hypothesis, $\mu_1 - \mu_2 = 0$, involves the assumptions that the populations are both normally distributed and that they have the same variance.

As usual, the probabilities are little affected by even considerable departures from normality. The matter of population variance will be discussed in section 4.8. More immediate is the question as to whether the estimate of variance, s^2, correctly evaluates the errors to which the experimental means are subject. In the present instance this is aimed at by choosing chicks of one breed and sex, all of the same age, then housing them together. Presumably no extraneous environmental factors differentiated the lots, only the hormone treatments being responsible for the population difference in means. The designs of many group comparisons leave these matters in doubt. If lots are kept in separate cages, or if two groups of lots are affected by positional differences in the greenhouse, the indicated population difference may be a combination of treatment and other environmental effects and s^2 may not be an appropriate estimate of error. The treatment differences are then said to be *confounded* with the others, and there may be no means of distinguishing them. In these circumstances, statistical evidence that the population averages are different may have little bearing on the problem of possible treatment effects. Although the statistics may lead correctly to rejection of the null hypothesis, and although this hypothesis may, in fact, be untrue, yet the treatments themselves may have no effects, or may tend to cause a difference opposite to that in the sample. Furthermore, there may be no way to estimate separately the amounts or directions of the two kinds of environmental effects, treatment and extraneous, the population difference being compounded of such effects in unknown proportions. If the experiment is conducted so as to avoid such confusion, σ^2 will be estimated by s^2 and real treatment effects may be expected to lead to significant differences.

4.5—Groups with different numbers of individuals. It is somewhat more efficient to have groups of the same size, but in much experimentation it is inconvenient or impossible to provide equal numbers. Two lots of chicks, for example, from two batches of eggs differently treated would nearly always differ in numbers of birds hatched. Furthermore, accidents and death usually befall the lots unequally. This may not change the statistical theory, and causes only a slight alteration in the method of making the comparison.

As an illustration, consider the gains in weight of two lots of rats fed different levels of protein, table 4.5.1. If n_1 and n_2 are the numbers of

TABLE 4.5.1

GAINS IN WEIGHT OF TWO LOTS OF FEMALE RATS ON DIFFERENT DIETS. THE GAINS
OCCURRED BETWEEN 28 AND 84 DAYS OF AGE

Diet	Number of Rats	Gains in Grams
High protein	12	134, 146, 104, 119, 124, 161, 107, 83, 113, 129, 97, 123
Low protein	7	70, 118, 101, 85, 107, 132, 94

observations in the two groups, the corresponding degrees of freedom are $n_1 - 1$ and $n_2 - 1$, a total of $n_1 + n_2 - 2$. The mean squares of the two group means are now different, s^2/n_1 and s^2/n_2, while the mean square of the difference of the means is now the sum of the two instead of $2s^2/n$:

$$s^2/n_1 + s^2/n_2 = s^2(1/n_1 + 1/n_2) = s^2 \frac{n_1 + n_2}{n_1 n_2}$$

so that finally,

$$s_{\bar{x}_1 - \bar{x}_2} = \sqrt{s^2 \frac{n_1 + n_2}{n_1 n_2}} = s \sqrt{\frac{n_1 + n_2}{n_1 n_2}}$$

If $n_1 = n_2$, this becomes, as it should, the same as that in table 4.3.2. The necessary computations are laid out in table 4.5.2.

TABLE 4.5.2

SUMMARY OF STATISTICS FOR COMPARISON OF TWO GROUPS OF DIFFERENT SIZES. RAT DATA OF TABLE 4.5.1

Diet	Number of Rats	Degrees of Freedom	Mean Gain (grams)	Sum of Squares
High	12	11	120	5,032
Low	7	6	101	2,552
		Sum = 17	Diff. = $\bar{x}_1 - \bar{x}_2 = 19$	Sum = $\Sigma x^2 = 7,584$

Pooled mean square $= s^2 = 7,584/17 = 446.12$
$s_{\bar{x}_1 - \bar{x}_2} = \sqrt{s^2(n_1 + n_2)/n_1 n_2} = \sqrt{446.12(12 + 7)/(12)(7)} = 10.04$ grams
$t = 19/10.04 = 1.89$, $d.f. = 17$, $P = 0.08$

Since $P > 0.05$, the null hypothesis may not be rejected. So far as this small sampling is competent, the levels of protein fed may not differentiate rat gains into two populations.

For evidence about homogeneity of variance, observe that $s_1^2 = 5,032/11 = 457$ and $s_2^2 = 2,552/6 = 425$.

The process of testing outlined above for groups of different sizes may be condensed into this formula:

$$t = (\bar{x}_1 - \bar{x}_2)\sqrt{\frac{n_1 n_2(n_1 + n_2 - 2)}{(n_1 + n_2)\Sigma x^2}},$$

$\bar{x}_1 - \bar{x}_2$, as before, being the difference between the group means and Σx^2 the pooled sum of squares. Applying this formula to the rat gains: $\bar{x}_1 - \bar{x}_2 = 120 - 101 = 19$ grams, $n_1 n_2 = (12)(7) = 84$, $n_1 + n_2 = 19$, $n_1 + n_2 - 2 = 17$, and $\Sigma x^2 = 5,032 + 2,552 = 7,584$. Upon substituting these values in the formula, $t = 1.89$ as in table 4.5.2.

If the investigator is interested more in estimates than in tests, he may choose to use the confidence interval rather than t. He may report that $\bar{x}_1 - \bar{x}_2 = 19$ grams with the 95% confidence interval, -2.2 to 40.2 grams.

EXAMPLE 4.5.1—The following are the rates of diffusion of carbon dioxide through two soils of different porosity (9). Through a fine soil (f): 20, 31, 18, 23, 23, 28, 23, 26, 27, 26, 12, 17, 25: through a coarse soil (c): 19, 30, 32, 28, 15, 26, 35, 18, 25, 27, 35, 34. Show that pooled $s^2 = 35.83$, $s_{\bar{x}_1 - \bar{x}_2} = 2.40$, $d.f. = 23$, and $t = 1.67$. The difference, therefore, is not significant.

EXAMPLE 4.5.2—The total nitrogen content of the blood plasma of normal albino rats was measured at 37 and 180 days of age (11). The results are expressed as grams per 100 cc. of plasma. At age 37 days, 9 rats had 0.98, 0.83, 0.99, 0.86, 0.90, 0.81, 0.94, 0.92, and 0.87; at age 180 days, 8 rats had 1.20, 1.18, 1.33, 1.21, 1.20, 1.07, 1.13, and 1.12 grams per 100 cc. Since significance is obvious, set a 95% confidence interval on the population mean difference. Ans. 0.21 to 0.35 g./100 cc.

EXAMPLE 4.5.3—Pearson and Catchpole (8) reported the means and standard errors of inorganic phosphorus per 100 ml. of blood serum as determined from 26 Percherons and 18 Shetlands, 3.29 ± 0.27 and 3.96 ± 0.40 mg., the numbers following the ± signs being the sample standard errors. To test the significance of the difference between means, 0.67 mg., compute the pooled sum of squares, 96.345, $s_{\bar{x}_1 - \bar{x}_2} = 0.464$, and $t = 1.44$. The difference is not significant, but may be easily a consequence of sampling variation.

EXAMPLE 4.5.4—It is reported that the mean percentage of bacon from the carcasses of 15 Poland China sows was 6.59% with the standard error, 0.300%. If you assume normal distribution, you can estimate the lowest and highest percentages in the sample as 4.6% and 8.6%. Would you have any reason to suspect the hypothesis of normality?

4.6—Individual vs. group comparisons.

The decision as to whether an experiment should be set up for individual or group comparisons is one of considerable import. It may even determine the success or failure of the trial. While there is no universal formula for determining the preferable design, there are numbers of relevant circumstances on which judgments may be founded. Most of them have been discussed already in sections 2.10 and 3.10. With some repetition, which I think is worth while, the attempt will be made to bring together the pertinent arguments.

Pairing is often indicated clearly in the experimental material. Crop yields in successive seasons tend to be so different that no one would think of comparing the results of one treatment last year with those of a second treatment this year. Both treatments must be applied every season with a consequent pairing of the yields. Much the same can be said of different localities in the same year.

On the other hand, pairing is not practicable in a variety of experiments. Among Breneman's chicks (section 4.3) there was no basis for matching individuals, hence, they were randomly assigned to the treatments. When yearling steers are shipped in from the range for fattening, so little is known of their history that estimating outcome seems to be doubtful. Again, if circumstances dictate different numbers of individuals for the two treatments, pairing is clearly impossible.

Aside from these rather obvious situations the design often depends upon the investigator's information about his experimental material and its environment. He may know, for example, that potted plants on two greenhouse benches will grow alike if treated alike. He could then apply one treatment to the pots on one bench and a second treatment to the others, then compare the two treatments by the methods of this chapter. But more often he will know that growing conditions on the two benches, and even on adjacent portions of the same bench, are different. He will avoid the effects of this variation by placing side by side pairs of pots with the two treatments, then replicating the pairs. The appropriate statistical method will be that of chapter 2.

With increasingly precise experimentation in any field, resulting from more exact knowledge of the behavior of the experimental material, group comparisons are likely to be replaced by those of individuals. In feeding trials with growing pigs, animals of the same litter, sex, and initial weight are paired because it has been learned that they are more likely to gain alike on the same ration than are two randomly assorted individuals. Hence, if from each pair one member, chosen at random, is given one feed while the other member receives the second, the differences in gain tend toward uniformity. This means that the experimental error, calculated as in chapter 2, is expected to be smaller than that in a group comparison where the pigs are allotted to the rations at random.

In such experiments the success of pairing depends upon knowledge of outcome. No advantage may be gained unless the experimenter can predict with some degree of success that the members of a pair have the same performing ability, this common ability being different from that of the members of other pairs.

A feature of the method of individual comparisons is that it enables the investigator to utilize all the knowledge he has about the behavior of his experimental material in the contemplated environment. In the absence of this knowledge of outcome, or of any pertinent relationship, group comparisons are more appropriate.

The beginner may learn to avoid pitfalls by observing the effects of applying an unwarranted statistical method to experimental data. Suppose, for example, the reduction of the paired virus data in section 2.9 had been mistakenly carried out by the method for group comparisons. The results would have been these:

Preparation of Virus	Number Half Leaves	Degrees of Freedom	Mean Number of Lesions	Sum of Squares
1	8	7	15	468
2	8	7	11	172
	Sum = 14		$\bar{x}_1 - \bar{x}_2 = 4$	$\Sigma x^2 = 640$

$s^2 = 45.71,\ t = 4\sqrt{(8)(7)/640} = 1.18,\ P = 0.26$, approximately

The investigator might have decided not to reject the null hypothesis, whereas he probably would have rejected it on the basis of the correctly computed statistics in table 2.9.1. This discussion of misapplication of statistical methods should be compared with that of section 2.10, where the purposes of pairing were examined.

Equally surprising effects follow an arbitrary pairing of data from an experiment designed for group comparison. When you remember that the latter design would be adopted only if the investigator were unable to foresee any advantage in pairing his experimental individuals, you will appreciate the mistake of arranging the randomly assembled measurements in pairs after the experiment is done. Perhaps the best way to illustrate is by use of the two samples discussed in section 4.2. The sample difference, 6.3 pounds, and mean square, 2(160.7) = 321.4, are unbiased estimates of $\mu_1 - \mu_2 = 0$ and $\sigma_D{}^2 = 200$. Furthermore, as you would expect in 95% of such comparisons, t is less than its 5% level. However, suppose someone had rearranged the items in the two samples, pairing the two smallest, the next smallest, and so on to the two largest as in the first part of table 4.6.1; or else pairing small with large and *vice versa* as in the second part of the table. While the means of the samples

TABLE 4.6.1

TWO OF THE POSSIBLE METHODS OF PAIRING THE DATA IN RANDOM SAMPLES, ILLUSTRATING THE ERRONEOUS CONCLUSIONS THAT MIGHT BE DRAWN

	Method I			Method II		
	Sample 1	Sample 2	Difference	Sample 1	Sample 2	Difference
	12	11	1	12	53	−41
	24	19	5	24	44	−20
	29	19	10	29	32	− 3
	33	24	9	33	31	2
	34	30	4	34	30	4
	36	30	6	36	30	6
	39	31	8	39	24	15
	39	32	7	39	19	20
	53	44	9	53	19	34
	57	53	4	57	11	46
SX	356	293	63	356	293	63
$\bar{x}$	35.6	29.3	$\bar{x}_1 - \bar{x}_2 = 6.3$	35.6	29.3	$\bar{x}_1 - \bar{x}_2 = 6.3$
s^2			8.01			627.34
t			7.04			0.80

and of the differences are unchanged, the mean squares of the two sets of differences form a notable contrast, neither being an unbiased estimate of the variance of random differences, $\sigma^2 = 200$, in the population. In the first method, the large value of t would certainly lead to rejection of the hypothesis of zero population difference. In the second, t is an underestimate of correct sample value, 1.11. It is clear from these illustrations that the statistical method fixed by the experimental design cannot be tampered with.

The reader who is pursuing a preliminary course of essentials is prepared for either chapter 6 on regression or for chapter 10 on analysis of variance. For the present, the remainder of this chapter may be omitted.

4.7—Size of sample. The methods here are only slight modifications of those in section 2.15. The basic estimate of σ is given directly by such tables as 4.3.2 or 4.5.2. Since differences between means are being estimated and tested, the factor $\sqrt{2}$ must be used. Either the largest allowable half confidence interval or the smallest interesting population mean difference is given by

$$\delta = \frac{\sqrt{2}\,s\,t}{\sqrt{n}},$$

where n is the size of each of the two experimental groups. Finally, $d.f. = 2(n - 1)$.

Illustrations will be based on example 4.3.4. The investigators were limited to 8 animals per lot and wished to know the size of the difference they had a 1:1 chance of detecting at the 5% level of significance. They usually encountered sample standard deviations of 0.12 to 0.18 lb. per day, so they chose $s = 0.15$. From these data they calculated

$$\delta = \frac{\sqrt{2}\,(0.15)(2.145)}{\sqrt{8}} = 0.16 \text{ lb./day}$$

as the difference they might expect to detect. (Notice that the degrees of freedom associated with s are not critical except for small samples.) As it turned out, the sample difference between means was 0.29 lb./day with 95% confidence interval, 0.13 to 0.45 lb./day.

If the investigators had wished to design a following experiment large enough to detect a difference of 5% of the sample average daily gain, that is, $(0.05)(1.985) = 0.1$ lb./day, they would determine the lot size from the statistic of the first experiment in which $s = 0.148$ lb./day. They would have

$$0.1 = \frac{\sqrt{2}\,(0.148)t_{.05}}{\sqrt{n}}$$

which, using the recursion methods of section 2.15, gives $n = 18$.

Greater assurance than 0.5 might be demanded; for example, 0.75. If so, it would be found by the method of section 10.18 that lots of 25 were required.

EXAMPLE 4.7.1—In example 4.3.3 the mean of all the crushing resistances was 45.5 lbs. It is thought that if the real difference were as much as 10% of the mean, it would be desirable to know that fact. How many replications per stage will be required to keep the half confidence interval below 4.55 lbs.? Ans. 38 kernels.

EXAMPLE 4.7.2—In example 4.3.1, the pooled mean square was 0.308 with $d.f. = 18$. What difference of sample means might this experiment be expected to detect at the 5% level of significance? Ans. 0.52%.

EXAMPLE 4.7.3—In the same example, 4.3.1, how many replications would be required to detect $\bar{x}_1 - \bar{x}_2 = 1.4\%$ at the 5% level? Ans. 3 bees per lot. Note: To raise the chance of detection to 3:1 would require 5 bees per lot.

4.8—A test for homogeneity of variance. If there is any suspicion that treatments will change the population variance, the matter properly should be decided upon in advance of the experiment. When it is only in the sample that the sums of squares are observed to differ greatly, sampling variation is strongly suspected and pooling should be done as usual. Occasionally, however, there may be reasons for expecting that the treatments will affect the variance. The experimenter may wish to test $H_0: \sigma_1^2 = \sigma_2^2$; indeed, he may design the experiment for that purpose.

For testing homogeneous variance, in contrast with the testing of section 2.14, a new sampling distribution is required, that of F. This will be discussed in section 10.5. A condensed table is 4.8.1. A more extensive table will be given in chapter 10.

TABLE 4.8.1

5% Level (Two-Tail) Distribution of F

$f_2 = d.f.$ for Smaller Mean Square	$f_1 = d.f.$ for Larger Mean Square									
	2	4	6	8	10	12	15	20	30	∞
2	39.00	39.25	39.33	39.37	39.40	39.42	39.43	39.45	39.46	39.50
3	16.04	15.10	14.74	14.54	14.42	14.34	14.25	14.17	14.08	13.90
4	10.65	9.60	9.20	8.98	8.84	8.75	8.66	8.56	8.46	8.26
5	8.43	7.39	6.98	6.76	6.62	6.52	6.43	6.33	6.23	6.02
6	7.26	6.23	5.82	5.60	5.46	5.37	5.27	5.17	5.07	4.85
7	6.54	5.52	5.12	4.90	4.76	4.67	4.57	4.47	4.36	4.14
8	6.06	5.05	4.65	4.43	4.30	4.20	4.10	4.00	3.89	3.67
9	5.71	4.72	4.32	4.10	3.96	3.87	3.77	3.67	3.56	3.33
10	5.46	4.47	4.07	3.85	3.72	3.62	3.52	3.42	3.31	3.08
12	5.10	4.12	3.73	3.51	3.37	3.28	3.18	3.07	2.96	2.72
15	4.76	3.80	3.41	3.20	3.06	2.96	2.86	2.76	2.64	2.40
20	4.46	3.51	3.13	2.91	2.77	2.68	2.57	2.46	2.35	2.09
30	4.18	3.25	2.87	2.65	2.51	2.41	2.31	2.20	2.07	1.79
∞	3.69	2.79	2.41	2.19	2.05	1.94	1.83	1.71	1.57	1.00

Use of the table is illustrated by means of the data in example 4.3.1. Different variances were not anticipated, but it is worth our while to examine the large discrepancy between the mean squares. For the 20% syrup, $s^2 = 0.027$; while for the 65% syrup, $s^2 = 0.589$. Each mean square has 9 $d.f.$ The value of F is the ratio, larger mean square over the smaller:

$$F = 0.589/0.027 = 22.1$$

To test the null hypothesis, $\sigma_1^2 = \sigma_2^2$, compare this sample value of F with the tabular value, 4.03, given in the row for 9 $d.f.$ and the column for 9 $d.f.$ (interpolated between 8 and 10). Since the sample F is larger than this 0.05 level, H_0 would ordinarily be rejected. If so, there is no common σ^2 to be estimated by the pooled mean square and the test in example 4.3.1 may be questioned. What to do about it is discussed in the next section.

EXAMPLE 4.8.1—In table 4.5.1, test the hypothesis that the two protein diets have not affected the variance of the rat gains. Ans. $F = 1.08$ to be compared to the tabular $F_{.05} = 5.41$. There is no evidence against pooling the sums of squares.

EXAMPLE 4.8.2—In example 4.5.3, test the hypothesis that the variance of the inorganic phosphorus per 100 ml. of blood serum is the same in Percherons and Shetlands. Ans. $F = 1.52$ for comparison with $F_{.05} = 2.37$.

4.9—Procedure if $\sigma_1 \neq \sigma_2$. If there is reason to believe that the standard deviations of two sampled normal populations are not the same, the tests which have been described in this chapter are not appropriate. One way of performing the proper test is the Behrens-Fisher method which requires special tables (1, 6, 12). An approximation (3) uses the more generally available tables and will be sufficiently accurate for our purposes.

Case 1: $\sigma_1 \neq \sigma_2$ but $n_1 = n_2$. If the groups are of the same size, carry out the calculations and the test as in section 4.3 with this exception: enter the t-table with $d.f. = n - 1$ instead of $2(n - 1)$. Example: From the two populations of tables 3.2.1 and 3.10.1, I selected the samples of table 4.9.1. The population means are the same, but the standard deviations differ. With the correct number of degrees of freedom, $n - 1 = 9$, the null hypothesis is accepted as it should be. But if the ordinary number of degrees of freedom, $2(n - 1) = 18$, had been used, the null hypothesis would have been rejected falsely. My carefully selected samples (not random) illustrate the fact that, for samples of equal size, the ordinary test, incorrectly applied when $\sigma_1 \neq \sigma_2$, would lead to more than 5% of rejections if the null hypothesis is true.

Case 2: $\sigma_1 \neq \sigma_2$ and $n_1 \neq n_2$. If the samples differ in size, a modification must be made in the calculations. This case is illustrated by

TABLE 4.9.1

Two Samples of the Same Size From Populations With Different Standard
Deviations, Together With the Test of H_0: $\mu_1 = \mu_2$; $n_1 = n_2 = 10$

Sample 1 from $\sigma = 10$, table 3.2.1	32	23	48	41	20	29	53	39	30	43
Sample 2 from $\sigma = 5$, table 3.10.1	27	30	32	26	31	27	23	29	35	20

Sample	Size	Degrees of Freedom	Mean	Sum of Squares
1	10	9	35.8	1,041.6
2	10	9	28.0	174.0
		Sum = 18	$\bar{x}_1 - \bar{x}_2 = 7.8$	$\Sigma x^2 = 1,215.6$

$$t = (\bar{x}_1 - \bar{x}_2) \sqrt{\frac{n(n-1)}{\Sigma x^2}} = 7.8 \sqrt{\frac{(10)(9)}{1,215.6}} = 2.122, \ d.f. = 9, \ P > 0.05$$

two more samples selected from the same pair of populations. Table 4.9.2 shows that the sums of squares are not pooled. Instead $s_{\bar{x}_1 - \bar{x}_2}{}^2$ is

TABLE 4.9.2

Two Samples, Differing in Size, From Populations With Different Standard Deviation, Together With the Test of H_0: $\mu_1 = \mu_2$; $n_1 = 13$, $n_2 = 7$

| Sample 1 from $\sigma = 10$ | 39 | 42 | 19 | 29 | 49 | 38 | 32 | 39 | 25 | 45 | 39 | 35 | 53 |
| Sample 2 from $\sigma = 5$ | 30 | 21 | 26 | 33 | 38 | 31 | 28 | | | | | | |

Sample	Size	Degrees of Freedom	$t_{.05}$	Sample Mean	s^2	$s_{\bar{x}}{}^2 = s^2/n$
1	13	12	2.179	37.23	88.53	6.810
2	7	6	2.447	29.57	28.95	4.136
		18		$\bar{x}_1 - \bar{x}_2 = 7.66$		$s_{\bar{x}_1 - \bar{x}_2}{}^2 = 10.946$

$$s_{\bar{x}_1 - \bar{x}_2} = \sqrt{10.946} = 3.308. \quad t' = (\bar{x}_1 - \bar{x}_2)/s_{\bar{x}_1 - \bar{x}_2} = 7.66/3.308 = 2.316$$

$$5\% \text{ level} = \frac{\Sigma s_{\bar{x}}{}^2 t_{.05}}{\Sigma s_{\bar{x}}{}^2} = \frac{(6.810)(2.179) + (4.136)(2.447)}{6.810 + 4.136} = 2.280$$

estimated by $\dfrac{s_1{}^2}{n_1} + \dfrac{s_2{}^2}{n_2}$. But the resulting quotient, $t' = (\bar{x}_1 - \bar{x}_2)/$ $s_{\bar{x}_1 - \bar{x}_2}$, is not distributed like "Student's" t. Cochran found that the 0.05 level of t' is given approximately by the weighted mean of two values of t taken from the regular table 2.7.1; t_1 corresponding to $n_1 - 1$ and t_2 to $n_2 - 1$. The weights are the mean squares of the two sample means, $s_1{}^2/n_1$ and $s_2{}^2/n_2$. The computations are illustrated in the table. Since $t' = 2.316$ exceeds the 5% level, 2.280, H_0 is rejected, this being one of those 1-in-20 samples leading to a Type I error. If, however, we had mistakenly applied the method of section 4.5, we should have had $\Sigma x^2 = 1,062.31 + 173.71 = 1,236.02$, with

$$t = 7.66 \sqrt{\frac{(91)(18)}{(20)(1,236.02)}} = 1.792,$$

which corresponds to $P = 0.07$, H_0 not being rejected. This kind of result is not typical though it may occur if the larger sample turns up the larger variance as in table 4.9.2. Typically, the ordinary t-test, incorrectly applied if $\sigma_1 \neq \sigma_2$, causes more than the expected 5% of rejections if H_0 is true.

In both cases, then, the ordinary t-test turns up more rejections than are expected—it is a biased test if $\sigma_1 \neq \sigma_2$. But these population standard deviations are seldom known. We really need to know what to do if the sample mean squares differ significantly. That is a difficult problem.

An oversimplified rule might be to use the regular t-test if the mean squares do not differ significantly and otherwise use the Behrens-Fisher test or the approximation to it. But such a procedure would introduce two possible errors, the first connected with the test of H_0: $\sigma_1 = \sigma_2$, the second with the test of H_0: $\mu_1 = \mu_2$. The combination would affect the final test in some complicated way, not in general known. The over-simplified rule is not desirable.

My recommendation is this: If it becomes evident that there is a large discrepancy between the mean squares, re-examine the experimental set-up to discover any possible explanation. It may be that you will find some cause for expecting the standard deviations to be different even though this cause had been overlooked in designing the experiment. In that case, use the Behrens-Fisher test or Cochran's approximation. If no reason for the discrepancy is found, stick to the regular tests but use greater caution in making decisions about the means because the sample estimates of σ^2 are questionable.

What about the experiment on bees, example 4.3.1 and section 4.8? If the 20% syrup were similar in concentration to the nectar usually encountered, one might conclude that the bees handled it with little variation because they were accustomed to it; but actually they are more accustomed to the higher concentration; or one might reason that with the lighter concentration little change was possible, the small variation being associated with the smaller mean. In that case no further test on the means is necessary. Dr. Park found no rational explanation of the discrepancy, so the ordinary test was made. Of course, in this experiment, H_0: $\mu_1 = \mu_2$ would be rejected by any test applied.

Warning: It is never appropriate to select a test according to the results got from it. The correct test is determined by the hypothesis made about the parameters, σ.

EXAMPLE 4.9.1—Young (13) examined the basal metabolism of 26 college women in two groups of $n_1 = 15$ and $n_2 = 11$; $\bar{x}_1 = 34.45$ and $\bar{x}_2 = 33.57$ cal./sq. m./hr.; $\Sigma x_1^2 = 69.36$, $\Sigma x_2^2 = 13.66$. Test H_0: $\sigma_1 = \sigma_2$. Ans. $F = 3.62$ to be compared with $F_{.05} = 3.55$.

BASAL METABOLISM OF 26 COLLEGE WOMEN
(Calories per square meter per hour)

7 or More Hours of Sleep				6 or Less Hours of Sleep			
1.	35.3	9.	33.3	1	32 5	7.	34.6
2.	35.9	10	33.6	2.	34.0	8	33.5
3.	37 2	11.	37.9	3.	34.4	9.	33.6
4.	33.0	12	35.6	4.	31.8	10	31.5
5.	31 9	13.	29.0	5	35 0	11	33.8
6	33 7	14	33.7	6	34.6	$\Sigma X_2 = 369.3$	
7	36.0	15	35.7				
8	35.0	$\Sigma X_1 = 516.8$					

$\bar{x}_1 = 34.45$ cal./sq. m./hr. $\bar{x}_2 = 33.57$ cal./sq. m./hr.

EXAMPLE 4.9.2—In the metabolism experiment there is little difference between the group means, so it seems unlikely that so mild a treatment difference would cause a differentiation between the standard deviations. A more credible explanation is that some unusual observations—29.0, 37.2, 37.9—appeared by chance in the larger sample, making its s^2 an overestimate of σ^2. However, assuming that some rational explanation were found for the hypothesis, $\sigma_1 \neq \sigma_2$, test H_0: $\mu_1 = \mu_2$. Ans. $t' = 1.31$, $t_{.05} = 2.17$. Compare this with $t = 1.19$ and $t_{.05} = 2.048$ which would result from taking $\sigma_1 = \sigma_2$. So far as conclusions are concerned, the hypothesis about standard deviations causes no change.

4.10—Statistics and the experiment. It will be increasingly evident that the statistician and the experimenter, who are usually the same person, must form a close cooperation to insure the success of an investigation. The experimenter specifies the conditions in which the trial is to be performed—materials and treatments, together with genetic and environmental circumstances, and the measurements that can be made. The statistician selects or invents a plan (experimental design) which will furnish unbiased and unconfounded estimates with adequate precision. The experimenter conducts the laboratory or field work, taking pains to eliminate as nearly as possible all extraneous effects. If he is successful, the ensuing measurements will contain the information for which the experiment is set up. The statistician uses appropriate methods for extracting all the information wrought into the data. Finally, the experimenter interprets this information in the light of existing knowledge in his science.

It is sometimes not understood that statistical methods can bring out only that information which has been incorporated into the data by careful design and execution of the sampling. Elaborate statistics are no substitute for meticulous experimentation. Population inferences are futile if dependent on carelessly collected data. It is equally often overlooked that extensive and conscientiously done measurements may contain little worth-while information if the experimental design is faulty. It is only by a combination of appropriate design, skillful conduct of the experiment and suitable statistical methods that the investigator is assured of reliable evidence upon which to base his decisions.

REFERENCES

1. W. U. BEHRENS. Landwirtschaftliche Jahrbucher, 68:807 (1929).

2. W. R. BRENEMAN. Personal communication.

3. W. G. COCHRAN and GERTRUDE M. COX. Experimental Designs. John Wiley and Sons, Inc., New York, (1950).

4. C. C. CULBERTSON and W. E. HAMMOND. Iowa Agricultural Experiment Station Animal Husbandry Leaflet 144 (1933).

5. HAROLD L. DEAN and R. H. WALKER. Journal of the American Society of Agronomy, 27:433 (1935).

6. R. A. FISHER. Annals of Eugenics, 11:141 (1941).

7. O. W. PARK. Iowa Agricultural Experiment Station Research Bulletin 151 (1932).

8. P. B. PEARSON and H. R. CATCHPOLE. The American Journal of Physiology, 115:90 (1936).

9. F. B. SMITH and P. E. BROWN. Soil Science, 35:413 (1933).

10. STEWART N. SMITH. Journal of the American Society of Agronomy, 26:792 (1934).

11. PEARL P. SWANSON and ARTHUR H. SMITH. The Journal of Biological Chemistry, 97:745 (1932).

12. P. V. SUKHATME. Sankhya, 4:39 (1938).

13. CHARLOTTE M. YOUNG. Thesis submitted for the degree, Ph.D., Iowa State University (1940).

CHAPTER 5

Short Cuts and Approximations. Less Than Fully Efficient and Non-Parametric Methods

5.1—Introduction. In the preceding chapters the effort has been made to keep the computations within moderate bounds. This was done by slight modifications in the data so as to provide integral means. Moreover, in sections 2.11 and 2.12 some short-cut and machine methods were described. There are other devices for reducing the burden of calculation. Some of the more useful are presented in this chapter. Others will be explained at appropriate places in succeeding chapters.

During recent years there has been great activity in devising quick and easy methods for dealing with samples from normal populations. In small samples, the range, as a substitute for the sample standard deviation, has been found to give remarkably high efficiency as compared to s. Roughly it may be said that the range of 10 observations furnishes about as much information as the sample standard deviation of 9. If the cost of the additional observation is less than that of calculating s, the range is an appropriate substitute. But even if observations are expensive, a quick appraisal using the range may show that there is no necessity for calculating s; the conclusions may be obvious. In this chapter will be given the range methods for paired and unpaired observations in two samples.

To this point in the text the normal distribution has been taken as the source of much of our sampling. The statistical methods described are fully efficient for that model. Fortunately the same methods are highly efficient for samples from moderately anormal populations. And that is not all. As sample sizes increase, the same methods approach full efficiency in samples from any population with finite standard deviation. In many cases this approach to full efficiency is rapid, even samples of $n = 3$ or $n = 4$ giving satisfactory approximations. Only with the more extreme anormalities are samples of 100 or more required. But for small samples drawn from populations which are notably anormal, there are some *non-parametric* methods available. The Sign Test is the most popular, but there are excellent methods based on ranks. These will be presented in the latter part of this chapter and at appropriate places later. It will be found that non-parametric methods also may be used as "quickies" for assessing samples from normal populations.

5.2—Linear transformations, or coding. In section 2.12 it was shown that machine calculation avoided the necessity of computing differences from $\bar{x}$ or G. But even when a machine is available, it is occasionally desirable to use deviations from some easily subtracted arbitrary origin. As an example, consider the weights of 10 tomatoes: 206, 217, 224, 227, 228, 231, 236, 241, 245, 258 grams. It is easy to subtract 200 grams from each item without rewriting the set. The machine is used to run up the deviations, $\Sigma X = 6 + 17 + \ldots + 58 = 313$, and $\Sigma X^2 = 6^2 + \ldots + (58)^2 = 11,741$. The mean, then, is $200 + 313/10 = 231.3$ grams, and the sum of squares is $11,741 - (313)^2/10 = 1,944.1$. Note that the subtracted number, 200, must be added to the mean deviation in order to get the correct sample mean. For the sum of squares, no such compensation is necessary; the whole set of observations has merely been moved down the scale of measurement with no change in the range or sample standard deviation. There is a worthwhile saving in the size of the numbers handled, with little chance of error in the subtractions.

This illustrates a simple type of *coding*. Code numbers are linear transforms of the observations, the operations being limited to addition and multiplication with the inverse operations, subtraction and division.

A slightly more complicated application of coding is illustrated in table 5.2.1. For present purposes, the hydrogen ion concentrations (pH)

TABLE 5.2.1

THE USE OF CODE NUMBERS IN CALCULATING MEAN AND STANDARD DEVIATION
Cyanogenetic nitrogen recovered from peach stems (2)

Initial pH	Grams per 50 Grams of Tissue X'	Code Numbers $X = 10,000X' - 200$
5.1	0.0238	38
5.0	0.0238	38
5.3	0.0241	41
5.3	0.0241	41
5.7	0.0250	50
5.7	0.0247	47
6.0	0.0241	41
6.1	0.0238	38
6.6	0.0226	26
6.5	0.0232	32

$n = 10$
$\Sigma X = 392$
$\bar{x} = 39.2$ code numbers
$\quad = 0.02392$ gram

$\Sigma X^2 = 15,784$
$(\Sigma X)^2/n = 15,366.4$
$\Sigma x^2 = 417.6$
$s^2 = 46.4$

$s = 6.81$ code numbers
$\quad = 0.000681$ gram

are ignored. The readings in the second column are coded by: (i) multiplication by 10,000, and (ii) subtraction of 200. The computations of $\bar{x}$
and s are done with code numbers. The resulting mean must first be
increased by 200 then divided by 10,000, these inverse operations being
applied in reverse order to the coding operations. You will notice that s
is not affected by the subtraction of 200; but it, like the mean, must be
compensated for the coding operation of multiplication by 10,000. Coding
by multiplication or division may be thought of as a change in the unit
measurement. If it is easier to carry on the calculations with a unit of
one ten-thousandth gram, little chance of error is introduced by the
change. At the end, the original unit is recovered by a mere shift of the
decimal point.

5.3—Rounding and coding. One use of code numbers arises from
a custom general among researchers. Both from necessary precaution
and from convenience they are prone to collect their data in finer units
than are suitable to statistical treatment. A good example appears in
the report of a survey of 145 Iowa farm families with the object of learning about their habits of food consumption (9). Naturally, the record
of the annual consumption of meat was in pound units, that of the first
20 families being 726, 296, 928, 668, 287, 1206, 517, 1638, 2414, 610,
494, 2489, 1198, 676, 1302, 440, 1247, 1053, 1029, 218 pounds. The
range is 2489 − 218 = 2271 units. In most statistical investigations a range
somewhere between 20 and 40 units is ample. It turns out, then, that the
hundredweight is a more suitable computing unit for the set above, the
appropriate code numbers being derived from dividing each item by 100,
then *rounding*: 7, 3, 9, 7, 3, 12, 5, 16, 24, 6, 5, 25, 12, 7, 13, 4, 12, 11, 10,
2 cwt. The statistics of this coded sample are, $\bar{x} = 9.65$, $s = 6.36$ cwt.
Of course, these must be multiplied by 100 to recapture the original unit,
so that $\bar{x} = 965$ pounds and $s = 636$ pounds.

In rounding, numbers like 13.51 are increased to 14, while such as
13.49 are lowered to 13. The dividing line being 13.50, what shall be done
if this particular number appears? In order to insure increases and decreases in approximately equal proportions a good rule is to round to
the nearest even number. Thus, 13.50 and 14.50 would each be rounded
to 14.

You will immediately wish to know whether any valuable information
has been lost owing to the rounding of the code numbers. The statistics
of the original sample are $\bar{x} = 972$, $s = 637$ pounds. Is the discrepancy
disturbing? Consider the standard error of the mean, $s_{\bar{x}} = 637/\sqrt{20} = 142$
pounds.

For the application of coding and rounding in making and calculating
frequency distributions, see section 8.2.

EXAMPLE 5.3.1—The dry weights of clippings from five bluegrass plants (5)
for the week ending July 7 were 1.2, 0.9, 1.0, 1.4, 0.9 grams. Before computing $\bar{x} = 1.08$

and $s = 0.217$ grams, imagine each item multiplied by 10; that is, ignore the decimal points. The correct results are got from dividing the coded statistics, $\bar{x}$ and s, by 10.

EXAMPLE 5.3.2—Do you have a name for such quantities as ΣX^2 and $\Sigma (X - G)^2$? You can't use "sum of squares" because that is reserved for Σx^2. You might say "sum of squares of the observations" and "sum of squares of deviations from G."

Here are three examples for those interested in the algebra of the preceding and following sections.

EXAMPLE 5.3.3—If $Y = A + X$, A being constant, prove that $\bar{y} = A + \bar{x}$ and $\Sigma y^2 = \Sigma x^2$.

EXAMPLE 5.3.4—If $Y = bX$ (b is another constant), prove that $\bar{y} = b\bar{x}$ and $\Sigma y^2 = b^2 \Sigma x^2$. You won't overlook the fact that b may be a fraction.

EXAMPLE 5.3.5—If $Y = A + bX$, prove that $\bar{y} = A + b\bar{x}$ and $\Sigma y^2 = b^2 \Sigma x^2$.

5.4—Rules and precautions about code numbers.

The objects of coding are to promote accuracy and save labor. Be sure that these advantages are great enough to more than counterbalance the time and risk of error involved in coding.

Every item in a set must be treated alike. If you were to add one number to some of the items and a different number to the others, the results would be meaningless.

The mean is affected by every coding operation. As an example, if items are coded by first subtracting 100 then dividing by 10, the coded mean must be first multiplied by 10 then increased by 100, the inverse operations being applied in reverse order.

The standard deviation is affected by only multiplication and division. It should be clear that addition and subtraction do not affect measures of variation such as range or s; such coding merely shifts the origin of measurement without contracting or expanding the unit. On the other hand, multiplication and division change the unit of measurement and must be compensated by applying the inverse operations to the coded statistics.

The accuracy of the final result is not affected by addition, subtraction, multiplication, or division, but is influenced by dropping off digits and rounding.

EXAMPLE 5.4.1—In example 6.9.6 are given percentages of water in apple twigs and corresponding measurements of specific heat. If you have a calculating machine available, compute $\bar{x}$ and s for each character. Note especially that you cannot round off the last digit in either column. If you were to do so, the range of rounded numbers in column 2 would be only $65 - 49 = 16$, which is less than desirable. Of course, you may omit the decimal point, then subtract 400 from each percentage if you wish. With a machine, however, the saving in time is questionable unless you are skilled enough to carry on the coding while operating the machine and without rewriting the column. Try it.

5.5—Significant digits.

The inference was made in section 5.3 that a range somewhere between 20 and 40 units is desirable. The reference was to code numbers, since they do not ordinarily involve decimals. A more general statement is that the range when expressed in *significant digits* should lie somewhere between 20 and 40. Significant digits (the term has no technical kinship with that employed in sections 1.13, 2.9, and 4.3) are independent of the position of the decimal point. The significant digits are the same in the numbers 647, 0.0647, and 6.47. If the range in one set is $0.067 - 0.031 = 0.036$ gram, and in another, $23.1 - 19.5 = 3.6$ pounds, the ranges in significant digits are the same, 36. When considering the number of digits to retain for computation, the decimal point may be ignored until it is time to make a record of the plan selected.

"How many decimals should be carried?" is a question often asked. In that form there is no definite answer. When the question is put in the form, "How many significant digits should be carried?" then answers are possible though various. The distinction, pointed out above, is made clearer by the following example. A weighing is made on a balance read directly to fifths of a gram, but estimated to tenths. The weight is 25.3 grams. But this result might be recorded as either 25,300 mg. or 0.0253 kg. In any of the three forms the significant digits are 253, quite unaffected by the unit of measurement. Even when the question above is limited to significant digits, however, there is an amazing array of considerations affecting the number of figures carried. It seems quite impossible to reduce them to rules. Throughout this text we have endeavored to display good form in handling numbers. At various points we have commented on unusual complications. In this section, we shall attempt little more than to suggest some trains of thought and some experiments in calculation.

If 25.3 g. is the dry weight of some forage plant grown in a pot, it may be necessary to convert the figure into pounds per acre. The conversion factor might be 94.327 pounds per acre per gram. How many significant digits should be carried in the product? Remembering that 25.3 grams really is an estimate of some weight between 25.25 and 25.35, the number of pounds per acre may be anywhere between

$$(25.25)(94.327) = 2,381.8 \text{ lbs. per acre}$$
and $\qquad (25.35)(94.327) = 2,391.2 \text{ lbs. per acre}$

The mean of these two products is equal to $(25.3)(94.327) = 2,386.5$. Three facts are clear: (i) Even the third significant figure may not be right, but (ii) it takes four significant figures, 2,386, to estimate the product satisfactorily, and (iii) the factor with the fewer significant figures limits the accuracy of the product—the weakest-link-in-the-chain idea. It is easy to verify the fact that the product of two three-figure measurements is even less accurate than the result considered above, but that the fourth figure still gives some information about the average value. A good rule in multiplication, then, is to carry one more significant digit than those in the shorter of the two factors.

You will find by a little experimentation that the facts about quotients are much the same as those about products. But consider the combination of subtraction and division illustrated in a report of the percentage decrease in amino nitrogen in a cabbage plant extract during distillation with calcium oxide (8). The number of milligrams before distillation was 14.3; after, 10.8, the percentage decrease being 24.5. At the limits of approximation, the decrease was between

$$14.35 - 10.75 = 3.60 \text{ mg.}$$
and
$$14.25 - 10.85 = 3.40 \text{ mg.}$$

The percentage decrease was, therefore, between

$$(3.60)/14.35 = 25.1\%$$
and
$$(3.40)/14.25 = 23.9\%$$

Thus, inaccuracy has crept into the second significant figure, all beyond the third being meaningless.

In computing the sum of a number of items similar to 25.3 grams, since there are likely to be about as many weights too small as too large, there is a tendency for the excesses to cancel the defects. The mean, therefore, can be carried safely one or two significant figures farther than the items.

Rules could be devised for the computations discussed above but they would have to be discarded promptly when a whole series of calculations is to be performed, as in the computation of the standard error of a mean. Continuous adherence to the rules would result in the introduction of exaggerations of inaccuracies. To be on the safe side, two or three extra figures must be carried, especially if calculating machines are available. The final results should be cut back to a reasonable number of significant figures.

What is a reasonable number? The errors of measurement considered above are relatively insignificant when compared with sampling variation. As an example, a mean, 55.957 mg., may be accurate to five significant digits in a large sample, and its standard error may be correctly computed as 1.754 mg. But since half of the 95% confidence interval ($t = \infty$) is $(1.960)(1.754) = 3.4$ mg., the report of the estimates might well be limited to 56.0 ± 3.4 mg. However, that brings up another complication. If we wish to reconstruct the normal sample from which these statistics were calculated, in the manner of example 4.5.4 for instance, it would be advantageous to have at least as many significant figures in $s_{\bar{x}}$ as there are in $\bar{x}$, the actual number depending somewhat upon the size of the sample (since $s_{\bar{x}}$ is to be multiplied by $\sqrt{n}$).

You begin to see why one can't follow any one set of specialized rules about significant digits. In simple products and ratios, it is easy to make the results compatible with the accuracy of the original measurements. If you are making a long sequence of calculations for the first time, carry along several more figures than you expect to retain in the final form. In preparing your report, limit all numbers to a size commensurate with their precision and contemplated utility.

EXAMPLE 5.5.1—A newspaper item dated November 2, 1952, claimed the world's record for underwater swimming—a descent of 127.957 feet without an oxygen mask in Naples harbor. How do you suppose the reporter got the last thousandth of a foot?

5.6—Inferences based on range in samples from normal distributions. In section 2.6 it was shown that while the range furnishes an easy estimate of σ, yet it is somewhat inefficient relative to s, especially in samples of $n > 10$. But for interval estimates the efficiency of the range stays above 90% for samples up to $n = 20$ (10). So the range is becoming popular as a short-cut in handling small samples from normal populations.

For interval estimates and testing hypotheses by use of the range, tables analogous to that of t have been prepared by Lord (6). The first at the left in table 5.6.1 is for unique samples such as those discussed in

TABLE 5.6.1

TWO LEVELS OF QUANTITIES ANALOGOUS TO t FOR INFERENCES ABOUT
NORMAL SAMPLES BY USE OF RANGE*

Two tails of distribution

	Single Samples Values of t_w			Two Samples of Equal Size Values of $t_{\bar{w}}$		
Size of Sample	Probability		Size of Each Sample	Probability		
	0.05	0.01		0.05	0.01
2	6.353	31.828	2	3.427	7.916
3	1.304	3.008	3	1.272	2.093
4	0.717	1.316	4	.813	1.237
5	.507	.843	5	.613	.896
6	.399	.628	6	.499	714
7	.333	.507	7	.426	600
8	.288	.429	8	.373	.521
9	.255	.374	9	.334	.464
10	.230	.333	10	.304	.419
11	.210	.302	11	.280	.384
12	.194	.277	12	.260	.355
13	.181	.256	13	.243	.331
14	.170	.239	14	.228	.311
15	.160	.224	15	.216	.293
16	.151	.212	16	.205	.278
17	.144	.201	17	.195	.264
18	.137	.191	18	.187	.252
19	.131	.182	19	.179	.242
20	.126	.175	20	.172	.232

* From more extensive tables by permission of E. Lord and the Editor of *Biometrika*.

chapter 2. The entries are values of $\dfrac{\bar{x} - \mu}{w}$, where w denotes the range of a sample. This ratio plays the role of t in section 2.7, so I shall call it t_w.

For an illustration of the setting of confidence intervals by means of table 5.6.1, return to the data for vitamin C in table 2.2.1. There $\bar{x} = 20$ and $w = 29 - 13 = 16$ mg./100 g., and $n = 17$. The new table has the entry 0.144 in the column headed 0.05 and the row for $n = 17$. This means that the probability of $t_w \leq 0.144$ is 0.95 in random samples of $n = 17$ from a normally distributed population. In the manner of section 2.8, the 95% confidence interval is fixed by the inequalities,

$$\bar{x} - t_w \omega \leq \mu \leq \bar{x} + t_w \omega$$

Substituting the vitamin C data,

$$20 - (0.144)(16) \leq \mu \leq 20 + (0.144)(16)$$
$$17.7 \leq \mu \leq 22.3 \text{ mg./100 g.}$$

This is to be compared with the interval based on s, $17.95 \leq \mu \leq 22.05$.

The test of a null hypothesis by means of t_w is illustrated by the tobacco virus data of table 2.9.1. Here $d = 4$ and $w = 14$ lesions, while $n = 8$. If H_0 is $\mu = 0$, we have

$$\frac{4 - 0}{14} = t_w = 0.286,$$

which is practically on the 5% level. The conclusion is the same as that reached before. If t_w is near either critical level, and if the test is to be decisive, the more efficient t-test should be made.

EXAMPLE 5.6.1—In example 2.5.3, for the alfalfa yields $\bar{x} = 1.70$ and $w = 1.4$ tons per acre, n being 10. Set the 0.95 confidence interval. Ans. From 1.38 to 2.02 tons per acre. Compare this with example 2.8.1.

EXAMPLE 5.6.2—Using the statistics of example 2.8.2, set the 0.99 confidence interval by use of ω and examples 2.5.5 and 2.6.1. Ans. 9 ± 16.9 bu./acre. Notice that, since the confidence interval covers zero, the null hypothesis, $\mu = 0$, would not be rejected.

EXAMPLE 5.6.3—Test H_0: $\mu = 0$ for the differences among the gladiolus florets in example 2.9.1. Ans. $t_w = 0.293$, $P = 0.08$. In close decisions like this, greater reliance is to be placed on "Student's" t.

We turn now to applications of the range in the type of experiment dealt with in chapter 4. For testing the significance of the difference between the means of two samples of equal size, n observations in each, the right-hand columns of table 5.6.1 are available. The mean of the two ranges, $\bar{w} = (w_1 + w_2)/2$, replaces the w of the foregoing paragraphs, and $\bar{x}_1 - \bar{x}_2$ takes the place of d.

As an example, turn to the chick experiment of table 4.3.1. There $n = 11$, $\bar{x}_1 - \bar{x}_2 = 41$ mg., $w_1 = 137 - 53 = 84$ mg., $w_2 = 96 - 22 = 74$ mg., and $\bar{w} = (84 + 74)/2 = 79$ mg. From this, $t_{\bar{w}} = (\bar{x}_1 - \bar{x}_2)/\bar{w} = 41/79 = 0.519$, which is far beyond the 0.01 level, 0.384, shown in the table. When the conclusion is so strongly indicated, there is no need to resort to the t-test.

If there is interest in the interval estimate of the population difference between means, it may be calculated first; then, if desired, it may be substituted for the test of significance. With the chick data, the 0.99 confidence interval is given by

$$\bar{x}_1 - \bar{x}_2 - t_{\bar{w}}\bar{w} \leq \mu_1 - \mu_2 \leq \bar{x}_1 - \bar{x}_2 + t_{\bar{w}}\bar{w}$$
$$41 - (0.384)(79) \leq \mu_1 - \mu_2 \leq 41 + (0.384)(79)$$
$$10.7 \leq \mu_1 - \mu_2 \leq 51.3 \text{ mg.}$$

Since the 99% confidence interval does not contain zero, it follows that H_0: $\mu_1 - \mu_2 = 0$ would be rejected at the 1% level.

In sampling from normal distributions the range is convenient as a substitute for s if a 5%–10% loss in information can be tolerated. But normal distributions are never available for sampling. It is known that inferences based on t are not greatly affected by moderate departures from normality; in fact, not by considerable departures as n grows larger. But inferences based on range are more sensitive to anormality, especially to skewness. So if skewness is suspected, somewhat less reliance should be placed on w as a substitute for s.

The efficiency of the range decreases as n increases. In some applications, $n = 8$ gives the greatest efficiency. For n between 12 and 22, the sample may be randomly divided into two equal subsamples and the average of the two ranges used for tests and estimates. Appropriate tables may be found in Lord's article.

For two samples of different size, use of the ranges is about as laborious as calculating Σx^2.

EXAMPLE 5.6.4—Try the range test on the pH experiment of example 4.3.2. Ans. $t_{\bar{w}} = 0.792$, $P > 0.05$ as compared to $t = 2.66$, $P = 0.04$.

5.7—Non-parametric methods: median and quartiles. If there is evidence that sampled populations are so far from normal as to invalidate the methods devised for normal samples, numerous *non-parametric* methods (11) are available. They do not depend on the shape of the population distribution and do not require the knowledge of a specific density function like that of the normal. Some of these methods will be described in this and following sections.

The most widely known non-parametric point estimate is the *median*. It is the middle item in an array; that is, if n is odd, the median is observation number $(n + 1)/2$, while if n is even, it is the mean of observations number $n/2$ and $(n + 2)/2$. Examples: In example 2.5.2, the median of the weights of 11 men is the weight of man number $(11 + 1)/2 = 6$ in in the array, 162 pounds. In example 2.5.6, the median of the 16 differences is the mean of differences number $n/2 = 8$ and number $(n + 2)/2 = 9$; that is, the median is $(3.7 + 4.0)/2 = 3.85$ bu./acre.

Corresponding to the median, there are other point estimates often used in samples from non-normal populations. For example, after the median is located, each half of the sample may again be divided into equal parts by the *quartiles*. The lower quartile, usually called the first quartile, is the observation which separates the lower quarter of the observations from the upper three-quarters. It is observation number $(n + 1)/4$. Among the corn yield differences, this is difference number $(16 + 1)4 = 4.25$. Ordinarily it would be satisfactory to say that the fourth difference, -4.0 bu./acre, is the first quartile. If refinement is required, a weighted mean of the fourth and fifth observations is used, the weights being 3 and 1:

$$Q_1 = \frac{3(-4) + 1(0)}{3 + 1} = -3 \text{ bu./acre,}$$

where Q_1 stands for the lower quartile. Similarly, the upper quartile is difference number $3(n + 1)/4 = 12.75$. The 13th difference is 7.1 bu./acre. More accurately,

$$Q_3 = \frac{1(6.4) + 3(7.1)}{4} = 6.92 \text{ bu./acre}$$

You will see that the median might be called Q_2.

In large samples or in finite populations, the process of subdivision may be continued; *deciles* separate the observations into 10 equal parts, *percentiles* into 100, and *permilles* into 1,000.

The quartiles lead to an estimate of variation. The *interquartile interval*, $Q_3 - Q_1$, includes half the observed values. One gives a rough description of a sample (or population) by saying, for example, that the median corn yield difference is 3.85 bu./acre with the interquartile range,

$$Q_3 - Q_1 = 6.92 - (-3) = 9.92 \text{ bu./acre}$$

Or, more simply, he might say that half the differences are between -3 and 7 bu./acre.

The chief utility of the median-quartile statistics is in describing large samples from anormal distributions. In the past, these statistics have been used extensively as short cuts for making estimates and tests in samples from normal populations; but with calculating machines the mean is about as easily computed as the median, and the mean-range short cut, described in the preceding section, is more efficient. For non-normal populations, also, we now have more useful methods for making inferences. Some of these will be presented in the next section and others from time to time as the need arises. In biology there seems to be little need for the median-quartile scheme.

To illustrate the method, table 5.7.1 is cited (1). For purposes of illustration, I have assumed that there were 179 cows in this experiment. Actually, the majority of the records are repeated observations after successive calvings. This raises doubts about the conclusions drawn below.

TABLE 5.7.1

DISTRIBUTION OF PERIODS FROM PARTURITION TO FIRST SUBSEQUENT OESTRUS IN NORMAL
CATTLE—A HOLSTEIN-FRIESIAN HERD IN WISCONSIN

Class mark (days)	10.5	30.5	50.5	70.5	90.5	110.5	130.5	150.5	170.5	190.5	210.5
Frequency	8	33	50	32	15	20	11	6	2	1	1
Accumulated frequency		41	91	123	138	158	169	175	177	178	179

The frequency rises to a peak at about 50 days. The day correspond-ing to the greatest frequency was called the *mode* by Karl Pearson. There is a secondary mode near 110 days. This *bimodal* feature, as well as the skewness, emphasizes the non-normality of the distribution.

The mean is 69.9 days, practically in the center of the class following the modal class. (For a method of calculating the mean and standard deviation, see section 8.3.) It does not represent the typical period in the sense that the mode does. Of what value is it in this anormal distribution? The fundamental character of the mean is that $\Sigma x = 0$; the sum of the positive deviations is equal to that of the negative. In this sense, it is the center of gravity of the distribution. If you draw the histogram on cardboard then cut it out, it should balance on a knife edge vertical to the X-axis at 69.9 days.

The quartiles are calculated by the formula,

$$Q = X_L + \frac{(n_Q - f_L)\,I}{f},$$

where

X_L = value of X at lower boundary of the class con-taining the quartile observation number

n_Q = the quartile observation number

f_L = accumulated frequency preceding the class containing n_Q

I = class interval

f = frequency of class containing n_Q

In the cattle data, the quartile observation numbers are $n_{Q1} = (179 + 1)/4 = 45$, $n_{Q2} = 90$, and $n_{Q3} = 135$.

For the median, $n_{Q2} = 90$ is in the class whose lower bound is $X_L = 40.5$ days, whose frequency is $f = 50$ cows, with a previously accumulated frequency of 41 cows. Hence,

$$Q_2 = \text{Median} = 40.5 + \frac{(90 - 41)(20)}{50} = 60 \text{ days}$$

The median, then, is practically on the upper boundary of the modal class. There are as many periods greater than 60 as less. Notice that the median is at the center of the number of periods while the mean is at the center of the lengths of periods. Neither coincides with the maximum frequency.

For the other quartiles,

$$Q_1 = 40.5 + \frac{(45 - 41)(20)}{50} = 42 \text{ days}$$

$$Q_3 = 80.5 + \frac{(135 - 123)(20)}{15} = 96 \text{ days}$$

You notice at once that the median, 60 days, is not at the middle of the interquartile interval.

One now describes the distribution of periods as having modes at 50 and 110 days, 50 days being the most fashionable period; as having the median at 60 days with lower and upper quartiles at 42 and 96 days; and as having an interquartile interval of $96 - 42 = 54$ days, an interval containing half the periods. This somewhat supplements the description given by the frequency distribution and its graphical representation.

If small samples (as a guess, $n < 20$) were drawn from a population shaped like the distribution of table 5.7.1, there would be some question about applying the normal methods which have been described. Suitable procedures are presented in following sections.

If the 179 periods can be considered a random sample from some larger population, say the population of periods in Holstein-Friesian cows, I would not hesitate to apply the central-limit theorem to so large a sample. I would calculate $s_{\bar{x}} = 2.9$ and set 95% confidence limits on μ,

$$69.9 - (1.96)(2.9) \le \mu \le 69.9 + (1.96)(2.9),$$

where

$$t_{.05} = 1.96 \text{ for } d.f. = \infty$$

Also, if this were a random sample, a confidence interval could be set for the population median (8). Two observation numbers, $t\sqrt{n}/2$, roughly equal to $\sqrt{n}$ for $t_{.05} = 1.96$, are selected, one on either side of n_{Q2}. These are $n_{Q2} \pm \sqrt{n} = 90 \pm \sqrt{179}$; that is, 77 and 103. The periods corresponding to these numbers are got by the formula for Q:

$$\text{For } 77: \quad 40.5 + \frac{(77 - 41)(20)}{50} = 55 \text{ days}$$

$$\text{For } 103: \quad 60.5 + \frac{(103 - 91)(20)}{32} = 68 \text{ days}$$

So the population median is between 55 and 68 days unless this is one of those unusual samples that occur about once in 20 trials.

But the records in table 5.7.1 may not constitute a sample; they may be the entire population consisting of the periods in a designated herd. The quartiles, the mean, and the standard deviation are then exact descriptions of this population, not subject to sampling variation. If so, the concepts of estimates, tests, and confidence intervals are irrelevant. This is because no cow outside the herd had a chance of being included in the experiment.

Of course, the dairy husbandman may refute these statements. He may know that the breeding and management practices in this herd do not affect the period between parturition and the first oestrus in Holstein-Friesian cows. This would be evidence that the herd represents a larger population of Holstein-Friesians in the manner of a random sample. This kind of evidence comes from knowledge about cows; it is not inherent in the statistical theory of sampling. But remember the other feature of this record; there were less than 179 cows, many of the records being repeats. This sample can represent only a population in which the proportion of single, double, triple, etc., observations is the same as that in the sample.

5.8—Non-parametric methods: rankings of two treatments. Often there is no scale for measuring a character, yet one believes that he can distinguish grades of merit. The animal husbandman, for example, judges body conformation, ranking the individuals from high to low, then assigning *ranks* 1, 2, ... *n*. In the same way, the foods expert arrays preparations according to flavor or palatability. If rankings of a set of individuals or treatments are made by a random sample of judges, inferences can be made about the ranking in the population from which the sample of judges was drawn; this despite the fact that the parameters of the distributions cannot be written down.

First, consider the rankings of two products by each of *m* judges. As an example, *m* = 8 judges ranked patties of ground beef which had been stored for 8 months at two temperatures in home freezers (4). Flavor was the basis of the ranking. Eight of the patties, one for each judge, were kept at 0°F.; the second sample of 8 were in a freezer whose temperature fluctuated between 0° and 15°F. The rankings are shown in table 5.8.1.

TABLE 5.8.1
RANKINGS OF THE FLAVOR OF PAIRS OF PATTIES OF GROUND BEEF
Eight judges. Rank 1 is high; rank 2, low

Judge	Sample 1 0° F.	Sample 2 Fluctuated
A	1	2
B	1	2
C	2	1
D	1	2
E	1	2
F	1	2
G	1	2
H	1	2

The null hypothesis to be tested is that there is no difference between the flavor ranking of the patties in the two freezers. As evidence we observe that one of the rankings is opposite to the other 7. May this be attributed to sampling variation, or should H_0 be rejected?

The test is made by setting up the 1:1 hypothesis for chi-square. In the sample, the orders of ranking are divided 7:1. The easiest formula is that of section 1.16 with $r = 1$; $a = 7$, $b = 1$. For such a small sample it is advisable to make an adjustment described in section 9.5. With this adjustment the formula becomes

$$\chi^2 = \frac{(a - b - 1)^2}{n}, \text{ where } n = a + b,$$

$$= \frac{(7 - 1 - 1)^2}{8} = 3.12, \, P = 0.08$$

This indicates non-significance, though the decision is close; it is questionable if the fluctuation of the temperature resulted in a detectable flavor difference.

Note: The adjusted chi-square test applied to m rankings of 2 things is equivalent to the "Sign Test" of Dixon and Mood (3). Since the computation of chi-square is trivial, no special tables for the sign test are necessary. Indeed, if one remembers $\chi^2_{.05} = 3.841$ and $\chi^2_{.01} = 6.635$, the chi-square test requires no reference to a table.

EXAMPLE 5.8.1—Cigarettes made by two manufacturers were prepared in identical wrappings and presented in random order to 6 randomly selected smokers. Five of them ranked the flavor of those by manufacturer A as high. If you reject the hypothesis that there is no difference in flavor, what is the chance of being wrong? Ans. $\chi^2 = 1.5$, $d.f. = 1$, $P = 0.25$. To what population would the inference apply?

EXAMPLE 5.8.2—Two ice creams were made with different flavors but with no other distinguishing marks such as color. A panel of 6 expert dairy industry men all ranked flavor A as preferred. Is this statistical evidence that the consuming public will prefer A?

5.9—Non-parametric methods: ranking of differences between measurements. A ranking test may be applied to samples of measurements which violate the assumptions made in the t-test. In that test for paired observations, it is assumed that the differences constitute a sample from $N(\mu_D, \sigma_D)$. Deviations from this model are of two kinds; the differences may not be normally distributed, or the variances of the differences may not be all the same. The second kind of deviation from the model may well have occurred in example 2.5.6. It is ordinarily assumed that the variance in large crops is greater than that in small, the coefficient of variation tending to be the same for all yields. If so, σ^2 in 1933 would be greater than that in 1934, and this would vitiate the t-test.

An appropriate non-parametric test is due to Wilcoxon (13). First, the absolute values of the differences are ranked, then signs are attached to the rankings according to the signs of the corresponding differences. For the corn yield data it is convenient, though not necessary, to array the absolute differences, keeping the signs at hand:

Array of absolute differences:	0.0,	0.4,	0.6,	1.0,	2.4,	3.4,	3.6,	3.7
Sign of difference:	+	−	−	+	−	+	−	+
Rank, with sign of difference:	1,	−2,	−3,	4,	−5,	6,	−7,	8

The ranks of the absolute value are written with the signs restored. The 8 higher ranks are not included because none of them have negative signs attached.

The sum of the negative ranks is $-2 -3 -5 -7 = -17$. This number, sign ignored, is referred to table 5.9.1. For 16 pairs a rank sum ≤ 19 would lead to rejection at the level $P = 0.01$. Since our sum is less than the tabular number, we presumably reject H_0: $\mu_D = 0$, the probability of a Type I error being < 0.01.

If it should happen that the sum of the positive ranks is less than the sum of the negative, enter the table with the former sum; always use the smaller.

TABLE 5.9.1

SUM OF RANKS AT 2 LEVELS OF $P*$

These numbers or smaller indicate rejection. Two-sided test

Number of Pairs	0.05	0.01	Number of Pairs	0.05	0.01
7	2	0	12	14	7
8	2	0	13	17	10
9	6	2	14	21	13
10	8	3	15	25	16
11	11	5	16	29	19

* Adapted from the article by Wilcoxon. More accurate probabilities are given in the original article.

Comparison of this result with that of example 2.12.4 shows that the two tests lead to the same conclusion. If there are differences among the variances in this experiment, they have little effect on the t-test. We have had occasion to remark before (and shall have again) that the t-test tolerates considerable deviations from the theoretical assumptions on which it is based.

If two or more differences are equal, it is often sufficiently accurate to assign to each of the ties the average of the ranks that would be assigned to the group. Thus, if two differences are tied in the fifth and sixth positions in the array, assign rank $5\frac{1}{2}$ to each of them.

EXAMPLE 5.9.1—From two J-shaped populations distributed like chi-square with $d.f. = 1$ (figure 1.11.1), I drew two samples of $n = 10$ and paired them at random:

Sample 1	1.98	3.30	5.91	1.05	1.01	1.44	3.42	2.17	1.37	1.13
Sample 2	0.33	0.11	0.04	0.24	1.56	0.42	0.00	0.22	0.82	2.54
Difference	1.65	3.19	5.87	0.81	−0.55	1.02	3.42	1.95	0.55	−1.41
Rank	6	8	10	3	−1.5	4	9	7	1.5	−5

The difference between the population means was 1, to be compared to $\bar{x}_1 - \bar{x}_2 = 1.65$. The smallest two absolute differences are tied, so each is assigned the rank $(1 + 2)/2 = 1.5$. The sum of the negative ranks is 6.5, between the critical sums, 3 and 8, in table 5.9.1. H_0 is rejected with $P = 0.04$, approximately.

EXAMPLE 5.9.2—If you had not known that the differences in the foregoing example were from a non-normal population, you would doubtless have applied the t-test. Would you have drawn any different conclusion? Ans. $t = 2.48$, $P = 0.04$.

EXAMPLE 5.9.3—If you had applied the method of section 5.8 (equivalent to the sign test) to the data of example 5.9.1, you would have got $\chi^2 = (8 - 2 - 1)^2/5 = 5$, $P = 0.03$.

EXAMPLE 5.9.4—Apply the sign test to the corn yield data discussed in the text Ans. $\chi^2 = 3.06$, $P = 0.08$. In the sign test, the numerical value of the negative rank is ignored, whereas in Wilcoxon's test a small rank with a negative sign plays a different role from that of a large one.

5.10—Non-parametric methods: ranking for unpaired measurements.

Turning now to the two-sample problems of chapter 4, we consider ranking as a non-parametric method for random samples of measurements which do not conform to the usual models. A method due to White (12) applies to unequal group sizes as well as to equal. All observations in both groups are put into a single array, care being taken to tag the numbers of each group so that they can be distinguished. Ranks are then assigned to the combined array. Finally, the smaller sum of ranks, T, is referred to table 5.10.3 to determine significance.

An example is drawn from the Corn Borer project in Boone County, Iowa, section 1.3. It is well established that, in an attacked field, more eggs are deposited on tall plants than on short ones. For illustration I took records of numbers of eggs found on 20 plants in a rather uniform field. The plants were in 2 randomly selected sites, 10 plants each. Table 5.10.1 contains the egg counts.

TABLE 5.10.1
NUMBER OF CORN BORER EGGS ON CORN PLANTS, BOONE COUNTY, IOWA, 1950

Height of Plant	Number of Eggs									
Less than 23″	0	14	18	0	31	0	0	0	11	0
More than 23″	37	42	12	32	105	84	15	47	51	65

In years such as 1950, the frequency distribution of egg numbers is much like that of chi-square with one degree of freedom, figure 1.11.1. Most plants have small numbers of eggs, but a few are heavily infested. The distribution of the population is J-shaped instead of normal. Moreover, the standard deviation tends to increase with numbers of eggs. Normal theory cannot be relied upon to yield correct inferences from small samples.

For convenience I have rearranged the 20 counts in the array of table

TABLE 5.10.2
ARRAY OF 20 EGG COUNTS TOGETHER WITH RANK
Boldface type indicates counts on plants 23″ or more

Array	0,	0,	0,	0,	0,	0,	11,	**12**,	14,	**15**,	18,	31
Rank	3½,	3½,	3½,	3½,	3½,	3½,	7,	**8**,	9,	**10**,	11,	12

5.10.2. The counts for the tall plants are in boldface. The remaining counts are omitted because they are all on tall plants.

TABLE 5.10.3
VALUES OF T AT TWO LEVELS
These values or smaller cause rejection. Two-sided test. Take $n_1 \leq n_2$*

0.05 Level of T

n_2 ↓ \ n_1 →	2	3	4	5	6	7	8	9	10	11	12	13	14	15
4			10											
5		6	11	17										
6		7	12	18	26									
7		7	13	20	27	36								
8	3	8	14	21	29	38	49							
9	3	8	15	22	31	40	51	63						
10	3	9	15	23	32	42	53	65	78					
11	4	9	16	24	34	44	55	68	81	96				
12	4	10	17	26	35	46	58	71	85	99	115			
13	4	10	18	27	37	48	60	73	88	103	119	137		
14	4	11	19	28	38	50	63	76	91	106	123	141	160	
15	4	11	20	29	40	52	65	79	94	110	127	145	164	185
16	4	12	21	31	42	54	67	82	97	114	131	150	169	
17	5	12	21	32	43	56	70	84	100	117	135	154		
18	5	13	22	33	45	58	72	87	103	121	139			
19	5	13	23	34	46	60	74	90	107	124				
20	5	14	24	35	48	62	77	93	110					
21	6	14	25	37	50	64	79	95						
22	6	15	26	38	51	66	82							
23	6	15	27	39	53	68								
24	6	16	28	40	55									
25	6	16	28	42										
26	7	17	29											
27	7	17												
28	7													

TABLE 5.10.3—*Continued*

0.01 Level of T

$n_1 \rightarrow$ $n_2 \downarrow$	2	3	4	5	6	7	8	9	10	11	12	13	14	15
5			15											
5				15										
6		10	16	23										
7		10	17	24	32									
8		11	17	25	34	43								
9		6	11	18	26	35	45	56						
10		6	12	19	27	37	47	58	71					
11		6	12	20	28	38	49	61	74	87				
12		7	13	21	30	40	51	63	76	90	106			
13		7	14	22	31	41	53	65	79	93	109	125		
14		7	14	22	32	43	54	67	81	96	112	129	147	
15		8	15	23	33	44	56	70	84	99	115	133	151	171
16		8	15	24	34	46	58	72	86	102	119	137	155	
17		8	16	25	36	47	60	74	89	105	122	140		
18		8	16	26	37	49	62	76	92	108	125			
19	3	9	17	27	38	50	64	78	94	111				
20	3	9	18	28	39	52	66	81	97					
21	3	9	18	29	40	53	68	83						
22	3	10	19	29	42	55	70							
23	3	10	19	30	43	57								
24	3	10	20	31	44									
25	3	11	20	32										
26	3	11	21											
27	4	11												
28	4													

* n_1 and n_2 are the numbers of cases in the two groups. If the groups are unequal in size, n_1 refers to the smaller.

Table is reprinted from White (12), who extended the method of Wilcoxon.

According to the rule already given, the 6 ties are given the mean rank,

$$\frac{1 + 2 + 3 + 4 + 5 + 6}{6} = 3\frac{1}{2}$$

In this instance, since all the tied ranks belong to one group, the averaging is not necessary; the sum of the 6 ranks is 21 whether they are all assigned the mean rank or whether they are arbitrarily ranked 1, . . . 6. But if the tied counts were in both groups, the averaging would be required.

The next step is to add the n_1 rank numbers in the group having the smaller sum, plants less than 23″:

$$T = 6(3\frac{1}{2}) + 7 + 9 + 11 + 12 = 60$$

This sum is referred to table 5.10.3 with $n_1 = n_2 = 10$. Since the sample T is less then $T_{.01} = 71$, the null hypothesis is rejected with $P < 0.01$. The anticipated conclusion is that plant height affects the number of eggs deposited.

The null hypothesis being tested is that the sum of ranks, T, is composed of n_1 ranks drawn at random from $n_1 + n_2$ ranks in the combined groups. This sum is

$$n_1(n_1 + n_2 + 1),$$

which is $(10)(21) = 210$ in the corn borer experiment.

It may happen that the ranks selected for addition may have a sum greater than half of the total. If so, subtract the sum from $n_1(n_1 + n_2 + 1)$ to get the value of T for testing; always use the smaller sum. One could get this smaller sum without use of the formula by numbering the ranks from the opposite end of the array.

EXAMPLE 5.10.1—In his article in *Biometrics*, White quoted Wright (14) on the survival time, under anoxic conditions, of the peroneal nerves of cats and rabbits. The survival times of the nerves of 4 cats were 25, 45, 33, and 43 minutes; of 14 rabbits, 28, 15, 35, 28, 35, 22, 23, 22, 17, 20, 30, 16, and 16 minutes. Test H_0: the survival time in the 2 species is the same. Ans. If rank 1 is low, $T = 58$, greater than half of $n_1(n_1 + n_2 + 1) = 76$. So take $T = 76 - 58 = 18$, or else make rank 1 high. $P = .04$.

EXAMPLE 5.10.2—There is no evidence given that the survival time in the preceding example is not normally distributed. Test H_0 by means of t. Ans. $t = 2.94$, $P = 0.01$.

EXAMPLE 5.10.3—In examples 4.9.1 and 4.9.2, there was some sample evidence of unequal variances in the sampled populations. Apply the non-parametric rank test. Ans. $T = 121.5$, $T_{.05} = 110$.

5.11—Non-parametric methods as short cuts in normal samples. There is a good deal of publicity for non-parametric methods as short cuts for the ordinary calculations for samples from normal populations. The question arises as to the relative costs of the two procedures. The answer depends on the cost per observation and the relative efficiencies of the tests. Also, since no normal distribution can exist in practice, the answer must specify the amount of anormality in the sampled population together with the consequent loss in efficiency of the t-test. This makes any overall statement impossible, but some general features may be discussed.

When the Wilcoxon rank tests are applied to normal samples, they have an efficiency of some 95% as the sample sizes approach infinity (7). Guessing 90% for ordinary situations, this means that a sample of $n = 9$ from a normal population using the original measurements would be about as informative as a sample of 10 with ranks substituted. If it costs 30 cents to calculate the t-test and only 15 cents to do the rank test, the two methods would be equally expensive if observations cost about 15 cents. In biological experimentation, there are not many observations so cheap. On the other hand, the efficiency of the t-test decreases with anormality of the sampled population. If the population is known to be far from normal, there would perhaps be more information in the rank test and at less cost. For expensive observations and near-normal distributions, I would stick to the t-test.

Warning: The decision as to which test to use should be made without reference to the data in hand. If you apply both methods and then choose the one that coincides with your preference, you introduce a bias. Of course, if the two methods indicate the same conclusion, you have assurance that it is not the population shape that controls the decision.

The rank tests are sometimes advocated as preliminary tests to be followed by the *t*-test if a close decision is to be made. This may occasionally be worth while, especially for inexperienced persons. Certainly time should not be wasted on calculation when the decision is obvious. But the labor involved in ranking, especially in the unpaired case, is little less than that in calculating *t*. If both are done in a substantial portion of experiments (in most experiments the decision is not obvious), time is lost, not saved.

As for the sign test (last paragraph of section 5.8) applied to a sample of normally distributed differences, there is little to be said in its favor except that it is quick and easy. Its efficiency, relative to *t*, is around 65%. As a short cut for normal differences, Wilcoxon's ranking test is preferable.

REFERENCES

1. A. B. CHAPMAN and L. E. CASIDA. Journal of Agricultural Research, 54:417 (1937).

2. O. W. DAVIDSON and J. W. SHIVE. Plant Physiology, 10:73 (1935).

3. W. J. DIXON and A. M. MOOD. Journal of the American Statistical Association, 41:557 (1946).

4. FLORENCE EHRENKRANTZ and HARRIETT ROBERTS. Journal of Home Economics, 44:441 (1952).

5 CARTER M. HARRISON. Plant Physiology, 9:94 (1934).

6. E. LORD. Biometrika, 34:56 (1947).

7. A. M. MOOD. Annals of Mathematical Statistics, 25:514 (1954).

8. A. M. MOOD. Introduction to the Theory of Statistics. McGraw-Hill Book Co., Inc., p. 388 (1950).

9. P. MABEL NELSON, ELIZABETH E. HOYT, LAURA McLAUGHLIN, and ETHEL CESSNA MORGAN. Iowa Agricultural Experiment Station Bulletin 337 (1935).

10. K. C. S. PILLAI. Annals of Mathematical Statistics, 22:469 (1951).

11. RICHARD SAVAGE. Journal of the American Statistical Association, 48:844 (1953).

12. COLIN WHITE. Biometrics, 8:33 (1952).

13. FRANK WILCOXON. Biometrics (Bulletin), 1:80 (1945).

14. E. B. WRIGHT. American Journal of Physiology, 147:78 (1946).

CHAPTER 6

Linear Regression

6.1—Introduction. In foregoing chapters the problems considered have involved mainly only a single measurement on each individual. This measurement may be of vitamin content or weight in which the variate is continuous, or of color or opinion, the variate being discrete. The observations are compared either singly or in groups, but generally it is one attribute or one kind of measurement per individual. Now attention is turned to inferences based on two or more observations on each member of the sample. For example, one may make more adequate judgments about the 120-day weight increase of a pig if he knows the related variates, initial weight, age, and feed eaten; increasing farm income during some periods may be explained partly by changes in the quantity of meat produced; or decisions about the comparative yielding abilities of varieties of corn may hinge on the numbers of plants in the several experimental plots.

In this chapter, attention will be centered primarily on the dependence of one variable Y on another, the *independent* variable X. In mathematical parlance Y is said to be a *function* of X, but in biological statistics Galton's descriptive term *regression* is generally used. The growth curve of height is spoken of as the regression of height on age; in toxicology the lethal effects of a drug are described by the regression of per cent kill on concentration. The origin of the term *regression* will be outlined in section 6.12.

The uses of regression are varied. Perhaps the objective is only to learn if Y does depend on X and, if so, to get a measure of the relationship. Or prediction of Y from X may be the goal. Some wish to determine the shape of the regression curve. Others, as indicated in section 3.10, are concerned with the real error involved in an experiment after the effect of a related variable is discounted. A few have theories about cause and effect and employ regression to test their hypotheses. To satisfy all needs we shall have to give an extensive account of the methods, leaving each reader to choose those which interest him most. As usual, we turn to an example for development of the subject.

6.2—The regression of blood pressure on age. A project, "The Nutritional Status of Population Groups," was set up by the Agricultural

Experiment Stations of 9 midwestern states. From the facts learned I have extracted data on systolic blood pressure among 58 women over 30 years of age, a random sample from a region near Ames, Iowa (18). For present purposes, the ages are grouped into 10-year classes and the mean blood pressure calculated for each class. The results are in the first two columns of table 6.2.1.

TABLE 6.2.1
MEAN SYSTOLIC BLOOD PRESSURE OF 58 WOMEN IN 10-YEAR AGE CLASSES

Midpoint of Age Class X	Mean Blood Pressure Y	Deviations From Means		Squares		Products xy
		x	y	x^2	y^2	
35	114	−20	−27	400	729	540
45	124	−10	−17	100	289	170
55	143	0	2	0	4	0
65	158	10	17	100	289	170
75	166	20	25	400	625	500
Sum 275	705	0	0	1,000	1,936	1,380
Mean 55	141					

Sample regression coefficient: $b = \dfrac{\Sigma xy}{\Sigma x^2} = \dfrac{1,380}{1,000} = 1.38$ units of blood pressure per year

As in most regression problems, the first thing to do is to draw a graph, figure 6.2.1. The independent variable X is plotted along the horizontal axis. Each measure of the dependent Y is indicated by a point above the corresponding X. Clearly, the trend of blood pressure with age is upward and roughly linear.

The straight line drawn in the figure is called the *sample regression of Y on X*. It contains the point $O'(\bar{x}, \bar{y})$ which, for the blood pressures, is (55, 141). It slopes upward at the rate of b units of Y per unit of X, where b is the *sample regression coefficient*, calculated as in table 6.2.1. This computation involves a process not encountered before, the *sum of products* of the deviations, x and y. This sum of products may be positive or negative according as the line slopes upward or downward. In the illustrative example, $b = 1.38$, meaning that blood pressure increases an average of 1.38 units per year of age.

The *sample regression equation of Y on X* is now written as

$$\hat{y} = bx,$$

where $\hat{y}$ is the *estimated* deviation of Y corresponding to any x-deviation. For example, if $x = 20$ years, $\hat{y} = (1.38)(20) = 27.6$ units of blood pressure.

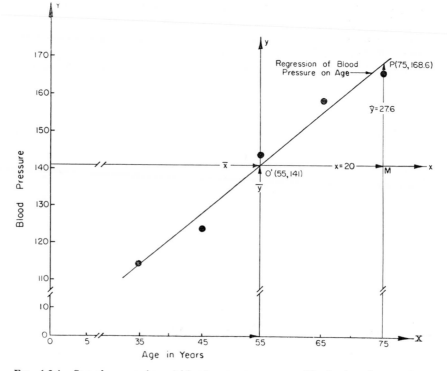

FIG. 6.2.1—Sample regression of blood pressure on age. The broken lines indicate omission of the lower parts of the scales in order to clarify the relations in the parts occupied by the data.

The sample regression equation enables us to complete figure 6.2.1 by drawing the sample regression line. Lay off $O'M = 20$ years to the right of O', then erect a perpendicular, $MP = 27.6$ units of blood pressure. The line $O'P$ then has the slope, 1.38 units of blood pressure per year.

In terms of the original units, the sample regression equation is

$$\hat{Y} - \bar{y} = b(X - \bar{x})$$

For the blood pressures, this becomes

$$\hat{Y} - 141 = 1.38 \ (X - 55)$$

or

$$\hat{Y} = 141 + 1.38 \ (X - 55)$$
$$= 65.1 + 1.38X$$

If $X = 75$ is entered in this equation, $\hat{Y}$ becomes $65.1 + (1.38)(75) = 168.6$ units of blood pressure. The corresponding point, (75, 168.6), is shown as P in the figure.

We can now compare the sample points with the corresponding $\hat{Y}$ to get measures of the *goodness of fit* of the line to the data. Each X is substituted in the regression equation and $\hat{Y}$ calculated. The 5 results are recorded in table 6.2.2. The *deviations from regression*, $Y - \hat{Y} = d_{y \cdot x}$, measure the failure of the line to fit the data. Note that, in this sample,

TABLE 6.2.2

CALCULATION OF $\hat{Y}$ AND DEVIATIONS FROM REGRESSION, $d_{y \cdot x} = Y - \hat{Y}$
Blood pressure data

Midpoint of Age Class X	Mean Blood Pressure Y	Estimated Blood Pressure $\hat{Y}$	Deviation From Regression $Y - \hat{Y} = d_{y \cdot x}$	Square of Deviation $d_{y \cdot x}^2$
35	114	113.4	0.6	0.36
45	124	127.2	−3.2	10.24
55	143	141.0	2.0	4.00
65	158	154.8	3.2	10.24
75	166	168.6	−2.6	6.76
Sum			$\Sigma d_{y \cdot x} = 0.0$	$\Sigma d_{y \cdot x}^2 = 31.60$

45-year-old women had below average blood pressure and 65-year-olds had an excess.

The sum of squares of deviations, $\Sigma d_{y \cdot x}^2 = 31.60$, is the basis for an estimate of error in fitting the line. The corresponding degrees of freedom are $n - 2 = 3$ because *two* averages have been used in calculating the deviations, $\bar{y}$ and b. We have then

$$s_{y \cdot x}^2 = \Sigma d_{y \cdot x}^2 / (n - 2) = 10.53,$$

where $s_{y \cdot x}^2$ is the *mean square deviation from regression*. The resulting *sample standard deviation from regression*,

$$s_{y \cdot x} = \sqrt{s_{y \cdot x}^2} = 3.24 \text{ units of blood pressure,}$$

corresponds to s in single-variable problems. In particular, it furnishes a *sample standard deviation of the regression coefficient*,

$$s_b = s_{y \cdot x} / \sqrt{\Sigma x^2}$$

This is $3.24/\sqrt{1,000} = 0.102$ units of blood pressure.

A test of significance of b is given by

$$t = b/s_b, \quad d.f. = n - 2$$

Applying this to the blood pressures,

$$t = 1.38/0.102 = 13.5**, d.f. = 3$$

Note: It is often convenient and sufficient to denote significance by asterisks. A single one indicates probabilities between 0.05 and 0.01; two indicate probabilities equal to or less than 0.01.

Often there is little interest in the $d_{y \cdot x}$ of table 6.2.2. If so, $\Sigma d_{y \cdot x}^2$ may be calculated directly by the formula,

$$\Sigma d_{y \cdot x}^2 = \Sigma y^2 - [(\Sigma xy)^2/\Sigma x^2]$$

Substituting the blood pressure data from table 6.2.1,

$$\Sigma d_{y \cdot x}^2 = 1,936 - [(1,380)^2/1,000] = 31.60$$

as before.

EXAMPLE 6.2.1—Following are measurements on heights of soybean plants in a field, a different random selection each week (21):

Age in weeks	1	2	3	4	5	6	7
Height in centimeters	5	13	16	23	33	38	40

Verify these results: $\bar{x} = 4$ weeks, $\bar{y} = 24$ cms., $\Sigma x^2 = 28$, $\Sigma y^2 = 1,080$, $\Sigma xy = 172$. Compute the sample regressions, $\hat{Y} = 6.143\,X - 0.572$ centimeters.

EXAMPLE 6.2.2—Plot on a graph the sample points for the soybean data, then construct the sample regression line. Do the points lie about equally above and below the line?

EXAMPLE 6.2.3—Calculate $s_b = 0.409$ cms./wk. Set the 95% confidence interval for the population regression. Ans. 5.09 — 7.20 cms./wk.

EXAMPLE 6.2.4—The soybean data constitute a growth curve. Do you suppose the population growth curve is really straight? How would you design an experiment to get a growth curve of the blood pressure in Iowa women?

EXAMPLE 6.2.5—Eighteen samples of soil were prepared with varying amounts of inorganic phosphorus, X. Corn plants, grown in each soil, were harvested at the end of 38 days and analyzed for phosphorus content. From this was estimated the plant-available phosphorus in the soil (section 14.2). Nine of the observations, adapted for ease of computation, are shown in this table:

Inorganic phosphorus in soil (ppm), X	1	4	5	9	13	11	23	23	28
Estimated plant-available phosphorus (ppm), Y	64	71	54	81	93	76	77	95	109

Calculate $b = 1.417$, $s_b = 0.395$, $t = 3.59**$.

Following this brief summary of the most common regression methods, the reader may wish to turn forward to Analysis of Variance in chapters 10 and 11.

6.3—Model I of the populations sampled: Fixed X. Before going further, it is necessary to specify the populations being sampled. They have three characteristics:

1. For each selected X there is a normal distribution of Y from which

the sample Y is taken at random. If desired, more than one Y may be drawn from each distribution (see section 6.13).

2. The means, μ, of all the sampled populations lie on a straight regression line.

3. All sampled populations are normally distributed and have a common σ. This Model I is specified concisely by the equation,

$$Y = a + \beta x + \epsilon,$$

where Y is any value of the dependent variable, a and β are parameters (to be explained), x is the deviation, $X - \bar{x}$, and ϵ is a random variable drawn from $\mathcal{N}(0, \sigma)$.

In this model, Y is the sum of a random part, ϵ, and a part fixed by x. The fixed part, according to 2 above, determines the means of the populations sampled, one mean for each x. The sequence of these means lie on the straight line represented by $\mu = a + \beta x$, the *population regression line*. The parameter a is the mean of the population corresponding to $x = 0$; in this sense, a specifies the height of the population regression above the X-axis. β is the *slope* or *trend* of the regression line, the *change in Y per unit change in* x. As for the variable part of Y, ϵ is drawn at random from $\mathcal{N}(0, \sigma)$; it is *independent of* x.

For non-mathematicians, the model is best explained by an arithmetical construction. For this, assign to X the values, 0, 2, 3, 7, 8, 10, as in table 6.3.1. This is done quite arbitrarily; the manner in which X is fixed has no bearing on the illustration

TABLE 6.3.1

CONSTRUCTION OF A SAMPLE FROM MODEL I, $Y = a + \beta x + \epsilon$, WITH $a = 4$, $\beta = 0.5$, AND ϵ DRAWN FROM $\mathcal{N}(0,1)$

X	x	$\beta x = 0.5x$	$a + \beta x = 4 + 0.5x$	ϵ	$Y = a + \beta x + \epsilon$
(1)	(2)	(3)	(4)	(5)	(6)
0	−5	−2.5	1.5	1.1	2.6
2	−3	−1.5	2.5	−1.3	1.2
3	−2	−1.0	3.0	−1.1	1.9
7	2	1.0	5.0	1.0	6.0
8	3	1.5	5.5	0.0	5.5
10	5	2.5	6.5	−1.0	5.5

Calculations of estimates for sample regression, Y on X:

$$\Sigma X = 30 \qquad\qquad\qquad\qquad\qquad\qquad\qquad\qquad \Sigma Y = 22.7$$
$$\bar{x} = 5 \qquad\qquad\qquad\qquad\qquad\qquad\qquad\qquad\quad \bar{y} = 3.78$$
$$\Sigma X^2 = 226 \qquad\qquad \Sigma XY = 149.1 \qquad\qquad \Sigma Y^2 = 108.31$$
$$C = 150 \qquad C = \Sigma X \Sigma Y/n = 113.5 \qquad\qquad C = 85.88$$
$$\overline{\Sigma x^2 = 76} \qquad\qquad \overline{\Sigma xy = 35.6} \qquad\qquad\qquad \overline{\Sigma y^2 = 22.43}$$

$$b = \Sigma xy/\Sigma x^2 = 35.6/76 = 0.468$$
$$\hat{Y} = 3.78 + 0.468 (X - 5) = 1.44 + 0.468X$$
$$\Sigma d_{y \cdot x}^2 = \Sigma y^2 - (\Sigma xy)^2/\Sigma x^2 = 22.43 - (35.6)^2/76 = 5.75$$
$$s_{y \cdot x}^2 = \Sigma d_{y \cdot x}^2/(n - 2) = 5.75/4 = 1.44. \quad s_{y \cdot x} = \sqrt{1.44} = 1.20$$

Next, calculate $\bar{x}$ and the deviations, $x = X - \bar{x}$, in column 2.

Now take $\beta = 0.5$; this implies that the means of the populations are to increase one-half unit with each unit change in x. From this, column 3 is calculated.

Choose $a = 4$, meaning that at $x = 0$ the population regression is 4 units above the X-axis.

The fixed X together with a and β determine the succession of means in column 4. These are indicated by open circles on the population regression line of figure 6.3.1. So far all quantities are *fixed*, without sampling variation.

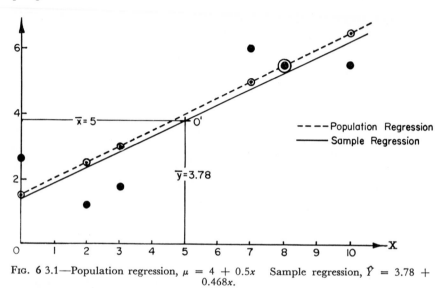

FIG. 6 3.1—Population regression, $\mu = 4 + 0.5x$ Sample regression, $\hat{Y} = 3.78 + 0.468x$.

Coming now to the variable part of Y, the ϵ are taken at random by this procedure:

1. In the table of random numbers (chapter 1), I started by chance at row 61, columns 55–56 and observed the integers, 86, 09, 14, 82, 52, 16. Matching these with the normally distributed items of table 3.2.1, I got 41, 17, 19, 40, 30, 20.

2. In order to make the mean equal to zero, I subtracted 30 from each item, getting the normal deviates, 11, -13, -11, 10, 0, -10.

3. To avoid the large variation, $\sigma = 10$, I divided each deviate by 10, changing the standard deviation to 1. The results, set down in column 5, make up the random sample from $N(0, 1)$.

The last column of the table contains the *sample of* Y, each item being the sum of the fixed part in column 4 and the corresponding random part in column 5. The *sample points* are plotted as black circles in the figure. Necessary calculations are appended to the table.

EXAMPLE 6.3.1—In table 6.3.1, $b = 0.468$. Calculate the 6 deviations from regression, $d_{y \cdot x}$, and identify each with the distance of the corresponding point from the sample regression line. The sum of the deviations should be zero and the sum of their squares about 5.75.

EXAMPLE 6.3.2—Construct a sample with $a = 6$ and $\beta = -1$. The negative β means that the regression will slope downwards to the right. Take $X = 1, 2, \ldots 9$, $\bar{x}$ being 5. Draw ϵ randomly from $N(0, 5)$, table 3.10.1. Make a table showing the calculation of the sample of Y. Graph the population regression and the sample points. Save your work for further use.

6.4—The point estimators of a and β.

As indicated before, $a = 4$ is estimated by $\bar{y} = 3.78$. The *sample regression line* is drawn through the point, $(\bar{x}, \bar{y})$, $(5, 3.78)$ as shown in the figure.

The slope, $\beta = 0.5$, is estimated by $b = 0.468$ (see table). The sample regression line is nearly parallel to that of the population but lies below it because of the slight under-estimation of a. The contrasts between the two lines are due wholly to the random sampling of the ϵ.

In the equation of the sample regression, the constant, 1.44, is the *intercept* on the Y-axis where $X = 0$.

Notice that there is no variation in the X; $\bar{x}$ is unaffected by the ϵ. This is one characteristic of Model I.

EXAMPLE 6.4.1—For your sample of example 6.3.2, calculate $\bar{y}$ and b, then plot the sample regression line on your graph. Calculate the deviations, $d_{y \cdot x}$, and compare them with the corresponding ϵ. It is a partial check on your accuracy if $\Sigma d_{y \cdot x} = 0$.

6.5—$\hat{Y}$ as an estimator of $\mu = a + \beta x$. Adjusted Y.

For any x, the sample $\hat{Y}$ estimates the corresponding $\mu = a + \beta x$. For example, you have already noticed that, at $x = 0$ (for which $X = 5$), $\hat{Y}_5 = \bar{y}$ estimates $\mu_5 = a$. As another example, at $x = 2$, for which $X = 7$, $\hat{Y}_7 = 1.44 + (0.468)(7) = 4.72$, estimating $\mu_7 = 4 + (0.5)(2) = 5$.

The difference, $\mu - \hat{Y}$, has two sources, both due to the random ϵ. One is the difference between the elevations of the sample and population regression lines, $a - \bar{y}$; the other, the difference between the two slopes, $\beta - b$.

Estimates of μ are often not confined to the populations sampled but are made at an X interpolated between two of the fixed X whose Y were sampled. For example, at $X = 4$,

$$\hat{Y}_4 = 1.44 + 0.468(4) = 3.31,$$

locating a point on the sample regression line perpendicularly above $X = 4$. It should be carefully observed that we are estimating μ in a population not sampled. There is no sample evidence for such an estimate; it is made on the cognizance of the investigator who has reason to believe that the intermediate population has the same σ as those sampled and has a μ on the sampled regression, $a + \beta x$.

Using the same argument, one may estimate μ at an X extrapolated beyond the range of the fixed X. Thus, at $X = 12$,

$$\hat{Y}_{12} = 1.44 + (0.468) \, 12 = 7.06$$

Extrapolation involves the extra hazard that the population regression of means may be curved with the curvature becoming more pronounced beyond the sample range of X.

Looking at the sample itself, $\hat{Y}$ enables us to judge whether an individual observed Y is above or below average, a fact that is obvious in the graph. Look, for example, at the first point on the left. $Y_0 = 2.6$, to be compared with $\hat{Y}_0 = 1.44$. The positive deviation, $Y_0 - \hat{Y}_0 = 1.16$, shows that Y_0 exceeds the estimated value by 1.16 units. This may mean that the observed Y, randomly drawn from the first selected population, exceeds the mean of that population. Actually, this is true in the constructed example; $Y_0 = 2.6$ does lie above $\mu_0 = 1.5$, a fact attributable to $\epsilon_0 = 1.1$.

It is often desirable to compare the deviations from regression at two values of X. At $X = 10$, $Y_{10} - \hat{Y}_{10} = 5.5 - [1.44 + (0.468)(10)] = -0.62$, the point being 0.62 units below the sample regression. *Relative to the sample regression*, this sixth observed Y is $1.16 - (-0.62) = 1.78$ units less than the first.

Such comparisons or *case studies* are readily made by means of *adjusted values* of Y. These are calculated by adding to $\bar{y}$ the several deviations from regression. Examples:

$$Y_{A,0} = \bar{y} + (Y_0 - \hat{Y}_0) = 3.78 + 1.16 = 4.94,$$

where $Y_{A,0}$ indicates adjusted Y at $X = 0$. Also,

$$Y_{A,10} = 3.78 + (-0.62) = 3.16$$

Note that the difference between the adjusted Y is the same as that between the deviations:

$$Y_{A,0} - Y_{A,10} = 4.94 - 3.16 = 1.78,$$

as before.

The meaning of Y_A, interpreted graphically, is shown in figure 6.5.1. It is the value Y might have if its X were moved to $\bar{x}$ and if Y followed

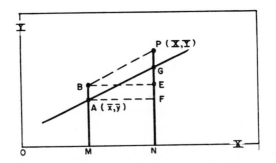

Fig. 6.5.1—Regression of Y on X. $NP = Y$ and $MB =$ (adjusted Y) $= \bar{y} + AB = \bar{y} + GP = \bar{y} +$ (deviation from regression). Also, $MB = NE = Y - EP = Y - FG = Y - b(AF) = Y - bx.$

parallel to the sample regression line. This involves assumptions about the biology which may or may not be realistic; the investigator must decide. Further discussion will be found in chapter 13.

EXAMPLE 6.5.1—Using the blood pressure data of section 6.2, estimate μ at age 30 years. Ans. 106.5 units.

EXAMPLE 6.5.2—Calculate adjusted Y for each age group in table 6.2.2, using the formula, $Y - bx$. Verify your results by the sum, $\Sigma Y_A = \Sigma Y$. Suggest several reasons for the differences among adjusted Y.

EXAMPLE 6.5.3—Mrs. A, 65 years old, has the blood pressure, 135 units. Mrs B, age 35, has the same blood pressure. The difference between the adjusted blood pressures is 41.4 units, that of Mrs. B's being higher. Explain the meaning. Is this a reasonable comparison?

EXAMPLE 6.5.4—In the plant available phosphorus data of example 6.2.5, calculate Y_A for the 9th soil sample. Ans. 87.7 ppm. Can you suggest a biological meaning for this result?

EXAMPLE 6.5.5—A growth curve for soybeans is given in example 6.2.1. Calculate Y_A for the 7-week plants. Ans. 21.6 cms., 2.4 cms. below $\bar{y}$. Can you suggest a realistic interpretation?

EXAMPLE 6.5.6—Prove that $\bar{y} + Y - \hat{Y} = Y - bx$.

EXAMPLE 6.5.7—Prove that $\mu - \hat{Y} = (a - \bar{y}) + x(\beta - b)$.

6.6—The estimator of σ^2. The deviations from sample regression, $d_{y \cdot x}$, are analogous to the ϵ. Since the ϵ are randomly drawn from $\mathcal{N}(0, \sigma)$, it seems natural to estimate σ^2 from the $d_{y \cdot x}$. That is what was done in table 6.2.2 where the deviations were squared, summed and later divided by the degrees of freedom, $n - 2$. It is now clear that $s_{y \cdot x}^2$ is estimating the parameter, σ^2; specifically, 1.44 is an estimate of $\sigma^2 = 1$ (or 1.20 is an estimate of $\sigma = 1$).

If nothing were known about X, the sample of Y would have yielded $s_y^2 = 22.43/5 = 4.49$ as the estimate of *experimental error*. By utilization of the knowledge of X, this is reduced to $s_{y \cdot x}^2 = 1.44$. Ignoring the change in degrees of freedom, the efficiency of this regression is said to be $4.49/1.44 = 312\%$.

EXAMPLE 6.6.1—In your sample taken in accord with example 6.3.2, calculate $s_{y \cdot x}^2$ and compare it with $\sigma^2 = 25$.

EXAMPLE 6.6.2—In example 6.2.5, estimate σ in the sampled population. Ans. $s_{y \cdot x} = 10.69$ ppm. Compare this with $s_y = 16.86$ ppm.

6.7—Model II of the population sampled: the bivariate normal. The investigator often does not select values of X; he draws an individual from some population, then measures two characters whose relation he wishes to investigate. These two variables are distributed in a *bivariate* population which will be described more at length in the following chapter. We shall consider only the *bivariate normal* population. Those who need more extensive information may find it in references (1, 13, 14).

TABLE 6.7.1

REGRESSION OF PERCENTAGE OF WORMY FRUIT ON SIZE OF APPLE CROP

Tree Number	Size of Crop on Tree (hundreds of fruits) X	Percentage of Fruits Wormy Y	Deviations From Mean x	Deviations From Mean y	Squares of Deviations x^2	Squares of Deviations y^2	Products of Deviations xy	Estimate of μ $\hat{Y}$	Deviation From Regression $Y - \hat{Y} = d_{y.x}$	Square $(Y - \hat{Y})^2 = d_{y.x}^2$
1	8	59	−11	14	121	196	−154	56.14	2.86	8.18
2	6	58	−13	13	169	169	−169	58.17	−0.17	0.03
3	11	56	−8	11	64	121	−88	53.10	2.90	8.41
4	22	53	3	8	9	64	24	41.96	11.04	121.88
5	14	50	−5	5	25	25	−25	50.06	−0.06	0.00
6	17	45	−2	0	4	0	0	47.03	−2.03	4.12
7	18	43	−1	−2	1	4	2	46.01	−3.01	9.06
8	24	42	5	−3	25	9	−15	39.94	2.06	4.24
9	19	39	0	−6	0	36	0	45.00	−6.00	36.00
10	23	38	4	−7	16	49	−28	40.95	−2.95	8.70
11	26	30	7	−15	49	225	−105	37.91	−7.91	62.57
12	40	27	21	−18	441	324	−378	23.73	3.27	10.69
Sum	228	540	0	0	924	1,222	−936	540.00	−0.00	273.88
Mean	19	45						45.00		

$$b = \frac{S_{xy}}{S_x^2} = \frac{-936}{924} = -1.013 \text{ per cent per 100 fruits}$$

$$s_{y.x}^2 = \Sigma d_{y.x}^2/(n - 2) = 273.88/10 = 27.388$$

$$\hat{Y} = \bar{y} + b(X - \bar{x}) = 45 - 1.013 (X - 19) = 64.247 - 1.013X \text{ hundreds of fruits}$$

Fortunately the methods which interest us are identical for the two models. The sample chosen to illustrate Model II contains another feature of interest, a regression which is negative instead of positive.

It is rather generally thought that the intensity of the injury by codling moth larvae is greater on apple trees bearing a small crop. Apparently the density of the flying moth tends towards uniformity, so that the chance of attack for any particular fruit is augmented if there are few fruits in the tree. The data in table 6.7.1 are adapted from the results of an experiment (10) containing evidence about this phenomenon. The 12 trees were all given a calyx spray of lead arsenate followed by five cover sprays made up of 3 pounds of manganese arsenate and 1 quart of fish oil per 100 gallons. There is a decided tendency, emphasized in figure 6.7.1, for the percentage of wormy fruits to decrease as the number of apples in the tree increases. In this particular group of trees, the relation of the two variates is even closer than usual.

The new feature in the calculations is the majority of negative products, *xy*, caused by the tendency of small values of Y to be associated with large values of X. The sample regression coefficient shows that the estimated percentage of wormy apples decreases, as indicated by the minus sign, 1.013 with each increase of 100 fruits in the crop. The sample regression line, and of course the percentage, falls away from the point, $0'(\bar{x}, \bar{y})$, by 1.013 for each unit of crop above 19 hundreds.

The regression line brings into prominence the deviations from this moving average, deviations which measure the failure of crop size to ac-

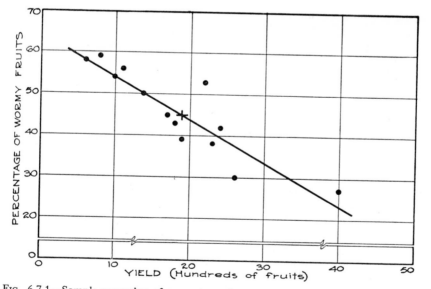

Fɪɢ. 6.7.1—Sample regression of percentage of wormy fruits on size of crop in apple trees. The cross indicates the origin for deviations, $0'(\bar{x}, \bar{y})$.

count for variation in the intensity of infestation. Trees number 4, 9, and 11 had notably discrepant percentages of injured fruits, while numbers 2 and 5 performed as expected. According to the model these are random deviations from the average (regression) values, but close observation of the trees during the flight of the moths might reveal some characteristics of this phenomenon. Tree 4 might have been on the side from which the flight originated or perhaps its shape or situation caused poor applications of the spray. Trees 9 and 11 might have had some peculiarities of conformation of foliage that protected them. Careful study of trees 2 and 5 might throw light on the kind of tree or location that receives normal infestation. This kind of *case study* usually does not affect the handling of the sample statistics, but it may add greatly to the investigator's knowledge of his experimental material and may afford clues to the improvement of future experiments. For example, it may be found that certain causes of variation can be predicted and so can be eliminated from experimental error by appropriate design (see chapter 11).

You have doubtless been impressed by the fact that when there is regression the statement, "One tree had only 27% wormy fruits in an orchard whose mean was 45%," may be inadequate. You immediately ask, "What was the size of the tree crop?" If you learn that it was 40 bushels you become aware that 27% was a greater rate of infestation than one would expect in a tree with so large a yield. It is not the orchard average with which the tree percentage should be compared, but it is the expected percentage for the individual crop size. The regression, in fact, replaces the mean as a standard of comparison. This new standard is not the same for all trees but varies according to the number of apples borne.

As in the case studies mentioned in section 6.5, two individual trees are compared, not directly by their percentages but by contrasting their deviations from regression. The rates of infestation of two trees are immediately comparable only if their yields are the same. Otherwise, it is their errors of estimate that must be compared. From table 6.7.1 it is seen that, while trees 1 and 4 differ by $59 - 53 = 6\%$ in actual percentages of wormy fruits, yet when they are compared on the basis of crop size the difference is $2.86 - 11.04 = -8.18\%$, meaning that if these trees had borne the same number of apples the percentage of injured fruits on 1 is estimated to have been less than that on 4 by 8.18%. This is another way of making the comparisons of section 6.5, using deviations from regression rather than adjusted Y.

There are two extremes among attitudes toward experimental data, both of which should be avoided. Some attend only to minute details of sample variation, neglecting the summarization of the data and the consequent inferences about the population. Others are impatient of the data themselves, rushing headlong toward averages and other generalizations. Either course fails to yield full information from the experiment. The competent investigator takes time to examine each datum together

with the individual measured. He attempts to distinguish normal variation from aberrant observations. He then judges his summaries and his
population inferences and draws his conclusions against this vivid background of sample facts.

EXAMPLE 6.7.1—Another group of 12 trees, investigated by Hansberry and
Richardson, was sprayed with lead arsenate throughout the season. In addition, the
fourth and fifth cover sprays contained 1% mineral oil emulsion and nicotine sulfate at
the rate of 1 pint per 100 gallons. The results are shown below. These facts may be
verified: $\Sigma X = 240$, $\Sigma Y = 384$, $\Sigma x^2 = 808$, $\Sigma y^2 = 1428$, $\Sigma xy = -582$, regression coefficient $= -0.7203$, $\hat{Y} = 46.41 - 0.7203X$, $Y - \hat{Y}$ for the first tree $= 16.40\%$.

Size of Crop, X Hundreds	15,	15,	12,	26,	18,	12,	8,	38,	26,	19,	29,	22
Percentage Wormy, Y	52,	46,	38,	37,	37,	37,	34,	25,	22,	22,	20,	14

EXAMPLE 6.7.2—In table 6.7.1, calculate $\Sigma d_{y \cdot x}^2 = 273.88$ by means of the
formula given in section 6.2.

EXAMPLE 6.7.3—The following weights of body and comb of 15-day-old White
Leghorn male chicks are adapted from Snedecor and Breneman (16):

Chick Number		1	2	3	4	5	6	7	8	9	10
Body weight (grams), X		83	72	69	90	90	95	95	91	75	70
Comb weight (milligrams), Y		56	42	18	84	56	107	90	68	31	48

Calculate the sample regression equation, $\hat{Y} = 60 + 2.302 (X - 83)$.

EXAMPLE 6.7.4—Construct the graph of the chick data, plotting body weight
along the horizontal axis. Insert the regression line.

6.8—Interval estimates and tests of null hypotheses. Being provided with point estimates of the parameters of the regression population,
we turn to their interval estimates and to tests of hypotheses about them.
These will be the same for Models I and II.

First in order of utility, there is the sample regression coefficient,
b, an estimate of β. As seen in section 6.2, in random sampling, b is distributed with a variance estimated by

$$s_b^2 = s_{y \cdot x}^2 / \Sigma x^2$$

Thus, in the apple sampling of table 6.7.1,

$$s_b^2 = 27.388/924 = 0.0296; \quad s_b = 0.172\%$$

Moreover, since the quantity $(b - \beta)/s_b$ follows the t-distribution with
$n - 2$ degrees of freedom, it may be said with confidence that

$$b - t_{.05}s_b \leq \beta \leq b + t_{.05}s_b$$

For the apples, $d.f. = 10$, $t_{.05} = 2.228$, $t_{.05}s_b = (2.228)(0.172) = 0.383$,
$b - t_{.05}s_b = -1.013 - 0.383 = -1.396$ per cent per 100 fruits,

$b + t_{.05}s_b = -1.013 + 0.383 = -0.630$ per cent per 100 fruits,

and, finally, $\qquad -1.396 \leq \beta \leq -0.630$

If it is said that the population regression coefficient is within these limits, the statement is right unless the sample is one of the divergent kind that occurs about once in 20 trials.

Graphically, the confidence limits are represented by two lines with slopes -1.396 and -0.630, crossing each other and the sample regression line at $0'(\bar{x}, \bar{y})$. We are confident that the population regression line slopes downward with an orientation somewhere between the indicated limits. But we are yet to set limits on the elevation of the line.

EXAMPLE 6.8.1—On the graph of figure 6.7.1, plot the 2 lines showing the confidence limits on β.

Instead of the interval estimate of β, interest may lie in testing some null hypothesis. While it is now rather obvious that H_0: $\beta = 0$ will be rejected, we proceed with the illustration; if there were any other pertinent value of β to be tested, we could use that instead. Since $(b - \beta)/s_b$ follows the t-distribution, we put

$$t = \frac{b - \beta}{s_b} = \frac{-1.013 - 0}{0.172} = -5.89, \quad d.f. = n - 2 = 10$$

The sign is ignored because the table contains both halves of the distribution. H_0 is rejected. One concludes that in the population sampled there is a regression of percentage wormy apples on crop size, the value likely being between -0.630 and -1.396 per cent per 100 fruits.

Next in order of usefulness are inferences about $\mu = a + \beta x$. The simplest case is that for which $x = 0$ and $\mu (= a)$ is estimated by $\bar{y}$. Since σ^2 is estimated by $s_{y \cdot x}^2$, the variance of the mean has the estimate, $s_{y \cdot x}^2/n$. For the apple data in which $\bar{y} = 45\%$,

$$s_{\bar{y} \cdot x}^2 = s_{y \cdot x}^2/n = 27.388/12 = 2.282, \quad s_{\bar{y} \cdot x} = 1.51\%$$

The confidence interval on μ for $x = 0$ is got from $s_{\bar{y} \cdot x}$ which has $n - 2$ $d.f.$ We have

$$\bar{y} - t_{.05}s_{\bar{y} \cdot x} \leq a \leq \bar{y} + t_{.05}s_{\bar{y} \cdot x}$$

which for the apples is

$$45 - (2.228)(1.51) \leq a \leq 45 + (2.228)(1.51)$$

$$41.6\% \leq a \leq 48.4\%$$

You may wonder why the mean square of $\bar{y}$ is not s_y^2/n, as might be inferred from chapter 3. What has been paid to get the smaller mean square, $s_{y\cdot x}^2/n$? Superficially it may be said that the measurement and use of X warrants the smaller estimate. More fundamentally, $s_{y\cdot x}^2/n$ is an estimate of σ^2/n, the variance of a sample mean from any one of our normal populations (Model I) or from our bivariate normal population (Model II). Included is that one under consideration, for which $X = \bar{x}$. The reason will be clear if you remember that in Model I the various X are fixed. In sampling from this model, the same set of X is always chosen. The only variation is that of the ϵ in the Y. In sampling blood pressure among women, if other ages were chosen—less than 30 years for example—the sample mean might have a considerably larger variation than that indicated by the sample in hand. The price of the small mean square is the restriction of the X to those chosen. In chapter 7, it will be found that Model II will provide the same estimate of $\sigma_{\bar{y}\cdot x}$.

If there is any relevant hypothesis about a, it may be tested by use of $s_{\bar{y}\cdot x}$. It might be that in a large apple-growing region the damage to fruits during the season was found to average 50%. To get evidence about the comparative rate of injury in the orchard of our sample one might set up the hypothesis that, for our set of X, $a = 50\%$. Then

$$t = \frac{\bar{y} - a}{s_{\bar{y}\cdot x}} = \frac{45 - 50}{1.51} = -3.31, \; d.f. = 10$$

H_0 would be rejected. The conclusion might be that (i) the spraying done was more effective than the usual practice in the region, or (ii) this orchard was, for some unknown reason, less heavily attacked than the average, or (iii) this orchard had more than the average number of apples per tree.

If $X \neq \bar{x}$, then $\hat{Y}$ is subject to a second source of variation. Not only may the sample mean, $\bar{y}$, be in error but also the sample regression coefficient, b. Since $\hat{Y} = \bar{y} + bx$, its mean square is the sum of two independent mean squares; that of $\bar{y}$, $s_{y\cdot x}^2/n$, and that of bx which is

$$\frac{s_{y\cdot x}^2 x^2}{\Sigma x^2}$$

The first is the same for all X, but the second changes in proportion to x^2. We have, then,

$$s_{\hat{Y}}^2 = \frac{s_{y\cdot x}^2}{n} + \frac{s_{y\cdot x}^2 x^2}{\Sigma x^2} = s_{y\cdot x}^2 \left(\frac{1}{n} + \frac{x^2}{\Sigma x^2} \right)$$

Hence,

$$s_{\hat{Y}} = s_{y\cdot x} \sqrt{1/n + x^2/\Sigma x^2}$$

For the apples, $s_{y\cdot x} = \sqrt{27.388}$ and

$$s_{\hat{Y}} = \sqrt{27.388} \sqrt{1/12 + x^2/924} = \sqrt{2.282 + 0.02964 x^2}$$

Thus, for trees with crops like that of No. 12, $x = 21$ and $s_{\hat{Y}} = 3.92\%$, notably greater than $s_{\bar{y} \cdot x} = 1.51\%$ at $x = 0$.

Often the second term of $s_{\hat{Y}}^2$ is relatively small within the sample range, but in forecasting beyond this range the term in x^2 may become predominant.

The reason for the increasing $s_{\hat{Y}}$ as X recedes from $\bar{x}$ is rather obvious if you think of the confidence interval on β. The two limiting slopes define a pair of limiting lines, passing through the origin, and diverging as $|x|$ increases. It is the increasing confidence limit on β that causes that on $\hat{Y}$.

Corresponding to any $\hat{Y}$, the point estimate of μ, there is an interval estimate,

$$\hat{Y} - t_{.05}\ s_{\hat{Y}} \leq \mu \leq \hat{Y} + t_{.05}\ s_{\hat{Y}}$$

One might wish to estimate the mean percentage of wormy apples, μ, at the point; $X = 30$ hundreds of fruits. If so,

$$x = X - \bar{x} = 30 - 19 = 11 \text{ hundreds of fruits}$$

$$\hat{Y} = \bar{y} + bx = 45 - (1.013)(11) = 33.86\%$$

$$t_{.05}\ s_{\hat{Y}} = (2.228)\sqrt{2.282 + (0.02964)(11^2)} = 5.40\%$$

$$33.86 - 5.40 \leq \mu \leq 33.86 + 5.40$$

Finally, $$28.46\% \leq \mu \leq 39.26\%$$

One says, then, that at $X = 30$ hundreds of fruits, the population mean Y is estimated as 33.86% wormy fruits with the 0.95 confidence limits from 28.46% to 39.26%. This confidence interval is represented by AB in figure 6.8.1.

If calculations like this are done for various values of X and if the confidence limits are plotted above and below the sample regression line, one has a confidence belt or zone with curved borders, as in figure 6.8.1. The curves are the branches of a hyperbola. We have confidence that μ_y for any X lies in the belt. The figure emphasizes the increasing hazard of making predictions at X far removed from $\bar{x}$.

If a person is making predictions, he is usually predicting individual events, not values of $\mu = \alpha + \beta x$. If so, the random element, ϵ, is an additional source of uncertainty. So, the mean square of Y contains another term, being

$$s_Y^2 = s_{y \cdot x}^2 + \frac{s_{y \cdot x}^2}{n} + \frac{s_{y \cdot x}^2\ x^2}{\Sigma x^2},$$

from which, $s_Y = s_{y \cdot x}\ \sqrt{1 + 1/n + x^2/\Sigma x^2}$

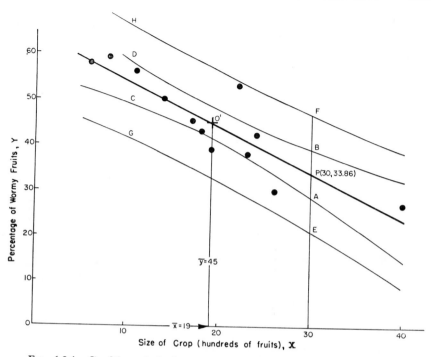

Fig. 6.8.1—Confidence belts for μ, *ABCD*; and for Y, *EFGH*; the apple data.

If you wish to predict the percentage of wormy apples on a tree yielding 30 hundreds of fruits,

$$t_{.05} \, s_Y = 2.228 \, \sqrt{27.388} \, \sqrt{1 + 1/12 + (11)^2/924} = 12.85\%$$

From this and $\hat{Y} = 33.86\%$, the confidence interval is given by

$$33.86 - 12.85 \leq \mu \leq 33.86 + 12.85$$

or, $$21.01\% \leq \mu \leq 46.71\%,$$

as shown by *EF*, figure 6.8.1. We conclude that for trees bearing 3,000 fruits, population values of percentage wormy fruits fall between 21.01% and 46.71% unless a 1-in-20 chance has occurred in the sampling.

Continuing this procedure, a confidence belt for Y may be plotted as in the figure. It is to be observed that all the sample points lie in the belt. In general about 5% of them are expected to fall outside.

Since $(\hat{Y} - \mu)/s_{\hat{y}}$ and $(Y - \mu)/s_Y$ both follow the t-distribution, any pertinent hypothesis about μ might be tested.

For purposes of illustration we have made all the probability statements above as though they were independent of each other. Statements about $\bar{y}$ and b are independent, but it is clear that probabilities related to $\hat{Y}$ and Y are determined in part by the same accidents of sampling that produced $\bar{y}$ and b. It is proper to consider the implications of all these statements. Only remember that if it should be found, for example, that the population mean lies beyond the sample based confidence limits, then the probability would be much greater than .05 that the population value of regression Y is outside the confidence limits based on $\hat{Y}$.

EXAMPLE 6.8.2—In the regression of comb weight on body weight, example 6.7.3, $n = 10$, $\bar{x} = 83$ grams, $\bar{y} = 60$ mg. $\Sigma x^2 = 1,000$, $\Sigma y^2 = 6,854$ and $\Sigma xy = 2,302$. Set 95% confidence limits on a, assuming the same set of body weights. Ans. 49.8 − 70.2 mg.

EXAMPLE 6.8.3—In the chick data, $b = 2.302$. Test the hypothesis that $\beta = 0$. Ans. $t = 5.22$, $P < .01$.

EXAMPLE 6.8.4—Since evidently there is a population regression of comb weight on body weight, set 95% confidence limits to the regression coefficient. Ans. 1.28 − 3.32 mg. per gram.

EXAMPLE 6.8.5—Predict the population average comb weight of 100-gram chicks. Ans. 99.1 mg. with 95% limits, 70.0 − 119.2 mg.

EXAMPLE 6.8.6—Set 95% confidence limits to the forecast of the comb weight of a randomly chosen 100-gram chick. Ans. 61.3 − 136.9 mg.

6.9—Short-cut methods of computation in regression. So far in this chapter you have not been greatly burdened with computation. In practice, regression calculations are rather tedious so that either machines are used or some form of coding is practiced. Short cuts in regression are mainly those already explained in chapter 5, only a single new feature being introduced. The data in table 6.9.1 will serve as illustration.

If a machine is available the methods of section 5.2 are easily extended to the calculation of regression. In most machines the sum of either variate is run up along with the sum of its squares; that is, both ΣX and ΣX^2 appear in the recording dials at the end of a single series of operations. As for the sum of products,

$$(50)(128) + (64)(159) + \ldots + (65)(104) = 108,530,$$

it is also read from the dials after the sequence of multiplications, none of the individual products being recorded. Your book of instructions, or

TABLE 6.9.1
INITIAL WEIGHTS AND GAINS IN WEIGHT (GRAMS) OF 15 FEMALE RATS ON HIGH PROTEIN DIET, 28TH TO 84TH DAYS OF AGE

	Rat Number														
	1	2	3	4	5	6	7	8	9	10	11	12	13	14	15
Initial weight, X	50	64	76	64	74	60	69	68	56	48	57	59	46	45	65
Gain, Y	128	159	158	119	133	112	96	126	132	118	107	106	82	103	104

the nearest agent, will furnish directions. In some machines the two sums, the two sums of squares, and the sum of products may all be accumulated at one run. If there are available machines for tabulating data punched in cards, they will be found convenient for handling large samples (200 or more sets of observations) (2). The results from any of these machines are entered in a table like 6.9.2. One advantage of a machine is the avoid-

TABLE 6.9.2

<small>COMPUTATIONS IN REGRESSION IF MACHINE IS USED. RAT DATA FROM TABLE 6.9.1</small>

$$\Sigma X = 901 \qquad\qquad \Sigma Y = 1{,}783 \qquad\qquad n = 15$$
$$\bar{x} = 60.07 \text{ grams} \qquad \bar{y} = 118.87 \text{ grams}$$
$$\Sigma X^2 = 55{,}465 \qquad \Sigma Y^2 = 218{,}297 \qquad \Sigma XY = 108{,}530$$
$$(\Sigma X)^2/n = 54{,}120.07 \qquad (\Sigma Y)^2/n = 211{,}939.27 \qquad (\Sigma X)(\Sigma Y)/n = 107{,}098.87$$
$$\Sigma x^2 = \overline{1{,}344.93} \qquad \Sigma y^2 = \overline{6{,}357.73} \qquad \Sigma xy = \overline{1{,}431.13}$$

ance of much copying of numbers. This enhances both the accuracy and the rapidity of calculation. The only entries that need be made are those in table 6.9.2. Note the one new feature, the correction term for the sum of products. This contains the product of ΣX by ΣY instead of the square of either, rather a reasonable method of correcting products. Don't overlook the fact that the correction term may be larger than ΣXY, making Σxy negative. This would indicate a downward sloping regression line.

The six quantities,

$$n, \bar{x}, \bar{y}, \Sigma x^2, \Sigma y^2, \Sigma xy,$$

constitute the entire information necessary for completing the computations of regression. We have, for example,

$$b = \Sigma xy/\Sigma x^2 = 1{,}431.13/1{,}344.93 = 1.0641$$

Gain in weight among such female rats is, therefore, partly predictable, each gram increase in initial weight corresponding to 1.0641 grams increase in gain. However,

$$\Sigma d_{y \cdot x}^2 = \Sigma y^2 - (\Sigma xy)^2/\Sigma x^2 = 6{,}357.73 - (1{,}431.13)^2/1{,}344.93 = 4{,}834.88$$
$$s_{y \cdot x}^2 = \Sigma d_{y \cdot x}^2/(n-2) = 4{,}834.88/13 = 371.91$$
$$s_b^2 = s_{y \cdot x}^2/\Sigma x^2 = 371.91/1{,}344.93 = 0.2765$$
$$s_b = \sqrt{0.2765} = 0.526$$
$$t = b/s_b = 1.0641/0.526 = 2.02$$

The large value of s_b relative to b will be obvious if you graph the data in the manner of example 6.8.1. Since t does not quite reach the 5% level one must not be too confident about population facts. Nevertheless, the sample estimate cannot be ignored. There is a good deal of evidence to support some relation between initial weight and gain. We have here some information about experimental design and shall return to these results in the succeeding section.

You are now prepared to read chapters 10 and 11, analysis of variance, or you may dip into chapters 7 and 9.

If a calculating machine is not available, one may profit by following directions for coding given in chapter 5. Each variate should be reduced to a series of integers centering on zero and having a range between 20 and 50 units. This not only makes the calculation relatively easy but also produces results sufficiently accurate for ordinary purposes. The process is illustrated in table 6.9.3. These data were taken from a study of the

TABLE 6.9.3

DRAFT AND SPEED OF PLOWS DRAWN BY TRACTORS
Illustration of coding in computation of regression

Speed Miles per Hour V	Draft Pounds D	Code Numbers $(10V - 30)/2$ (rounded) X	$(D/10) - 50$ (rounded) Y	Squares of Code Numbers X^2	Y^2	Products of Code Numbers XY
0.9	425	−10	−8	100	64	80
1.3	420	−8	−8	64	64	64
2.0	480	−5	−2	25	4	10
2.7	495	−2	0	4	0	0
3.4	540	2	4	4	16	8
3.4	530	2	3	4	9	6
4.1	590	6	9	36	81	54
5.2	610	11	11	121	121	121
5.5	690	12	19	144	361	228
6.0	680	15	18	225	324	270
34.5	5460	48 −25	64 −18	727	1044	841
		23	46			

$$\Sigma X = 23$$
$$\bar{x} = 2.3 \text{ code units}$$
$$\bar{v} = \frac{(2)(2.3) + 30}{10}$$
$$= 3.46 \text{ mi./hr.}$$
$$\Sigma X^2 = 727$$
$$(\Sigma X)^2/n = 52.9$$
$$\Sigma x^2 = \overline{674.1}$$
$$\Sigma v^2 = (674.1)(2/10)^2$$
$$= 26.964$$

$$\Sigma Y = 46$$
$$\bar{y} = 4.6 \text{ code units}$$
$$\bar{d} = (4.6 + 50)(10)$$
$$= 546 \text{ pounds}$$
$$\Sigma Y^2 = 1,044$$
$$(\Sigma Y)^2/n = 211.6$$
$$\Sigma y^2 = \overline{832.4}$$
$$\Sigma d^2 = (832.4)(10)^2$$
$$= 83,240$$

$$\Sigma XY = 841$$
$$(\Sigma X)(\Sigma Y)/n = 105.8$$
$$\Sigma xy = \overline{735.2}$$
$$\Sigma vd = (735.2)(2/10)(10) = 1,470.4$$

forces necessary to draw plows at the speeds commonly attained by tractors (3). The character of the soil and depth of the furrow were experimentally controlled as closely as possible. Within the limits of the trial the draft was roughly proportional to the speed, as a graphical representation of the data will indicate.

In order to avoid large numbers and decimals, the coding was carried to an extreme. Doubtless some will prefer the decimals and large numbers; an argument against coding is the opportunity for mistakes in the procedure itself. However, familiarity makes the process less forbidding, and there are data whose coding is certainly convenient.

The decoding offers some novel features. The sums of squares must be decoded by use of the squares of the coding ratios and the sum of products by means of their product. If this doesn't seem reasonable, try extracting the square roots of the sums of squares, decoding in the usual manner, then squaring the results.

The regression coefficient, $b = \Sigma vd/\Sigma v^2 = 1{,}470.4/26.964 = 54.53$, shows that the drawbar pull increased an average of 54.53 pounds for each mile per hour increase in speed. The formula for estimating draft at various speeds is

$$\hat{D} = 546 + 54.53 \,(V - 3.46) = 54.53V + 357.3 \text{ pounds}$$

Since the use of this regression formula may lead to the prediction of drawbar pulls in individual trials, it is pertinent to calculate the variance, s_D^2, of a randomly selected D:

$$\Sigma(D - \hat{D})^2 = \Sigma d^2 - (\Sigma vd)^2/\Sigma v^2 = 83{,}240 - (1{,}470.4)^2/26.964 = 3{,}056$$
$$s_{d \cdot v}^2 = \Sigma(D - \hat{D})^2/(n - 2) = 3{,}056/8 = 382.0$$
$$s_D^2 = s_{d \cdot v}^2(1 + 1/n + v^2/\Sigma v^2) = 382.0(1 + 0.1 + v^2/26.964)$$
$$= 420.2 + 14.167v^2$$

As an example, let us estimate the drawbar pull of a tractor making 5 miles per hour.

$$\hat{D} = 54.53(5) + 357.3 = 630 \text{ pounds}$$
$$v = 5 - 3.46 = 1.54 \text{ miles per hour}$$
$$s_D^2 = 420.2 + 14.167(1.54)^2 = 453.8$$
$$\text{Standard error} = 21.3 \text{ pounds}, \quad t_{.05} = 2.306$$

The confidence limits are given by,

$$630 - (21.3)(2.306) \leq \mu \leq 630 + (21.3)(2.306)$$
$$581 \leq \mu \leq 679$$

EXAMPLE 6.9.1—Speed records attained in the Indianapolis Memorial Day automobile races, 1911–1955 (miles per hour) are as follows:

Year	1911	1912	1913	1914	1915	1916	1917	1918	1919	1920
Speed, Y	74.6	78.7	75.9	82.5	89.8	83.3	(no races)		88.1	88.6

	1921	1922	1923	1924	1925	1926	1927	1928	1929	1930
	89.6	94.5	91.0	98.2	101.1	95.9	97.5	99.5	97.6	100.4

	1931	1932	1933	1934	1935	1936	1937	1938	1939	1940
	96.6	104.1	104.2	104.9	106.2	109.1	113.6	117.2	115.0	114.3

	1941	1942	1943	1944	1945	1946	1947	1948	1949	1950
	115.1	....	(no races)	....		114.8	116.3	119.8	121.3	124.0

	1951	1952	1953	1954	1955
	126.2	128.9	128.7	130.8	128.2

For the 29 pre-World-War-II races, 1911–1941, calculate $\Sigma x^2 = 2{,}325.03$, $\Sigma y^2 = 4{,}039.81$, $\Sigma xy = 2{,}971.23$, $\hat{Y} = 1.278\,X + 63.51$ miles per hour (code the dates by subtracting 1900 from each).

EXAMPLE 6.9.2—Estimate the speed for the years 1946 and 1952, remembering that it is individual speeds being forecasted, not $\hat{Y}$. Ans. In 1946, $Y = 122.3$ miles per hour with 95% confidence interval, $118.9 - 125.7$; in 1952, $Y = 130.0$, $126.0 - 134.0$ miles per hour. Notice that in the latter year the confidence interval covers the observed speed.

EXAMPLE 6.9.3—On the graph of speed against date one can draw curves representing the confidence intervals for every year's speed. For the prewar races, these will be closest to the regression line in $\bar{x} = 26.59$ (or 1926.59 uncoded) and will deviate further from regression as X departs from its mean either way. The curves are the two branches of a hyperbola. If $t_{.05}$ is selected, about 95% of the records should fall between the curves if the sampling is random.

EXAMPLE 6.9.4—In *time series* such as the Speedway records, regression Model I may not be suitable; the ϵ may not be randomly assorted and one may not be independent of the next. Changes in rules, new discoveries, winning of successive races by the same man, and wars all bring Model I into question. The complications of time series will not be dealt with in this book.

EXAMPLE 6.9.5—It was desired to forecast the yields of 29 double and three-way crosses of maize under heavy second brood chinch bug infestation (11). The basis of prognostication was the known mean yields of top crosses of the parental lines grown under the same conditions. A formula designed by Jenkins (12) was used. The forecasted yields, X, and the actual experimental yields, Y, read from a scatter diagram, were as follows: 20, 20; 24, 29; 25, 34; 26, 35; 29, 43; 31, 11; 33, 24; 34, 35; 34, 45; 35, 34; 36, 34; 36, 36; 37, 35; 37, 46; 37, 42; 41, 41; 42, 43; 43, 43; 43, 55; 50, 53; 50, 55; 51, 54; 51, 55; 52, 42; 55, 55; 56, 54; 56, 51; 57, 50; 71, 61 bushels per acre. Construct the scatter diagram. Do you think the regression is linear? Assuming that it is, calculate the sample regression of Y on X, $\hat{Y} = 0.79X + 9.4$.

EXAMPLE 6.9.6—In the course of his investigations of winter hardiness in apple trees, Stark (17) wished to determine the specific heat, Y, of the twigs. The laboratory technique was difficult and inaccurate. Since more than half the weight of the twigs was water, and since the heat capacity of water is great, he tried estimating Y from the percentage of water, X, in the twigs, the latter being easily and accurately measured. Twenty-one pairs of Stark's measurements, X and Y, are as follows: 49.4, 0.646; 50.1, 0.644; 50.8, 0.665; 51.2, 0.670; 51.5, 0.666; 51.9, 0.653; 52.5, 0.669; 52.7, 0.657; 53.1, 0.689; 53.6, 0.669; 55.7, 0.685; 56.3, 0.696; 57.0, 0.700; 58.0, 0.690; 58.5, 0.711; 59.2, 0.704; 59.7, 0.696; 61.3, 0.713; 62.0, 0.719; 63.1, 0.731; 64.9, 0.731. Compute $\bar{x} = 55.83\%$, $\Sigma x^2 = 431.31$, $\bar{y} = 0.6859$, $\Sigma y^2 = 0.0142$, $\Sigma xy = 2.3536$, $\hat{Y} = 0.005457X + 0.3812$. Since $s_y = 0.027$ and $s_{y \cdot x} = 0.0086$, about a third of the variation of Y is unassociated with X. Since X is determined with very little error, Stark concluded that Y could be determined with sufficient accuracy by first measuring the percentage of water in the apple twigs, then estimating specific heat from the regression equation.

EXAMPLE 6.9.7—Derive the formula, $\Sigma xy = \Sigma XY - (\Sigma X)(\Sigma Y)/n$. Hint: Start with $X = x + \bar{x}$ and $Y = y + \bar{y}$. Multiply and add, remembering that $\Sigma x = \Sigma y = 0$.

6.10—Use of regression in experimental design. Statistical control.

As anticipated in section 3.10, regression is one means of reducing the unexplained error encountered in experimentation. Variation not controlled in the conduct of the experiment is often associated with some measurable variate, and the measurement of this variate enables the investigator to use regression for increasing the information available. An example is found in the rat gains of table 6.9.1. Though it was known that gain is usually associated with initial weight, it was not feasible to control this extraneous variate; that is, to use only rats all having the same starting weight. It was easy, however, to measure the variate, X, and to calculate the regression of gain upon it. What advantage was attained? Without this precaution experimental error would have been based on the rat mean square,

$$s^2 = \Sigma y^2/(n - 1) = 6{,}357.73/14 = 454.12$$

But utilization of known initial weights reduced the error mean square to

$$s_{y \cdot x}^2 = 371.91$$

Following the argument of section 3.10, it may be said that the information *per rat* has been increased in the ratio, $454.12/371.91 = 122\%$. Another way of saying it is that, for the same reliability, 22% more rats would have been required if the facts about initial weight had not been utilized. The relatively inexpensive measurement and use of initial weight increased the information from this experiment by 22%.

Even if experimental control is feasible it is not always desirable. Thus, in the experiment with tractor-drawn plows one would certainly not wish to confine his trials to a single speed. On the other hand, he would get little information if he considered

$$s^2 = \Sigma d^2/(n-1) = 83,240/9 = 9,249$$

as the experimental error. This experiment having been designed for use of regression, the appropriate estimate of random experimental error is

$$s_{v \cdot d}^2 = 382.0$$

Not only is the experiment founded on a broader basis of experience, but the information has been increased in the ratio of $9,249/382.0 = 2421\%$; that is, the information per trial is 2321% greater than it would have been if no use had been made of the speed records.

It appears, then, that in many situations where it is either not convenient or not desired to control experimentally a variate associated with the one under invesigation, *statistical control* (19) may be introduced. By measuring the auxiliary quantity and using regression one may accomplish the same end as by keeping this quantity constant in the experiment. The error, $s_{y \cdot x}$, is presumably no greater than s_y would be in an experimentally controlled sample with constant X. Indeed, it seems that in many cases statistical control is more to be desired; the actual situation is studied instead of one artificially produced, the observations are extended over a greater range, thus broadening the foundation for inference, and in the end one has knowledge of the variation of two quantities instead of one, together with the relation between them. In each line of research it must be learned by experience which type of control is more readily available, and which produces information more quickly and cheaply.

EXAMPLE 6.10.1—The chick data of example 6.7.3 were adapted from the original records of 13 birds whose body weights (X grams) and comb weights (Y mg.) were as follows: 83, 54; 72, 42; 69, 29; 78, 37; 69, 18; 90, 84; 90, 56; 95, 107; 95, 90; 91, 68; 75, 31; 70, 48; 76, 41. From these records, $n = 13$, $\bar{x} = 81.0$ grams, $\bar{y} = 54.2$ mg., $\Sigma x^2 = 1,218.00$, $\Sigma y^2 = 8,292.31$, $\Sigma xy = 2,834.00$. If decisions are to be based on comb weight, estimate the increase in information due to use of body weight as a statiticals control. Ans. 348%.

EXAMPLE 6.10.2—From the apple data of table 6.7.1, estimate the decrease in precision (information) that would result from omitting crop size as a statistical control. Ans. 75.3%.

EXAMPLE 6.10.3—For 1,594 farms in Crop Estimates District 9 of eastern South Dakota for the year 1942, X = acres in farm and Y = acres in corn were recorded. The mean square of corn acres was $s_y^2 = 1,859$, while that of deviations from regression was $s_{y \cdot x}^2 = 1,002$. If you collected a random sample of 100 farms from which to estimate the average number of acres in corn, s_y^2 would be 18.59. If you used farm size as a statistical control, how many farms would be required in the sample to get the same amount of information? Ans. 54 farms.

6.11—Partitioning the sum of squares of the dependent variate. Regression computations may be looked upon as a process of partitioning ΣY^2 into 3 parts which are both useful and meaningful. You have become accustomed to dividing ΣY^2 into $(\Sigma Y)^2/n$ and the remainder, Σy^2; then

TABLE 6.11.1
DATA SET UP TO ILLUSTRATE THE PARTITION OF ΣY^2

X	2	4	6	8	10	12	14	$\Sigma X = 56$
Y	4	2	5	9	3	11	8	$\Sigma Y = 42$

$$n = 7, \; \bar{x} = 8, \; \bar{y} = 6, \; \Sigma x^2 = 112, \; \Sigma y^2 = 68, \; \Sigma xy = 56$$

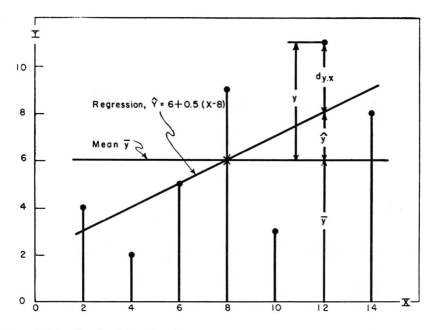

FIG. 6.11.1—Graph of data in table 6.11.1. The ordinate at $X = 12$ is shown divided into 2 parts, $\bar{y} = 6$ and $y = 5$. Then y is subdivided into $\hat{y} = 2$ and $d_{y \cdot x} = 3$. Thus $Y = \bar{y} + \hat{y} + d_{y \cdot x} = 6 + 2 + 3 = 11$.

subdividing Σy^2 into $(\Sigma xy)^2 / \Sigma x^2$ and $\Sigma d_{y \cdot x}^2$. This means that you have divided ΣY^2 into three portions:

$$\Sigma Y^2 = (\Sigma Y)^2 / n + (\Sigma xy)^2 / \Sigma x^2 + \Sigma d_{y \cdot x}^2$$

Each of these portions can be associated exactly with the sum of squares of a segment of the ordinates, Y. To illustrate this a simple set of data has been set up in table 6.11.1 and graphed in figure 6.11.1.

In the figure the sixth ordinate is shown partitioned into 3 segments:

$$Y = \bar{y} + \hat{y} + d_{y \cdot x}$$

Each of the other ordinates may be divided similarly, though negative segments make the geometry less obvious. The lengths are all set out in table 6.11.2 and the several segments are emphasized in figure 6.11.2. Observe that in each line of the table (including the two at the bottom) the sum of the last three numbers is equal to the number in column Y.

TABLE 6.11.2

LENGTHS OF ORDINATES IN TABLE 6.11.1 TOGETHER WITH SEGMENTS INTO WHICH THEY ARE PARTITIONED

Pair Number	Ordinate Y	Mean $\bar{y}$	Deviation $\hat{y}$	Deviation From Regression $d_{y \cdot x}$
1	4	6	−3	1
2	2	6	−2	−2
3	5	6	−1	0
4	9	6	0	3
5	3	6	1	−4
6	11	6	2	3
7	8	6	3	−1
	42	42	0	0
Sum of squares	320	252	28	40

It is notable that, though

$$Y = \bar{y} + \hat{y} + d_{y \cdot x},$$

yet the sum of squares is

$$\Sigma Y^2 = \Sigma \bar{y}^2 + \Sigma \hat{y}^2 + \Sigma d_{y \cdot x}^2,$$

each of the three product terms being zero (example 6.11.5). The sums of squares of the ordinates, $\Sigma Y^2 = 320$, and of the deviations from regression, $\Sigma d_{y \cdot x}^2 = 40$, are already familiar. It remains only to identify $(\Sigma Y)^2 / n$ with $\Sigma \bar{y}^2$ and $(\Sigma xy)^2 / \Sigma x^2$ with $\Sigma \hat{y}^2$.

First,

$$(\Sigma Y)^2 / n = n \frac{(\Sigma Y)^2}{n^2} = n\bar{y}^2 = \Sigma \bar{y}^2$$

That is, the correction for mean is simply the sum of the squares of the mean taken n times. The reason it is not so used in calculation is that any rounding inaccuracy in $\bar{y}$ would be exaggerated both by squaring and by multiplication with n.

Second,

$$\frac{(\Sigma xy)^2}{\Sigma x^2} = \frac{(\Sigma xy)^2}{(\Sigma x^2)^2} \Sigma x^2 = b^2 \Sigma x^2 = \Sigma b^2 x^2 = \Sigma \hat{y}^2$$

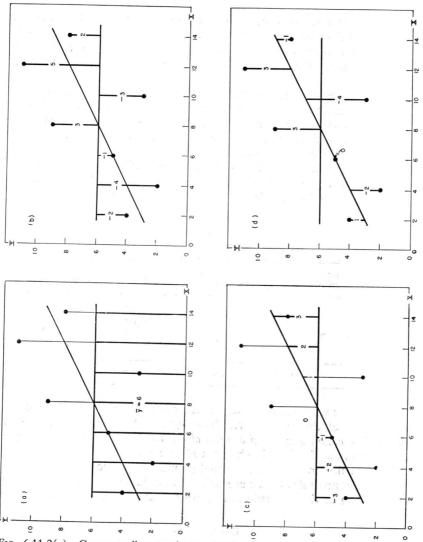

FIG. 6.11.2(a)—Corresponding to the mean, $\bar{y}$, these are the segments subtracted from Y leaving the deviations from mean, y, shown in figure 6.11.2(b). The sum of the squares of these 7 segments, $7(6^2) = 252$, corresponds to the 1 degree of freedom for the correction term, $(\Sigma Y)^2/n = (42)^2/7 = 252$.

FIG. 6.11.2(b)—These are deviations from mean, y, further subdivided in figures 6.11.2 (c) and (d).

FIG. 6.11.2(c)—Heavy lines show the deviations of regression values, $\hat{Y}$, from their mean, $\bar{y}$. They are completely determined by $\bar{y}$, b and a fixed set of x's. The sum of their squares, $\Sigma \hat{y}^2 = 28$, is the portion of ΣY^2 attributable to regression.

FIG. 6.11.2(d)—Random deviations from regression, $d_{y \cdot x}$. Each $d_{y \cdot x}$ added to the corresponding $\bar{y}$ and $\hat{y}$ of figures 6.11.2 (a) and (c) comprises an ordinate, Y, in figure 6.11.1. The sum of the squares of these deviations, $\Sigma d_{y \cdot x}^2 = 40$, corresponding to 5 degrees of freedom, furnishes an estimate, $s_{y \cdot x}^2 = 40/5 = 8$, of σ^2.

So the sum of squares attributable to regression turns out to be the sum of the squares of the n deviations of $\hat{Y}$ from its mean, $\bar{y}$. Certainly, it would be a tedious job to calculate $\Sigma \hat{y}^2$ every time one wished the sum of squares due to regression. You are now in a position to evaluate the short cut, $(\Sigma xy)^2/\Sigma x^2$.

I hope you appreciate the beauty of these regression computations. Make each formula meaningful, not merely a jumble of letters and figures. Associate each with a column in the table and with a line segment in the figure as well as with the descriptive phrase which has been used. Familiarity breeds not only utility but admiration.

The partition of ΣY^2 is intimately associated with the division of the total available degrees of freedom into 3 parts, one part corresponding to each portion of ΣY^2 (table 6.11.3). This identification of the several

TABLE 6.11.3

ANALYSIS OF VARIANCE OF Y IN TABLE 6.11.1

Description of Source of Variation	Symbol	Degrees of Freedom	Sum of Squares	Mean Square
The Mean	$\bar{y}$	1	$(\Sigma Y)^2/n = 252$	
Regression	b	1	$(\Sigma xy)^2/\Sigma x^2 = 28$	
Deviation from Regression	$d_{y\cdot x}$	$n-2=5$	$\Sigma d_{y\cdot x}^2 = 40$	$s_{y\cdot x}^2 = 8$
Total	Y	$n=7$	$\Sigma Y^2 = 320$	

$$\Sigma y^2 = 28 + 40 = 68, \quad d.f. = n - 1 = 6$$

sums of squares with corresponding degrees of freedom is one of the useful contributions of Professor R. A. Fisher (8). The method is shown in table 6.11.3, called a table of *analysis of variance*, a name with which you will become more familiar in chapters 10 and 11.

The first line in this table is usually omitted, the common and more useful form of analysis of variance being that of table 6.11.4.

Returning to the discussion of figure 6.11.2, it will be observed that

TABLE 6.11.4

ANALYSIS OF VARIANCE OF y IN TABLE 6.11.1

Source of Variation	Degrees of Freedom	Sum of Squares	Mean Square
Regression	1	28	
Deviations from Regression	5	40	8
Deviations from Mean	6	68	11.3

zero is the sum of the deviations from the horizontal line in (a) and (b) as well as from the regression line of (d). In fact, this would be true of any line drawn through the origin of deviations, $(\bar{x}, \bar{y})$. The sum of the squares of the deviations in (b) is less than the corresponding sum from any other *horizontal* line. But if you begin to rotate this line counterclockwise about the center, $(\bar{x}, \bar{y})$, the sum of squares becomes smaller and smaller till the position of the regression line is reached. It is the introduction of a second variate, such as crop size in the apple data, that gives meaning to this rotation. So long as there is only injured apples to consider, with no hint as to differences in crop size, the horizontal line is the only one interpretable. In fact, all the points might as well be plotted on some vertical line, such as OY of figure 6.2.1. In that event, the deviations from the origin, $\bar{y}$, would be exactly those considered in the earlier chapters. But added information about crop size warrants the extension of our ideas to include regression. Much of the variation in percentage injured fruits is eventually explained by differences in crop size. The only remaining variation is that associated with the deviations from the regression line due, according to our hypothesis, to sampling variation of injury to the apple crop. The selection of that line for which the sum of such deviations is zero, and the sum of their squares a minimum, is an effect of the logical extension of those ideas that led to the selection of the mean as an appropriate average of concentration. The principle of least squares is simply a statement of the unity in our ideas of averages for single variates and regressions for two or more.

EXAMPLE 6.11.1—Dawes (5) determined the "density" of the melanin content of the skin of 24 male frogs together with their weights. Since "Some of the 24 males . . . were selected for extreme duskiness or pallor so as to provide a measure of the extent of variability," that is, since selection was exercised on density this variate cannot be estimated (section 6.3) from the sample. Assuming random weights, they may be taken as Y. The data follow:

| Density, X | 0.13 | 0.15 | 0.28 | 0.58 | 0.68 | 0.31 | 0.35 | 0.58 |
| Weight, Y | 13 | 18 | 18 | 18 | 18 | 19 | 21 | 22 |

| Density, X | 0.03 | 0.69 | 0.38 | 0.54 | 1.00 | 0.73 | 0.77 | 0.82 |
| Weight, Y | 22 | 24 | 25 | 25 | 25 | 27 | 27 | 27 |

| Density, X | 1.29 | 0.70 | 0.38 | 0.54 | 1.08 | 0.86 | 0.40 | 1.67 |
| Weight, Y | 28 | 29 | 30 | 30 | 35 | 37 | 39 | 42 |

Calculate $\bar{x} = 0.6225$ units, $\bar{y} = 25.79$ grams, $\Sigma x^2 = 3.3276$, $\Sigma y^2 = 1{,}211.96$, $\Sigma xy = 40.022$.

EXAMPLE 6.11.2—In example 6.11.1 test the hypothesis, $\beta = 0$. Ans. $t = 3.81$, $P < 0.01$.

EXAMPLE 6.11.3—Analyze the variance of the frog weights, as follows:

Source of Variation	Degrees of Freedom	Sum of Squares	Mean Square
Mean	1	15,965.04	
Regression	1	481.36	
Deviations	22	730.60	33.21
Total	24	17,177.00	

EXAMPLE 6.11.4—How nearly free from error is the measurement of melanin density, X? After preparation of a solution from the skin of the frogs, the intensity of the color was evaluated in a colorimeter and the readings then transferred graphically into neutral densities. The figures reported are means of from 3 to 6 determinations. The error of this kind of measurement is usually appreciable, so that the estimate of regression may be biased downwards. Had not the investigator wished to learn about extremes of density, the regression of density on weight might have been not only unbiased but more informative.

EXAMPLE 6.11.5—Prove that the sums of the cross products in ΣY^2 are all zero. The only one that offers any difficulty is $\Sigma \hat{y} d_{y \cdot x}$: set $\hat{y} = bx$ and $d_{y \cdot x} = y - \hat{y} = y - bx$. Multiply and add, noting that $\Sigma xy = b\Sigma x^2$.

6.12—Galton's use of the term "regression." In his studies of inheritance Galton developed the idea of regression. Of the "law of universal regression" (9) he said, "Each peculiarity in a man is shared by his kinsman, but *on the average* in a less degree." His friend, Karl Pearson (15), collected more than a thousand records of stature, cubit and span in family groups. Figure 6.12.1 shows his regression of son's stature on father's. Though tall fathers do tend to have tall sons, yet the average

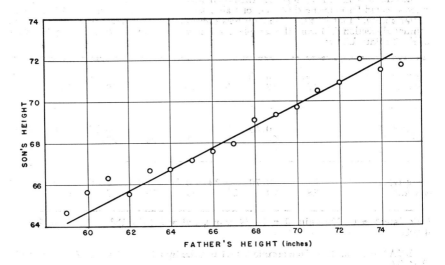

Fɪɢ. 6.12.1—Regression of son's stature on father's (12). $\hat{Y} = 0.516X + 33.73$. 1,078 families.

height of sons of a group of tall fathers is less than their father's height. There is a *regression*, or going back, of son's heights toward the average height of all men.

As part of Galton's evidence he reported the results of an experiment on the inheritance of size in sweet pea seeds. For planting he selected 100 seeds in each of seven size groups, then ascertained the average size of the offspring. He gives the following data on diameter of parent sweet peas and mean diameter of filial seeds: 21, 17.5; 20, 17.3; 19, 16.0; 18, 16.3; 17, 15.6; 16, 16.0; 15, 15.3; all measurements in hundredths of an inch.

The regression coefficient of filial size on parent size, that is Y on X, was 0.3. Galton thought that regression was generally about one-third, the average of the offspring deviating from the racial mean only about a third as much as the deviation of the same measurement in the lot of parents having a common measure.

If you are a student of genetics you will realize that this is not a simple phenomenon, involving as it does such concepts as heterozygosity, dominance, etc. An additional complexity in stature is the tendency toward the *selective mating* of men and women of similar stature. Apparently this law of universal regression summarizes those tendencies in a species to preserve its unique characteristics. If tall fathers begot taller daughters and tall daughters bore taller sons there would be no regression, and the two related concepts, *species* and *average*, would presumably not exist. The average of concentration in statistics is that measurement of a character toward which regression is directed, while the average of variation stays constant from generation to generation because of this regression.

EXAMPLE 6.12.1—Warren (20) investigated the magnitude of regression in parthenogenetic generations of aphids. He measured the frontal breadth in units of 0.0221 mm., the results for parents (X) and offspring (Y) being as follows: 14.8, 13.7; 18.4, 14.6; 17.5, 14.5; 16.3, 14.3; 16.9, 14.7; 15.8, 14.2; 15.4, 14.8; 15.2, 15.0; 15.9, 15.8; 16.1, 15.7; 16.3, 15.1; 16.7, 15.6; 17.0, 15.5; 17.8, 15.9; 18.1, 15.4; 18.5, 15.8; 18.9, 15.2; 15.8, 16.2; 16.0, 16.0; 16.2, 16.7; 16.6, 16.6; 16.8, 16.9; 17.5, 16.4; 18.2, 16.3; 18.8, 16.7; 19.0, 16.9; 15.7, 17.2; 16.1, 17.0; 16.5, 17.6; 16.8, 17.4; 17.1, 17.8; 17.7, 17.5; 18.0, 17.7; 18.8, 17.9; 19.5, 17.6; 16.0, 18.1; 17.5, 18.8; 19.0, 18.4; 18.9, 19.5. Compute the regression coefficient, 0.4469.

6.13—Regression Model IA: σ proportional to X, $a = 0$. The principle of least squares produces various models, varying partly according to the assumptions made about ϵ. In Models I and II the ϵ are randomly and independently drawn from a common σ. But not infrequently, σ varies with X. In the model now to be considered, σ is directly proportional to X; that is, $\sigma = kX$, or $\sigma/X = k$, some constant ratio. While this model has some utility in itself, the chief purpose for introducing it here is to throw light on the widespread practice of using rates and ratios instead of regression.

Model IA has only two characteristics different from Model I; $\sigma = kX$ and the regression line passes through the origin, $O(0, 0)$. The latter restriction applies to both the population and the sample lines.   The model, then, is

$$Y_{ij} = \beta X_i + \epsilon_{ij}, \, i = 1, 2, \ldots n, j = 1, 2, \ldots m,$$

where the subscripts specify the correspondence of the quantities to which they are attached and where ϵ_{ij} is randomly drawn from $\mathcal{N}(0, \sigma_i)$, $\sigma_i = kX_i$. The second subscript shows that m of the Y were drawn for each of the n values of X.

The data in table 6.13.1 are taken from a survey of the percentage of farm land in corn among eastern South Dakota farms in 1942.   Five of the more frequently occurring farm sizes were selected, then 5 records were drawn at random for each size.

In further explanation of the symbols used in the model, X_i is successively $X_1 = 80$, $X_2 = 160$, etc., i going from 1 to 5.   For each X_i, j also goes from 1 to 5.   As examples, $Y_{11} = 25$, $Y_{12} = 10$, $Y_{21} = 60$, $Y_{34} = 85$.

TABLE 6.13.1

NUMBER OF ACRES IN CORN ON 25 FARMS IN SOUTH DAKOTA (1942)

SELECTED BY FARM SIZE

Size of Farm (acres) X	Acres in Corn Y	Range	Standard Deviation s_y	Ratio s_y/X	Ratio Y/X
80	25				0.312
	10				.125
	20				.250
	32				.400
	20	22	8.05	0.101	.250
160	60				0.375
	35				.219
	20				.125
	45				.281
	40	40	14.58	0.091	.250
240	65				0.271
	80				.333
	65				.271
	85				.354
	30	55	21.51	0.090	.125
320	70				0.219
	110				.344
	30				.094
	55				.172
	60	80	29.15	0.091	.188
400	75				0.188
	35				.088
	140				.350
	90				.225
	110	105	39.21	0.098	.275
Mean	56.28				0.243

$$N = nm = 25, \quad b = \frac{\Sigma(Y/X)}{N} = 0.243 \text{ corn acre/farm acre}$$

The ranges of the several groups of Y indicate that σ is increasing with X. The same thing is shown in figure 6.13.1. To get more detailed information on this, s_y was calculated for each group, then the ratio of s_y to X. These ratios are so nearly constant as to justify the assumption that in the population σ/X is a constant. Also it seems reasonable to

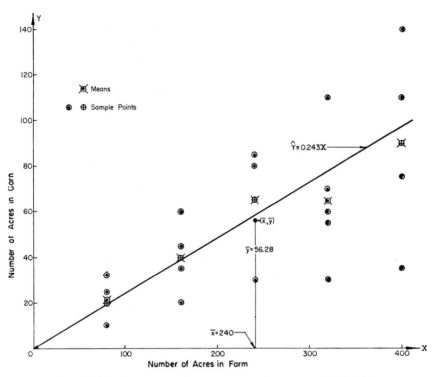

FIG. 6.13.1—Regression of corn acres on farm acres; Model IA.

suppose that $O(0, 0)$ is a point on the regression line. These two characteristics specify Model IA, it being taken for granted that the regression is linear and that the distributions sampled are normal.

Taking b as the least squares estimate of β, the sample regression equation is

$$\hat{Y} = bX$$

The computation of b is surprisingly different from that used heretofore; it is simply the mean of the sample ratios, Y/X, in the last column of the table. That is,

$$b = \frac{\Sigma(Y/X)}{N} = 0.243,$$

where N is the total number of observations, $N = nm$. The sample regression equation is $\hat{Y} = 0.243X$. The sample regression coefficient is the average increase in corn acres per acre increase in farm size. It is also the average ratio of corn acres to farm acres. In this way of thinking, $\hat{Y}/X = 0.243$ is the average of the individual farm ratios, Y/X. Notice that these ratios are somewhat stable, varying only from 0.088 to 0.400. This stability is attained because both the numerator Y and its standard deviation σ increase with X.

A characteristic of this Model IA is that the point $(\bar{x}, \bar{y})$ may not lie on the regression line. You will see that (240, 56.28) falls below the line in the figure. It is plain that $\bar{y}/\bar{x}$ is in general not the same as the mean of Y/X.

A confidence interval may be set on β and any relevant hypothesis about it may be tested by means of the sample standard deviation of the ratios Y/X. The inferences may not be exact because such ratios are usually not normally distributed, but this need not disturb us much. The mean square of the 25 ratios is calculated in the usual way, resulting in $s_{Y/x}^2 = 0.008069$. From this, the mean square of b is

$$s_b^2 = \frac{s_{Y/x}^2}{N} = \frac{0.008069}{25} = 0.0003228$$

$$s_b = 0.0180, \quad d.f. = N - 1 = 24$$

The 95% interval estimate of β is set in the usual manner:

$$b - t_{.05}\, s_b \leq \beta \leq b + t_{.05}\, s_b,$$

the result being $0.206 \leq \beta \leq 0.280$. In Model IA, this is also the interval estimate of the population mean ratio of Y to X.

If there were any hypothesis about β, it could be tested by calculating

$$t = \frac{b - \beta}{s_b}, \quad d.f. = N - 1$$

Other tests and estimates are complicated by the changing value of σ. The methods will not be given here but may be found in (6).

EXAMPLE 6.13.1—Dungan (7) studied the effect on yield consequent upon the removal of various fractions of the leaves of maize plants in Illinois. In one experiment the leaves were stripped off when the grain was in the milk stage, the total leaf area being reduced by $16\frac{2}{3}$, $33\frac{1}{3}$, 50, $66\frac{2}{3}$, $83\frac{1}{3}$ and 100% in six lots of plants. The corresponding reductions in the yield of shelled grain were 13, 17, 28, 22, 37, and 50%. Assuming a regression line through the origin and σ proportional to age, calculate, the sample regression of percentage yield reduction on percentage leaf reduction. Ans. $\hat{Y} = 0.52X$, $s_b = 0.06$.

6.14—On a common misuse of rates and ratios. In view of the extensive use of rates and ratios, it may be well to examine a situation in which the practice is questionable. Employing appropriate regression methods, Crampton (4) reported the gains in weight (Y) of pigs eating recorded amounts of feed (X). For his Lot I (table 6.14.1), $n = 10$,

TABLE 6.14.1
DATA ON LOT I OF CRAMPTON'S PIGS

Feed Eaten (pounds) X	Gain (pounds) Y	Ratio Y/X	Predicted Gains	
			Model I $\hat{Y} = 0.2627X - 22.1$	Model IA $\hat{Y} = 0.1999X$
382	66	0.1728	78.3	76.4
335	72	0.2149	65.9	67.0
388	84	0.2165	79.8	77.6
316	47	0.1487	60.9	63.2
319	75	0.2351	61.7	63.8
399	87	0.2180	82.7	79.8
358	75	0.2095	72.0	71.6
355	73	0.2056	71.2	71.0
344	59	0.1715	68.3	68.8
339	70	0.2065	67.0	67.8
Mean 353.5	70.8	0.1999	70.8	70.7

$\bar{x} = 353.5$ pounds of feed, $\bar{y} = 70.8$ pounds gain, $\Sigma x^2 = 7,334.5$, $\Sigma y^2 = 1,207.5$, $\Sigma xy = 1,927.0$. Figure 6.14.1 displays the scatter diagram with his sample regression, $\hat{Y} = 0.2627X - 22.1$. Crampton called attention to the fact that this regression does not contain the origin because feed is required to maintain the animal even with no increase in weight. Furthermore, the sample evidence admits the hypothesis of constant variance in Y over the range found, and there is no appreciable error in the measurement of X. It would seem correct, therefore, to employ regression Model I.

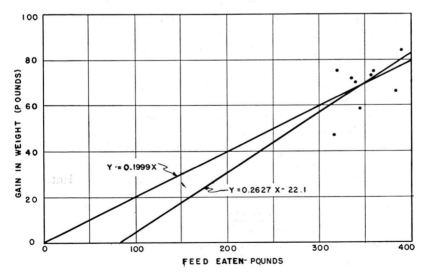

FIG. 6.14.1—Graph of regressions of gain on food consumed. Crampton's pigs, Lot I.

Yet many an experimenter confines his attention to the ratios, Y/X, ignoring the fact that he is inappropriately applying Model IA. He uses the mean, $b = 0.1999$ pounds gain per pound of feed consumed, without being aware that it underestimates the performance of pigs eating heavily and overestimates the others. He overlooks the passage of the Model IA regression through the origin, contrary to the manner in which the pigs grow.

Another consequence of the incorrect use of Model IA is that the changing value of Y/X is lost sight of. In this model, Y/X is assumed constant for all X, but in the correct Model I, Y/X increases with X. This is shown by calculating the sample regression equation, $\hat{Y} = 0.2627X - 22.1$, then dividing by X:

$$\frac{\hat{Y}}{X} = 0.2627 - \frac{22.1}{X}$$

Clearly, $\hat{Y}/X$ increases with X; that is, the efficiency of gain is greater for the heavier eating pigs. To use Model IA in this kind of situation is to lose some of the information contained in the experimental data.

Unless there is reason to believe that the regression equation contains the origin and that σ is directly proportional to X, the ratio, Y/X, is of dubious value. It may do for rough work but careful experimental procedure deserves the more efficient statistical method.

6.15—Summary. For Models I and II, the most widely used, the 6 sample values, n, $\bar{x}$, $\bar{y}$, Σx^2, Σy^2, Σxy, furnish all regression information:

1. The regression coefficient of Y on X: $b = \Sigma xy / \Sigma x^2$.
2. The sample regression equation of Y on X: $\hat{Y} = a + bX$.
3. Y adjusted for X: Adjusted $Y = Y - bx$.
4. The sum of squares attributable to regression:
   $(\Sigma xy)^2 / \Sigma x^2 = \Sigma \hat{y}^2$.
5. The sum of squares of deviations from regression:
   $\Sigma y^2 - (\Sigma xy)^2 / \Sigma x^2 = \Sigma d_{y \cdot x}^2$.
6. The mean square deviation from regression:
   $\Sigma d_{y \cdot x}^2 / (n - 2) = s_{y \cdot x}^2$.
7. The sample standard error of Y estimated from X:
   $s_{\bar{y} \cdot x} = s_{y \cdot x} / \sqrt{n}$.
8. The sample standard deviation of the regression coefficient:
   $s_b = s_{y \cdot x} / \sqrt{\Sigma x^2}$.
9. The sample standard deviation of $\hat{Y}$:
   $s_{\hat{y}} = s_{y \cdot x} \sqrt{1/n + x^2 / \Sigma x^2}$.
10. The sample standard deviation of Y:
    $s_Y = s_{y \cdot x} \sqrt{1 + 1/n + x^2 / \Sigma x^2}$.

REFERENCES

1. R. L. ANDERSON and T. A. BANCROFT. Statistical Theory in Research. McGraw-Hill Book Company, Inc., New York (1952).

2. A. E. BRANDT. Journal of the American Statistical Association, 23:291 (1928).

3. E. V. COLLINS. Transactions, American Society of Agricultural Engineers, 14:39 (1920).

4. EARLE WILCOX CRAMPTON. Journal of Nutrition, 7:305 (1934).

5. BEN DAWES. Journal of Experimental Biology, 18:26 (1941).

6. W. EDWARDS DEMING. Statistical Adjustment of Data. John Wiley and Sons, Inc., New York (1943).

7. GEORGE H. DUNGAN. Plant Physiology, 9:749 (1934)

8. R. A. FISHER. Statistical Methods for Research Workers. Oliver and Boyd, Edinburgh (1925–50).

9. FRANCES GALTON. Natural Inheritance. Macmillan and Company, London (1889).

10. T. ROY HANSBERRY and CHARLES H. RICHARDSON. Iowa State Journal of Science, 10:27 (1935).

11. J. R. HOLBERT, W. P. FLINT, J. H. BIGGER, and G. H. DUNGAN. Iowa State Journal of Science, 9:413 (1935)

12. M. T. JENKINS. Journal of the American Society of Agronomy, (1934).

13. M. G. KENDALL. The Advanced Theory of Statistics. Charles Griffin and Company, Ltd., London (1947).

14. ALEXANDER MCFARLANE MOOD. Introduction to the Theory of Statistics. McGraw-Hill Book Company, Inc., New York (1950).

15. KARL PEARSON and ALICE LEE. Biometrika, 2:357 (1903).

16. GEORGE W. SNEDECOR and W. R. BRENEMAN. Iowa State Journal of Science, 19:333 (1945).

17. ARVIL L. STARK. Plant Physiology, 8:168 (1933).

18. PEARL P. SWANSON, RUTH LEVERTON, MARY GRAM, HARRIETT ROBERTS, and ISABEL PESEK. Journal of Gerontology, 10:41 (1955).

19. H. A. WALLACE and GEORGE W. SNEDECOR. Correlation and Machine Calculation. Iowa State University Official Publication 30, No. 4 (1931).

20. ERNEST WARREN. Biometrika, 1:129 (1902).

21. J. B. WENTZ and R. T. STEWART. Journal of the American Society of Agronomy, 16:534 (1924).

CHAPTER 7

Correlation

7.1—Introduction. Bivariate populations are often interesting, not because one quantity is to be predicted from the other, but because of the mutual relationship between the measurements. Some evaluation of this relation is needed even if there is no reason for thinking of one variable as dependent on the other. Galton's proposal of this problem sprang from his study of inherited characteristics, a study attaining scientific rank during the latter half of the nineteenth century. Biologists and mathematicians vied with each other in developing the theory and its applications. It turned out that the subject of *correlation*, as it came to be called, acquired a group of the concepts of regression, so that in many writings the two are scarcely distinguished.

Correlations among stature, span, and cubit (length of forearm) were reported by Pearson and Lee (17), who collected data from more than a thousand British families. The measurements of brother and sister heights in table 7.1.1 are selected to illustrate one of their tables. Since there is here no distinction between the dependence of the two variables, they are designated merely as X_1 and X_2 instead of X and Y. You will have no difficulty in verifying the calculation of the sums of squares and products. The new feature is the *sample correlation coefficient*, universally symbolized by

TABLE 7.1.1
STATURE (INCHES) OF BROTHER AND SISTER
Illustration taken from Pearson and Lee's sample of 1,401 families

Family Number	1	2	3	4	5	6	7	8	9	10	11
Brother, X_1	71	68	66	67	70	71	70	73	72	65	66
Sister, X_2	69	64	65	63	65	62	65	64	66	59	62

$n = 11$, $\bar{x}_1 = 69$, $\bar{x}_2 = 64$, $\Sigma x_1^2 = 74$, $\Sigma x_2^2 = 66$, $\Sigma x_1 x_2 = 39$

$r = \Sigma x_1 x_2 / \sqrt{(\Sigma x_1^2)(\Sigma x_2^2)} = 39/\sqrt{(74)(66)} = 0.558$. Pearson and Lee's $r = 0.553$

r. It is a numeralization of that commonly observed similarity among children of the same parents, the tendency of the taller sisters to have the taller brothers. This is represented graphically by a diagram such as figure 7.1.1. The value, $r = 0.558$, reflects the propensity of the dots to

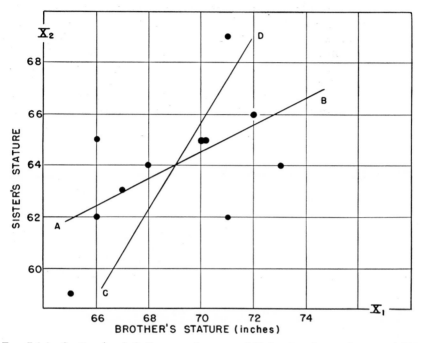

Fɪɢ. 7.1.1—Scatter (or dot) diagram of stature of 11 brother-sister pairs. $r = 0.558$.

lie in a band extending from lower left to upper right, not scattered randomly over the whole field. These points are confined to an elliptical area with the major axis inclined upward toward the right. Biologically, $r = 0.558$ measures the common inheritance of stature by these siblings.

EXAMPLE 7.1.1—Calculate $r = 1$ for the following pairs:
  X_1: 1, 2, 3, 4, 5
  X_2: 3, 5, 7, 9, 11
Represent the data in a graph similar to figure 7.1.1.

EXAMPLE 7.1.2—Verify $r = 0.91$ in the pairs:
  X_1: 2, 5, 6, 8, 10, 12, 14, 15, 18, 20
  X_2: 1, 2, 2, 3, 2, 4, 3, 4, 4, 5
Plot the elliptical band of points.

EXAMPLE 7.1.3—In the following, show that $r = 0.20$:
  X_1: 3, 5, 8, 11, 12, 12, 17
  X_2: 11, 5, 6, 8, 7, 18, 9
Observe the scatter of the points in a diagram.

EXAMPLE 7.1.4—In the apple data of table 6.7.1, $\Sigma x^2 = 924$, $\Sigma y^2 = 1{,}222$, $\Sigma xy = -936$. Calculate $r = -0.88$.

7.2—The sample correlation coefficient, *r*. The expression, $\Sigma x_1 x_2/\sqrt{(\Sigma x_1^2)(\Sigma x_2^2)}$, is designed to vary between -1 and $+1$ according to the closeness of the relationship in the population sampled. Negative values of r, like those of b, indicate an inclination of the ellipse of points downward toward the right, large values of one variable being associated with small values of the other. To help you acquire some experience of the nature of r, a number of simple tables with the corresponding graphs are displayed in figure 7.2.1. In each of these tables $n = 9$, $\bar{x}_1 = 12$, $\bar{x}_2 = 6$, $\Sigma x_1^2 = 576$, $\Sigma x_2^2 = 144$. Only $\Sigma x_1 x_2$ changes, and with it the value of r. Since $\sqrt{(\Sigma x_1^2)(\Sigma x_2^2)} = \sqrt{(576)(144)} = 288$, the correlation is easily evaluated in the several tables by calculating $\Sigma x_1 x_2$ and dividing by 288 (or multiplying by $1/288 = 0.0034722 \ldots$ if a machine is used).

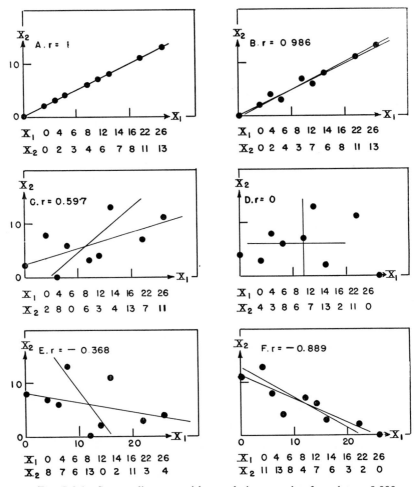

FIG. 7.2.1—Scatter diagrams with correlations ranging from 1 to -0.889.

In *A*, the nine points lie on a straight line, the condition for $r = 1$. The line is a "degenerate" ellipse—it has length but no width. In this relation between the two variables they keep in perfect step, any change in one being accompanied by a proportionate change in the other. *B* depicts some deviation from linearity, the ellipse being long and thin with r slightly reduced below 1. In *C*, the ellipse widens, then reaches circularity in *D* where $r = 0$. This denotes no relation between the two variables. *E* and *F* show negative correlations tending towards -1. To summarize, the thinness of the ellipse of points exhibits the magnitude of r, while the inclination of the axis upward or downward shows its sign. It should be observed that the slope of the axis is determined by the scales of measurement adopted for the two axes of the graph and is therefore not a reliable indicator of the magnitude of r. It is the concentration of the points near the axis of the ellipse that signifies high correlation, especially if the regression is large.

I think you will agree that the larger correlations, either positive or negative, are fairly obvious from the graphs. It is not so easy to make a visual evaluation if the absolute value of r is less than 0.5; even the direction of inclination of the ellipse may elude you if r is between -0.3 and $+0.3$. In these small samples a single dot can make a lot of difference. In *D*, for example, if the point (26, 0) were changed to (26, 9), r would be increased to 0.505. This emphasizes the fact that sample correlations from a bivariate population in which the correlation is ρ (the Greek rho distinguishes the parameter from the statistic) are quite variable if n is small. The sampling distribution of r will be considered in section 7.5. In assessing the value of r in a table, select some extreme values of one variable and note whether they are associated with extreme values of the other. If no such tendency can be detected, r is likely small.

Perfect correlation ($r = 1$) rarely occurs in biological data, though values as high as 0.99 are not unheard of. Each field of investigation has its own range of coefficients. Inherited characteristics like height ordinarily have correlations between 0.35 and 0.55. Among high school grades r averages around 0.35 (3). Pearson and Lee got "organic correlations," that is, correlations between two such measurements as stature and span *in the same person*, ranging from 0.60 to 0.83. Brandt (2) calculated the sample correlation, 0.986, between live weight and warm dressed weight of 533 swine. Evvard *et al.* (6) estimated $r = -0.68$ between average daily gain of swine and feed required per pound gained.

It is clear that judgment about the size of a correlation should be made in the light of similar correlations encountered in the same field, sometimes with little reference to the theoretical limits, ± 1.

7.3—The bivariate normal population: Model II in regression.
It has been assumed that r is based on a sample from some two-variable population, but so far little has been said about the structure of it (section 6.7). This structure is most easily shown by a large sample such as the

one displayed in table 7.3.1. The data are from the article by Galton (10) in 1888 where "co-relation" was first proposed.

To be observed in the table are these five features: (i) Each row and each column in the body of the table is a frequency distribution. Also, the column at the right, headed f_2, is the total frequency distribution of X_2, length of forearm, and the third-to-the-last row below is that of X_1, height. (ii) The frequencies are concentrated in an elliptical area with the major axis inclined upward to the right. There are no very short men with long forearms nor any very tall men with short forearms. (iii) The frequencies pile up along the major axis, reaching a peak near the center of the distribution. They thin out around the edges, vanishing entirely beyond the borders of the ellipse. (iv) The center of the table is at $\bar{x}_1 = 67.5$ inches, $\bar{x}_2 = 18.1$ inches. This point happens to fall in the cell containing the greatest frequency, 28 men. (v) The bivariate frequency histogram can be presented graphically by erecting a column over each cell in the table, the heights of columns being proportional to the cell frequencies. The tallest column could be in the center, surrounded with shorter columns. The heights would decrease toward the perimeter of the ellipse, with no columns at all beyond the edges. A ridge of tall columns would extend along the major axis.

The shape of the bivariate normal population now becomes clear if you imagine an indefinite increase in the total frequency with a corresponding decrease in the areas of the table cells. A smooth surface would overspread the table, rising to its greatest height at the center (μ_1, μ_2), fading away to tangency with the XY plane at infinite distances away.

Some of the properties of this new model are as follows: (i) Each section perpendicular to the X_1 axis is a normal distribution, and likewise, each section perpendicular to the X_2 axis. This means that each column and each row in table 7.3.1 is a sample from a normal frequency distribution. (ii) The frequency distributions perpendicular to the X_1 axis all have the same standard deviation, $\sigma_{2.1}$, and they have means all lying on a straight regression line, $\mu_{2.1} = a_2 + \beta_{2.1}X_1$. (These are the properties of Model II in chapter 6.) The sample means and standard deviations are recorded in the last two lines of the table. While there is considerable variation in $s_{2.1}$, each is an estimate of the common parameter, $\sigma_{2.1}$. (iii) The frequency distributions perpendicular to the X_2 axis have a common standard deviation, $\sigma_{1.2}$ (note the estimators in the right-hand column of the table), and their means lie on a second regression line, $\mu_{1.2} = a_1 + \beta_{1.2}X_2$. (To this there was no corresponding property in Model I of chapter 6.) Both of the sample regression lines have been drawn in figures 7.1.1 and 7.2.1. (iv) Each border frequency distribution is normal. That on the right is $N(\mu_2, \sigma_2)$, while the one below the body of the table is $N(\mu_1, \sigma_1)$.) (v) The distribution of the bivariate frequency distribution has the coefficient, $1/2\pi\sigma_1\sigma_2\sqrt{1-\rho^2}$, followed by e with this exponent:

$$-1/(2)(1-\rho^2)[(X_1-\mu_1)^2/\sigma_1{}^2 - 2\rho(X_1-\mu_1)(X_2-\mu_2)/\sigma_1\sigma_2 + (X_2-\mu_2)^2/\sigma_2{}^2]$$

TABLE 7.3.1

FREQUENCY OF PAIRS OF MEASUREMENTS OF HEIGHT AND LENGTH OF FOREARM. GALTON'S DATA WITH THE OUTER CLASSES DISTRIBUTED IN PROPORTION TO TABLE 9 BY PEARSON AND LEE

Height in Inches, X_1

Length of Forearm X_2	59–60	60–61	61–62	62–63	63–64	64–65	65–66	66–67	67–68	68–69	69–70	70–71	71–72	72–73	73–74	74–75	f_2	$\bar{x}_{1.2}$	$s_{1.2}$
21.0–21.5																1	1	74.4	0.00
20.5–21.0													1	1			2	72.0	0.71
20.0–20.5														1			1	72.4	0.00
19.5–20.0										2			1		2		5	71.0	2.51
19.0–19.5									2	4	6	11	8	4	2	1	38	70.6	1.62
18.5–19.0					1		2	6	8	7	15	13	2	1			55	68.8	1.77
18.0–18.5						3	8	15	28	14	25	5	2	2			102	68.0	1.67
17.5–18.0				2	1	2	12	18	15	7	2	1	1				61	66.7	1.62
17.0–17.5			1	3	6	11	10	7	7	3	1						49	65.4	1.80
16.5–17.0			1	5	6	5	4	1	1	1	1						25	64.4	1.97
16.0–16.5	1	1	1	3	2												8	62.0	1.41
15.5–16.0		1															1	60.4	0.00
Frequency, f_1	1	2	3	13	16	21	36	47	61	38	50	30	15	9	4	2	348		
Mean, $\bar{x}_{2.1}$	16.2	16.0	16.8	16.9	17.1	17.3	17.7	17.9	18.1	18.3	18.4	18.8	19.1	20.2	19.5	20.2	18.1		
Std. Dev., $s_{2.1}$	0.0	0.36	0.50	0.52	0.60	0.48	0.54	0.42	0.51	0.68	0.48	0.41	0.70	0.83	0.29	1.41	0.905		

This distribution has five parameters. Four of them are familiar in character; μ_1, μ_2, σ_1, σ_2. The fifth is the correlation coefficient, ρ, of which r is an estimator.

The parameter, ρ, measures the closeness of the relation between X_1 and X_2; that is, it determines the elongation or narrowness of the ellipse containing the major portion of the observations; its effect in samples was indicated in figure 7.2.1. In the height-forearm table, ρ is estimated by $r = 0.7$. For tables like 7.3.1, the calculation of the estimators will be explained in section 8.9.

Small sample calculations have been presented already. One added word about them: If the data have been coded (section 5.4), the correlation coefficient may be computed directly from the coded sums of squares and products. Unlike the regression coefficient, r does not require the decoding of the calculated values. For example, in table 6.9.3, $r = 735.2/\sqrt{(674.1)(832.4)} = 0.98$. The same result would attend the use of the decoded values, $r = 1{,}470.4/\sqrt{(26.96)(83{,}240)}$.

EXAMPLE 7.3.1—Make a graph of $\bar{x}_{2.1}$ in the next-to-the-last line of table 7.3.1. The values of X_1 are the class marks at the top of the columns. The first class mark may be taken as 59.5 inches. Compare your graph with figure 6.12.1.

EXAMPLE 7.3.2—Graph the $\bar{x}_{1.2}$ on the same sheet with that of $\bar{x}_{2.1}$. The class marks for X_2 are laid off on the vertical axis. The first class mark may be taken as 21.25 inches. If you are surprised that the two regression lines are different, remember that $\bar{x}_{2.1}$ is the mean of a column while $\bar{x}_{1.2}$ is the mean of a row. The pairs have only one measure in common, that of the cell which is at the intersection of the row and column.

EXAMPLE 7.3.3—Graph $s_{2.1}$ against X_1. You will see that there is no trend, indicating that all the $s_{2.1}$ may be random samples from a common $\sigma_{2.1}$.

EXAMPLE 7.3.4—The data in example 6.7.3 may be taken as a random sample from a bivariate normal population. You had $\bar{x} = 83$ grams, $\bar{y} = 60$ mg., $\Sigma x^2 = 1{,}000$, $\Sigma y^2 = 6{,}854$, $\Sigma xy = 2{,}302$. Calculate the regression of body weight, X, on comb weight, Y. Ans. $\hat{X} = 83 + 0.336\,(Y - 60)$ grams. Draw the graph of this line along with that of example 6.7.4. Notice that the angle whose tangent is 0.336 is measured from the Y axis.

EXAMPLE 7.3.5—In the chick experiment, estimate $\sigma_{y \cdot x}$. Ans. $s_{y \cdot x} = 13.9$ mg. Also estimate $\sigma_{x \cdot y}$. Ans. $s_{x \cdot y} = 15.1$ grams. In $s_{x \cdot y}$, the deviations from regression are measured horizontally.

EXAMPLE 7.3.6—From the chick data, estimate ρ. Ans. $r = 0.88$.

EXAMPLE 7.3.7—Grout (11) measured the wing length and tongue length, both in millimeters, of 44 bees:

Wing	9.68	9.81	9.59	9.68	9.84	9.59	9.61	9.55	9.25	9.08	9.70
Tongue	6.53	6.71	6.70	6.69	6.70	6.62	6.59	6.55	6.35	6.25	6.61
	9 60	9.50	9.74	9.72	9.64	9.73	9.77	9.72	9.54	9.65	9.74
	6 51	6.55	6 74	6.75	6 45	6.75	6.70	6.65	6.68	6.77	6.44
	9 59	9.71	9.56	9.61	9 61	9.55	9.78	9.74	9.48	9.71	9.20
	6 54	6.64	6.55	6.57	6.61	6.64	6.64	6.63	6.62	6.55	6.22
	9.53	9.74	9.67	9.56	9.49	9.64	9.45	9.52	9.58	9.60	9.68
	6.43	6.67	6.68	6.62	6.71	6.70	6.50	6.41	6.50	6.62	6.69

Code by subtracting 9 from each wing length and 6 from each tongue length. Calculate $r = 0.731$.

EXAMPLE 7.3.8—Thirty students scored as follows in two mathematics achievement tests:

I	73	41	83	71	39	60	51	41	85	88	44	71	52	74	50
II	29	24	34	27	24	26	35	18	33	39	27	35	25	29	13

	42	85	53	85	44	66	60	33	43	76	51	57	35	40	76
	13	40	23	40	22	25	21	26	19	29	25	19	17	17	35

Calculate $r = 0.774$.

EXAMPLE 7.3.9—After reviewing examples 5.3.3, 5.3.4, and 5.3.5, prove that if $Y = a + bX$ and $U = c + dZ$, then $r_{yu} = \pm r_{xz}$.

7.4—Relation between the sample coefficients of correlation and regression. If X_2 were designated as dependent, its regression on X_1 would be $b_{21} = \Sigma x_1 x_2 / \Sigma x_1^2$, but if X_1 were dependent, the regression of X_1 on X_2 would become $b_{12} = \Sigma x_1 x_2 / \Sigma x_2^2$. These expressions differ in their denominators only. The regression lines corresponding to the two circumstances are drawn in the several diagrams of figure 7.2.1. If r is near ± 1, the lines are close together, becoming identical in A; if $r = 0$, they are perpendicular. Note: if X_2 is the independent variable, the slope, b_{12}, is measured from the X_2 axis, vertical in the figures. The regression of X_1 on X_2 is always the line that makes the lesser angle with the vertical axis.

Now, it is easily seen that

$$b_{21}b_{12} = \frac{\Sigma x_1 x_2}{\Sigma x_1^2} \frac{\Sigma x_1 x_2}{\Sigma x_2^2} = \frac{(\Sigma x_1 x_2)^2}{\Sigma x_1^2 \Sigma x_2^2} = r^2$$

Thus,

$$r = \sqrt{b_{21}b_{12}}$$

In other words, r is the *geometric mean* of the two regression coefficients that might be calculated; it is intermediate in value between them. Let us illustrate.

If we were interested in estimating the statures of sisters from those of their brothers, we should have (table 7.1.1),

$b_{21} = 39/74 = 0.527$ inch sister's height per inch brother's, graphed as AB in figure 7.1.1. On the other hand, if the interest were in estimating brothers' heights,

$b_{12} = 39/66 = 0.591$ inch brother's height per inch sister's, the regression line being CD. Usually, however, it is the mutual relationship that attracts attention because this is taken to represent the heritability of stature, so we calculate

$$r = \sqrt{(0.527)(0.591)} = 0.558,$$

an average of the two regression coefficients.

This serves to clarify the relation of the two coefficients, correlation and regression, in measuring relationship. The latter is the appropriate one if one variable, Y, may be designated as dependent upon the other, X. Y may be partly controlled or caused by X, as when the available amounts of some glandular secretion cause differences in the sizes of organisms. Or, Y may be subsequent to X, as weight gain in nutrition experiments follows the measurement of initial weight. In such cases, the regression of Y on X is usually the statistic that furnishes the information desired. It is then appropriate to attempt to estimate the value of Y from a knowledge of the corresponding value of X. Correlation, on the other hand, is the appropriate measure of the relation between two variables like statures of sister and brother. The two heights are known to be associated through the complex mechanism of inheritance, but neither may be looked upon as a consequence of the other; they are both consequences of common elements. In this sense correlation is a two-way average of relationship, while regression is directional. Of course, there are many variables whose relation may be studied by means of either correlation or regression, or both. It is necessary only to keep clearly in mind the character of the relation being considered.

A characteristic of r is revealed by dividing both numerator and denominator of the ratio by $n - 1$:

$$r = \frac{\Sigma x_1 x_2}{\sqrt{(\Sigma x_1^2)(\Sigma x_2^2)}} = \frac{\dfrac{\Sigma x_1 x_2}{n-1}}{\sqrt{\dfrac{\Sigma x_1^2}{n-1}\cdot\dfrac{\Sigma x_2^2}{n-1}}} = \frac{\text{covariance}}{\sqrt{(s_1^2)(s_2^2)}}$$

$$= \frac{\text{covariance}}{\text{geometric mean of variances}}$$

Correlation is thus seen to be the quotient of two averages of variation: one, the covariance of the two measurements, X_1 and X_2; the other, an average of the two sample variances (i.e., mean squares). It is an abstract number measuring *covariation*: if of two related characters each occurs in various sizes, their correlation is a measure of the extent to which their variations are concomitant.

Similarly, b takes on new meaning from the changes below:

$$b_{12} = \frac{\Sigma xy}{\Sigma x^2} = \frac{\Sigma xy}{\sqrt{\Sigma x^2 \Sigma y^2}}\cdot\frac{\sqrt{\Sigma y^2}}{\sqrt{\Sigma x^2}} = r\frac{\sqrt{\Sigma y^2/(n-1)}}{\sqrt{\Sigma x^2/(n-1)}} = r\frac{s_y}{s_x}$$

In this manner b is intimately related to r. Either can be calculated from the other if the sample standard deviations of the two variables are known.

It is often convenient to use the sample standard deviation as the unit for measuring the deviate, $x = X - \bar{x}$. The *standard deviate*, $x' = x/s$, may be thought of as randomly drawn from $\mathcal{N}(0, 1)$. As an example, suppose two aptitude tests have been applied, one to fourth grade and the other to sixth grade pupils. Designate the tests as IV and VI. Now IV may have $\bar{x} = 40$ and $s = 10$, while VI has $\bar{x} = 60$, $s = 20$. If pupil A scores 60 in IV and his brother B is graded 80 in VI, their standard deviates (or standard measures),

$$A: x' = \frac{60 - 40}{10} = 2, \qquad B: x' = \frac{80 - 60}{20} = 1,$$

show their relative standing in the tests.

It is clear that every sample of standard deviates has $\bar{x}' = 0$ and $s' = 1$. Take for illustration the set,

$$X: \quad 6, \ 6, \ 2, \ 8, \ 6, \ 8, \ 6$$

Since the mean is 6, the deviations are

$$x: \quad 0, \ 0, \ -4, \ 2, \ 0, \ 2, \ 0$$

Now, $s = 2$, so the set of standard deviates is

$$x': \quad 0, \ 0, \ -2, \ 1, \ 0, \ 1, \ 0,$$

in which $\bar{x}' = 0$ and $s' = 1$.

It may be interesting to write the sample regression of section 6.4 in this form:

$$\hat{Y} - \bar{y} = b(X - \bar{x})$$

If we now put $\hat{y} = \hat{Y} - \bar{y}$ and $x = X - \bar{x}$, we have:

$$\hat{y} = bx = r \cdot \frac{s_y}{s_x} \cdot x$$

Substituting standard measure for each variable, we have the simple form,

$$\hat{y} = rx',$$

because $s_y = s_x = 1$, and r is therefore the same as b. Thus, in standard measure r is the regression coefficient, the average change in y' per standard deviation change in x'. We have already noticed that r is unaffected by units of measurement. Now it appears that if we use standard measure, also independent of units of measurements, the distinction between the correlation and regression coefficients disappears.

7.5—Sampling variation of the correlation coefficient. Common elements. A convenient way to draw samples from a normal bivariate population is by use of an old device called *common elements* (7). You may go back to the random sampling scheme of section 3.3, or to the samples already drawn from table 3.2.1. In a new table, such as 7.5.1, record some convenient number, say three, of the random pig gains. These gains, or

TABLE 7.5.1

CALCULATION OF THREE PAIRS OF VALUES OF THE VARIABLES X_1 AND X_2 HAVING COMMON ELEMENTS

The elements are pig gains from table 3.2.1

Pair	Elements		
1	23 44 ← common → 43 37 ← different →	23 44 43 30 33	
	$X_1 = 147$	$173 = X_2$	
2	40 16 ← common → 19 30 ← different →	40 16 19 29 13	
	$X_1 = 105$	$117 = X_2$	
3	23 38 ← common → 37 30 ← different →	23 38 37 31 41	
	$X_1 = 128$	$170 = X_2$	

elements, are written twice in the table. Then continue the drawing, adding, for example, one more randomly drawn gain to the left-hand column, and two more to the right. The sums constitute the paired values of X_1 and X_2. Three uch pairs are computed in the table. It is clear that there is a relation between the two sums in each pair. If the three common elements all happen to be large. then both X_1 and X_2 are likely large, irrespective of the extra elements contained in each. Naturally, owing to the noncommon elements, the relation is not perfect If you continue this process, drawing a hundred or more pairs, then compute the correlation, you will get a value of r not greatly different from the population value,

$$\rho = 3/\sqrt{(4)(5)} = 0.67$$

The numerator of this fraction is the number of common elements, while the denominator is the geometric mean of the total numbers of elements in the two sums, X_1 and X_2. A formula may be written for this parameter. If n_{12} represents the number of common elements, with n_1 and n_2 designating the total numbers of elements making up the two sums, then the correlation between these two sums is theoretically,

$$\rho = n_{12}/\sqrt{n_1 n_2}$$

Of course, there will be sampling variation in the values calculated from drawings. You may be lucky enough to get a good verification with only 10 or 20 pairs of sums. With 50 pairs we have usually got a coefficient within a few hundredths of the expected parameter, but once we got 0.28 when the population was

$$n_{12}/\sqrt{n_1 n_2} = 6/\sqrt{(9)(16)} = 0.5$$

If you put the same numbers of elements into X_1 and X_2, then $n_1 = n_2$. Denoting this common number of total elements by n, the parameter may be symbolized by

$$\rho = n_{12}/n,$$

the ratio of the number of common elements to the total number in each sum. In this special case, the correlation coefficient is simply the fraction of the elements which are common. Roughly, this is the interpretation of the sister-brother correlation in stature (table 7.1.1), usually not far from 0.5: an average of some 50% of the genes determining height are common to sister and brother.

Another illustration of this special case arises from the determination of some physical or chemical constant by two alternative methods. As an example, consider the estimation of the potassium content of the expressed sap of corn stems as made by two methods, the colorimetric and the gravimetric (15). Two samples are taken from the same source, one being treated by each of the two techniques. The common elements in the two results must be associated with the actual weights of potassium in the pair of samples. Extraneous elements may be attributed to the differences in the accuracy with which the potassium is determined by the two procedures, as well as to the random variation in the two samples. The sample correlation between 24 pairs of determinations was 0.87. On the assumption that each determination is the sum of some constant number of elements chosen at random from a homogeneous population, it may be asserted that 87% of the elements in the two determinations are common. Thus, 87% of the elements are associated with the actual weight of potassium in the sap, the remaining 13% being attributed to errors of measurement and sampling variation.

A less specific illustration is contained in the correlation, $r = 0.70$, between the weights of cob and grain in 250 ears of Country Gentleman sweet corn (12). If you are willing to postulate an equal number of elements determining cob weight and grain weight, then 70% of them may be common. But what are they? Some of them inherited, perhaps, and some environmental.

The reader will have no difficulty in extending this list of illustrations. The disturbing necessity is to keep in mind the limitations. The elements in the two variables must not only be equal in number, but must be drawn from a normally distributed population. Further, the effects of the elements must be describable by a sum. If one element, included by chance, should double the effects of other elements, then the interpretation would be faulty. Despite these limitations, the careful thinker can greatly enhance his ideas of correlation by this concept of common elements.

Unless there is the same unit of measurement in X_1 and X_2, there is little hope of applying the theory of common elements. For instance, in Dungan's study of hail injury to maize (example 6 13.1), while both the variables are percentages, yet one is based on areas, the other on weights. It would be hard to specify the nature of the common elements, though undoubtedly there are some.

When you have carried through one or more of the calculations of r with common elements, you are well aware of the sampling variation of this statistic. However, it would be too tedious a task to compute enough coefficients to gain even a rough picture of the distribution curve. This must be left to the mathematicians to be done from theoretical considerations. In figure 7.5.1 are the curves for samples of 8 drawn from popula-

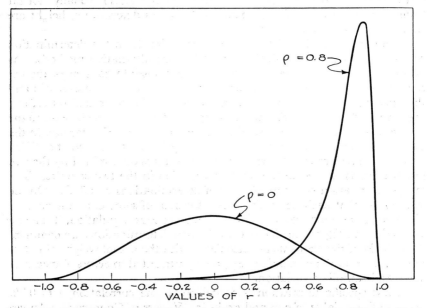

Fig. 7.5.1—Distribution of sample correlation coefficients in samples of 8 pairs drawn from two normally distributed bivariate populations having the indicated values of ρ.

tions with correlations zero and 0.8. Even the former is not quite normal. The reason for the pronounced skewness of the latter is not hard to see. Since the parameter is 0.8, sample values can exceed this by no more than 0.2, but may be in defect of it by as much as 1.8. Wherever there is a limit to the variation of a statistic at one end of the scale, with practically none at the other, the distribution curve is likely to be asymmetrical. Of course, with increasing sample size this skewness tends to disappear. Samples of 300 pairs, drawn from a population with a correlation even so great as 0.8, would have little tendency to range more than 0.05 on either side of the parameter. Consequently, the upper limit, unity, would not constitute a restriction, and the distribution would be almost normal.

EXAMPLE 7.5.1—Suppose all the elements of X_1 are included in X_2. Then $n_{12} = n_1$ and $\rho = \sqrt{n_1/n_2}$. This is the relation that may exist when the whole, X_2, is correlated with one of its parts, X_1. An example is the correlation between the live weight and warm dressed weight of swine (2). Among the 533 animals studied, the mean live weight was 222.6 pounds while the mean dressed weight was 185.1 pounds. If one assumes that each pound of dressed weight represents a common element, then r might be an estimate of $\sqrt{185.1/222.6} = 0.91$. Compare this with the sample $r = 0.986$ and the discussion of section 7.11.

EXAMPLE 7.5.2—In a tea plantation (5), the production of 16 plots during one 14-week period was correlated with the production of the same plots in the following period of equal length. The correlation coefficient was 0.91. Can you interpret this in terms of common elements?

7.6—Estimating the correlation coefficient: confidence statements and tests of hypotheses.

If random samples are drawn from a normal bivariate population with correlation, ρ, the statistic, r, is an appropriate estimate of ρ. Errors in either X_1 or X_2 will bias the coefficient. Unlike regression samples, neither X_1 nor X_2 may be selected. You see, then, that in samples such as the soybean heights of example 6.4.1, the correlation coefficient provides no estimate of ρ because X_1 is selected. This is a marked distinction between samplings for estimating β and ρ.

Fisher (8) showed that the null hypothesis, $\rho = 0$, may be tested by use of t whose sample value is

$$t = r\sqrt{(n-2)/(1-r^2)}, \quad d.f. = n - 2$$

For illustration, assume that the $r = 0.597$ in C of figure 7.2.1 is randomly drawn under the conditions specified above. What is the probability of a larger $|r|$ in sampling from $\rho = 0$? We have

$$t = 0.597\sqrt{(9-2)/(1-0.597^2)} = 1.969, \quad d.f. = 7$$

Interpolation in the t-table elicits the approximate probability, 0.09, of a larger value of t. Hence, a greater value of $|r|$ could happen about 9 times per 100 in sampling from $\rho = 0$, and the null hypothesis would not likely be rejected. This throws light on the difficulty (section 7.2) of graphical evaluation of small correlations, especially if the number of degrees of freedom is small—they may be no more than accidents of sampling (see example 7.7.4).

TABLE 7.6.1

CORRELATION COEFFICIENTS AT THE 5% AND 1% LEVELS OF SIGNIFICANCE

Degrees of Freedom	5%	1%	Degrees of Freedom	5%	1%
1	.997	1.000	24	.388	.496
2	.950	.990	25	.381	.487
3	.878	.959	26	.374	.478
4	.811	.917	27	.367	.470
5	.754	.874	28	.361	.463
6	.707	.834	29	.355	.456
7	.666	.798	30	.349	.449
8	.632	.765	35	.325	.418
9	.602	.735	40	.304	.393
10	.576	.708	45	.288	.372
11	.553	.684	50	.273	.354
12	.532	.661	60	.250	.325
13	.514	.641	70	.232	.302
14	.497	.623	80	.217	.283
15	.482	.606	90	.205	.267
16	.468	.590	100	.195	.254
17	.456	.575	125	.174	.228
18	.444	.561	150	.159	.208
19	.433	.549	200	.138	.181
20	.423	.537	300	.113	.148
21	.413	.526	400	.098	.128
22	.404	.515	500	.088	.115
23	.396	.505	1,000	.062	.081

Portions of this table were taken from Table VA in "Statistical Methods for Research Workers" by permission of Professor R. A. Fisher and his publishers, Oliver and Boyd.

The test of H_0: $\rho = 0$, H_A: $\rho \neq 0$ is made at sight in table 7.6.1. Simply look along the row for *d.f.* = 7 and observe the position of the sample r relative to the tabular values. Our $r = 0.597$ is considerably less than the 5% level, 0.666, leading to the same conclusion as before. The test is made without considering the sign of r. Among the following correlations, observe particularly how conclusions are affected by both sample size and the size of r:

Number of Pairs	Degrees of Freedom	r	Conclusion About Hypothesis, $\rho = 0$
20	18	0.60	Reject at 1% level
100	98	0.21	Reject at 5% level
10	8	0.60	Not rejected
15	13	−0.50	Not rejected
500	498	−0.15	Reject at 1% level

Those who wish a sketch of the main features of statistics at first reading may well omit the remainder of this chapter, together with all of the next. Go to chapter 9 if you wish to learn more of enumeration statistics, or to chapter 10 for analysis of variance.

In figure 7.5.1 was shown the asymmetry of the distribution of small sample r's from a population with a large value of ρ. Only under the hypothesis, $\rho = 0$, can the t-distribution be used precisely for testing significance. It is unsuited for testing other null hypotheses, such as $\rho = 0.05$ for example, or $\rho_1 - \rho_2 = 0$. Equally, t cannot be used for making confidence statements about small sample correlations. A convenient and sufficiently accurate solution of these problems was provided by Fisher (9) who devised a transformation from r to a quantity, z, distributed almost normally with variance,

$$\sigma_z{}^2 = \frac{1}{n-3},$$

"practically independent of the value of the correlation in the population from which the sample is drawn." The relation of z to r is given by

$$z = \tfrac{1}{2}[\log_e(1 + r) - \log_e(1 - r)],$$

but figure 7.6.1 enables us to change from one to the other with sufficient accuracy for ordinary sampling. Following are some examples of the use of z.

1. *It is required to set confidence limits to the value of ρ in the population from which a sample r has been drawn.* As an example, consider $r = -0.889$, based on 9 pairs of observations, figure 7.2.1F. From figure 7.6.1, $z = 1.417$ corresponds to $r = 0.889$. Since $n = 9$, $s_z = \sqrt{1/(9-3)} = 0.408$. Now, z is distributed almost normally, independent of sample size, so $t_{.01} = 2.576$, corresponding to $d.f. = \infty$. This value may be taken from table 2.7.1, or approximately from the table of probability in the normal distribution, table 8.8.1. For $P = 0.99$, we have as confidence limits of z,

$$1.417 - (2.576)(0.408) \leq z \leq 1.417 + (2.576)(0.408),$$

$$0.366 \leq z \leq 2\,468$$

Returning to the figure for the corresponding r, and restoring the sign, the 0.99 confidence limits on ρ are given by

$$-0.986 \leq \rho \leq -0.350$$

Emphasis falls on two facts: (i) in small samples the estimate, r, is not very reliable; and (ii) the limits are not equally spaced on either side of r, a consequence of its skewed distribution.

2. *Occasionally there is reason to test the hypothesis that ρ has some particular value, other than zero, in the sampled population* ($\rho = 0$, you recall, is tested by use of table 7.6.1). An example was given in section 7.5, where $r = 0.28$ was observed in a sample of 50 pairs from $\rho = 0.5$. What is the probability of a larger deviation? For $r = 0.28$, take from the figure $z = 0.288$, and for $\rho = .5$, $z = 0.549$. The difference, $0.549 - 0.288 = 0.261$, has

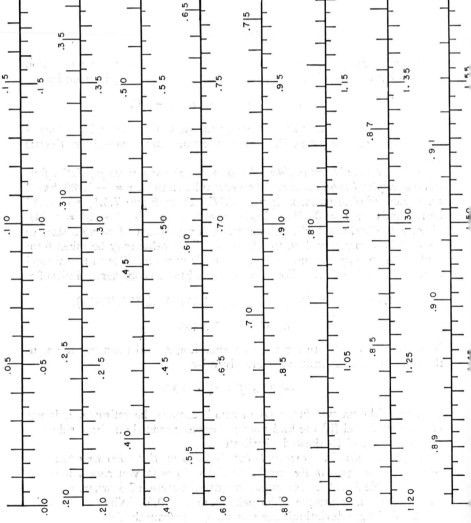

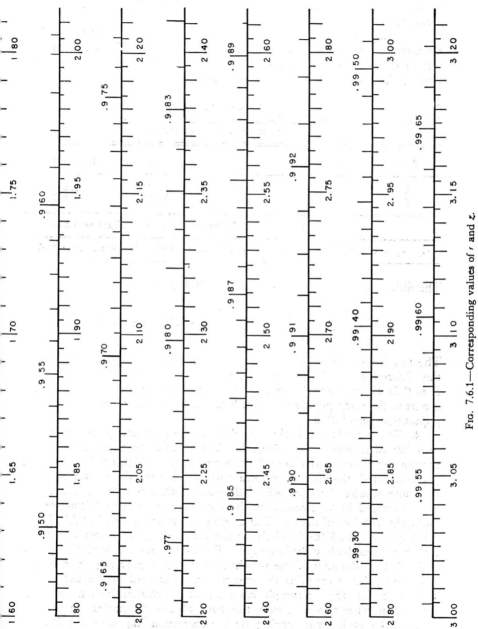

Fig. 7.6.1—Corresponding values of r and z.

the standard error, $1/\sqrt{n-3} = 1/\sqrt{47} = 0.1459$. Hence, $t = 0.261/0.1459 = 1.80$, with $d.f. = \infty$, does not reach the 5% level: the sample is not as unusual as 1 in 20.

3. *To test the hypothesis that two sample values of* r *are drawn at random from the same population*, convert each to z, then test the significance of the difference between the two z's. For two lots of pigs the correlations between gain in weight and amount of feed eaten are recorded in table 7.6.2.

TABLE 7.6.2

TEST OF SIGNIFICANCE OF THE DIFFERENCE BETWEEN TWO CORRELATIONS OF GAIN
WITH FEED EATEN AMONG SWINE

Lot	Pigs in Lot	r	z	$1/(n-3)$
1	5	0.870	1.333	0.500
2	12	0.560	0.633	0.111
		Difference = 0.700	Sum = 0.611	

$s_{z_1-z_2} = \sqrt{0.611} = 0.782$. $t = 0.700/0.782 = 0.895$. $d.f. = \infty$. $P = 0.37$

The difference between the z-values, 0.700, has the mean square

$$\frac{1}{n_1-3} + \frac{1}{n_2-3} = \frac{1}{2} + \frac{1}{9} = 0.611, \quad d.f. = \infty$$

The test is completed in the usual manner, calculating t as the ratio of the difference of the z's to the standard error of this difference. With $P = 0.37$ there is clearly no reason to reject the hypothesis that the z's are from the same population, and hence that the r's are from a common population correlation.

4. *To test the hypothesis that several* r's *are from the same* ρ, *and to combine them into an estimate of* ρ. There is often occasion to think that several sample correlations are drawn from a common ρ. If this null hypothesis is not rejected, then it is appropriate to combine the r's into an estimate of ρ more reliable than that afforded by any of the separate r's. Lush (14) was interested in an average of the correlations between initial weight and gain in 6 lots of steers. The computations are shown in table 7.6.3. Each z is weighted (multiplied) by the reciprocal of its mean square, so that small samples have little weight. The sum of the weighted z's, 15.478, is divided by the sum of the weights, 39, to get the average $z = 0.397$. The next column contains the calculations that lead to the test of the hypothesis that the six sample correlations are drawn from a common population correlation. From the sum of the quantities, $(n-3)z^2$, obtained by multiplying each z by the corresponding $(n-3)z$, is subtracted a correction,

$$[\Sigma(n-3)z](\text{average } z) = (15.478)(0.397) = 6.145,$$

TABLE 7.6.3

TEST OF HYPOTHESIS OF COMMON ρ AND ESTIMATION OF ρ. CORRELATIONS BETWEEN INITIAL WEIGHT AND GAIN OF STEERS

Samples	No. $= n$	$n - 3$	r	z	Weighted z $= (n - 3)z$	Weighted Square $= (n - 3)z^2$	Corrected z
1927 Herefords	4	1	0.929	1.651	1.651	2.726	1.589
1927 Brahmans	13	10	0.570	0.648	6.480	4.199	0.633
1927 Backcrosses	9	6	0.455	0.491	2.946	1.446	0.468
1928 Herefords	6	3	−0.092	−0.092	−0.276	0.025	−0.055
1928 Brahmans	11	8	0.123	0.124	0.992	0.123	0.106
1928 Backcrosses	14	11	0.323	0.335	3.685	1.234	0.321
	57	39			15.478	9.753	14.941
				Average $z = 0.397$		6.145	$z = 0.383$
	Average $r = 0.377$					$\chi^2 = 3.608$	$r = 0.365$

the result being a value of chi-square. This value, 3.608, has 5 degrees of freedom, less by 1 than the number of lots. From table 1.14.1, $P = 0.61$, so that H_0 is not rejected.

Since the 6 sample correlations may all have been drawn from the same population, it is appropriate to ask their average value, an estimate of the common ρ. This is got by taking from figure 7.6.1 the correlation 0.377 (with 0.95 confidence interval, $0.083 - 0.611$) corresponding to the average $z = 0.397$. Don't fail to note the great variation in these small sample correlations.

Fisher pointed out that there is a small bias in z, each being too large by

$$\frac{\rho}{2(n - 1)}$$

You see that the bias usually may be neglected in all the foregoing calculations. It might be serious, however, if large numbers of correlations were averaged, because the bias accumulates, one bit being added with every z. It would be easy to subtract the bias from each z were the population ρ not involved. If there is need to increase accuracy in the calculation of table 7.6.3, the average $r = 0.377$ may be substituted for ρ; then the approximate bias for each z may be deducted, and the calculation of the average z repeated. Since this will decrease the estimated r, it is well to take ρ slightly less than the first average. For instance, it may be guessed that $\rho = 0.37$, then the correction in the first z is $0.37/2(4 - 1) = 0.062$, and corrected z is $1.651 - 0.062 = 1.589$ The other corrected z's are in the last column of the table. The sum of the products,

$$\Sigma(n - 3)(\text{corrected } z) = 14.941,$$

appearing in the calculating machine with no intermediate recording, is divided by 39 to get the corrected mean value of z, 0.383. The corresponding correlation is 0.365   Before straining to reach precision, remember two facts: the true ρ is known only approximately, and the values of r and z are read from a graph inaccurate in the third decimal place. For tables of the distribution of r, see reference (4).

EXAMPLE 7.6.1—To get an idea of how the selection of pairs affects correlation, try picking the 5 lowest values of test II (example 7.3.8) together with the 6 highest. The correlation between these 11 scores and the corresponding scores on test I turns out to be 0.89, indicating the unreality that can be introduced into r by non-random choice.

EXAMPLE 7.6.2—Set 95% confidence limits to the correlation, 0.986, $n = 533$, between live and dressed weights of swine. Ans. 0.983 − 0.988.
What would have been the confidence limits if the number of swine had been 25? Ans. 0.968 − 0.994.

EXAMPLE 7.6.3—The correlation, 0.731, between wing and tongue length in bees (example 7.3.7) was one among 4 similar correlations calculated by Grout, the other three being 0.354, 0.690, and 0.740, each based on a sample of 44. Test the hypothesis that these are samples from a common ρ. Ans. $\chi^2 = 9.164$, $d.f. = 3$, $P = 0.03$. In only about 3 trials per 100 would you expect such disagreement among 4 correlations drawn from a common population. One would like to know more about the discordant correlation, 0.354, before drawing conclusions.

EXAMPLE 7.6.4—Estimate ρ in the population from which the 3 bee correlations, 0.731, 0.690, and 0.740, were drawn. Ans. 0.721.

EXAMPLE 7.6.5—Set 99% confidence limits on the foregoing bee correlation. Note: $r = 0.721$ is based on $3 \times 41 = 123$ $d.f.$ It is therefore equivalent to a single r from a sample of $123 + 3 = 126$ bees. The confidence limits: 0.590 − 0.815.

EXAMPLE 7.6.6—Although there is evidence against the hypothesis that the 4 bee correlations were drawn from a common ρ, it would not be appropriate ordinarily to ask if the small one differs significantly from the average of the 3 larger. For sake of illustration, however, let us test the hypothesis that $r = 0.354$, which might have been derived under one set of circumstances, is randomly drawn from the same ρ as the average of the other 3, which could have come from another hive, say. You have found that these 3 larger correlations average 0.721. Show that this differs significantly from the small correlation. Ans. $t = 2.99$, $d.f. = \infty$, $P < 0.01$ (or $\chi^2 = 8.97$, $d.f. = 1$).

7.7—Correlation and regression. Every pair of columns in the apple data of table 6.7.1 will yield a correlation coefficient, some of them of notable interest. Consider the series of equal correlations,

$$r_{XY} = r_{xy} = r_{Y\hat{Y}} = r_{Y\hat{y}} = r_{y\hat{y}}$$

Each of the corresponding pairs of columns consists of coded values of another pair so that these correlations are all the same (section 7.3). As examples: (i) The deviations, x and y, are coded values of X and Y got by subtracting $\bar{x}$ from each X and $\bar{y}$ from each Y; thus, $r_{xy} = r_{XY}$. (ii) Since $\hat{Y} = a + bX$, then $\hat{Y}$ is a coded X, each X being multiplied by b and the product increased by a; hence, the correlation between X and Y is equal to that between $\hat{Y}$ and Y.

This correlation between Y and $\hat{Y}$ is especially enlightening. Restating it, we may say that the correlation between Y and its regression estimate is identical with that between Y and X. This means that if Y is uniformly near the regression line, then $r_{Y\hat{Y}}$ and its equal, r_{XY}, are close to ± 1. Thus, the value of r_{XY} is, in this specific sense, a measure of success in estimating Y by means of regression.

Another correlation worth noticing is the one that you may compute from the columns, X and $\hat{Y}$. Since $\hat{Y}$ is the coded value of X, this correlation between X and its own coded value is ± 1 w th sign the same as that of b. Rounding errors may prevent you from verifying this exactly. The meaning of this correlation is that $\hat{Y}$ changes in steps proportional to changes in X, the successive points, $(X, \hat{Y})$, all lying exactly on the regression line.

The correlations of $d_{y \cdot x}$ with x and y may also be calculated and interpreted. The first, $r_{x d_{y \cdot x}} = 0$, recalls one of the assumptions made in fitting this regression: the standard deviation of $d_{y \cdot x}$ is, in the population, uniform throughout the range, and therefore is uncorrelated with x. The second, $r_{y d_{y \cdot x}} = \sqrt{1 - r_{xy}^2}$, may be visualized in this manner: if the regression is zero, the regression line is horizontal, and $d_{y \cdot x}$ coincides with y; that is, $r_{y d_{y \cdot x}}$ is unity when $r_{xy} = 0$. At the opposite extreme, as the points cluster more and more closely around the line, r_{xy} approaches 1; and since all the deviations, $d_{y \cdot x}$, approach zero, there is nothing for y to keep step with and $r_{y d_{y \cdot x}}$ approaches zero.

It will be observed that in this section r has been treated merely as a calculated quantity without reference to estimation or probability statements. The formulas giving the relation of correlation to regression would be just as true of the soybean data (example 6.2.1) as of the apple data despite the fact that, on account of the selection of X, the correlation between time and height is not an estimate of any population parameter. This distinction between r as an estimate of ρ and r as a convenient computational device must be observed carefully. Not only in the present section but also in the three to follow, r is used merely as a fraction related to a group of regression concepts. Whether or not it be considered an estimate of ρ depends on whether the sampling conditions of section 7.3 have been met.

EXAMPLE 7.7.1—Prove that the correlation of $d_{y \cdot x}$ with x is zero. Hint: using deviations, $d_{y \cdot x} = y - bx$. Then the sum of products, $\Sigma x d_{y \cdot x} = \Sigma xy - b\Sigma x^2$. Since $b = \Sigma xy / \Sigma x^2$, this reduces to 0.

EXAMPLE 7.7.2—Prove that the correlation of $d_{y \cdot x}$ with y is $\sqrt{1 - r_{xy}^2}$.

EXAMPLE 7.7.3—Show that $b = r\sqrt{\Sigma y^2}/\sqrt{\Sigma x^2} = r s_y / s_x$.

EXAMPLE 7.7.4—Show that the test of H_0: $\beta = 0$ is identical with the test of H_0: $\rho = 0$. Hint: Prove that the value of t for testing b is equal to that for testing r.

7.8—Correlation and the partition of Σy^2. The sum of squares attributable to regression (section 6.11) is readily changed as follows:

$$\frac{(\Sigma xy)^2}{\Sigma x^2} = \frac{(\Sigma xy)^2}{\Sigma x^2 \Sigma y^2} \cdot \Sigma y^2 = r^2 \Sigma y^2$$

That is, r^2 is the fraction of Σy^2 due to regression. The remainder is

$$\Sigma d_{y \cdot x}{}^2 = \Sigma y^2 - r^2 \Sigma y^2 = (1 - r^2)\Sigma y^2$$

You see how intimate is the relation between r and the partitioning of Σy^2 in regression. r^2 is the fraction of Σy^2 associated with the correlated changes in Y and X, while $(1 - r^2)$ is the remaining fraction quite independent of X.

These facts are summarized in a table of analysis of variance, table 7.8.1, similar to table 6.11.4. The earlier data are copied in the last line. Note: $r^2 = (\Sigma xy)^2/(\Sigma x^2)(\Sigma y^2) = (56)^2/(112)(68) = 7/17$.

TABLE 7.8.1
ANALYSIS OF VARIANCE OF y IN TABLE 6.11.4

Source of Variation	Degrees of Freedom	Sum of Squares	Mean Square
Regression	1	$r^2\,\Sigma y^2 = 28$	
Deviations from Regression	5	$(1 - r^2)\,\Sigma y^2 = 40$	8
Deviations from Mean	6	$\Sigma y^2 = 68$	11.3

$\Sigma x^2 = 112, \quad \Sigma y^2 = 68, \quad \Sigma xy = 56, \quad r^2 = 7/17 = 0.41, \quad r = 0.64$

It may be said again that this use of r is non-parametric; it is merely an algebraic relation associated with the calculations for linear regression as in Models I and II. So far as the calculations are concerned, it makes no difference whether or not the sample is drawn from either of these models or neither of them, providing the regression is linear. The symbols are so much simpler than those of regression that their use has become almost universal. The beginner must guard against thinking that r is always used as an estimator of some ρ.

If you can bring together these ideas and consider them in relation to figure 6.7.1 and table 6.7.1, it is illuminating to study the manner in which this entire complex is affected by different values of r. Take, for example, the extreme case in which $r = 0$, and therefore $1 - r^2 = 1$. None of the variation in percentage of wormy apples would then be accounted for by differences in crop size. The regression line would be horizontal, cutting the vertical scale at the point of $\bar{y} = 45\%$. The regression percentages in the table would be all the same and equal to $\bar{y}$. The deviations from regression would be simply deviations from mean value. The computation of $s_{y \cdot x}$ would be identical with that of s_y, except for degrees of freedom.

The opposite extreme is that in which $r = \pm 1$ and $1 - r^2 = 0$. Now all the variation in wormy apples would be attributable to regression, every dot in the figure would lie on the regression line, the regression percentages would be identical with the corresponding observed values, and the deviations from regression together with the standard deviation from regression would all be zero.

7.9—Correlation, common elements, and regression. Common elements help to clarify some of the facts of regression. To understand this one must make a slight alteration in the ideas presented in section 7.5. In table 7.5.1, think of four elements being drawn, their sum constituting X_1. Transfer three of them, taken at random, to X_2; then add two more. The resulting value of X_2 is con rolled, to some extent, by the elements transferred from X_1. In this sense, X_1 is one of the causes of X_2. While the computation of r is unaffected by this new attitude, the emphasis has been shifted to regression. It has been shown (7) that, using x_1 and x_2 as deviations from mean, the regression of x_2 on x_1 is

$$\hat{x}_2 = (n_{12}/n_1)x_1$$

the regression coefficient being the ratio of the number of transferred elements to the number in x_1.* As an example, consider the inheritance of stature. An average of half the genes controlling height are transferred to the son by his father. If this were undisturbed by complicating circumstances, one would expect the regression of son's height on father's to be $\hat{x}_2 = 0.5x_1$, the expected deviations of sons' heights from their mean averaging just half the deviations of fathers' heights from theirs. If you are a student of genetics, you will know that this coefficient is often less.

The equation, $\hat{x}_2 = (n_{12}/n_1)x_1$, emphasizes the fact that the estimated value, $\hat{x}_2$, is not affected by the number of elements in x_2. This estimated value depends entirely upon two quantities: (i) the fraction of the elements transferred from x_1, and (ii) the value of the sum, x_1. Neither the number of elements in x_2, nor their sum, influences $\hat{x}_2$. The values, x_2 and $\hat{x}_2$ are correlated (section 7.7) only because they contain the n_{12} common elements.

7.10—Correlation and differences. Any set of paired observations might be interesting from either or both of two viewpoints; correlation-regression as in chapters 6 and 7, or differences as in chapters 2, 3, and 4. Actually, the two viewpoints are not without connections, some of which we wish to examine now.

In section 3.9 you learned about differences between randomly paired observations from a normal population with $\sigma^2 = 100$. Such differences, centering on the mean, zero, had double the variance of the items; that is, $\sigma_D^2 = 2\sigma^2$. Again, corresponding facts about differences between means were pointed out; the differences clustered around zero with variance, $2\sigma^2/n$. Now it is necessary to consider differences of a more general type. In the difference, $X_D = X_1 - X_2$, imagine X_1 drawn from a population with mean, μ_1, and variance, σ^2, while X_2 is from μ_2, σ^2. You could draw samples from this population of differences by taking X_1 from the pig gains of table 3.2.1 and X_2 from those of table 3.10.1, deducting for con-

---

* It is convenient to think of x_1 and x_2 as variates instead of X_1 and X_2. These new variates are the sums you would have got in table 7.5.1 is you had subtracted $\bar{x} = 30$ pounds from every pig gain in table 3.2.1.

venience 10 pounds from each of the latter items so as to make $\mu_2 = 20$ pounds. Such differences would be normally distributed with

$$\mu_D = \mu_1 - \mu_2 = 30 - 20 = 10 \text{ pounds}$$

$$\sigma_D^2 = \sigma_1^2 + \sigma_2^2 = 100 + 25 = 125$$

Table 7.10.1 shows three samples of this kind. Of course, there is sampling variation in both mean and variance as can be seen by comparison of each with its parameter indicated above. This sampling variation leads to a contrast between the relationship among the sums of squares in the sample and in the population. In the sample, it is easily shown (example 7.10.6) that

$$\Sigma x_D^2 = \Sigma x_1^2 + \Sigma x_2^2 - 2\Sigma x_1 x_2$$

Illustrating with sample 1, $918.4 = 408.9 + 268.1 - 2(-120.7)$, and similarly in the other samples. Sample 3 was chosen so that $\Sigma x_1 x_2 = 0$, and therefore $1,352 = 1,206 + 146$.

If we substitute for $\Sigma x_1 x_2$ its equal, $r_{12}\sqrt{(\Sigma x_1^2)(\Sigma x_2^2)}$, then divide both members of the equation by $n - 1$, there results,

$$s_D^2 = s_1^2 + s_2^2 - 2r_{12}s_1 s_2$$

These equations hold exactly for every set of differences irrespective of sampling variation. Why doesn't the last term appear in the population formula for σ_D^2? For this reason: on account of the random pairing of X_1 and X_2, the correlation in the population of such pairs is zero. Through vagaries of random drawing, a small correlation usually shows up in samples, but the sign is as likely to be plus as minus and the sum of a lot of such correlations would tend towards zero.

If you compare the r's of samples 1 and 2 with those of table 7.6.1, you will see that the calculated values may well be samples from $\rho = 0$. Naturally, if you continue the sampling, you will get $|r| > 0.632$ about once in each 20 trials.

The foregoing discussion applies to differences from uncorrelated populations. What happens if X_1 and X_2 are drawn from a population in which there is a correlation, ρ? Such a population could result from the common elements of section 7.5, and samples can be drawn from it as illustrated in table 7.5.1; that population, you may recall, had a correlation, $\rho_{12} = 0.67$. If the difference, $X_D = X_1 - X_2$, is calculated from each pair, then

$$\sigma_D^2 = \sigma_1^2 + \sigma_2^2 - 2\rho_{12}\sigma_1\sigma_2,$$

a formula that follows the pattern of that for sample differences from uncorrelated populations So far as samples are concerned there is no distinction between the formulas. In samp'es of differences from both correlated and noncorrelated populations,

$$s_D^2 = s_1^2 + s_2^2 - 2r_{12}s_1 s_2$$

TABLE 7.10.1

THREE SAMPLES OF 10 DIFFERENCES, $X_D = X_1 - X_2$. X_1 IS FROM TABLE 3.2.1, AND X_2 FROM 3.10.1 WITH EACH ITEM DECREASED 10 POUNDS

Item Number	Sample 1			Sample 2			Sample 3		
	X_1	X_2	X_D	X_1	X_2	X_D	X_1	X_2	X_D
1	39	13	26	19	22	−3	32	18	14
2	34	19	15	14	20	−6	31	13	18
3	22	20	2	57	25	32	28	22	6
4	27	23	4	34	26	8	24	17	7
5	33	25	8	39	22	17	44	11	33
6	42	20	22	34	16	18	53	19	34
7	36	7	29	39	23	16	9	16	−7
8	24	16	8	13	22	−9	35	23	12
9	25	24	1	39	22	17	33	23	10
10	29	20	9	23	16	7	31	18	13
Mean	31.1	18.7	12.4	31.1	21.4	9.7	32	18	14
Sum of squares	408.9	268.1	918.4	1,706.9	98.4	1,480.1	1,206	146	1,352
Sum of products	−120.7			162.6			0		
Mean square	45.43	29.79	102.04	189.66	10.93	164.46	134.00	16.22	150.22
Covariance	−13.41			18.07			0		
Correlation	−0.365			0.102			0		

Of course, if the sample is from a correlated population you may expect r to be significant, especially if ρ and n are fairly large.

This formula for the variance of sample differences explains the effects of arbitrary pairing, examined in section 4.6 The randomly paired differences in the first two columns of table 3.3.1 are 1, 22, 23, -1, 20, 33, -41, -20, 20, and 6: their variance is, $s_D{}^2 = 513.79$. In the first column of table 7.10.2 this variance is verified from the formula above. You will notice that the correlation is negative; hence, the third term in the formula is added to the other two to make up the total, $s_D{}^2 = 513.79$. Now consider the arbitrary pairing of method I, table 4.6.1. This arrangement changes the random correlation of -0.59962 to the high positive value, 0.97664, with the consequent reduction in variance to 8.01 (middle column, table 7.10.2.) The pairing of method II, on the contrary, accentuates the random negative correlation and so increases the variance to $s_D{}^2 = 627.35$.

The success of pairing in an experiment depends upon the extent to which positive correlation can be introduced. If the investigator knows his material well enough to bring together into each pair individuals that will react alike, he will tend to get differences like those of method I with a small resultant variation. But if he should try pairing without adequate knowledge of his material he might get a negative correlation with the large experimental error of method II. In that case, he would have been better off with the group comparison of chapter 4.

Occasionally it may be useful to know that the correlation in a sample of pairs can be calculated from the foregoing formula by rearranging it thus:

$$r_{12} = \frac{s_1{}^2 + s_2{}^2 - s_D{}^2}{2s_1s_2} = \frac{\Sigma x_1{}^2 + \Sigma x_2{}^2 - \Sigma x_D{}^2}{2\sqrt{(\Sigma x_1{}^2)(\Sigma x_2{}^2)}}$$

TABLE 7.10.2

ILLUSTRATIONS OF THE EFFECT OF CORRELATION ON THE STANDARD DEVIATION OF DIFFERENCES. DATA FROM TABLES 3.3.1 AND 4.6.1

	From the First Two Columns of Table 3.3.1	Method I, Table 4.6.1	Method II, Table 4.6.1
r_{12}	$-\ 0.59962*$	$0.97664*$	$-\ 0.95353*$
$s_1{}^2$	169.82		
$s_2{}^2$	151.57		
$s_1{}^2 + s_2{}^2$	321.39	321.39	321.39
$2r_{12}s_1s_2$	-192.40	313.38	-305.96
$s_D{}^2$	513.79	8.01	627.35

* This number of decimals is necessary to verify the arithmetic.

where $x_D = x_1 - x_2$, the deviation of X_D from its mean. An example may be found in the tobacco virus data of table 2.9 1 where $\Sigma x_D{}^2 = 130$ is already known. The sums of squares of the numbers of lesions on the two sets of half leaves are easily computed: $\Sigma x_1{}^2 = 468$ and $\Sigma x_2{}^2 = 172$. Substituting,

$$r_{12} = \frac{468 + 172 - 130}{2\sqrt{(468)(172)}} = 0.90$$

The efficiency of this experiment, discussed in section 3.10, arises from the similarity of the reaction of the leaf halves to the inoculation, a similarity reflected in this high correlation, 0.90.

Although the chief interest here is in differences, it is useful to observe, also, the formula for the variance of the sum, $X_S = X_1 + X_2$:

$$s_S{}^2 = s_1{}^2 + s_2{}^2 + 2r_{12}s_1s_2$$

EXAMPLE 7.10.1—In table 7.1.1, subtract each sister height from her brother's, then compute the corrected sum of squares of the differences. From this, together with $\Sigma x_1{}^2 = 74$ and $\Sigma x_2{}^2 = 66$, verify $r_{12} = 0.558$ by means of the formula just above.

EXAMPLE 7.10.2—Notice that, in the last formula given above, if $s_D{}^2 = s_1{}^2 + s_2{}^2$ as in sample 3, table 7.10.1, then $r_{12} = 0$; if $s_D{}^2 < s_1{}^2 + s_2{}^2$ as in sample 2, then r_{12} is positive.

EXAMPLE 7.10.3—Haber (12) furnished the following information about 300 ears of sweet corn:

Character	Mean (grams)	Standard Deviation (grams)
Ear weight, E	106.55	27.68
Cob weight, C	15.59	
Grain weight, G	90.96	24.62

Observe that $E = C + G$; also, $r_{eg} = 0.9940$. Calculate $s_c = 4.19$ grams, and $r_{cg} = 0.6906$.

EXAMPLE 7.10.4—If $r_{12} = 1$, show that $s_D = s_1 - s_2$.

EXAMPLE 7.10.5—If $r_{12} = -1$, show that $s_D = s_1 + s_2$.

EXAMPLE 7.10.6—Assuming successively that the correlation between X_1 and X_2 is first zero then r_{12}, derive the corresponding formulas for $\Sigma x_D{}^2$ and $\Sigma x_S{}^2$.

7.11—Correlations with sums and ratios. Correlations due to common causes.

It is often informative to correlate a variable, X_1, with the sum of itself and another variable, X_2; that is, X_1 with $X_S = X_1 + X_2$. As an example, there is the correlation, 0.986 (cited in section 7.2) between warm dressed weight, X_1, and live weight X_S, in swine, the variable X_2 denoting the weight of discarded portions. Again, one may gain information from correlating X_1 with $X_P = X_1/X_2$ or with $X_Q = X_2/X_1$(18). An example of r_{1P} is the correlation between the standard deviation and the coefficient of variation; that is, between s and $s/\bar{x}$. For illustration,

50 pairs of these statistics were taken at random from the samples of pig gains, section 3.3. The mean of the 50 standard deviations was 9.87, that of the means, 29.76. The correlation between s and $\bar{x}$ was 0.140, an estimate of $\rho = 0$, because these two statistics are theoretically uncorrelated in this kind of sampling. But the correlation between s and C was 0.932. A familiar instance of r_{1Q} is the correlation of live weight, X_1, with dressing percentage, X_Q:

$$X_Q = \frac{\text{carcass weight, } X_2}{\text{live weight, } X_1}$$

An even more complicated relation is found in the correlation, -0.68, between average daily gain of swine and feed required per pound gained (6), where the gain is in the numerator of the first rate and in the denominator of the second.

Having observed some unwarranted interpretations of such correlations, Karl Pearson dubbed them "spurious" (16), and this rather derogatory title has led people to distrust them. Of course, it is the interpretation that may be spurious. The correlations are on the same footing as any others: they are appropriate estimates of parameters if they satisfy the conditions laid down in section 7.3 (1). As for the interpretation, any explanation of a correlation between X_1 and the sums or ratios involving it would seem to require knowledge of r_{12} as well.

An especially simple case, in which $r_{12} = 0$, is illustrated in table 7.11.1. The correlation, $r_{1S} = 0.9445$, is like the one between dressed weight (X_1) and live weight (X_S) except that here there is no correlation between the two parts. It would be interesting to know the correlation between dressed weight and the weight of discarded parts.

TABLE 7.11.1

CORRELATIONS OF X_1 WITH $X_S = X_1 + X_2$ AND $X_Q = X_2/X_1$. X_1 AND X_2 COMPRISE SAMPLE 3 IN TABLE 7.10.1, WHERE $r_{12} = 0$

	X_1	X_2	X_1	X_S	X_1	X_Q
	32	18	32	50	32	0.562
	31	13	31	44	31	0.419
	28	22	28	50	28	0.786
	24	17	24	41	24	0.708
	44	11	44	55	44	0.250
	53	19	53	72	53	0.358
	9	16	9	25	9	1.778
	35	23	35	58	35	0.657
	33	23	33	56	33	0.697
	31	18	31	49	31	0.581
Sum	320	180	320	500	320	6.796
Sum of squares	1,206	146	1,206	1,352	1,206	1.59887
Sum of products	0		1,206		-37.516	
Correlation	0		0.9445		-0.8543	

The *part-whole* correlation can be computed from the original samples by means of the formula,

$$r_{1S} = \frac{s_1 + r_{12}s_2}{\sqrt{s_1^2 + 2r_{12}s_1s_2 + s_2^2}}$$

If $r_{12} = 0$, as in table 7.11.1, this formula reduces to

$$r_{1S} = \frac{s_1}{\sqrt{s_1^2 + s_2^2}} = \frac{1}{\sqrt{1 + s_2^2/s_1^2}} = \frac{1}{\sqrt{1 + \Sigma x_2^2/\Sigma x_1^2}}$$

The calculation of the part-whole correlation in the table may now be verified by substitution from the first sample:

$$r_{1S} = \frac{1}{\sqrt{1 + 146/1206}} = 0.9445,$$

as before. If, in addition to $r_{12} = 0$, $s_2 = s_1$ also, then

$$r_{1S} = 1/\sqrt{2} = 0.707$$

This gives some idea of the size of spurious correlations in special cases and shows that both of the standard deviations are involved, as well as the correlation between the added variables.

This part-whole correlation may be considered a special case of common elements. X_1 is common to both X_1 and X_S, while X_2 is the different part. If X_1 and X_2 are drawn from the same normal population, then one may put $n_{12} = 1$, $n_1 = 1$, $n_2 = 2$, and each sample correlation is an estimate of

$$\rho = n_{12}/\sqrt{n_1n_2} = 1/\sqrt{2} = 0.707$$

as in the special case of r_{1S} above.

The correlation, $r_{1Q} = -0.8543$, is negative partly because X_1 is the denominator of the fraction, X_Q, so that a large X_1 tends to make a small X_Q. This correlation, also, can be got directly from the sample. The formula is an approximate one:

$$r_{1Q} = \frac{r_{12}C_2 - C_1}{\sqrt{C_1^2 + 2r_{12}C_1C_2 + C_2^2}}$$

where C is the coefficient of variation, $s/\bar{x}$, expressed as a fraction (not percentage). In the first pair of columns in table 7.11.1, $r_{12} = 0$, $C_1^2 = 0.13090$, $C_2^2 = 0.05007$ and $C_1 = 0.3618$. Substituting,

$$r_{1Q} = \frac{-0.3618}{\sqrt{0.05007 + 0.13090}} = -0.8505$$

The small discrepancy is due partly to the approximate nature of the formula. In this ratio correlation, the means as well as the standard deviations of the original sample have come into the picture.

The correlation between two variables may be due, wholly or in part, to their common relation to one or more other factors. The organic correlations already mentioned are examples. A big animal tends to be big all over, so that any two parts are likely correlated because of their participation in the general size. Again, two quantities that change in time may show a high correlation. As an example, there is a correlation of -0.98 between the birth rate in Great Britain, from 1875 to 1920, and the production of pig iron in the United States. The matter was discussed by Yule as a question, "Why do we sometimes get nonsense-correlations between time series (20)?" Among the answers suggested only one is pertinent at this point: pairs of observations ordered in time are not randomly drawn in the usual sense and may not come from any normal bivariate population. Hence, they may not conform to the conditions we have set for estimates and probability statements. For another answer, see "partial correlation," chapter 14.

7.12—Non-parametric methods. Rank correlation. Often there is reason to suspect that a bivariate population is far from normal. In that case, there is no parameter, ρ, to be estimated. But there may be evidence that the two variables are not independent; and, in that sense, they are said to be correlated.

The best known "population" of this kind is the one in which the variables are not measurements at all, but are merely the result of an arrangement of the individuals according to some criterion observed. Thus, a group of swine may be placed from high to low on the basis of back fat. Each has a rank—first, second, etc. Two such rankings of the same things, or of related things, led Spearman (19) to devise a formula for *rank correlation*,

$$r_s = 1 - \frac{6\Sigma d^2}{n(n^2 - 1)},$$

whose calculation is explained in table 7.12.1. Like r, the rank correlation can range in samples from -1 (complete discordance) to $+1$ (complete concordance).

The distribution of r_s is known only if $\rho = 0$. This means that, in general, interval estimates are not available but that H_0: $\rho = 0$ can be tested. For samples greater than 8 ranks, use the normal approximation as described for table 7.6.1. If n is 8 or less, use table 7.12.2. From this table one observes that at the 5% level the null hypothesis cannot be rejected in samples of 4 or less. The correlation, $r_s = 0.857$, in table 7.12.1 is significant at the 5% level but not at the 1%; that is, there are

TABLE 7.12.1
RANKING OF 7 RATS BY 2 OBSERVERS OF THEIR CONDITION AFTER 3 WEEKS
ON A DEFICIENT DIET

Rat Number	Ranking by		Difference, d	d^2
	Observer 1	Observer 2		
1	4	4	0	0
2	1	2	-1	1
3	6	5	1	1
4	5	6	-1	1
5	3	1	2	4
6	2	3	-1	1
7	7	7	0	0
			$\Sigma d = 0$	$\Sigma d^2 = 8$

$$r_S = 1 - \frac{6\Sigma d^2}{n(n^2 - 1)} = 1 - \frac{6 \times 8}{7(49 - 1)} = 0.857$$

about 2 chances in 100 of getting a rank correlation greater than 0.857 even if the rats were all in the same condition so that the judgments of the observers had no foundation.

If the continuous variables in a bivariate distribution are far from normally distributed, some idea of the relationship between them may be got from a sample, as follows: Arrange the observed values of each variable in order of size, from high to low. Number the successive values of each $1, 2, \ldots n$, calling these numbers *ranks* (for a discussion of the theory, see reference 13, section 16.25). Substitute the rank numbers for the originally observed measures; then calculate r_S. The null hypothesis $\rho = 0$ may be tested by table 7.12.2.

Some people have used r_S as a short-cut method for estimating r in a sample from a bivariate normal distribution. There is little justification for such a procedure. It is true that, for samples up to about $n = 30$,

TABLE 7.12.2
SIGNIFICANT LEVELS IN SMALL SAMPLES OF THE RANK CORRELATION COEFFICIENT
UNDER THE HYPOTHESIS, $\rho = 0$

Size of Sample	5% Level	1% Level
4 or less	none	none
5	1	none
6	0.886	1
7	0.750	0.893
8	0.714	0.857
9 or more	use table 7.6.1	

a little time is saved and the resulting values of r and r_s are not greatly different. The latter fact is illustrated as follows: Using common elements (section 7.5), I drew 10 samples, each with $n = 20$, from a bivariate normal population with

$$\rho = \frac{n_{12}}{\sqrt{n_1 n_2}} = \frac{10}{\sqrt{(20)(16)}} = 0.559$$

then calculated r and r_s in each. The results are tabulated in table 7.12.3. Both averages in the last line of the table are got by use of z (section 7.6) despite the fact that the theory does not apply to r_s. In this small sample of coefficients, r_s averages a little less than r and is somewhat more vari-

TABLE 7.12.3

PRODUCT-MOMENT AND RANK CORRELATIONS IN 10 SAMPLES FROM A BIVARIATE NORMAL
POPULATION IN WHICH $\rho = 0.559$

Sample	r	r_s	Sample	r	r_s
1	0.663	0.505	6	0.712	0.680
2	.708	.738	7	.627	.474
3	.505	.584	8	.444	.352
4	.374	.311	9	.529	.398
5	.536	.562	10	.546	.484
Average				0.564	0.512

able. The correlation between the 10 pairs of r and r_s is 0.64. If your data aren't worth much, the short-cut method may be good enough, but if they have cost you much money and/or time, the product-moment correlation seems worth while.

REFERENCES

1. G. A. BAKER. Journal of the American Statistical Association, 37:537 (1942).

2. A. E. BRANDT. Thesis submitted for the degree Doctor of Philosophy, Iowa State University (1932).

3. A. R. CRATHORNE. Reorganization of Mathematics in Secondary Education. Mathematical Association of America, Inc., page 105 (1923).

4. F. W. DAVID. Tables of the correlation coefficient. Cambridge University Press (1938).

5. T. EDEN. Journal of Agricultural Science, 21:547 (1931).

6 JOHN M. EVVARD, M. G. SNELL, C. C. CULBERTSON, and GEORGE W. SNEDECOR. Proceedings of the American Society of Animal Production, 1927, page 2.

7. CARL H. FISCHER. The Annals of Mathematical Statistics, 4:103 (1933).

8. R. A. Fisher. Biometrika, 10:507 (1915).

9. R. A. Fisher. Metron, 1:3 (1921).

10. Francis Galton. Proceedings of the Royal Society of London, 45:135 (1888).

11. R. A. Grout. Iowa Agricultural Experiment Station Research Bulletin No. 218 (1937).

12. E. S. Haber. Data from the Iowa Agricultural Experiment Station.

13. Maurice G. Kendall. The advanced theory of statistics, Vol. 1. Charles Griffin and Company, Limited, London (1943).

14. Jay L. Lush. Journal of Agricultural Research, 42:853 (1931).

15. V. H. Morris and R. W. Gerdel. Plant Physiology, 8:315 (1933).

16. Karl Pearson. Proceedings of the Royal Society, A, 60:489 (1897).

17. Karl Pearson and Alice Lee. Biometrika, 2:357 (1902–1903).

18. Lowell J. Reed. Journal of the Washington Academy of Science, 11:449 (1921).

19. C. Spearman. American Journal of Psychology, 15:88 (1904).

20. G. Udny Yule. Journal of the Royal Statistical Society, 89:1 (1926)

CHAPTER 8

Large Sample Methods

8.1—Introduction. Large samples randomly drawn from single populations are seldom encountered. If n is greater than, say, 500, the individuals usually come from several populations. The statistician who examines such samples spends a considerable amount of his effort in separating the observations into more or less homogeneous groups. He then endeavors to compare the several portions of the sample or to discover relationships within the component parts, adapting his conclusions to the various populations found. This may be his objective; or he may be seeking for the elements common to all the populations.

Large random samples from a single population can be relied upon to reflect the shape and parameters of the population rather faithfully. The sample statistics estimate closely the population parameters. Interval estimates and tests of hypotheses are not so essential as in small samples.

The first arrangement of a large sample is nearly always in the form of a frequency distribution. Our initial job will be to learn some appropriate methods of calculation. Afterwards we shall be concerned with various methods suitable to large samples from single normal populations. In chapter 17 some account will be given of planned large samples drawn from several populations.

8.2—Computation of mean and standard deviation of a frequency distribution. In section 3.4 you were promised a short method for computing the statistics of a frequency distribution. That of the 511 sample means is copied in the first two columns of table 8.2.1. The actual sample means are grouped into classes with midpoints at 19, 20, . . . pounds, the number of means in each class being recorded in the second column. For convenience, the arbitrary origin, G, is selected as 29 pounds because that is the middle class mark and also because that class carries one of the greater frequencies. The code numbers are simply the deviations of the class marks from G. In the fourth column are recorded the sums of the deviations in the several classes. For example, in the fourth class, class mark 22, the deviation is -7 and there are 7 of them: the sum is therefore $(-7)(7) = -49$. At the foot of the column are set down separately

TABLE 8.2.1

FREQUENCY DISTRIBUTION OF 511 MEANS OF SAMPLES OF 10 ITEMS (TABLE 3.4.1).
COMPUTATION OF MEAN AND STANDARD DEVIATION
$G = 29$ pounds

Class Mark, Pounds	Frequency f	Code Numbers X	Sum of Code Numbers fX	Sum of Squares of Code Numbers fX^2
19	1	−10	−10	100
20	1	− 9	− 9	81
21	0	− 8	0	0
22	7	− 7	−49	343
23	5	− 6	−30	180
24	10	− 5	−50	250
25	19	− 4	−76	304
26	30	− 3	−90	270
27	41	− 2	−82	164
28	48	− 1	−48	48
29	66	0	0	0
30	72	1	72	72
31	56	2	112	224
32	46	3	138	414
33	45	4	180	720
34	22	5	110	550
35	24	6	144	864
36	12	7	84	588
37	5	8	40	320
38	0	9	0	0
39	1	10	10	100

$$n = \Sigma f = 511 \qquad\qquad \begin{array}{r} -444 \\ 890 \\ \hline 446 \end{array} \quad \Sigma fX^2 = 5{,}592$$

$$\begin{aligned}
\Sigma fX &= 446 \\
\Sigma fX/n &= 446/511 \\
&= 0.87 \\
\bar{x} &= G + \Sigma fX/n \\
&= 29 + 0.87 = 29.87 \text{ pounds} \\
s_{\bar{x}} &= \sqrt{s^2/n} = \sqrt{10.2014/511} = 0.141 \text{ pound}
\end{aligned}$$

$$\begin{aligned}
\Sigma fX^2 &= 5{,}592 \\
(\Sigma fX)^2/n &= (446)^2/511 = 389.27 \\
\Sigma x^2 &= 5{,}202.73 \\
s^2 &= \Sigma x^2/(n-1) = 5{,}202.73/510 \\
&= 10.2014 \\
s &= 3.194 \text{ pounds}
\end{aligned}$$

the sums of the negative and positive deviations together with their total, 446.

The sums of the squares of the deviations in the last column are calculated conveniently by multiplying fX by X. Again using class mark 22 as an example, $(-7)(-49) = 343$ is easier than $(-7)^2(7)$. Merely multiply twice by each code number, first f to get fX, then fX to get fX^2. The calculations at the bottom of the table involve no innovations.

Do you see the identity of the code numbers, X, with those discussed in chapter 5? Each mean weight is coded, implicitly, by first subtracting 29, then rounding. Consider a mean whose value was calculated in section 3.4, such as 33.2 pounds. The code is $33.2 - 29 = 4.2$, rounded to $X = 4$.   In the actual process of making the frequency distribution the rounding, accomplished by grouping, was the first step.   For example, the mean, 33.2 pounds, fell into the class whose mark was 33 pounds.   The subtraction of the class mark completed the coding.   It is easy to verify the code numbers for such means as 31.6, 25.1, and 26.8 pounds; namely, 3, -4, and -2.   How about 30.5?   You remember the rule—round to the adjacent even number.   Hence $30.5 - 29 = 1.5$ rounds to 2.   But $31.5 - 29 = 2.5$ also rounds to 2.   The result is a slight excess of frequency in the even-numbered classes.   In effect, these classes are wider than the others.

Another rule must be brought forward from chapter 5, the one requiring the range of code numbers to be not less than 20.   In new terms, there must be at least 20 classes for precise work, preferably more.   After the computations are done, you can apply this criterion: the sample standard deviation should be at least four times as great as the class interval.   You will notice that this requirement was not fulfilled in table 8.2.1, s being only a little more than three times the class interval of one pound.   It would have been better to make the class interval one-half or three-quarters of a pound.

It is well to keep in mind that the only lack of precision in using code numbers derives from the grouping or rounding.   This process is usually limited to that type of variable known as *continuous*, an item being likely to fall at any point on the scale.   There is no sacrifice of precision in the computations when the variable results from such an enumeration as that of the following example.

EXAMPLE 8.2.1—Edwards (3) planted 20 soybeans on each of 183 agar plates, then observed the numbers germinating.   The frequency distribution follows:

Number germinating on each plate, X	6	7	8	9	10	11	12	13	14	15	16
Number of plates, f	5	9	8	19	26	34	26	22	21	10	3

Compute the mean number of beans germinating on a plate, 11.2, together with the sample standard error, 0.17 bean.   Is any inaccuracy introduced by the use of the arbitrary origins?   Notice the use of enumeration data as though they were measurements. This is often convenient.   If the sample is large and the distribution is a symmetrical binomial, one may safely make all inferences appropriate to normal measurement data.

8.3—Computation of mean and standard deviation of a frequency distribution—continued.   In the last section the unit of measurement, one pound, was conveniently used as the class interval, but in the distribution of table 8.3.1 it takes an interval of 10 pounds to provide a satisfactory number of classes.   The first class interval extends from 75 pounds up to (but not including) 85 pounds, the midpoint being 80 pounds.

TABLE 8.3.1
FREQUENCY DISTRIBUTION OF LIVE WEIGHTS OF 533 SWINE. COMPUTATION OF MEAN
AND STANDARD DEVIATION WITH A CLASS INTERVAL DIFFERENT FROM ONE UNIT
Class interval, $I = 10$ pounds $G = 170$ pounds

Class Mark, Pounds	Frequency f	Code Numbers X	Sum of Code Numbers fX	Squares fX^2
80	1	− 9	− 9	81
90	0	− 8	0	0
100	0	− 7	0	0
110	7	− 6	−42	252
120	18	− 5	−90	450
130	21	− 4	−84	336
140	22	− 3	−66	198
150	44	− 2	−88	176
160	67	− 1	−67	67
170	76	0	0	0
180	55	1	55	55
190	57	2	114	228
200	47	3	141	423
210	33	4	132	528
220	30	5	150	750
230	23	6	138	828
240	11	7	77	539
250	5	8	40	320
260	5	9	45	405
270	4	10	40	400
280	5	11	55	605
290	2	12	24	288

$n = 533$ -446 $\Sigma fX^2 = 6,929$
     $1,011$

$$\Sigma fX = \quad 565$$

$\Sigma fX = 565$ $\Sigma fX^2 = 6,929$
$I(\Sigma fX)/n = 10(565/533)$ $(\Sigma fX)^2/n = (565)^2/533 = \quad 598.92$
     $= 11$ pounds   For code numbers, $\Sigma x^2 = \overline{6,330.08}$
     $\bar{x} = G + I(\Sigma fX)/n$ $s^2 = I^2(\Sigma x^2)/(n-1)$
     $= 170 + 11$ $= (10)^2 (6,330.08)/532$
     $= 181$ pounds $= 1,189.86$
     $s_{\bar{x}} = \sqrt{s^2/n} = \sqrt{1,189.86/533} = 1.49$ pounds $s = 34.5$ pounds

G was selected as the midpoint of the class of greatest frequency despite the fact that this was not the middle class. (The size of the correction for mean, 11 pounds shows that G might well have been taken as 180 pounds.) The class interval, $I = 10$ pounds, enters the calculations of both mean and variance, since both must be decoded.

You will observe that we still haven't provided enough classes. The standard deviation falls short of being four times the class interval, but the discrepancy is not serious.

EXAMPLE 8.3.1—Compute the sample mean and standard deviation of the live weights in table 8.3.1, taking $G = 180$ pounds.

EXAMPLE 8.3.2—The yields in grams of 1,499 rows of wheat are recorded by Wiebe (11). They have been tabulated as follows:

Class Mark	Fre-quency	Class Mark	Fre-quency	Class Mark	Fre-quency
375	3	600	127	825	10
400	13	625	140	850	10
425	41	650	122	875	4
450	99	675	94	900	4
475	97	700	64	925	2
500	118	725	49	950	3
525	138	750	31	975	1
550	146	775	26	1,000	1
575	136	800	20		
				Total	1,499

Compute $\bar{x} = 587.74$ grams, and $s = 100.55$ grams. Are there enough classes in this distribution?

EXAMPLE 8.3.3—Lindstrom (6) reported the numbers of rows of kernels on 327 ears of F_2 generation derived from a cross of inbred lines of maize:

Number of rows of kernels	12	14	16	18	20	22
Number of ears	25	75	133	68	21	5

The sample mean is 16.00 rows, the sample standard deviation 2.136 rows. Is any inaccuracy introduced by the small number of classes?

8.4—Miscellaneous remarks about frequency distributions. There exists some confusion about the desirable number of classes for a frequency distribution. One thinks of two distinct objectives: (i) the presentation of data in summary form, accompanied often by a graph, and (ii) the calculation of the sample statistics. It is only for the latter that 20 or more classes are required. For tabular and graphical presentation it is usually desirable to keep the number of classes less than 10.

It requires care to get the class mark in the center of its interval. Suppose weights are recorded in whole pounds with no fractional values. It is the usual practice to estimate such weights to at least the closest half pound; that is, the record of 25 pounds probably included all weights between 24½ and 25½ pounds. If the class intervals are chosen as 20–29 pounds, 30–39 pounds, etc., the first class really extends from 19.5 to 29.5 pounds. In such a scheme, the class mark is $(19.5 + 29.5)/2 = 24.5$ pounds, not 25. Fix the class limits as precisely as feasible, then compute the midpoint to get the class mark.

It is assumed that the items falling into a class are somewhat evenly distributed throughout the interval. When this expectation is realized, the mean of the items will be not greatly different from the class mark. This is especially likely in the high frequency intervals bearing the greatest weights in the computations. Caution should be exercised, then, if there are natural groupings in the interval.   An instance was observed where the number of locules (seed compartments) in tomatoes was the variable, its values being confined to whole numbers and halves.   Only a few of the fruits had half locules.   At first, the class intervals were chosen to extend from 2 up to but not including 3, etc., the class marks falling at $2\frac{1}{2}$, $3\frac{1}{2}$, etc.   Actually, the mean numbers of locules in the classes were almost at the lower boundaries, 2, 3, etc.   This systematic error led to an over-statement of almost half a locule in the mean.

Those desiring to refine the estimate of standard deviation of a continuous variable may use Sheppard's correction for grouping (10).   This consists in deducting one-twelfth of a unit from the coded mean square, provided the code numbers differ by unity as in tables 8.2.1 and 8.3.1.   In table 8.2.1 the correction would be $10.2014 - 0.0833 = 10.1181$ with $s = 3.181$ pounds.   This estimate, however, should not be used in a test of significance (5).

EXAMPLE 8.4.1—In table 8.3.1, apply Sheppard's correction to derive the estimate, $s = 34.37$ pounds.   Before correction, the coded mean square is 11.8986.

EXAMPLE 8.4.2—Compute the corrected value of s, 100.55 grams, in example 8.3.2.

EXAMPLE 8.4.3—In examples 8.2.1 and 8.3.3, whose variables are discrete, is there any error of grouping to be corrected?

EXAMPLE 8.4.4—Two lots of mice inoculated with different isolations of typhoid (see section 12.16 for reference) survived during the numbers of days indicated by the following frequency distributions:

Days to death	1	2	3	4	5	6	7	8	9	10	11	12
Strain 9D	7	5	2	16	11	7	2	5	2	2	0	0
Strain DSC 1	1	0	0	1	6	8	4	6	3	3	1	3

Test the significance of the difference between the means of days to death (chapter 4).   The sums of squares are 316.88 and 209.64; the difference between sample means, 2.628 days, $t = 5.22$, and $d.f. = 93$.

8.5—A test of symmetry.   At various points in this text where you have been asked to judge of the normality of sets of data the only criteria available were symmetry and the proportion of items in the interval $x \pm s$.   Adequate tests of normality will be described in this and following sections (4).   We shall consider two types of departure from the normal.   In one, the distribution of the data is asymmetrical or skewed, the mean and median being different.   The other occurs in symmetrical sets, characterized by either an excess or a deficit of items concentrated near the center of the range.   For the sake of simplicity in presentation, we shall first illustrate the test for symmetry only, using a small sample.

In example 2.5.4 the array of weights of 11 men was cited as an example of an asymmetrical set.   Let us measure the skewness and test significance.   The calculations are set out in table 8.5.1.   The first unfamiliar feature is the column of cubes with their sum, $S_3 = 248,628$. Next appear the two k statistics, k_2 being our friend, mean square, and k_3 a corresponding average of the third powers of the deviations from mean. The measure of skewness is $g_1 = 1.96$. You will see immediately that S_3 and therefore g_1 might be positive, negative, or zero. If g_1 were zero, symmetry in the sample would be demonstrated. A positive g_1 as in our illustration, indicates an excess in the number of items smaller than the mean. If g_1 proves to be significantly different from zero, the excess of small values

TABLE 8.5.1

THE TEST OF SYMMETRY IN A SMALL SAMPLE
Weights (pounds) of 11 men

Weight X	Deviation x	Square x^2	Cube x^3
148	-24	576	$-13,824$
154	-18	324	$-\ 5,832$
158	-14	196	$-\ 2,744$
160	-12	144	$-\ 1,728$
161	-11	121	$-\ 1,331$
162	-10	100	$-\ 1,000$
166	$-\ 6$	36	$-\ \ \ 216$
170	$-\ 2$	4	$-\ \ \ \ \ 8$
182	10	100	1,000
195	23	529	12,167
236	64	4,096	262,144

| $\bar{x} = 172$ | $S_1 = 0$ | $S_2 = 6,226$ | $S_3 = 248,628$ |

$n = 11$

$$k_2 = S_2/(n-1)$$
$$= 6,226/10$$
$$= 622.6$$

$$k_3 = nS_3/(n-1)(n-2)$$
$$= (11)(248,628)/(10)(9)$$
$$= 2,734,908/90 = 30,387.9$$

$g_1 = k_3/\sqrt{k_2^3} = k_3/(k_2)(\sqrt{k_2})$
$= 30,387.9/(622.6)(\sqrt{622.6})$
$= 30,387.9/15,535 = 1.96$
$\quad s_{g1} = 0.661, \quad t = g_1/s_{g1} = 1.96/0.661 = 2.96, d.f. = \infty$

$s_{g1}^2 = 6n(n-1)/(n-2)(n+1)(n+3)$
$= (6)(11)(10)/(9)(12)(14)$
$= 660/1,512 = 0.437$

may then be ascribed to asymmetry in the population from which the sample is drawn. The standard error of g_1 turns out to be 0.661, so that $t = 2.96$. The test of significance is carried out with an infinite number of deg ees of freedom, the 1% level of t being 2.576.

To assist you in following the computations we have carried an unnecessary number of significant figures in table 8.5.1. For practice, you might recalculate the statistics with the use of no more than four significant figures in any one number.

As a second illustration, let us test the symmetry of the weights of neutral fats in the blood plasma of 64 normal men (8):

419, 162, 149, 219, 248, 313, 211, 169 91, 281, 264, 172, 124, 235, 94, 62,

224, 58, 92, 205, 132, 145, 305, 285, 174, 107 240, 269, 396, 416, 662, 703, 249, 179, 136, 157, 198, 95, 100 178, 145, 199, 54, 407, 166, 94, 248, 235, 66, 120, 239, 128, 560, 233, 80, 557, 217, 542, 252, 175, 103, 165, 351, 107 mg. per 100 cc.

These data call for the introduction of the machine method of calculation. Accumulate the sum of the 64 weights, $s_1 = 14,361$; the sum of their squares, $s_2 = 4,518,741$; and the sum of cubes, $s_3 = 1,878,426,855$. The last sum is obtained most easily by taking the cubes from one of the many available tables containing the first three powers of the integers (1) (2) (7).

From s_2 compute in the usual manner the sum of the squares of deviations from mean,

$$S_2 = s_2 - s_1^2/n = 4,518,741 - (14,361)^2/64 = 1,296,267,$$

s_1 being the sum of the X's.   For S_3, the sum of the cubes of deviations from the mean, the corresponding formula is

$$\begin{aligned} S_3 &= s_3 - 3s_1s_2/n + 2s_1^3/n^2 \\ &= 1,878,426,855 - 3(14,361)(4,518,741)/64 + 2(14,361)^3/(64)^2 \\ &= 282,723,308 \end{aligned}$$

Armed with these results, complete the computations indicated in table 8.5.1, ending with $g_1 = 1.5696$ and $t = 5.24$.   Certainly, there is no doubt of asymmetry in the population from which this sample was drawn.   The positive g_1 indicates a mean greater than the median.

8.6—Tests of normality in large samples.   One can test both skewness and *kurtosis*, two ways in which distributions may depart from normal.   Kurtosis is measured by g_2, a statistic based on the sum of the fourth powers of deviations from mean.   If g_2 is zero, there is no departure from normality so far as this measure is concerned.   A positive value of g_2 indicates an excess of items near the mean and far from it, with a corresponding depletion of the flanks of the distribution.   This is the manner in which the distribution of t departs from normal.   Negative values of g_2 result from flat-topped distribution curves.

The computations are shown in table 8.6.1.   The first five columns correspond to those of tables 8.2.1 and 8.3.1.   The numbers in the last four columns are calculated by repeated multiplication by X.   Take line 3 as an example: $(4)(-6) = -24$, $(-24)(-6) = 144$, $(144)(-6) = -864$, and $(-864)(-6) = 5,184$.   You are already familiar with the remaining calculations save those of S_4, k_4, g_2, and s_{g2}.   The formulas are intricate but may be followed with a little care.

You notice that both g_1 and g_2 are small, each being exceeded by its standard error.   The negative g_1 indicates a slight asymmetry with an excess of items larger than the mean drawing the peak of the frequency curve toward the right.   The negative g_2 shows a moderate kurtosis de-

TABLE 8.6.1

TEST OF NORMALITY IN A FREQUENCY DISTRIBUTION
Diameter (mm.) of ears in F_2 generation of yellow dent inbreds
of maize. (Lindstrom)

Class Mark	Frequency f	Code X	fX	fX^2	fX^3	fX^4
36	1	−8	− 8	64	− 512	4,096
37	0	−7	0	0	0	0
38	4	−6	−24	144	− 864	5,184
39	7	−5	−35	175	− 875	4,375
40	18	−4	−72	288	−1,152	4,608
41	26	−3	−78	234	− 702	2,106
42	28	−2	−56	112	− 224	448
43	51	−1	−51	51	− 51	51
44	47	0	0	0	0	0
45	49	1	49	49	49	49
46	31	2	62	124	248	496
47	33	3	99	297	891	2,673
48	19	4	76	304	1,216	4,864
49	4	5	20	100	500	2,500
50	8	6	48	288	1,728	10,368
51	1	7	7	49	343	2,401
	327		$s_1 = 37$	$s_2 = 2,279$	$s_3 = 595$	$s_4 = 44,219$

$S_2 = s_2 - s_1^2/n = 2,274.81$
$S_3 = s_3 - 3s_1s_2/n + 2s_1^3/n^2 = -177.659$
$S_4 = s_4 - 4s_1s_3/n + 6s_1^2s_2/n^2 - 3s_1^4/n^3 = 44,124.6$

$k_1 = s_1/n = 0.1131$
$k_2 = S_2/(n - 1) = 6.9779$
$k_3 = nS_3/(n - 1)(n - 2) = -0.5483$
$k_4 = n[(n + 1)S_4 - 3(n - 1)S_2^2/n]/(n - 1)(n - 2)(n - 3) = -9.563$

$g_1 = k_3/(k_2\sqrt{k_2}) = -0.0297$ $g_2 = k_4/k_2^2 = -0.1964$

$s_{g1}^2 = 6n(n - 1)/(n - 2)(n + 1)(n + 3) = 0.0182$
$s_{g2}^2 = 24n(n - 1)^2/(n - 3)(n - 2)(n + 3)(n + 5) = 0.0723$
Sample standard deviations: of g_1, 0.135; of g_2, 0.269
Values of t: for g_1, 0.22; for g_2, 0.73; $d.f. = \infty$

scribed by a distribution curve plateau-like near the center with an excess of moderate deviations. Since neither g is significant, however, there is little evidence of departure from normality in the population.

EXAMPLE 8.6.1—Compute the mean ear diameter from table 8.6.1, together with its standard error, 44.11 ± 0.146 mm.

EXAMPLE 8.6.2—In table 3.2.2, compute $g_1 = -0.0139$ and $g_2 = 0.0460$, showing that the distribution is practically normal.

EXAMPLE 8.6.3—In table 3.5.2 is the sampling distribution of 511 standard deviations. Calculate $g_1 = 0.3074$ with standard error, 0.108. This indicates that the anticipated departure from normality is significant. g_1 is positive because the mode is to the left of the mean.

EXAMPLE 8.6.4—The 511 values of t discussed in section 3.7 were distributed as follows:

Class Mark	f	Class Mark	f	Class Mark	f	Class Mark	f
−3.13	3	−1.13	29	0.87	31	2.87	1
−2.88	5	−0.88	35	1.12	23	3.12	1
−2.63	1	−0.63	38	1.37	17	3.37	2
−2.38	3	−0.38	40	1.62	11	3.62	0
−2.13	6	−0.13	52	1.87	8	3.87	0
−1.88	12	0.12	57	2.12	10	4.12	0
−1.63	21	0.37	43	2.37	6	4.37	1
−1.38	16	0.62	37	2.62	2		
						Total 511	

The highly significant value of $g_2 = 0.5340$ shows that the frequencies near the mode and in the tails are greater than in the normal distribution, those in the flanks being less. This was expected. But $g_1 = 0.1356$ is nonsignificant, which is also expected because the theoretical distribution of t is symmetrical.

8.7—Constructing the graph of a normal distribution. You were introduced to the normal distribution in section 2.1; a graph was shown in figure 2.1.1. The equation of the distribution is

$$y = \frac{1}{\sigma\sqrt{2\pi}}\, e^{-(X-\mu)^2/2\sigma^2}$$

In figure 8.7.1, μ is set at zero and σ at 1; that is, the graph depicts $\mathcal{N}(0, 1)$.

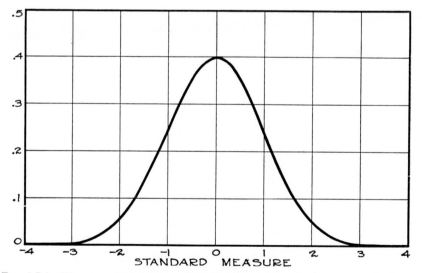

FIG. 8.7.1—The normal frequency curve. Abscissas are standard measure. Ordinates are taken from table 8.7.1.

It is convenient to put $\tau = (X - \mu)/\sigma$, where τ is the standard measure of the abscissa. The equation then takes the simpler form,

$$ y = \frac{1}{\sqrt{2\pi}} \, e^{-\tau^2/2} $$

The ordinates of this curve, for various values of τ, are given in table 8.7.1.

TABLE 8.7.1

ORDINATES OF THE NORMAL CURVE

τ	Second decimal place in τ									
	0.00	0.01	0.02	0.03	0.04	0.05	0.06	0.07	0.08	0.09
0.0	.3989	.3989	.3989	.3988	.3986	.3984	.3982	.3980	.3977	.3973
0.1	.3970	.3965	.3961	.3956	.3951	.3945	.3939	.3932	.3925	.3918
0.2	.3910	.3902	.3894	.3885	.3876	.3867	.3857	.3847	.3836	.3825
0.3	.3814	.3802	.3790	.3778	.3765	.3752	.3739	.3725	.3712	.3697
0.4	.3683	.3668	.3653	.3637	.3621	.3605	.3589	.3572	.3555	.3538
0.5	.3521	.3503	.3485	.3467	.3448	.3429	.3410	.3391	.3372	.3352
0.6	.3332	.3312	.3292	.3271	.3251	.3230	.3209	.3187	.3166	.3144
0.7	.3123	.3101	.3079	.3056	.3034	.3011	.2989	.2966	.2943	.2920
0.8	.2897	.2874	.2850	.2827	.2803	.2780	.2756	.2732	.2709	.2685
0.9	.2661	.2637	.2613	.2589	.2565	.2541	.2516	.2492	.2468	.2444
1.0	.2420	.2396	.2371	.2347	.2323	.2299	.2275	.2251	.2227	.2203
1.1	.2179	.21 ɔ5	.2131	.2107	.2083	.2059	.2036	.2012	.1989	.1965
1.2	.1942	.1919	.1895	.1872	.1849	.1826	.1804	.1781	.1758	.1736
1.3	.1714	.1691	.1669	.1647	.1626	.1604	.1582	.1561	.1539	.1518
1.4	.1497	.1476	.1456	.1435	.1415	.1394	.1374	.1354	.1334	.1315
1.5	.1295	.1276	.1257	.1238	.1219	.1200	.1182	.1163	.1145	.1127
1.6	.1109	.1092	.1074	.1057	.1040	.1023	.1006	.0989	.0973	.0957
1.7	.0940	.0925	.0909	.0893	.0878	.0863	.0848	.0833	.0818	.0804
1.8	.0790	.0775	.0761	.0748	.0734	.0721	.0707	.0694	.0681	.0669
1.9	.0656	.0644	.0632	.0620	.0608	.0596	.0584	.0573	.0562	.0551
2.0	.0540	.0529	.0519	.0508	.0498	.0488	.0478	.0468	.0459	.0449
2.1	.0440	.0431	.0422	.0413	.0404	.0396	.0387	.0379	.0371	.0363
2.2	.0355	.0347	.0339	.0332	.0325	.0317	.0310	.0303	.0297	.0290
2.3	.0283	.0277	.0270	.0264	.0258	.0252	.0246	.0241	.0235	.0229
2.4	.0224	.0219	.0213	.0208	.0203	.0198	.0194	.0189	.0184	.0180
2.5	.0175	.0171	.0167	.0163	.0158	.0154	.0151	.0147	.0143	.0139
2.6	.0136	.0132	.0129	.0126	.0122	.0119	.0116	.0113	.0110	.0107
2.7	.0104	.0101	.0099	.0096	.0093	.0091	.0088	.0086	.0084	.0081
2.8	.0079	.0077	.0075	.0073	.0071	.0069	.0067	.0065	.0063	.0061
2.9	.0060	.0058	.0056	.0055	.0053	.0051	.0050	.0048	.0047	.0046

τ	First decimal place in τ									
	0.0	0.1	0.2	0.3	0.4	0.5	0.6	0.7	0.8	0.9
3	.0044	.0033	.0024	.0017	.0012	.0009	.0006	.0004	.0003	.0002
4	.0001	.0001	.0001	.0000	.0000	.0000	.0000	.0000	.0000	.0000

As an example, at $\tau = 1$ the ordinate is 0.2420 as plotted in the figure. The same ordinate is plotted at $\tau = -1$. As another example, at $\tau = 2.46$ the ordinate is read from the column headed 0.06 in the table, opposite the entry $\tau = 2.4$ in the left column, the length being 0.0194. You will notice that as the curve recedes from the origin, it descends faster and faster until it reaches the ordinate at $\tau = 1$. Beyond that point, the descent is ever slower.

It is easy to identify the ordinates in the table with those in such a distribution as that of ear diameters in table 8.6.1. You may have already constructed the histogram for the sample. Applying Sheppard's correction to the variance k_2 in table 8.6.1, you have $s = \sqrt{(k_2 - 0.0833)} = \sqrt{6.8946} = 2.626$ mm. as the suitable estimate of the value of this parameter. There remains only a constant multiplier to transform the ordinates in table 8.7.1 to those appropriate for the sample. It is

$$\frac{n}{s} = \frac{327}{2.626} = 124.5$$

Start with the ordinate at the mean, 44.11 mm. Its value is (124.5) (0.3989) = 49.66 ears, the second factor being taken from the table at $\tau = 0$. This ordinate is plotted on the same scale of frequencies used in making your histogram. Next, compute the ordinate at one of the class marks, say 39 mm. The standard measure of this point is $\tau = (39 - 44.11) /2.626 = -1.95$. The tabular ordinate corresponding is 0.0596; whence the ordinate to be plotted is (124.5)(0.0596) = 7.42 ears. As a final illustration, compute the ordinate at one of the class boundaries, say 47.5 mm. You get $\tau = 1.29$, and thence 21.61 ears as the ordinate to be plotted. Proceeding in this manner, you compute as many ordinates as may seem necessary for plotting the normal curve. The final graph will have the same general appearance as figure 8.7 1.

8.8—Cumulative normal frequency distribution.

Table 8.8.1 differs from the usual frequency distribution in one major and several minor respects. The chief difference is that the frequencies (percentages or areas) are cumulative. To illustrate, look in the second column, opposite $\tau = 1.0$ in the first, where you find 3413. The meaning is that 34.13% of the total frequency of 10,000 falls on values of τ lying between zero and 1.00. This corresponds to the fact that 34.13% of the area of the curve in figure 8.7.1 lies between the ordinates at $\tau = 0$ and $\tau = 1$. The figure 34.13% is approximately half of the familiar 68.27%. Again, opposite 2.0 you find 4772, meaning that 47.72% of the frequency lies between $\tau = 0$ and $\tau = 2$. Doubling this percentage, you have 95.44% of the frequency within the interval $\tau = \pm 2$. The remaining 4.56% of the frequency lies beyond these limits. In general, the numbers in this table correspond to areas in figure 8.7.1 between ordinates at 0 and τ.

Some minor differences between table 8.8.1 and an ordinary frequency distribution are: (i) Since τ is standard measure, its values are measured in terms of the population standard deviation, σ, as a unit. Thus, $\tau = 2$ means $x = 2\sigma$ or $x/\sigma = 2$; (ii) the values of τ are not midpoints of class intervals, but are distances to their outer boundaries; (iii) only the positive values of τ are listed, corresponding to the right half of figure 8.7.1; (iv) values of τ are given to two decimal places, the second being read at

TABLE 8.8.1

CUMULATIVE NORMAL FREQUENCY DISTRIBUTION
τ is standard measure. $n = 10,000$

τ	.00	.01	.02	.03	.04	.05	.06	.07	.08	.09
.0	0000	0040	0080	0120	0160	0199	0239	0279	0319	0359
.1	0398	0438	0478	0517	0557	0596	0636	0675	0714	0753
.2	0793	0832	0871	0910	0948	0987	1026	1064	1103	1141
.3	1179	1217	1255	1293	1331	1368	1406	1443	1480	1517
.4	1554	1591	1628	1664	1700	1736	1772	1808	1844	1879
.5	1915	1950	1985	2019	2054	2088	2123	2157	2190	2224
.6	2257	2291	2324	2357	2389	2422	2454	2486	2517	2549
.7	2580	2611	2642	2673	2704	2734	2764	2794	2823	2852
.8	2881	2910	2939	2967	2995	3023	3051	3078	3106	3133
.9	3159	3186	3212	3238	3264	3289	3315	3340	3365	3389
1.0	3413	3438	3461	3485	3508	3531	3554	3577	3599	3621
1.1	3643	3665	3686	3708	3729	3749	3770	3790	3810	3830
1.2	3849	3869	3888	3907	3925	3944	3962	3980	3997	4015
1.3	4032	4049	4066	4082	4099	4115	4131	4147	4162	4177
1.4	4192	4207	4222	4236	4251	4265	4279	4292	4306	4319
1.5	4332	4345	4357	4370	4382	4394	4406	4418	4429	4441
1.6	4452	4463	4474	4484	4495	4505	4515	4525	4535	4545
1.7	4554	4564	4573	4582	4591	4599	4608	4616	4625	4633
1.8	4641	4649	4656	4664	4671	4678	4686	4693	4699	4706
1.9	4713	4719	4726	4732	4738	4744	4750	4756	4761	4767
2.0	4772	4778	4783	4788	4793	4798	4803	4808	4812	4817
2.1	4821	4826	4830	4834	4838	4842	4846	4850	4854	4857
2.2	4861	4864	4868	4871	4875	4878	4881	4884	4887	4890
2.3	4893	4896	4898	4901	4904	4906	4909	4911	4913	4916
2.4	4918	4920	4922	4925	4927	4929	4931	4932	4934	4936
2.5	4938	4940	4941	4943	4945	4946	4948	4949	4951	4952
2.6	4953	4955	4956	4957	4959	4960	4961	4962	4963	4964
2.7	4965	4966	4967	4968	4969	4970	4971	4972	4973	4974
2.8	4974	4975	4976	4977	4977	4978	4979	4979	4980	4981
2.9	4981	4982	4982	4983	4984	4984	4985	4985	4986	4986
3.0	4987	4987	4987	4988	4988	4989	4989	4989	4990	4990
3.1	4990	4991	4991	4991	4992	4992	4992	4992	4993	4993
3.2	4993	4993	4994	4994	4994	4994	4994	4995	4995	4995
3.3	4995	4995	4995	4996	4996	4996	4996	4996	4996	4997
3.4	4997	4997	4997	4997	4997	4997	4997	4997	4997	4998
3.6	4998	4998	4999	4999	4999	4999	4999	4999	4999	4999
3.9	5000									

the head of the column. To illustrate this last point, consider the number 4535 in the column headed 0.08 opposite 1.6 in column one. The interpretation is that 45.35% of the frequency lies between $\tau = 0$ and $\tau = 1.68$.

In the following paragraphs will be given various applications of the table of the normal frequency distribution, or the normal density function as it is now often called.

1. *Levels of* τ. These are values of $|\tau|$ outside which specified percentages of frequency may be found. As an example, let us determine the 5% level of τ, denoted by $\tau_{.05}$. On the positive side, 2.5% of the frequency is to be beyond $\tau_{.05}$ so that 47.5% is to be between 0 and $\tau_{.05}$. From the table the value of τ corresponding to 0.4750 is 1.96. Above 1.96 is to be found 2.5% of the total frequency while below -1.96 is another 2.5%. The 5% level, then, is $\tau_{.05} = 1.96$. This is the same as the 5% level of t, table 2.7.1, for infinite degrees of freedom. That is, as n increases indefinitely, the distribution of t tends toward the normal distribution of τ. Roughly, in large samples ($n > 50$, say) the 5% level of either t or τ is often taken as 2.

2. *The sample standard error of the difference between two means.* In large samples, the distinction between n and degrees of freedom is usually ignored. Instead of pooling sums of squares, as in chapter 4, the formulas of section 7.10 are used. If the means are taken from random samples, they are theoretically uncorrelated, and

$$s_{\bar{x}_1 - \bar{x}_2}^2 = s_1^2/n_1 + s_2^2/n_2 = s_{\bar{x}_1}^2 + s_{\bar{x}_2}^2$$

As an example, it is reported that for 841 13-year-old boys the mean height was $\bar{x}_1 = 57.30$ inches with $s_1 = 2.76$ inches, while for 784 girls of the same age, $\bar{x}_2 = 58.60$ and $s_2 = 2.44$ inches. The difference of the means is therefore 1.30 inches with standard error,

$$\sqrt{[(2.76)^2/841 + (2.44)^2/784]} = 0.129 \text{ inch}$$

The 95% confidence interval is given by

$$1.30 - (1.96)(0.129) \leq \mu_1 - \mu_2 \leq 1.30 + (1.96)(0.129)$$

One is confident, then, that the population difference between is 1.05 inches and 1.55 inches; the superior height of the girls at age 13 is clearly a population characteristic. The same conclusion would result from a test of H_0: $\mu_1 - \mu_2 = 0$. Here $\tau = 1.30/0.129 = 10$, far greater than the 1% level, 2.576.

3. *The distribution of chi with a single degree of freedom.* This is the same as that of t with infinite degrees of freedom. Consequently, the probability of exceeding large values of chi-square, beyond the limits of table 1.12.1 (which is the first line of table 1.14.1), may be evaluated by table 8.8.1; but notice, the 5% level of t is the same as the 2.5% po nt of τ. Illustration: In example 1.13.1 you were referred to this section for he probability of $\chi^2 > 8$. We have $t_{d.f. = \infty} = \chi_{d.f. = 1} = \sqrt{8} = 2.83$. From

the table, the probability of $\tau > 2.83 = 0.5 - 0.4977 = 0.0023$; whence the probability of $|t| > 2.83 = 0.0046$, which is the probability of $\chi^2 > 8$. Other illustrations of the use of the table will be given in the examples to follow.

EXAMPLE 8.8.1—Using table 8.8.1, show that 92.16% of the items in a normally distributed population lie between -1.76σ and 1.76σ.

EXAMPLE 8.8.2—Show that 65.24% of the items in a normal population lie between $\tau = -1.1\sigma$ and $\tau = 0.8\sigma$.

EXAMPLE 8.8.3—Show that 13.59% of the items are between $\tau = \sigma$ and $\tau = 2\sigma$.

EXAMPLE 8.8.4—Using table 8.8.1, show that approximately 50% of the items lie in the interval from -0.6745σ to 0.6745σ. The deviation 0.6745σ is called the *probable deviation*, and $0.6745\sigma/n$ the *probable error*.

EXAMPLE 8.8.5—Show that the 1% level is at $x/\sigma = 2.575$. You will find a slightly more precise value in table 2.7.1 at $n = \infty$.

EXAMPLE 8.8.6—Verify the statement that the interval $\bar{x} \neq 1.645\sigma$ contains 90% of a normal frequency.

EXAMPLE 8.8.7—The statement was made that of 1,000 13-year-old boys, 390 had heights within 1.4 inches of the mean height, 57.3 inches. Show that $s = 2.75$ inches on the assumption of normal distribution.

EXAMPLE 8.8.8—The mean of 1,000 normally distributed plot yields of corn was 20.50 pounds per plot. It was observed that 200 of the plots yielded 17.75 pounds or less. Estimate the standard deviation of the yields. Ans. 3.27 pounds per plot.

EXAMPLE 8.8.9—The mean and standard error of the dressing percentages in one large group of swine were $81.7 \pm 0.46\%$; in another, $80.0 \pm 0.37\%$. Show that, for testing the mean difference, $t = 2.88$, a highly significant value.

EXAMPLE 8.8.10—In table 8.6.1, compute the frequency expected in the class whose mark is 42; that is, whose interval is 41.5–42.5. Hints: In standard measure, the boundaries are

$$\frac{41.50 - 44.11}{2.626} = -0.994 \text{ and } \frac{42.50 - 44.11}{2.626} = -0.613$$

From table 8.8.1, the cumulative percentage frequencies are 0.3399 and 0.2301. Hence, the percentage frequency within the interval is $0.3399 - 0.2301 = 0.1098$. Finally, the expected frequency is $(0.1098)(327) = 35.9$, to be compared with the observed frequency of 28 ears.

EXAMPLE 8.8.11—In table 8.6.1, compute the frequency expected in the class whose mark is 44. Ans. 49.2 ears. Continuing, expected frequencies may be computed for all the intervals in the table and for the tails in which no ears were observed. This process is referred to as the *graduation* of the distribution—the fitting of the class frequencies to those of some standard distribution, in this case, the normal. The sum of the percentage frequencies should be 1, while that of the expected frequencies should be 327. The resulting normal distribution has for its parameters the statistics, $\mu = 44.11$ ears $\sigma = 2.626$ ears, but it is only an approximation to the $N(\mu, \sigma)$ from which the sample of ears was drawn.

The goodness of fit of the observed distribution to the calculated normal may be tested by chi-square, the degrees of freedom being *three less than the number of classes*. In section 1.14, the degrees of freedom were only one less than the number of classes, but here we are using as additional restrictions two statistics, $\bar{x}$ and s, which have been calculated from the sample. One degree of freedom must be deducted for each added restriction.

EXAMPLE 8.8.12—Verify the probability, 0.0002, in the answer to example 1.13.5.

8.9—The calculation of r in a random sample from a bivariate normal population. The double entry table 8.9.1 contains in compact form the record of two measurements on each of 327 ears of corn (6). The diameters, X, were grouped into millimeter classes as in table 8.6.1, the frequencies and code numbers appearing in the bottom rows of the table. The weight classes, Y, are 10 grams each with frequency and code at the right. Correlation in these data is evidenced by the tendency of high frequencies to lie along the diagonal of the table, leaving two corners blank—there are no very heavy ears with small diameters. In each diameter array (column) there is notable variation in weight, but it is not nearly so great as the entire range displayed in the left-hand column. The regression of weight on diameter could be represented by a line following the upward trend of the data. This line would be fitted by the method of least squares to the means of the successive diameter arrays.

The calculations follow patterns already familiar. Those leading to Σx^2 are taken from that part of table 8.6.1 which is the counterpart of table 8.2.1. The corresponding calculations for weight are carried through with the data in columns f_y and Y. The results are summarized in table 8.9.2.

The device for arriving at ΣXY, displayed in the last two columns of table 8.9.1, has not been explained before. Each number in column ΣXf_x is calculated from the frequencies in that row together with the code numbers in the bottom line. As examples:

   (i) In the 3rd line: $(3)(4) = 12$
   (ii) In the 4th line: $(1)(2) + (1)(4) = 6$
   (iii) In the 5th line: $(1)(1) + (2)(2) + (1)(3) + (4)(6) = 32$
   (iv) In the 7th line: $(1)(-2)+(3)(-1)+(7)(1)+(3)(3)+(3)(4)=23$

The products in the last column are got from the two columns preceding. The sum at the end of this column is the desired ΣXY. You remember that no decoding is necessary for r. Incidentally, the sum of the column, ΣXf_x, checks s_1 in table 8.6.1.

There are numerous devices for calculating r in a two-way frequency distribution. They all lead to the same result and all take about the same amount of time. If a punched card system is available, the sums, sums of squares, and sum of products can be run up on the tabulator economically if $n > 300$ (approximately).

A vast amount of time has been wasted in calculating correlation coefficients for samples not randomly drawn or not drawn from bivariate populations which are normal. (See section 7.3.) In such cases, r estimates no parameter. It is true that r^2 is the fraction of Σy^2 which is attributable to linear regression—this is merely a matter of arithmetic. But that has to do with regression, not correlation. Even regression can be meaningless if linearity is assumed when the sample regression is obviously nonlinear. Before starting any computation on a large sample, examine the data carefully to see that they conform to the model described in section 7.3. Among other things it will pay to plot both regressions to learn if they are reasonably linear. In chapter 10 you will find some tests of homogeneity of variance and in chapter 15, of linearity of regression.

TABLE 8.9.1

COMPUTATION OF SAMPLE CORRELATION COEFFICIENT IN TWO-WAY FREQUENCY TABLE

Frequency of occurrence of ears of maize having each diameter and weight

Weight, Grams	Diameter, Millimeters																f_v	Code Y	ΣXf_z	Product $Y(\Sigma Xf_z)$
	36	37	38	39	40	41	42	43	44	45	46	47	48	49	50	51				
320													1				1	12	4	48
310												1					1	11	3	33
300													3				3	10	12	120
290										1	1	1	1				2	9	6	54
280									1	1	2	3	2	1	4	1	8	8	32	256
270							1	3	2		1	2	3	1			7	7	23	161
260								1	2	7	3	6	2	2			19	6	23	138
250				1				1	4	3	5	4					11	5	24	120
240							3	6	4	4	3	1	1		1		23	4	30	120
230							1	7	7	3	1	3		2			20	3	26	78
220							2	6	5	4	3	1	2		1		23	2	5	10
210						1	1	5	6	4	3	5	1				28	1	4	4
200				1		1	2	6	6	11	2	4	1				29	0	-7	0
190					1	4	4	5	3	2	2						32	-1	-22	-22
180			1	2		3	5	2	1	4	3		1				28	-2	-14	-28
170				1	5	4	1	4	4	2		1			1		21	-3	-20	-60
160					1	2	1	1	1	1		1					19	-4	-15	-60
150				1	3	2	2				1						14	-5	-15	-75
140						3	1										11	-6	-22	-132
130					5	2		2									3	-7	-8	-56
120			1			2											9	-8	-33	-264
110					1		1				1						3	-9	-4	-36
100				1		1	1	1			1						2	-10	-5	-50
90			1		1	1	1		2								4	-11	-8	-88
80				1													3	-12	-9	-108
70					1		1										1	-13	-5	-65
60			1				1										1	-14	-4	-56
50	1								2								1	-15	-8	-120
f_z	1	0	4	7	18	26	28	51	47	49	31	33	19	4	8	1	327		37	2318
Code X	-8	-7	-6	-5	-4	-3	-2	-1	0	1	2	3	4	5	6	7				

TABLE 8.9.2

CALCULATION OF CORRELATION COEFFICIENT IN TABLE 8.9.1

$$\Sigma Xf_x = 37 \qquad \Sigma Yf_y = -46 \qquad \Sigma XY = 2,318$$
$$\Sigma X^2 f_x = 2,279 \qquad \Sigma Y^2 f_y = 7,264 \qquad (\Sigma Xf_x)(\Sigma Yf_y)/n = -5.20$$
$$(\Sigma Xf_x)^2/n = 4.19 \qquad (\Sigma Yf_y)^2/n = 6.47$$
$$\overline{} \qquad\qquad \overline{} \qquad\qquad \Sigma xy = 2,323.20$$
$$\Sigma x^2 = 2,274.81 \qquad \Sigma y^2 = 7,257.53$$

$$r = \frac{\Sigma xy}{\sqrt{(\Sigma x^2)(\Sigma y^2)}} = \frac{2,323.20}{\sqrt{(2,274.81)(7,257.53)}} = 0.5718$$

EXAMPLE 8.9.1—Using the data in columns f_y and Y, table 8.9.1, calculate $\Sigma y^2 = 7,257.53$, together with the sample mean and standard error, 198.6 ± 2.61.

EXAMPLE 8.9.2—Calculate the sample mean, 44.1, and standard deviation, 2.64, in the 42-millimeter array of weights, table 8.9.1.

EXAMPLE 8.9.3—In the 200-gram array of diameters, compute $\bar{x} = 198.6$ and $s = 47.18$.

EXAMPLE 8.9.4—Compute the sample regression coefficient of weight on diameter, 1.0213, together with the regression equation, $\hat{Y} = 1.0213X + 154.81$.

EXAMPLE 8.9.5—Calculate the sample mean weight of the ears in each of the 16 diameter arrays of table 8.9.1. Present these means graphically as ordinates with the corresponding diameters as abscissas. Plot the graph of the regression equation on the same figure. Do you get a good fit? Is there any evidence of curvilinearity in the regression of means?

EXAMPLE 8.9.6—Calculate the mean diameter in each of the 28 weight arrays. Plot these means against the weight class marks. Does there seem to be any pronounced curvilinearity in the regression of these mean diameters on the weight? Can you write the regression equation giving estimated diameter for each weight?

EXAMPLE 8.9.7—If you are interested in mathematics, you will naturally wish to derive the formula for ΣXY in table 8.9.1. This table, in fact, introduces many fascinating problems. You will find an excellent discussion, with bibliography, in (9).

REFERENCES

1. PETER BARLOW. Tables. E. and F. N. Spon, Ltd., London (1921).

2. C. B. DAVENPORT and MERLE P. EKAS. Statistical Methods in Biology, Medicine and Psychology. John Wiley and Sons, Inc., New York (1936).

3. T. I. EDWARDS. Plant Physiology, 9:8 (1934).

4. R. A. FISHER. Statistical Methods for Research Workers. Oliver and Boyd, Edinburgh. See section 13 and Appendix D to chapter III.

5. R. A. FISHER. Biometrics, 11:237, Query No. 114 (1955).

6. E. W. LINDSTROM. The American Naturalist, 49:311 (1935).

7. Mathematical Tables. Chemical Rubber Publishing Co., Cleveland.

8. IRVINE H. PAGE, ESBEN KIRK, WILLIAM H. LEWIS, JR., WILLIAM THOMPSON, and DONALD D. VAN SLYKE. The Journal of Biological Chemistry, 111:613 (1935).

9. H. L. RIETZ, Editor-in-Chief. Handbook of Mathematical Statistics. Houghton Mifflin Co., New York (1924).

10. W. F. SHEPPARD. Proceedings of the London Mathematical Society, 29:353 (1898).

11. GUSTAV A. WIEBE. Journal of Agricultural Research, 50:331 (1935).

CHAPTER 9

Enumeration Data With More
Than One Degree of Freedom

9.1—Introduction. The chief purpose of chapter 1 was the easy introduction of sample-based inferences about populations. Point and interval estimates, together with tests of hypotheses, were explained with as little diversion as seemed feasible. Those primarily interested in enumeration statistics were referred to this chapter for further exposition.

In the intervening chapters a good deal has been said about the normal distribution; it is the basis for many of the statistical methods devised for measurement data. Most of the methods of the present chapter, like those of chapter 1, are appropriate for samples from binomially or multinomially distributed populations, together with those from Poisson distributions. These latter distributions will be described in more detail in chapter 16.

With the exception of section 1.14, the methods in chapter 1 were for single samples with only two classes of individuals involving a single degree of freedom. We are now ready to consider more than one sample as well as more than two classes.

In the next two sections of this chapter, as in chapter 1, the hypotheses tested will be those concerned with *goodness of fit*; the conformity of a sample with some theoretical subdivision, like 3:1 or 9:3:3:1, or like the classes of a binomial distribution. Later, the hypotheses will be those of *independence* or *homogeneity*.

9.2—An experiment with more than one sample. It is often convenient and informative to collect data in several small samples rather than in a single large one. This provides substantially more information. An illustration is furnished by some experiments on chlorophyll inheritance in maize (14) reported in table 9.2.1. The series consisted of 11 progenies of heterozygous green plants, self-fertilized, segregating into dominant green and recessive yellow. The hypothetical ratio was 3:1.

Chi-square is calculated for each progeny and entered in the last column. As an illustration, consider the first progeny with 122 plants,

98 green and 24 yellow.   Under the 3:1 hypothesis the numbers anticipated are three-fourths of 122 = 91.5 green, and one-fourth, 30.5, yellow;
then chi-square (review section 1.10 if necessary) is,

$$\chi^2 = \frac{(98 - 91.5)^2}{91.5} + \frac{(24 - 30.5)^2}{30.5} = 1.85,$$

not an excessive value in random sampling from homogeneous material
(see table 1.14.1).

Since most of the chi-squares are small and all nonsignificant, they
furnish little evidence that the 11 progeny samples may not have been

TABLE 9.2.1

NUMBERS OF GREEN AND YELLOW SEEDLINGS IN 11 PROGENIES OF SELF-FERTILIZED,
HETEROZYGOUS GREEN PLANTS, WITH NUMBERS EXPECTED UNDER THE 3:1 HYPOTHESIS,
AND VALUES OF CHI-SQUARE

Number of Plants	Green	Yellow	Ratio, G/Y	Hypotheti- cal Green	Hypotheti- cal Yellow	Chi-square
122	98	24	4.1	91.50	30.50	1.85
149	110	39	2.8	111.75	37.25	0.11
86	68	18	3.8	64.50	21.50	0.76
55	42	13	3.2	41.25	13.75	0.05
71	54	17	3.2	53.25	17.75	0.04
179	141	38	3.7	134.25	44.75	1.36
150	120	30	4.0	112.50	37.50	2.00
36	27	9	3.0	27.00	9.00	0.00
91	70	21	3.3	68.25	22.75	0.17
53	39	14	2.8	39.75	13.25	0.05
111	85	26	3.3	83.25	27.75	0.15
Pooled 1,103	854	249		827.25	275.25	3.46

drawn from a 3:1 population.   In fact, somewhat more variation might
have been expected; you remember that, in sampling from binomial
populations, about one random sample among twenty has chi-square
greater than 3.841.

A valuable property of chi-square is that the sum of n sample values
is itself distributed as chi-square with n degrees of freedom.   Though each
component chi-square may be short of significance, yet the sum may be
highly significant.   Thus the information in the small samples is accumulated, giving clearer evidence of population facts.   For illustration, look
at the first line of table 1.14.1 under $P = 0.10$; $\chi^2 = 2.706$.   Suppose
there were five similar samples each of which happened to turn up th'is
same chi-square.   The sum would be $5(2.706) = 13.53$, with 5 $d.f.$,
which exceeds the 0.025 point.

In the corn progenies the sum of the 11 chi-squares is only 6.54, a smaller-than-usual value for 11 *d.f.* The accumulated information emphasizes the conformity of the progenies to the 3:1 ratio.

There are two other chi-squares that may elicit information about the populations sampled as in this experiment. First, there is the chi-square calculated from the pooled data in the last line of the table. Here the 11 progenies are treated as a single large sample. Using the formula (section 1.16),

$$\chi^2 = \frac{(a - rb)^2}{r(a + b)} = \frac{\{854 - 3(249)\}^2}{3(1,103)} = 3.46$$

With one *d.f.* this chi-square almost reaches the 5% point. The reason is that nine of the eleven ratios, G/Y, are larger than 3. This persisting tendency might have been strong enough to lead to rejection of the 3:1 hypothesis. See example 9.2.1.

Finally, there is a chi-square that measures the *inconsistency* of the deviations of the sample ratios from the hypothetical. Fisher and Mather (11) called this *"heterogeneity."* Its calculation is simple:

	Degrees of Freedom	Chi-square
Sum of 11 chi-squares	11	6.54
Pooled chi-square	1	3.46
Heterogeneity (difference)	10	3.08

A surprising feature of this maize experiment is the smallness of the heterogeneity chi-square with 10 *d.f.* Under the null hypothesis, larger values would be expected in 98% of random samples. The oscillations above and below the hypothetical ratio are much less than is usual in sampling. Such pronounced consistency might lead the experimenter to examine his procedure for constraints leading to lack of ordinary random variation. Compare example 9.2.2.

We now have three over-all chi-squares testing the same null hypothesis, that the several samples are all drawn from a common population with some specified ratio. It is the alternative hypotheses that differ. For the sum of chi-squares, the alternative is that the population ratios deviate from the hypothetical with no distinction between excess and defect; the squaring of the deviation obliterates the sign. The alternative for pooled chi-square is that there is a predominating tendency toward deviations with a common sign. In the case of heterogeneity chi-square, the signs of the deviations are recognized and their inconsistency evaluated.

Further discussion of heterogeneity chi-square will be found in sections 9.6 and 9.9.

EXAMPLE 9.2.1—From a population expected to segregate 3:1, samples were drawn with the following ratios; 98:41, 71:31, 127:52, 61:25, 86:36. Calculate the sample ratios and chi-squares. (The formula of section 1.16 makes the work easier.) The sum of the 5 chi-squares is 6.73, $P = 0.25$. Pooled chi-square is 6.66, $P < 0.01$, showing significance in the persistent excess of recessive plants. Heterogeneity chi-square is only 0.07, verifying the obvious consistency in the sample ratios.

EXAMPLE 9.2.2—Samples with the following ratios were drawn from a population expected to segregate 1:1; 47:33, 40:26, 30:42, 24:34. Note the discrepancies among the sample ratios. These result in a large heterogeneity chi-square equal to 9.01, $P = 0.03$. The conclusion is that there are two populations being sampled, not one.

9.3—An experiment with more than two classes of individuals. An introduction to this type of experiment was given in section 1.14. With liberation from the restriction of a single degree of freedom, all the theoretical genetic ratios may be tested, both in single samples and in combinations. As examples, two groups of progenies are recorded in table 9.3.1, each being F_2 plants from a cross between japonica colored maize

TABLE 9.3.1

F_2 Seedlings From a Cross of Japonica With Fine-Striped Maize
Lindstrom's data (14)
Hypothetical ratios, 9:3:3:1. Hypothetical numbers in parenthesis

Progeny Numbers	Number of Seedlings	Green	Japonica	Fine-Striped	Combination	Chi-square
1, 4, 6	168	117(94.5)	26(31.5)	18(31.5)	7(10.5)	13.28
2, 3	135	82(76.0)	12(25.3)	33(25.3)	8(8.4)	9.82
Sum	303	199	38	51	15	

plants and fine-striped. The seedlings were expected to segregate in 9:3:3:1 ratios. Hence, from the 168 plants in the first group, one would expect nine-sixteenths green, three-sixteenths japonica, etc. The formula for chi-square, section 1.14, specifies the sum of the four component parts:

$$(117 - 94.5)^2/94.5 = 5.36$$
$$(26 - 31.5)^2/31.5 = 0.96$$
$$(18 - 31.5)^2/31.5 = 5.79$$
$$(7 - 10.5)^2/10.5 = 1.17$$
$$\chi^2 = \overline{13.28}$$

This value of χ^2 is based on three degrees of freedom, one less than the number of subsamples contributing. It is larger than the 1% point, 11.34. The null hypothesis being tested is that the segregation in the population is in the ratios 9:3:3:1. There is little chance, therefore, that the seedlings in this group are a sample from such a population. That is, the sample departs significantly from the hypothetical ratios.

In the second group of progenies, $\chi^2 = 9.82$, $d.f. = 3$, is just at the 2% point. The departure from hypothetical is significant but less pronounced than in the first sample.

The sum of the 2 chi-squares, $13.28 + 9.82 = 23.10$, $d.f. = 6$, accentuates the deviations from the hypothetical frequencies but gives no evidence about the directions of the departures.

Pooled chi-square, calculated from the sums in the last line of the table, is 12.37 with $d.f., = 3$, also significant. The tendency is for the ratios in the two samples to deviate in the same direction from hypothetical, though the tendency is reversed in the two fine-striped classes.

Heterogeneity chi-square is calculated this way:

	Degrees of Freedom	Chi-square
Sum of 2 chi-squares	6	23.10
Pooled	3	12.37
Heterogeneity	3	10.73

The deviations, signs considered, are significant, but not so pronounced as those of the other types.

Lindstrom remarked: "This F_2 distribution suggests independent inheritance between the japonica and fine-striped factors, although the data are rather uncertain because of the difficulty in classifying the various types of striping and also because of the differential viability of the types."

This brings us to the end of the applications of chi-square to goodness-of-fit problems. In chapter 1 and in most of the present one we have been testing data against theoretical distributions and ratios. After two intervening sections, applications will be switched to tests of dependence and homogeneity in contingency tables, where there is no prior knowledge about the ratios in the population.

EXAMPLE 9.3.1—Bateson and Punnett (2) worked with sweet peas having blue flowers (B) dominant to red (b) and long pollen (L) to round (l). Instead of the expected 9:3:3:1 ratios in F_2, they got the following distributions in two of their trials:

	BL	*Bl*	*bL*	*bl*
Number 61,1910	85	33	41	1
F 32,1910	72	35	28	0
Pooled	157	68	69	1

Among several hypotheses about the phenomenon, they were ". . . inclined to regard the partial repulsion between B and L . . . " as of a type which would produce the ratios 129:63:63:1. On the basis of this null hypothesis, analyze chi-square as follows:

	Degrees of Freedom	Chi-square
Sum of two	6	3.249
Pooled	3	0.961
Heterogeneity	3	2.288

Since the hypothesis was selected to fit the data, tests of hypotheses are not appropriate. It is merely to be observed that heterogeneity chi-square is the major portion of the sum.

9.4—Combination of probabilities.
Evidence on a treatment effect may be available from more than one type of experiment. The data

cannot be pooled and there are no chi-squares to be added. But if each experiment has yielded a probability, these may be combined to accumulate the evidence from the several sources. Fisher (10, section 21.1. See also reference 21) showed that $-2 \log_e P$ is distributed as chi-square with 2 degrees of freedom. This leads to the following method applied to hypothetical data.

The difference between two nutritive elements was evaluated in three experiments on small animals. In one, there was merely an enumeration of those that did and did not exceed a standard gain. The resulting chi-square was 2.7 with one degree of freedom; $P = 0.10$. The second

TABLE 9.4.1

COMBINATION OF PROBABILITIES FROM THREE EXPERIMENTS

Experiment	P	$Log_{10}P$
1	0.10	$9.0000 - 10$
2	0.12	$9.0792 - 10$
3	0.08	$8.9031 - 10$
Sum		$26.9823 - 30 = -3.0177$

$$Log_e P = (2.3026)(-3.0177) = -6.95$$
$$\chi^2 = -2 \log_e P = 13.90, \ d.f. = (3)(2) = 6, \ P = 0.035$$

experiment was a comparison of two lots with $t = 1.65$, $d.f. = 18$, $P = 0.12$. Individuals were compared in the third experiment; $t = 2.00$, $d.f. = 9$, $P = 0.08$. Each experiment indicated an effect but none was significant at the 5% level. One feels that the accumulated evidence would be more convincing. Table 9.4.1 shows how to combine the probabilities. From the results, the experimenter would be justified in rejecting the hypothesis of no effect.

If the probabilities average around $P = 0.3$, the accumulated evidence does not alter that of the several experiments. Suppose you have three experiments, each with $P = 0.3$; you will find the combined probability is still about 0.3.

9.5—Adjustment for continuity. In chapters 1 and 9, the theoretical continuous distribution of chi-square is used to test discrete data. The jumps from unit to unit in the observed data prevent the calculated chi-square from corresponding exactly with probabilities read in table 1.14.1. The result is a bias in the probability taken from the table, a tendency to underestimate it, causing too many rejections of the null hypothesis. In cases involving a single degree of freedom, the bias is corrected quite simply. The formulas are adjusted by subtracting 0.5 from the absolute values of the deviations. The subsequent calculation and reading of the table go forward as usual. In large samples this small adjustment has little effect on the calculated chi-square; but it is so easily made that it might as well be the routine procedure.

As an example, consider one of the samples of digits drawn as in section 1.5. Suppose 8 odds turned up in a sample of 10. The theoretical ratio, you remember, is 0.506. We have, then,

$$f_1 = 8, f_2 = 2, F_1 = 5.06, F_2 = 4.94$$

Substituting in the formula for adjusted chi-square,

$$\chi^2 = \Sigma(|f - F| - 0.5)^2 / F$$

$$= \frac{(|8 - 5.06| - 0.5)^2}{5.06} + \frac{(|2 - 4.94| - 0.5)^2}{4.94}$$

$$= \frac{(2.94 - 0.5)^2}{5.06} + \frac{(2.94 - 0.5)^2}{4.94}$$

$$= \frac{(2.44)^2}{5.06} + \frac{(2.44)^2}{4.94}$$

$$= 2.38$$

The only change is that the absolute values of the two deviations are changed from 2.94 to 2.44, the signs being ignored because of the squaring.

The special formula of section 1.11 is even easier to adjust.

$$\chi^2 = (|f - F| - 0.5)^2 (1/F_1 + 1/F_2)$$
$$= (|8 - 5.06| - 0.5)^2 (1/5.06 + 1/4.94)$$
$$= (2.44)^2 (0.40006)$$
$$= 2.38, \text{ as before.}$$

It is clear that adjusted chi-square is always less than the unadjusted value, the latter being 3.46 in the illustrative example. This leads to the reading of larger probabilities in the table, probabilities that are less extreme; consequently, the null hypothesis is less liable to rejection. For theoretical discussions of the correction for continuity see (6, 10, 21, 22).

If it happens that $|f - F|$ is less than 0.5, the adjustment should not be made. In this case, chi-square is small so that conclusions will not be affected.

The adjustment should be omitted in all situations where several chi-squares are combined. Examples are found in the sampling of chi-square (sections 1.11 and 1.12) and in the analysis of chi-square discussed in section 9.2. In the latter section, the additive relationship would be destroyed if the adjustment were made.

The adjustment described does not apply to data with more than one degree of freedom.

The formula of section 1.16 is adjusted by subtracting $(r + 1)/2$ from $|a - rb|$. Applying the adjustment to the data in that section,

$$\chi^2 = \frac{(|a - rb| - (r + 1)/2)^2}{r(a + b)}$$

$$= \frac{(|310 - 270| - 4/2)^2}{3(400)}$$

$$= 1.20,$$

instead of the unadjusted value of 1.33. Notice that if the population is equally divided then

$$r = 1 \text{ and } \chi^2 = \frac{(|a - b| - 1)^2}{a + b}$$

EXAMPLE 9.5.1—In example 1.13.5, $a = 2$, $b = 19$, $r = 1$. Adjusted chi-square is

$$(|2 - 19| - 1)^2/21 = 12.2$$

instead of the unadjusted 13.76. Conclusions are unchanged.

EXAMPLE 9.5.2—In the illustrative example of section 9.2, segregation in the first sample was in the ratio of 98 green plants to 24 yellow, with unadjusted chi-square equal to 1.85. Calculate adjusted chi-square by each of the appropriate formulas. Ans. 1.57.

9.6—Test for independence. The fourfold contingency table.
After a sample has been divided on the basis of one attribute, the individuals in each part may be subdivided according to a second. An illustration is taken from the Boone County survey cited in section 1.3. One attribute observed between August 14 and September 6 was the presence of second brood eggs of the corn borer. Table 9.6.1 shows that 125 of the 176 sample fields were so infested. A second attribute investigated

TABLE 9.6.1

PRESENCE AND ABSENCE OF SECOND BROOD EGGS IN BOONE COUNTY SAMPLE, SUBDIVIDED ACCORDING TO APPLICATION OF FERTILIZER

| Second Brood Eggs | Fertilizer or Manure | | Total |
	Some	None	
Present	31	94	125
Absent	9	42	51
Total	40	136	176

was the use of fertilizer or manure. The 2 × 2 table shows the subdivision of the sample according to the two attributes.

Since this is a random sample of fields, many inferences can be made by use of the methods of chapter 1. Three examples will serve to indicate the possibilities.

1. In 31/176 = 17.6% of the fields both attributes were observed, second brood eggs being found in fertilized fields. The 0.95 confidence interval is from 11.6% to 24.6%. If the number of fields in the population were known, both the point and interval estimates could be expanded to the total number of infested, fertilized fields in Boone County.

2. Among the sample fields, 125/176 = 71.0% were infested with second brood eggs, the 95% confidence interval being 63.0% to 78.5%.

3. Of the 40 sample fields which had been fertilized, 31 were infested and 9 free. We may test any interesting null hypothesis; for example, that in the population of fertilized fields in Boone County, half are infested. This would be in answer to the question, "Is there a significant difference between the fractions of infested and free fertilized fields?" Using the third formula of section 9.5, $a = 31$, $b = 9$, $r = 1$, and

$$\chi^2 = (31 - 9 - 1)^2/40 = 11.0$$

The significance of the difference is manifest.

Coming now to the new feature of fourfold tables, this question arises: Does fertilizing affect the occurrence of second brood eggs or are these two attributes *independent*? Another way to ask the question involves the two ratios of fertilized to unfertilized fields, the ratios being

$$31/94 = 0.330 \text{ for infested fields, and}$$
$$9/42 = 0.214 \text{ for clean fields.}$$

Are these ratios significantly different? A third form of the question might be about the two percentages of infested fields,

$$31/125 = 24.8\% \text{ for fertilized fields, and}$$
$$9/51 = 17.6\% \text{ for unfertilized.}$$

Do these percentages differ significantly?

The three questions are logically the same; they are all answered by setting up the null hypothesis of independence, then testing it by chi-square. If the null hypothesis is true, the two ratios in each of the foregoing pairs may be samples from equal population ratios. The argument will be presented in the next section; meanwhile, a convenient formula will be explained.

The 2 × 2 table may be represented symbolically in this way:

a	b	$a + b$
c	d	$c + d$
$a + c$	$b + d$	$a + b + c + d = n$

An easily calculated chi-square formula for testing the hypothesis of independence is

$$\chi^2 = \frac{n(|ad - bc| - n/2)^2}{(a + b)(c + d)(a + c)(b + d)}$$

The fraction, $n/2$, effects the correction for continuity. In samples of several hundreds and in situations where the correction is not appropriate this term may be omitted.

For the Boone County sample, $a = 31$, $b = 94$, $c = 9$, $d = 42$, and $n = 176$. Substituting,

$$\chi^2 = \frac{176(31 \times 42 - 94 \times 9 - 176/2)^2}{125 \times 51 \times 40 \times 136}$$

$$= \frac{176 \times 368 \times 368}{125 \times 51 \times 40 \times 136}$$

Only the first 3 or 4 digits are needed in the answer. Cumbersome calculations may be avoided by dividing both numerator and denominator by some convenient power of 10, in this case, 10^6. This is done by moving the decimal points a total of 6 places to the left in each term of the fraction:

$$\chi^2 = \frac{1.76 \times 3.68 \times 3.68}{1.25 \times 5.1 \times 4.0 \times 1.36} = \frac{23.8}{34.7} = 0.69$$

As will be shown later, the test for independence in the 2 × 2 table is based on only a single degree of freedom; so P is about 0.42 and the null hypothesis is not rejected. Each pair of ratios discussed above may well be the same in the population. The conclusion is that fertilization of a field does not affect the deposition of second brood eggs; the two processes are independent.

Theoretically, the conclusion might as well be that the deposition of second brood eggs does not affect the practice of fertilizing fields. It is practical considerations alone that dictate the form of the conclusion.

If the conclusion were different, we should have to review the second of the three inferences proposed in the second paragraph of this section. Should the fraction of infested fields depend on fertilization, the over-all percentage of infested fields would lose much of its interest. Instead, we should wish to know the two different percentages, one for fertilized and another for unfertilized fields. The over-all percentage may have little utility in situations where heterogeneity (or dependence) is present.

EXAMPLE 9.6.1—Dr. C. H. Richardson of the Iowa Agricultural Experiment Station has furnished the following numbers of aphids (*Aphis rumicis* L.) alive and dead after being sprayed with two solutions of sodium oleate:

Concentration of Sodium Oleate (per cent)	Alive	Dead	Total	Per Cent Dead
1.10	3	62	65	95.4
0.65	13	55	68	80.9
Total	16	117	133	

Calculate adjusted chi-square, 5.31. Estimate the 95% confidence intervals, 86% to 99%, for the population percentage dead in the higher concentration; and 69% to 90% in the lower. Is there any reason for considering the per cent dead in the entire sample? Note that the totals, 65 and 68, were selected for convenience; they do not contain information about the relative sizes of two populations.

EXAMPLE 9.6.2—Here are data on the germination of samples from two bags of blue grass seed.

Bag Number	Number of Seeds Germinating	Number Not Germinating	Total	Per Cent Germinating
1	340	60	400	85
2	356	44	400	89
Total	696	104	800	87

Calculate adjusted $\chi^2 = 2.49$. The difference between the percentages of germination may be attributed to sampling variation, and 87% considered as an unbiased estimate of the per cent germination in the two bags. Set 0.99 confidence limits to the population percentage. Ans. 84%–90%.

EXAMPLE 9.6.3—In 1933 Davis (8) was trying to determine the causes of unusual development of smut (*Ustilago zeae*) in corn plants. Since all the plants were inoculated, the chances of infection seemed equal. Bags were placed over the ears of 174 plants just before silking, thus preventing pollination and inhibiting development. Of these plants, 38 were smutted. Among 262 unbagged plants 31 were found smutted on September 15. Chi-square is 7.13, indicating a significant difference in the percentages of smutted plants, attributable to the effects of bagging.

EXAMPLE 9.6.4—In examining the effects of different sprays in the control of codling moth injury to apples, Hansberry and Richardson (12) counted the wormy apples on each of 48 trees. Two trees sprayed with lead arsenate yielded:

A: 2,130 fruits, 1,299 or 61% of which were injured
B: 2,190 fruits, 1,183 or 54% of which were injured

Chi-square = 21.16 is conclusive evidence that on these two trees the chance of injury was different. Yet they were treated in all respects alike. This is characteristic of spray experiments. For some unknown reasons, injuries under identical experimental treatment differ significantly. Hence, it is undesirable to compare sprays on single trees, because a difference in percentages of injured apples might be attributable either to the treatments or to the unknown sources of variation. A statistical determination of the homogeneity or heterogeneity of experimental material under identical conditions is called a *test of technique*. Hansberry and Richardson combined a study of technique with their experiment on sprays.

9.7—The fourfold table; frequencies based on hypothesis of independence. If the null hypothesis of independence is true, then the frequencies in the four cells of the table are proportional. Denote these hypothetical frequencies by

F_1	F_2	$a + b$
F_3	F_4	$c + d$
$a + c$	$b + d$	n

The border totals are assumed to be unchanged; that is, $F_1 + F_2 = a + b$, etc. Then $F_1/F_2 = F_3/F_4$ and $F_1/F_3 = F_2/F_4$ if the attributes are independent.

The hypothetical frequencies are easily computed from the border totals. Thus,

$$F_1 = \frac{(a + b)(a + c)}{n}, \text{ etc.}$$

Applying this to the Boone County sample,

F_1	F_2	125
F_3	F_4	51
40	136	176

$F_1 = [(125)(40)]/176 = 28.4$, etc. Only one of the hypothetical frequencies need be calculated; the others are got by subtraction from the border totals;

$$F_2 = 125 - F_1 = 125 - 28.4 = 96.6, \text{ etc.}$$

The resulting hypothetical frequencies, F, are

28.4	96.6
11.6	39.4

In calculating chi-square, these hypothetical frequencies are to be compared with the sample frequencies, f:

31	94
9	42

The four deviations, $f - F$, are

2.6	−2.6
−2.6	2.6

The sum of these deviations is zero in each row and in each column, and except for the signs they are all equal.

Since the absolute values of the four differences, $|f - F|$, are the same, the usual formula for uncorrected chi-square,

$$\chi^2 = \Sigma \frac{(f - F)^2}{F},$$

becomes

$$\chi^2 = (f - F)^2 \Sigma \frac{1}{F}$$

Substituting the Boone County data,

$$\chi^2 = (2.6)^2 \left(\frac{1}{28.4} + \frac{1}{96.6} + \frac{1}{11.6} + \frac{1}{39.4} \right)$$

$$= 1.06$$

The correction for continuity is made by deducting 0.5 from $|f - F|$. The formula for corrected chi-square is

$$\chi^2 = (|f - F| - 0.5)^2 \Sigma(1/F)$$

$$= (2.6 - 0.5)^2 (0.1572)$$

$$= 0.69$$

This has brought us back to the same answer as that given by the shorter method of the previous section. The formulas are equivalent.

The reason for only one degree of freedom is now apparent. Since the theoretical frequencies are based on the border totals, only one F is free, the other three being determined by the first F and the totals.

With acceptance of the hypothesis of independence, there is little further interest in the fourfold table. The sample of 176 fields may be considered independently from two viewpoints. First, the second brood eggs were found in 71% of the fields, the 95% interval estimate being 63.0% to 78.5%. Second, about 23% of the fields were fertilized, with a 95% interval estimate of 16% to 31%. Other questions that might have been raised, such as 1 and 3 in section 9.6, now have little relevance.

Like all applications of chi-square to contingency tables, the foregoing methods, even with the correction for continuity, are approximate. The approximation becomes poorer as the size of sample decreases. If the frequency observed in any cell is less than 5, close decisions may be affected. For such unusual cases the reader is referred to (10) where an exact method is explained, and to (7) for additional discussion.

EXAMPLE 9.7.1—Following is a record of clinical trials on 171 white patients therapeutically inoculated by anophelines infected with the McCoy strain of *Plasmodium vivax*, employing sporozoites not exceeding 50 days of age (3).

NUMBERS OF TAKES AND FAILURES OF INOCULATIONS WITH VIVAX MALARIA IN THE MONTHS JANUARY TO MARCH CONTRASTED WITH APRIL TO DECEMBER

Months	Result of Inoculation		Total
	Take	Failure	
January–March	13	6	19
April–December	142	10	152
Total	155	16	171

Calculate adjusted $\chi^2 = 9.67$. With rejection of H_0, there are only two further inferences to be made about populations; these are based on the two pairs of estimates (point and interval) about the percentage of (i) takes (or failures) in January–March, and (ii) takes (or failures) in April–December. These estimates cannot be expanded because there is no information about the size of the population which was randomly sampled.

EXAMPLE 9.7.2—In the Boone County survey, notice that among the hypothetical frequencies this relation is true: $F_1/F_2 = F_3/F_4$, or $F_1F_4 = F_2F_3$. This verifies the calculations.

EXAMPLE 9.7.3—In the fall of 1943 approximately one in every 1,000 families of Iowa was asked about the canning of fruits or vegetables during the preceding season Of the 392 rural families interviewed 378 had done canning, while among the 300 urban (from places of 2,500 or more inhabitants) families 274 had canned. Test the hypothesis that the percentage of families doing canning was the same in rural and urban communities of Iowa in 1943. Ans. $\chi^2 = 7.19$.

Two comments: (i) Assuming that every family in Iowa had the probability 0.001 of being interviewed, estimates and expansions can be made from each of the four cell frequencies and from the four border totals. Interpretation of two of the latter four is subject to the heterogeneity which is evident. (ii) The assumption of complete randomness is not realistic; such randomization is too costly. Practical devices have been found for overcoming this difficulty. See chapter 17.

9.8—Test of independence in an R × C table.

If one or both of two attributes are recorded in more than two classes, the resulting table having R rows and C columns, independence may be tested by chi-square with $(R - 1)(C - 1)$ degrees of freedom. As in section 9.7, hypothetical frequencies, F, are based on the border totals. These with the observed frequencies, f, lead to the familiar form,

$$\chi^2 = \Sigma(f - F)^2/F$$

Strand and Jessen (19) examined the distribution of tenancy on various levels of soil fertility in Audubon County, Iowa. The results from a random sample of farms are summarized in table 9.8.1. Before drawing conclusions from the border totals, this question is asked: Is tenancy in this county dependent on fertility; or is the county distribution of tenancy the same on the three levels of fertility?

TABLE 9.8.1
NUMBERS OF FARMS ON 3 SOIL FERTILITY GROUPS IN AUDUBON COUNTY, IOWA,
CLASSIFIED ACCORDING TO TENURE

Soil		Owned	Rented	Mixed	Total
I	f	36	67	49	152
	F	36.75	62.92	52.33	
	$f - F$	−0.75	4.08	−3.33	
II	f	31	60	49	140
	F	33.85	57.95	48.20	
	$f - F$	−2.85	2.05	0.80	
III	f	58	87	80	225
	F	54.40	93.13	77.47	
	$f - F$	3.60	−6.13	2.53	
Total		125	214	178	517

$$\chi^2 = \Sigma \frac{(f - F)^2}{F} = \frac{(-0.75)^2}{36.75} + \ldots + \frac{(2.53)^2}{77.47} = 1.54, \, d.f. = (R - 1)(C - 1) = 4$$

As before, the hypothetical frequency for any cell is computed from the border totals in the corresponding row and column:

$$F = \frac{(\text{row total})(\text{column total})}{n}$$

$$= \frac{\text{row total}}{n} (\text{column total})$$

Examples: For the first row,

$$\frac{\text{row total}}{n} = \frac{152}{517} = 0.29400$$

$$F_1 = (0.29400)(125) = 36.75$$
$$F_2 = (0.29400)(214) = 62.92$$
$$F_3 = (0.29400)(178) = 52.33$$

This procedure makes the computation fairly easy if a calculating machine is available. For verification, notice that (i) the sum of the F in any row or column is equal to the observed total, and consequently (ii) the sum of the deviations in each row and in each column is zero.

The facts just stated dictate the number of degrees of freedom. One is free to put $R - 1$ theoretical frequencies in any column, but the remaining cell is then fixed as the column total minus the sum of the $R - 1$ values of F. Similarly, there are $C - 1$ degrees of freedom in each of $R - 1$ rows. Therefore, $d.f. = (R - 1)(C - 1)$.

The calculation of chi-square proceeds as indicated in the table. Since $P > 0.8$, the null hypothesis of independence is not rejected.

Since there is no evidence of heterogeneity in the soil-tenure data, it is proper to test any pertinent hypothesis the investigator may have about the border totals. For example, if he should know that in the state as a whole, tenancy is distributed in the ratios 25:45:30, he could test (as in sections 1.14 and 9.3) whether his sample is randomly drawn from the state population or whether Audubon County has a different pattern from that in the state. Or he might ask if the farms having the several levels of fertility are equally numerous in the county sampled; this would specify the null hypothesis, the ratios being 1:1:1.

If one or more cells of the table contribute unusually large values of $(f - F)^2/F$, they may warrant special consideration. Shall the large components be attributed to sampling vagaries or may there be a useful interpretation?

If an experimenter does not need to examine the components in the several cells of his $R \times C$ table, he can save up to half the time of computation by use of a short cut devised by P. H. Leslie (13). This is especially useful if there are many such tables to be calculated.

EXAMPLE 9.8.1—In three experiments on artificial insemination of cows, successes and failures were recorded as follows:

Experiment	Successes	Failures
1	194	158
2	80	86
3	165	151

Calculate chi-square. Ans. 2.21, $d.f. = 2$.

EXAMPLE 9.8.2—In table 9.2.1, suppose it had been found that the progenies were not segregating 3:1, or suppose there had been no theoretical genetic ratio to apply. The investigator might wish to test independence as in the present section. Calculate chi-square. Ans. 3.31, $d.f. = 10$. You will observe that this is not the same as the heterogeneity chi-square of section 9.2. The distinction will be discussed in the next section.

9.9—A special method of computing chi-square in an R × 2 table.

In scientific writings many tables of enumeration data are presented in some such fashion as the first three columns of table 9.9.1. These data are selected from an experiment in which uniform doses of Danysz bacillus were injected into rats. The sizes of the sub-samples were dictated by the numbers of animals available at the several dates of injection.

The probabilities of survival, p_i, in the third column of the table are emphasized. For such tables a convenient method of computing chi-square has been devised by Snedecor and Irwin (18). (This is sometimes referred to as the Brandt and Snedecor method.) The results, of course, are the same as those obtained by applying the method of the foregoing section. The second and third columns might as well refer to the numbers dead, but computation is easier with the smaller probabilities. In the last column the sum of the products is usually accumulated in the dials of a calculating machine with no listing of the separate items.

The results indicate that the probability of death is independent of the group and may therefore be characteristic of the amount of inoculum

TABLE 9.9.1

PERCENTAGE OF RATS LIVING AFTER INJECTION WITH DANYSZ BACILLUS

Number in Group	Number Living X_i	Probability* of Survival p_i	Products $p_i X_i$
40	9	0.2250	2.0250
12	2	0.1667	0.3334
22	3	0.1364	0.4092
11	1	0.0909	0.0909
37	2	0.0541	0.1082
20	3	0.1500	0.4500

$n = 142$ $\Sigma X_i = 20$ $\bar{p} = \Sigma X_i/n = 20/142 = 0.1408$ $\Sigma p_i X_i = 3.4167$

$$\bar{q} = 1 - \bar{p} = 0.8592$$

$$\chi^2 = \frac{\Sigma p_i X_i - \bar{p} \Sigma X_i}{\bar{p}\bar{q}} = \frac{3.4167 - 2.8160}{(0.1408)(0.8592)} = 4.97, \ d.f. = 5, \ P = 0.43$$

* If you prefer percentages, see example 9.9.4.

injected. The experimental technique was rather difficult to control—the rats were probably variable in their reaction to the injected organism, the organism doubtless changed somewhat in virulence, and the amounts of the inoculum introduced were likely not entirely uniform—yet the probability of death throughout the sample was no more divergent than would be expected in groups randomly drawn from a population with constant probability of death.

This special method (11) may be convenient if crossing over or linkage is suspected in genetic material which should theoretically segregate $r:1$. For the sake of easy comparison, let us apply it to the data of table 9.2.1, rearranged as in table 9.9.2. The new features are in the lower part of the table where chi-square is computed on two assumptions: (i) that the population ratio is 3:1, the value of chi-square being identical with the heterogeneity chi-square calculated as a difference in section 9.2; and (ii) that there is no theoretical ratio. What are the advantages?

First, since $\chi^2 = 3.08$, $d.f. = 10$ is so small as to indicate no heterogeneity among the sample ratios, the pooled chi-square is of interest and may conveniently be calculated by means of the formula (section 1.16),

$$\chi^2 = \frac{(a - rb)^2}{r(a + b)} = \frac{(854 - 3 \times 249)^2}{3(1,103)} = 3.46$$

We now have both the pooled and the heterogeneity chi-squares which are essential: the total chi-square may be got by addition if it is needed. The calculations are notably less burdensome than those of table 9.2.1.

TABLE 9.9.2

SEGREGATION OF GREEN AND YELLOW SEEDLINGS IN 11 PROGENIES.
DATA OF TABLE 9.2.1
Alternative method of computation

Number Examined	Number Yellow X_i	Probability of Yellow p_i	Products $p_i X_i$
122	24	0.1967	4.7208
149	39	0.2617	10.2063
86	18	0.2093	3.7674
55	13	0.2364	3.0732
71	17	0.2394	4.0698
179	38	0.2123	8.0674
150	30	0.2000	6.0000
36	9	0.2500	2.2500
91	21	0.2308	4.8468
53	14	0.2642	3.6988
111	26	0.2342	6.0892
1,103	$\Sigma X_i = 249$	$\bar{p} = 0.22575$ $\bar{q} = 0.77425$	$\Sigma p_i X_i = 56.7897$ $\bar{p}\Sigma X_i = 56.2118$
			$\Sigma p_i X_i - \bar{p}\Sigma X_i = 0.5779$

Assuming 3:1 ratio, $p = 0.75$, $q = 0.25$

$$\chi^2 = \frac{\Sigma p_i X_i - \bar{p}\Sigma X_i}{pq} = \frac{0.5779}{(0.75)(0.25)} = 3.08$$

With no assumption about ratio,

$$\chi^2 = \frac{\Sigma p_i X_i - \bar{p}\Sigma X_i}{\bar{p}\bar{q}} = \frac{0.5779}{(0.2258)(0.7742)} = 3.31$$

Second, we have as before the evidence to decide whether there is crossing over or not. While pooled chi-square is short of the 5% point, it does emphasize a bias—a deficit in the recessive yellows. If the investigator attributes this to crossing over (or to some other genetic phenomenon) he will reject the 3:1 hypothesis. He then has available the appropriate $\chi^2 = 3.31$ based only on the assumption of independence, and this with a negligible amount of extra computation.

We now have two chi-squares measuring inconsistency in the sizes or signs of deviations from theoretical, numerically not greatly different. In the computations they are distinguished only by their denominators. If one needs the heterogeneity chi-square of section 9.2, he divides by the hypothetical probabilities. If it is independence he wishes to test, he uses probabilities based on the border totals of the sample as in section 9.8.

EXAMPLE 9.9.1—In another sample of inoculated rats the data were: 25, 21; 50, 48; 20, 15; and 20, 17—the first number in each pair being the sub-sample size, the second, the number dying. Calculate $\chi^2 = 6.69$, $P = 8.6\%$.

EXAMPLE 9.9.2—Combine the values of chi-square for the two samples of rats, yielding $\chi^2 = 11.66$, $d.f. = 8$, $P = 17\%$.

EXAMPLE 9.9.3—If you are willing to accept the hypothesis that each sample of rats was drawn from a homogeneous population, it is appropriate to test the hypothesis that the probabilities of death in the two populations are the same; that is, that the two sample probabilities, 85.9% and 87.8%, differ only as may be expected in random sampling from a common population. Ans. Adjusted $\chi^2 = 0.070$ (section 9.6).

EXAMPLE 9.9.4—Apply the method of table 9.9.2 to the data of example 9.2.1, using percentages instead of probabilities. Note the slight modification in the formula when percentages instead of probabilities are used.

Number in Group	Number Yellow X_i	Percentage Yellow p_i		
139	41	29.4964*		
102	31	30.3922		
179	52	29.0503		
86	25	29.0698		
122	36	29.5082		
628	$\Sigma X_i = 185$	$\bar{p} = 29.4586$	$\Sigma p_i X_i = 5,451.17$	
		$\bar{q} = 70.5414$	$\bar{p}\Sigma X_i = 5,449.84$	
			$\Sigma p_i X_i - \bar{p}\Sigma X_i =$	1.33

For testing heterogeneity, $\chi^2 = \dfrac{100(\Sigma p_i X_i - \bar{p}\Sigma X_i)}{(25)(75)} = 0.071$

For testing independence, $\chi^2 = \dfrac{100(\Sigma p_i X_i - \bar{p}\Sigma X_i)}{\bar{p}\bar{q}} = 0.064$

*I carried 2 extra digits in order to verify the result in example 9.2.1.

Since we know from the earlier computations that pooled chi-square is significant at the 1% point, some such bias as crossing over may be decided upon. If so, the 3:1 hypothesis is abandoned and heterogeneity calculated as 0.064. Clearly, heterogeneity is negligible under either hypothesis—3:1 or independence.

EXAMPLE 9.9.5—Burnett (4) tried the effect of five storage locations on the viability of seed corn. In the kitchen garret, 111 kernels germinated among 120 tested; in a closed toolshed, 55 among 60; in an open toolshed, 55 among 60; out-of-doors, 41 among 48; and in a dry garret, 50 among 60. Calculate $\chi^2 = 5.09$, $d.f. = 4$, $P = 28\%$. The calculations are somewhat shorter if the numbers of non-germinating seeds are used. The results contain slight evidence against the hypothesis that there is a uniform probability of germination, irrespective of location.

EXAMPLE 9.9.6—Among some experiments reported by Lindstrom (15), the number of ears of corn displaying the presence of a recessive gene producing sugar was 18 among 33 having 8 rows of kernels, 37 among 63 with 10 rows, 27 among 70 with 12 rows, and none among 4 with 14 rows. It is easy to see that the expected number of sugary ears among the last four is less than five, the minimum expected number that should be used in applying chi-square. The 12-row and 14-row ears, may, therefore, be merged into one sub-sample having 27 sugary ears among 74. If this is done, $\chi^2 = 7.4$, $d.f. = 2$, and $P = 3\%$. The evidence is against homogeneity, though not strongly so. Apparently the sugary gene is associated with ears having few rows of kernels.

EXAMPLE 9.9.7—Using the data of the preceding example, calculate chi-square by means of the formula of section 9.8. Since 48.24% of the total 170 ears were sugary, one would expect 48.24% of the 33 eight-row ears to bear the gene; that is, 15.92 ears. The deviation from expected is $18 - 15.92 = 2.08$ ears. Similarly, five more deviations from expected are calculated (3 pairs in each of which the deviations are equal in absolute value but opposite in sign), the resulting chi-square being 7.4 as before.

9.10—Three sets of attributes; the 3-way contingency table. Not infrequently observations are made on more than two attributes; for example on species, on sex, and on treatments. The table may be thought of as having layers, L, built on the $R \times C$ table, making a rectangular column with dimensions $R \times C \times L$.

In biology, most 3-way tables have one classification with only two categories, success or failure, alive or dead, male or female, etc. In such tables the chief interest is usually in the behavior of the percentage of successes, not in the ratio of successes to failures. Such tables reduce to the 2-way with a percentage as the variable. Methods for dealing with this type are presented in examples 12.4.4, 12.14.1, and 12.15.2.

If each classification has three or more categories, methods for testing two hypotheses about independence may be found in (17). The use of hypothetical frequencies leads to similar values of chi-square and they serve to indicate the location of the big deviations.

In a $2 \times 2 \times 2$ table,

$$
\begin{array}{cccc}
a & b & \quad a' & b' \\
c & d & \quad c' & d'
\end{array}
$$

one might wish to test this hypothesis of independence,

$$
\frac{a/b}{c/d} = \frac{a'/b'}{c'/d'}, \text{ or } \frac{ad}{bc} = \frac{a'd'}{b'c'}
$$

Now, in a 2×2 table, the test of the ratios, $a/b = c/d$, is identical with the test of the percentages, $a/(a + b) = c/(c + d)$, but the corresponding relation does not hold in the $2 \times 2 \times 2$. It must be rare, then, that in a 3-way table one would be interested in the hypothesis stated above. If he is, he will find a method in (1). An account of it was given in section 9.8 of the 4th edition of this text.

9.11—An experiment requiring a test of technique. When novel experimental methods are used, the investigator must determine, among other things, whether he can reproduce his results; that is, whether he has adequate control over the conditions under which the experiment is performed. Reference to this problem was made in section 9.9. If results cannot be verified under controlled conditions assumed to be identical, then it is idle to try the effect of changing these conditions— one cannot know whether differences (or likenesses) in the results are to be charged to the controlled situation or to those unknown causes that elude control.

Decker and Andre (9) were faced with this problem when they started to investigate the effect of a short, sudden exposure to cold, the adults of the chinch bug being the organism studied. The experimental insects had to be gathered in the field, so that the degree of heterogeneity was unknown. Ten individuals were placed in each of 50 tubes and exposed for 15 minutes at $-8°$ C. Since the chi-square method may not yield accurate results unless the expected numbers are all at least as great as five, the counts of the numbers dead in the individual tubes were combined at random in 5 lots of 10 tubes each; that is, lots of 100 nymphs. The mortalities were 14, 14, 23, 17, and 20 insects. From these data, $\chi^2 = 4.22$, $d.f. = 4$, and $P = 39\%$. This indicates approximately the variation that would be expected in sampling from homogeneous material. The mean probability of death was 17.6%. The results are in accord with the hypothesis that every individual was subject to this same chance of being killed by the exposure.

In a second sample of 500 adults, handled in the same manner except that they were exposed at $-9°$ C., the mortalities in groups of 100 were 38, 30, 30, 40, 27. The chi-square of 5.79 verifies the technique and shows only sampling variation from the estimated mortality of 33%. While no particular advantage is gained in this case, it is interesting to add the two values of chi-square, $\chi^2 = 4.22 + 5.79 = 10.01$, $d.f. = 8$, $P = 27\%$.

The gratifying uniformity in the experimental results leads one to place confidence in the rather surprising finding that the mortalities at $-8°$ C. and $-9°$ C. were significantly different. The total numbers dead in the two samples of 500 were 88 and 165. The value, $\chi^2 = 31.4$, $d.f. = 1$, P less than 0.0002 (section 8.8), constitutes convincing evidence that a rise in mortality with the lowering of temperature from $-8°$ C. to $-9°$ C. is a population characteristic, not merely an accident of sampling.

The ease of applying such a test of experimental technique makes its use almost a routine procedure except in highly standardized processes. It is necessary merely to collect the data in several small groups instead of in one mass. The additional information available may modify conclusions profoundly.

EXAMPLE 9.11.1—Dr. R. H. Walker of the Intermountain Forest and Range Experiment Station has provided the following unpublished data on counts of bacteria in suspensions of soil and indigo particles, following the method of Thornton and Gray (20).   The number of indigo particles in a field specifies the amount of soil present. Good technique will be indicated if the numbers of bacteria vary from proportionality to the indigo particles only so much as would be expected in random sampling from a population in which this ratio is constant.   On a slide, 16 fields were counted, four in each of four drops.   The data are records of the total slide counts, four slides to each soil suspension.   For purposes of computation, we shall give only two figures: (i) the total count of both bacteria and indigo particles, and (ii) the number of bacteria. For the four plates of soil suspension 1: 204, 78; 260, 75; 246, 76; 278, 95. Chi-square = 5.22, $d.f.$ = 3, P = 16%.   For suspension 2: 260, 60; 196, 50; 198, 45; 186, 50. Chi-square = 1.30, $d.f.$ = 3, P = 73%.   For suspension 3: 177, 22; 177, 23; 150, 16; 177, 20.   Chi-square = 0.53, $d.f.$ = 3, P = 91%.   For suspension 4: 289, 46; 356, 63; 281, 45; 250, 42.   Chi-square = 0.48, $d.f.$ = 3, P = 92%.   The agreement is closer than one would ordinarily expect in random sampling.

EXAMPLE 9.11.2—To determine whether the four soil suspensions differed significantly in the numbers of bacteria per unit voulme, the totals are taken from the records of the foregoing example: for suspension 1: 988, 324; 2:840, 205; 3:681, 81; 4:1176, 196.   Chi-square = 130, $d.f.$ = 3, P less than 1%.   There is no doubt of differences among the four soil suspensions.

EXAMPLE 9.11.3—In computing chi-square by the method of table 9.9.1, the numbers of observations in the groups may be either equal or different.   If they are equal, the mathematician can easily reduce the formula to the special one, $\chi^2 = k\Sigma x^2/\bar{x}(k - \bar{x})$, where k is the size of the sub-sample, Σx^2 is the sum of the squares of the deviations from mean, $\bar{x}$, obtained in the usual manner by using the formula, $\Sigma x^2 = \Sigma X^2 - (\Sigma X)^2/n$.   Those who work extensively with chi-square will find some saving in time by using this special formula when their group numbers are equal.   They may practice by applying it to the Decker and Andre data.   This formula was first used by "Mathetes" (16).

9.12—An experiment in which the presence of an attribute is recorded quantitatively.

In the enumeration data heretofore considered, the mere presence of some attribute was recorded.   There is another kind in which presence may be observed in more than one unit, so that the record becomes quantitative even at this initial stage.   Both kinds are employed in many studies of insect populations.   In investigations of the intensity of attack by codling moth, for example, the fruits may be designated qualitatively as merely injured or free; or they may be described as containing 0, 1, 2, etc., larvae.   The latter kind of data often follows a distribution known as the Poisson, further account of which will be given in chapter 16.   An example is found in an experiment designed to investigate various treatments for the control of cabbage loopers (5). Certain parts of the data are summarized in table 9.12.1.   The original record of the counts on the individual plants in plot 2 of treatment four was like this: 0, 1, 0, 0, 1, 2, 1, 0, 0, 0, 0, 4, 0, etc.   In the four plots receiving one of the treatments not entered in the table only a single looper was found.   For this illustration we selected only those treatments yielding at least five as the expected number for each plot.   On plots with less loopers there was even greater uniformity than on those selected for this investigation.

For treatment 1, the expected number in each plot is simply the mean of the four plot counts, 6 loopers. The deviations from expected are, therefore, just the same as deviations from mean in measurement data, $11 - 6$, $4 - 6$, etc. To make up chi-square, each of these deviations must be squared, then divided by the expected number. Since the latter is the same for the four plots, division may be delayed until the addition has been completed. Thus,

$$\chi^2 = \frac{(5)^2 + (-2)^2 + (-2)^2 + (-1)^2}{6} = \frac{34}{6} = 5.67$$

In the table, the computation is done by the usual machine method. It is easy to see that the formula used is merely an adaptation of the customary formula for chi-square.

TABLE 9.12.1

NUMBER OF LOOPERS OBSERVED ON 50 CABBAGE PLANTS IN A PLOT
Four plots treated alike. Five treatments

Treatment	Number of Loopers in Each of 4 Plots X	Total for Treatment ΣX	Mean $\bar{x}$	Chi-square $\Sigma x^2/\bar{x}$
1	11, 4, 4, 5	24	6.00	5.67
2	6, 4, 3, 6	19	4.75	1.42
3	8, 6, 4, 11	29	7.25	3.69
4	14, 27, 8, 18	67	16.75	11.39
5	7, 4, 9, 14	34	8.50	6.24
Total		173		28.41

Computation for treatment 1
$\Sigma x^2 = \Sigma X^2 - (\Sigma X)^2/n = (11)^2 + (4)^2 + (4)^2 + (5)^2 - (24)^2/4 = 34$
$\chi^2 = \Sigma x^2/\bar{x} = 34/6.00 = 5.67, d.f. = 3, P = 14\%$

Computation for five treatments
$\Sigma x^2 = \Sigma X^2 - (\Sigma X)^2/n = (24)^2 + (19)^2 + (29)^2 + (67)^2 + (34)^2 - (173)^2/5 = 1437.2$
$\bar{x} = 173/5 = 34.6$
$\chi^2 = \Sigma x^2/\bar{x} = 1437.2/34.6 = 41.5, d.f. = 4, P$ less than 0.0002

For treatment 1, the value of chi-square, computed in the table, would be exceeded 14 times in 100 trials from homogeneous material. The uniformity of infestation need not be questioned. The sum of the chi-squares for the five treatments is 28.41, $d.f. = 15$, $P = 2\%$. This indicates significant variation from uniformity of infestation among plots treated alike. From the original records, this lack of homogeneity seemed to be confined chiefly to the plots more severely attacked. However, the departure from uniformity appears to be slight compared with the variation induced by the treatments. This is shown by the last computation in the table where five treatment totals are examined. The chi-square of 41.5, $d.f. = 4$, leaves little doubt of the treatment effects, even though an unknown amount of variation may have been introduced by the heterogeneity of the plots treated alike.

EXAMPLE 9.12.1—Davis (8) counted the number of nodal smut galls in the corn plants of eight plots. The plants of four plots had been inoculated with the organism producing the galls. The numbers of galls observed in these plots were 56, 60, 41, and 75. Chi-square $= 10.1$, $d.f. = 3$, $P = 2\%$. In the four plots whose plants were not inoculated, the numbers of galls were 20, 12, 26, 22. Chi-square $= 5.2$, $d.f. = 3$, $P = 17\%$. For the two groups, $\chi^2 = 15.3$, $d.f. = 6$, $P = 2\%$. These figures indicate a significant lack of uniformity among the plots treated alike. Nevertheless, since the heterogeneity is not great, it is proper to test the difference between the totals for the two groups of plots. For the sums, 232 and 80, $\chi^2 = 74$, $d.f. = 1$, P less than 1%. There is little question of a population difference between the totals.

EXAMPLE 9.12.2—In example 9.11.1, soil suspension 1, ignore the numbers of indigo particles and compute, for the bacteria alone, $\chi^2 = 3.3$, $d.f. = 3$, $P = 36\%$. Neither the bacteria nor the ratios of bacteria to totals depart significantly from sampling variation in a homogeneous population. The ratios, as shown by the larger chi-square, are more variable, possibly because the test is more critical; the former test was based on the variation of both bacteria and indigo particles.

EXAMPLE 9.12.3—Davis (8) counted the numbers of ears on two plots of corn whose plants had been inoculated with an organism producing smut, and also on two check plots. The numbers were 436 and 432, respectively. The obvious failure of the inoculation to affect the number of ears is verified by unadjusted $\chi^2 = 0.02$, $d.f. = 1$. The numbers of smutted ears, however, were 69 and 39. That the percentages differ significantly is shown by adjusted $\chi^2 = 8.59$, $d.f. = 1$.

REFERENCES

1. M. S. BARTLETT. Supplement to the Journal of the Royal Statistical Society, 2:248 (1935).

2. W. BATESON and R. C. PUNNETT. Journal of Genetics, 1:297 (1911).

3. MARK F. BOYD, S. F. KITCHEN, and HUGO MUENCH. The American Journal of Tropical Medicine, 16:589 (1936).

4. L. C. BURNETT. Thesis submitted for the degree of Master of Science, Iowa State University (1906).

5. D. J. CAFFREY and C. E. SMITH. Bureau of Entomology and Plant Quarantine, U.S.D.A. (Baton Rouge) (1934).

6. W. G. COCHRAN. Iowa State Journal of Science, 16:421 (1942).

7. W. G. COCHRAN. Annals of Mathematical Statistics, 23:315 (1952). Biometrics, 10:417 (1954).

8. GLEN N. DAVIS. Iowa Agricultural Experiment Station Research Bulletin 199 (1936).

9. GEORGE C. DECKER and FLOYD ANDRE. Iowa State Journal of Science, 10:403 (1936).

10. R. A. FISHER. Statistical Methods for Research Workers. Oliver and Boyd, Edinburgh (1934 and later).

11. R. A. FISHER and K. MATHER. Annals of Eugenics, 7:265 (1936).

12. T. Roy Hansberry and C. H. Richardson. Iowa State College Journal of Science, 10:27 (1935).

13. P. H. Leslie. Biometrics, 7:283 (1951).

14. E. W. Lindstrom. Cornell University Agricultural Experiment Station Memoir 13 (1918).

15. E. W. Lindstrom. Iowa Agricultural Experiment Station Bulletin 142 (1931).

16. "Mathetes." Annals of Applied Biology, 11: 220 (1924).

17. A. M. Mood. Introduction to the Theory of Statistics. McGraw-Hill Book Company, Inc., New York (1950).

18. George W. Snedecor and M. R. Irwin. Iowa State College Journal of Science, 8:75 (1933).

19. Norman V. Strand and Raymond J. Jessen. Iowa Agricultural Experiment Station Research Bulletin 315 (1943).

20. H. P. Thornton and P. H. H. Gray. Proceedings of the Royal Society of London, Series B, 115:522 (1934).

21. W. Allen Wallis. Econometrica, 10:229 (1942)

22. F. Yates. Supplement to the Journal of the Royal Statistical Society, 1:217 (1934).

CHAPTER 10

Two or More Random Samples of Measurement Data. Analysis of Variance

10.1—Extension from two samples to many. Statistical and experimental methods for two samples were presented in chapter 4, but the needs of the investigator are seldom confined to only two treatments. More than two require extensions of the methods. For enumeration data such extensions were made in the foregoing chapter. We are now ready to do the same for measurement data, expand chapter 4 to allow for the simultaneous trial of three or more treatments.

During the early 1920's great progress was made in handling the statistics of multiple groups (5). Near the beginning of the decade Fisher (6) was able to solve some problems of distribution that completed his *analysis of variance*. This device has led to tremendous expansion in the design of experiments, each with an appropriate statistical analysis. Some of these form the topic of the present chapter.

10.2—Multiple samples from a common population. Analysis of variance. In the earlier sections of chapter 4 we considered two samples of equal size: three or more such samples now concern us. As examples, there may be several lots of animals, every lot receiving a different ration; or several classes of children in the 6th grade on which different methods of instruction are being tried. The statistical analysis of the ensuing experimental data is most easily explained by reference to the sampling of chapter 3. There we drew at random a number of samples from a normally distributed set of pig gains with mean, 30 pounds, and variance, 100. If we put together several of these samples, say 4, we shall have in effect an experiment with 40 pigs divided into 4 lots of 10 animals each. Ordinarily the lots would receive different treatments, but our data simulate a *dummy experiment*, or *uniformity trial*, in which all lots are treated alike.

The results of an experiment of the kind just described are recorded in table 10.2.1. For ease in calculation the lots have been reduced to 5 pigs each and the gains in weight changed slightly so as to avoid fractions. There are *a* samples or lots (treatments), each with *n* observations (replications) on weight. Thus, the experiment is comprised of *an* individuals.

The data in the table lead to 3 estimates of the variance, $\sigma^2 = 100$, in the population sampled by the experiment. The first is taken from the right-hand column where the 20 weight gains are summarized. This estimate is the mean square, $1{,}918/19 = 100.9$.

A second estimate of the population variance is got from the sums of squares within the 4 lots. Following the method of chapter 4, these sums of squares are added or pooled:

$$472 + 396 + 616 + 164 = 1{,}648$$

What about degrees of freedom? One must be deducted from the original 5 in each lot because the mean of that lot has been used as the origin

TABLE 10.2.1

GAINS IN WEIGHT (POUNDS) OF 4 LOTS OF SWINE, 5 PER LOT. SAMPLES FROM TABLE 3.2.1

	$a = 4$ Lots, $n = 5$ Pigs Per Lot				Entire Experiment
	1	2	3	4	
	40	29	11	17	
	24	27	31	21	
	46	20	17	28	
	20	39	37	33	
	35	45	39	21	
ΣX	165	160	135	120	580
$\bar{x}$	33	32	27	24	29
ΣX^2	5,917	5,516	4,261	3,044	18,738
$(\Sigma X)^2/n$	5,445	5,120	3,645	2,880	16,820
Σx^2	472	396	616	164	1,918

for deviations. Altogether, then, there are 4 degrees of freedom in each of the 4 lots, these 16 corresponding to the sum of squares, 1,648. The resulting mean square, $1{,}648/16 = 103$, is the second estimate of σ^2 furnished by the sample.

The lot means lead to a third estimate of the population variance. Because these 4 means are random samples from the same normal population, their mean square is an unbiased estimate of $\sigma^2/n = 100/5 = 20$. The mean square of these means is

$$\frac{(33 - 29)^2 + (32 - 29)^2 + (27 - 29)^2 + (24 - 29)^2}{3} = 18$$

instead of 20. Since 18 is an estimate of $\sigma^2/5$, then $5 \times 18 = 90$ is the third estimate of σ^2, this one based on the lot means with 3 degrees of freedom.

The foregoing analysis is summarized in table 10.2.2. One additional feature: the mean square of lot means has been multiplied by its degrees of freedom to form a sum of squares, 270, the utility of which will be clear from what follows.

The table brings into prominence two notable facts: not only the total sum of squares but also the corresponding degrees of freedom have been

TABLE 10.2.2
ANALYSIS OF VARIANCE OF PIG GAINS IN TABLE 10.2.1

Source of Variation	Degrees of Freedom	Sum of Squares	Mean Square
Individuals of the several lots	16	1,648	103
Lot means	3	270	90
Total	19	1,918	100.9

separated into two parts, both associated with the structure of the experiment. Since the parts as well as the total were computed independently, their additive relationship is emphasized. You will recall similar addition theorems in section 6.11. This partition of degrees of freedom and corresponding sums of squares is called *analysis of variance*. With the random sampling employed, each sum of squares is an estimate of the population σ^2

EXAMPLE 10.2.1—Analyze the variance in the following data selected for ease in computation.

		Sample Number		
1	2	3	4
11	13	21	10
4	9	18	4
6	14	15	19

Analysis of Variance

Source of Variation	Degrees of Freedom	Sum of Squares	Mean Square
Individuals	8	172	21.5
Samples	3	186	62.0
Total	11	358	32.5

EXAMPLE 10.2.2—Calculate the sum squares for samples, 186, by adding the four sample correction terms, 147, 432, etc., then deducting the experiment correction term, 1,728.

EXAMPLE 10.2.3—Calculate the sum of squares for samples as follows:

$$\frac{(21)^2 + (36)^2 + (54)^2 + (33)^2}{3} - \frac{(144)^2}{12}$$

The numbers squared in the numerator are the sample and experiment totals, while those in the denominators are n and an.

Which method of calculation seems easiest?

10.3—Usual method of calculation. One of the reasons for the popularity of analysis of variance is the elegance of its computations. Those in table 10.2.1 may be shortened considerably as soon as their meaning is learned. With adequate facilities for checking calculations, most people prefer to omit the last three lines of the central section of the table, calculating the two sums of squares, Total and Lot Means, then subtracting for Individuals. Here is the usual method. (Those who prefer an algebraic symbolism will find it in section 10.10.)

1. The sum of all observations: $\Sigma X = 40 + 24 + \ldots + 21 = 580$.
2. The *correction for mean*: $C = (\Sigma X)^2/an = (580)^2/20 = 16,820$.
3. The *total sum of squares*:
   $$\Sigma X^2 - C = 40^2 + 24^2 + \ldots + 21^2 - C = 18,738 - 16,820$$
   $$= 1,918$$
4. The sum of squares for *lot means*:

$$\frac{\Sigma(\Sigma X)^2}{n} - C = \frac{165^2 + 160^2 + \ldots + 120^2}{5} - C = \frac{85,450}{5} - C$$

$$= 17,090 - 16,820 = 270$$

The results from the last 2 steps, with corresponding degrees of freedom, are entered in table 10.3.1, where the computations for Individuals are completed.

TABLE 10.3.1
ANALYSIS OF VARIANCE OF PIG GAINS: USUAL FORM

Source of Variation	Degrees of Freedom	Sum of Squares	Mean Square
Total	19	1,918	
Lot Means	3	270	90
Individuals	16	1,648	103

Comments: (i) The degrees of freedom and sum of squares in the last line are got by subtraction, taking advantage of the addition theorem characterizing this analysis. (ii) There is no verification of the computations such as was provided in table 10.2.1. Beginners would do well to calculate independently the several sums of squares for individuals within lots. (iii) For the mechanism of step 4, review examples 10.2.2 and 10.2.3.

If this seems a bit complicated at first, be assured that practice will make it almost automatic.

If no calculating machine is available, proceed as follows: (i) In each lot, calculate the deviations, $x = X - \bar{x}$, then sum their squares to get Σx^2. The sum of all such Σx^2 is the sum of squares for individuals, 1,648. (ii) Calculate the deviation of each lot mean from the experiment mean, sum the squares, then multiply by $n = 5$; this gives the sum of squares for lot means, 270. (iii) If desired, the total sum of squares may be got by adding the other two, but there is little occasion for computing it. (iv) If the means do not "come out even," use the method of section 2.11 for calculating sums of squares.

EXAMPLE 10.3.1—As part of a larger experiment (25), 3 lots each containing 3 pigs were fed a basal ration supplemented by antibiotics and 3 levels of vitamin B_{12}. The average daily gains of the pigs (to 75 lbs. live weight) were:

Level of B_{12}(μg/lb ration)	Average Daily Gains		
5	1.52	1.56	1.54
10	1.63	1.57	1.54
20	1.44	1.52	1.63

Analyze the variance as follows:

Source of Variation	Degrees of Freedom	Sum of Squares	Mean Square
Total	8	0.0274	0.0034
Lot Means	2	0.0042	0.0021
Individuals	6	0.0232	0.0039

Hint: If you subtract 1.00 from each gain you will save time (section 5.4).

EXAMPLE 10.3.2—The percentage of clean wool in 7 bags was estimated by taking 3 batches at random from each bag. The percentages of clean wool in the batches were as follows:

Bag Number						
1	2	3	4	5	6	7
41.8	33.0	38.5	43.7	34.2	32.6	36.2
38.9	37.5	35.9	38.9	38.6	38.4	33.4
36.1	33.1	33.9	36.3	40.2	34.8	37.9

Calculate the mean squares for bags (11.11) and batches (8.22).

EXAMPLE 10.3.3—A mean square, M, which is an estimate of some σ^2 of a normal distribution, has a known sampling distribution which was discussed in section 3.5. Calculate s_M for Individuals in table 10.3.1. Ans. 34. (See example 3.5.4. $n - 1 = 16$, $n + 1 = 18$.)

EXAMPLE 10.3.4—Set the 95% confidence interval for σ^2 basing it on the estimate, M, for Individuals in table 10.3.1 (see section 2.14). Ans. $57 \le \sigma_M^2 \le 239$. Plenty of latitude, isn't there?

10.4—Random samples from two or more populations.   So far, discussion has been confined to the analysis of variance of random samples from a single population.   But in most applications the treatments of the lots affect the means.   In effect, the lots become samples from different populations.   These populations are thought of as having means characterized by the treatments but with a common variance unaffected by treatment.   Theoretically they are normal populations all having the variance, σ^2, but each with its peculiar mean, μ.   In the analysis of variance of such an experiment, the mean square for individuals estimates σ^2 as before, but the mean square for lot means is augmented by the differences among the μ.

Table 10.4.1 contains the data from such an experiment.   During

TABLE 10.4.1

GRAMS OF FAT ABSORBED BY 6 BATCHES OF DOUGHNUTS IN EACH OF 4 FATS
(100 grams subtracted from each batch)

Fats	Grams Absorbed − 100						Sum	Mean (decoded)
1	64	72	68	77	56	95	432	172
2	78	91	97	82	85	77	510	185
3	75	93	78	71	63	76	456	176
4	55	66	49	64	70	68	372	162

The calculations:
  1. $\Sigma X = 64 + 72 + \ldots + 70 + 68 = 1{,}770$
  2. $C = (1{,}770)^2/24 = 130{,}537.5$
  3. Total: $\Sigma x^2 = 64^2 + 72^2 + \ldots + 70^2 + 68^2 - C = 134{,}192 - C = 3{,}654.5$
  4. Fat means: $\dfrac{432^2 + \ldots + 372^2}{6} - C = 132{,}174 - C = 1{,}636.5$

cooking, doughnuts absorb fat in various amounts.   Lowe (19) wished to learn if the amount absorbed is characteristic of the fat used.   Six batches, each containing 24 doughnuts, were cooked in each of 4 fats. The numbers in the table are the grams of fat absorbed per batch, coded by deducting 100 grams from each datum.   The means are decoded (section 5.4).   Table 10.4.2 shows the analysis of variance.

TABLE 10.4.2

ANALYSIS OF VARIANCE OF DOUGHNUT DATA

Source of Variation	Degrees of Freedom	Sum of Squares	Mean Square
Total	23	3,654.5	
Fats	3	1,636.5	545.5
Batches	20	2,018.0	100.9

Under the assumptions outlined above, sampling from normal populations with common σ^2, 100.9 is an estimate of this σ^2. But the mean square for fats, 545.5, seems to have an additional component due to differing fats. To estimate this and to test its significance are the next objectives.

As to the constancy of the variance, the ranges in the samples are evidence. For fat 1, the range is $95 - 56 = 39$; for the others, 20, 30, 21. From your experience with samples from table 3.2.1, with similar σ^2, you will no doubt consider these ranges rather uniform. More exact evidence will be available in section 10.20.

EXAMPLE 10.4.1—In table 9.12.1 there was recorded the number of loopers observed on 50 cabbage plants per plot after the application of 4 treatments to each of 4 plots, completely randomized. The numbers were:

Treatment	1	11	4	4	5
	2	6	4	3	6
	3	8	6	4	11
	4	14	27	8	18
	5	7	4	9	14

Counts like these are not expected to be normally distributed, and the treatment effects may not be additive as they are assumed to be in this chapter. (See section 11.11.) But for illustration, analyze the variance as follows:

Source of Variation	Degrees of Freedom	Sum of Squares	Mean Square
Total	19	670.55	
Treatments	4	359.30	89.82
Plots having same treatment	15	311.25	20.75

EXAMPLE 10.4.2—Construct an experiment like that with doughnuts by changing the means in table 10.2.1, leaving the variance as it was. As an example, increase the mean for lot 1 from its population value, 30 pounds, to 45 pounds. The 5 gains will then be $40 + 15 = 55$, etc. Leaving lot 2 unchanged, decrease the mean in lot 3 by 6 pounds and that in lot 4 by 9 pounds. The experimental data will then be as follows:

55	29	5	8
39	27	25	12
61	20	11	19
35	39	31	24
50	45	33	12

Analyze the variance of this new experiment:

Source of Variation	Degrees of Freedom	Sum of Squares	Mean Square
Total	19	4,798	
Lots	3	3,150	1,050
Individuals	16	1,648	103

Since the Σx^2 (and the ranges) within the lots are unchanged, the mean square for individuals remains 103. But the mean square for lots has been increased from 90 to 1,050 by the changes in the lot means. This new mean square does not estimate $\sigma^2 = 100$; another component has been added by the different μ. This will be examined further in section 10.11.

EXAMPLE 10.4.3—In the sum of squares for lots, the surprising increase from 270 to 3,150 is because the large original means were increased while the smaller were decreased. Construct another set of data from table 10.2.1 by subtracting 9 from the first lot mean, 6 from the second, and adding 15 to the fourth, leaving the third unchanged. Analyze the variance. Ans. Sum of squares for lots = 690.

EXAMPLE 10.4.4—It is not hard to show just how the mean square in example 10.4.2 changed from 270 to 3,150.

Original $\bar{x}$	Change	New $\bar{x}$	Deviations From 29	(Deviations)^2
33	15	33 + 15	4 + 15	16 + 120 + 225
32	0	32	3	9
27	− 6	27 − 6	−2 − 6	4 + 24 + 36
24	− 9	27 − 9	−5 − 9	25 + 90 + 81
29	0	29	0	54 + 234 + 342

The new sum of squares of deviations *of means* is 54 + 234 + 342 = 630. Since $n = 5$, the sum of squares for observations is $(630)(5) = 3,150$.

10.5—Test of the equality of the μ. The variance ratio, F. The doughnut data introduce a familiar question; is ordinary random sampling accountable for the large discrepancy between the mean squares for fats and batches, or shall we conclude that the fat means are differentiated by causes other than sampling fluctuations? Lowe suspected that the nature of the several fats might result in different amounts of absorption. If so, the batches are samples from different populations instead of a common one.

The appropriate null hypothesis to be tested is H_0: $\mu_1 = \mu_2 = \ldots = \mu_a$, which specifies the population sampled by the lots of pig gains, table 10.2.1. In order to test H_0, we must examine a sampling distribution based on multiple samples from a common population. For this we go back to the drawings from table 3.2.1. Now, the original samples of $n = 10$ are to be collected into experiments of $a = 10$ like that of table 10.5.1. The analysis of variance of each such experiment is computed. Finally, a new test criterion is calculated, the ratio

$$\frac{\text{Mean square of sample means}}{\text{Mean square of individuals}}$$

This ratio has a distribution discovered by R. A. Fisher (6). I named it F in his honor (26). Fisher tabulated the distribution in the form, $z = \log_e \sqrt{F}$. Fisher and Yates (8) designate F as the *variance ratio*, while Mahalanobis (20), who first calculated it, called it x.

In table 10.5.1, $F = 1.51$, and we know that sampling variation

TABLE 10.5.1

TEN SAMPLES, EACH WITH 10 ITEMS, RANDOMLY DRAWN FROM THE NORMAL DISTRIBU-
TION OF TABLE 3.2.1. THIS SIMULATES A DUMMY EXPERIMENT WITH 10 LOTS OF PIGS

1	2	3	4	5	6	7	8	9	10
35	34	17	39	18	7	33	42	7	39
42	38	29	34	7	22	29	35	48	34
42	26	30	22	31	40	25	31	43	33
30	17	36	27	41	29	27	33	53	33
15	42	41	42	21	31	21	53	7	33
31	28	30	33	17	41	46	21	33	39
29	35	3	24	21	30	19	41	17	36
29	33	23	36	40	12	43	29	57	32
17	16	38	29	14	44	22	34	42	32
21	40	30	25	14	30	21	49	42	30

Source of Variation	Degrees of Freedom	Mean Square
Sample means	9	172.3
Individuals	90	114.0

$$F = 172.3/114.0 = 1.51$$

accounts for the failure of the two mean squares to be equal; each is an estimate of $\sigma^2 = 100$.

Table 10.5.2 displays the sampling distribution of 100 values of F, each derived from a randomly drawn experiment like that of table 10.5.1. One notices first the skewness; a concentration of small values and a long tail of larger. Next, there is the fact that 65 of the F are less than 1. If you remember that both terms of the ratio are estimates of σ^2, you may be surprised that 1 is not the median. However, the mean, calculated as in section 8.3.1, is 0.96, about the average one would expect. Finally it is to be observed that 5% of the values lie beyond 2.25 and 1% beyond 2.75, so that these points are roughly comparable with those of the theoretical distribution next to be considered.

Table 10.5.3 contains the *theoretical* 5% and 1% points of F for con-

TABLE 10.5.2

DISTRIBUTION OF F IN 100 SAMPLES FROM TABLE 3.2.1. DEGREES OF FREEDOM 9 AND 90

Class Interval	Frequency	Class Interval	Frequency
0. –0.24	7	1.50–1.74	5
0.25–0.49	16	1.75–1.99	2
0.50–0.74	16	2.00–2.24	4
0.75–0.99	26	2.25–2.49	2
1.00–1.24	11	2.50–2.74	2
1.25–1.49	8	2.75–2.99	1

TABLE 10.5.3
5% (Roman Type) and 1% (Bold Face Type) Points for the Distribution of F

f_1 degrees of freedom (for greater mean square)

Each cell shows the 5% point (Roman) / **1% point (Bold)**.

f_2	1	2	3	4	5	6	7	8	9	10	11	12	14	16	20	24	30	40	50	75	100	200	500	∞
1	161 / **4,052**	200 / **4,999**	216 / **5,403**	225 / **5,625**	230 / **5,764**	234 / **5,859**	237 / **5,928**	239 / **5,981**	241 / **6,022**	242 / **6,056**	243 / **6,082**	244 / **6,106**	245 / **6,142**	246 / **6,169**	248 / **6,208**	249 / **6,234**	250 / **6,258**	251 / **6,286**	252 / **6,302**	253 / **6,323**	253 / **6,334**	254 / **6,352**	254 / **6,361**	254 / **6,366**
2	18.51 / **98.49**	19.00 / **99.00**	19.16 / **99.17**	19.25 / **99.25**	19.30 / **99.30**	19.33 / **99.33**	19.36 / **99.34**	19.37 / **99.36**	19.38 / **99.38**	19.39 / **99.40**	19.40 / **99.41**	19.41 / **99.42**	19.42 / **99.43**	19.43 / **99.44**	19.44 / **99.45**	19.45 / **99.46**	19.46 / **99.47**	19.47 / **99.48**	19.47 / **99.48**	19.48 / **99.49**	19.49 / **99.49**	19.49 / **99.49**	19.50 / **99.50**	19.50 / **99.50**
3	10.13 / **34.12**	9.55 / **30.82**	9.28 / **29.46**	9.12 / **28.71**	9.01 / **28.24**	8.94 / **27.91**	8.88 / **27.67**	8.84 / **27.49**	8.81 / **27.34**	8.78 / **27.23**	8.76 / **27.13**	8.74 / **27.05**	8.71 / **26.92**	8.69 / **26.83**	8.66 / **26.69**	8.64 / **26.60**	8.62 / **26.50**	8.60 / **26.41**	8.58 / **26.35**	8.57 / **26.27**	8.56 / **26.23**	8.54 / **26.18**	8.54 / **26.14**	8.53 / **26.12**
4	7.71 / **21.20**	6.94 / **18.00**	6.59 / **16.69**	6.39 / **15.98**	6.26 / **15.52**	6.16 / **15.21**	6.09 / **14.98**	6.04 / **14.80**	6.00 / **14.66**	5.96 / **14.54**	5.93 / **14.45**	5.91 / **14.37**	5.87 / **14.24**	5.84 / **14.15**	5.80 / **14.02**	5.77 / **13.93**	5.74 / **13.83**	5.71 / **13.74**	5.70 / **13.69**	5.68 / **13.61**	5.66 / **13.57**	5.65 / **13.52**	5.64 / **13.48**	5.63 / **13.46**
5	6.61 / **16.26**	5.79 / **13.27**	5.41 / **12.06**	5.19 / **11.39**	5.05 / **10.97**	4.95 / **10.67**	4.88 / **10.45**	4.82 / **10.27**	4.78 / **10.15**	4.74 / **10.05**	4.70 / **9.96**	4.68 / **9.89**	4.64 / **9.77**	4.60 / **9.68**	4.56 / **9.55**	4.53 / **9.47**	4.50 / **9.38**	4.46 / **9.29**	4.44 / **9.24**	4.42 / **9.17**	4.40 / **9.13**	4.38 / **9.07**	4.37 / **9.04**	4.36 / **9.02**
6	5.99 / **13.74**	5.14 / **10.92**	4.76 / **9.78**	4.53 / **9.15**	4.39 / **8.75**	4.28 / **8.47**	4.21 / **8.26**	4.15 / **8.10**	4.10 / **7.98**	4.06 / **7.87**	4.03 / **7.79**	4.00 / **7.72**	3.96 / **7.60**	3.92 / **7.52**	3.87 / **7.39**	3.84 / **7.31**	3.81 / **7.23**	3.77 / **7.14**	3.75 / **7.09**	3.72 / **7.02**	3.71 / **6.99**	3.69 / **6.94**	3.68 / **6.90**	3.67 / **6.88**
7	5.59 / **12.25**	4.74 / **9.55**	4.35 / **8.45**	4.12 / **7.85**	3.97 / **7.46**	3.87 / **7.19**	3.79 / **7.00**	3.73 / **6.84**	3.68 / **6.71**	3.63 / **6.62**	3.60 / **6.54**	3.57 / **6.47**	3.52 / **6.35**	3.49 / **6.27**	3.44 / **6.15**	3.41 / **6.07**	3.38 / **5.98**	3.34 / **5.90**	3.32 / **5.85**	3.29 / **5.78**	3.28 / **5.75**	3.25 / **5.70**	3.24 / **5.67**	3.23 / **5.65**
8	5.32 / **11.26**	4.46 / **8.65**	4.07 / **7.59**	3.84 / **7.01**	3.69 / **6.63**	3.58 / **6.37**	3.50 / **6.19**	3.44 / **6.03**	3.39 / **5.91**	3.34 / **5.82**	3.31 / **5.74**	3.28 / **5.67**	3.23 / **5.56**	3.20 / **5.48**	3.15 / **5.36**	3.12 / **5.28**	3.08 / **5.20**	3.05 / **5.11**	3.03 / **5.06**	3.00 / **5.00**	2.98 / **4.96**	2.96 / **4.91**	2.94 / **4.88**	2.93 / **4.86**
9	5.12 / **10.56**	4.26 / **8.02**	3.86 / **6.99**	3.63 / **6.42**	3.48 / **6.06**	3.37 / **5.80**	3.29 / **5.62**	3.23 / **5.47**	3.18 / **5.35**	3.13 / **5.26**	3.10 / **5.18**	3.07 / **5.11**	3.02 / **5.00**	2.98 / **4.92**	2.93 / **4.80**	2.90 / **4.73**	2.86 / **4.64**	2.82 / **4.56**	2.80 / **4.51**	2.77 / **4.45**	2.76 / **4.41**	2.73 / **4.36**	2.72 / **4.33**	2.71 / **4.31**
10	4.96 / **10.04**	4.10 / **7.56**	3.71 / **6.55**	3.48 / **5.99**	3.33 / **5.64**	3.22 / **5.39**	3.14 / **5.21**	3.07 / **5.06**	3.02 / **4.95**	2.97 / **4.85**	2.94 / **4.78**	2.91 / **4.71**	2.86 / **4.60**	2.82 / **4.52**	2.77 / **4.41**	2.74 / **4.33**	2.70 / **4.25**	2.67 / **4.17**	2.64 / **4.12**	2.61 / **4.05**	2.59 / **4.01**	2.56 / **3.96**	2.55 / **3.93**	2.54 / **3.91**
11	4.84 / **9.65**	3.98 / **7.20**	3.59 / **6.22**	3.36 / **5.67**	3.20 / **5.32**	3.09 / **5.07**	3.01 / **4.88**	2.95 / **4.74**	2.90 / **4.63**	2.86 / **4.54**	2.82 / **4.46**	2.79 / **4.40**	2.74 / **4.29**	2.70 / **4.21**	2.65 / **4.10**	2.61 / **4.02**	2.57 / **3.94**	2.53 / **3.86**	2.50 / **3.80**	2.47 / **3.74**	2.45 / **3.70**	2.42 / **3.66**	2.41 / **3.62**	2.40 / **3.60**
12	4.75 / **9.33**	3.88 / **6.93**	3.49 / **5.95**	3.26 / **5.41**	3.11 / **5.06**	3.00 / **4.82**	2.92 / **4.65**	2.85 / **4.50**	2.80 / **4.39**	2.76 / **4.30**	2.72 / **4.22**	2.69 / **4.16**	2.64 / **4.05**	2.60 / **3.98**	2.54 / **3.86**	2.50 / **3.78**	2.46 / **3.70**	2.42 / **3.61**	2.40 / **3.56**	2.36 / **3.49**	2.35 / **3.46**	2.32 / **3.41**	2.31 / **3.38**	2.30 / **3.36**
13	4.67 / **9.07**	3.80 / **6.70**	3.41 / **5.74**	3.18 / **5.20**	3.02 / **4.86**	2.92 / **4.62**	2.84 / **4.44**	2.77 / **4.30**	2.72 / **4.19**	2.67 / **4.10**	2.63 / **4.02**	2.60 / **3.96**	2.55 / **3.85**	2.51 / **3.78**	2.46 / **3.67**	2.42 / **3.59**	2.38 / **3.51**	2.34 / **3.42**	2.32 / **3.37**	2.28 / **3.30**	2.26 / **3.27**	2.24 / **3.21**	2.22 / **3.18**	2.21 / **3.16**

TABLE 10.5.3—(Continued)

f_1 degrees of freedom (for greater mean square). Each cell gives the upper value (5%) over the lower value (1%).

f_2	1	2	3	4	5	6	7	8	9	10	11	12	14	16	20	24	30	40	50	75	100	200	500	∞	f_2
14	4.60 / 8.86	3.74 / 6.51	3.34 / 5.56	3.11 / 5.03	2.96 / 4.69	2.85 / 4.46	2.77 / 4.28	2.70 / 4.14	2.65 / 4.03	2.60 / 3.94	2.56 / 3.86	2.53 / 3.80	2.48 / 3.70	2.44 / 3.62	2.39 / 3.51	2.35 / 3.43	2.31 / 3.34	2.27 / 3.26	2.24 / 3.21	2.21 / 3.14	2.19 / 3.11	2.16 / 3.06	2.14 / 3.02	2.13 / 3.00	14
15	4.54 / 8.68	3.68 / 6.36	3.29 / 5.42	3.06 / 4.89	2.90 / 4.56	2.79 / 4.32	2.70 / 4.14	2.64 / 4.00	2.59 / 3.89	2.55 / 3.80	2.51 / 3.73	2.48 / 3.67	2.43 / 3.56	2.39 / 3.48	2.33 / 3.36	2.29 / 3.29	2.25 / 3.20	2.21 / 3.12	2.18 / 3.07	2.15 / 3.00	2.12 / 2.97	2.10 / 2.92	2.08 / 2.89	2.07 / 2.87	15
16	4.49 / 8.53	3.63 / 6.23	3.24 / 5.29	3.01 / 4.77	2.85 / 4.44	2.74 / 4.20	2.66 / 4.03	2.59 / 3.89	2.54 / 3.78	2.49 / 3.69	2.45 / 3.61	2.42 / 3.55	2.37 / 3.45	2.33 / 3.37	2.28 / 3.25	2.24 / 3.18	2.20 / 3.10	2.16 / 3.01	2.13 / 2.96	2.09 / 2.89	2.07 / 2.86	2.04 / 2.80	2.02 / 2.77	2.01 / 2.75	16
17	4.45 / 8.40	3.59 / 6.11	3.20 / 5.18	2.96 / 4.67	2.81 / 4.34	2.70 / 4.10	2.62 / 3.93	2.55 / 3.79	2.50 / 3.68	2.45 / 3.59	2.41 / 3.52	2.38 / 3.45	2.33 / 3.35	2.29 / 3.27	2.23 / 3.16	2.19 / 3.08	2.15 / 3.00	2.11 / 2.92	2.08 / 2.86	2.04 / 2.79	2.02 / 2.76	1.99 / 2.70	1.97 / 2.67	1.96 / 2.65	17
18	4.41 / 8.28	3.55 / 6.01	3.16 / 5.09	2.93 / 4.58	2.77 / 4.25	2.66 / 4.01	2.58 / 3.85	2.51 / 3.71	2.46 / 3.60	2.41 / 3.51	2.37 / 3.44	2.34 / 3.37	2.29 / 3.27	2.25 / 3.19	2.19 / 3.07	2.15 / 3.00	2.11 / 2.91	2.07 / 2.83	2.04 / 2.78	2.00 / 2.71	1.98 / 2.68	1.95 / 2.62	1.93 / 2.59	1.92 / 2.57	18
19	4.38 / 8.18	3.52 / 5.93	3.13 / 5.01	2.90 / 4.50	2.74 / 4.17	2.63 / 3.94	2.55 / 3.77	2.48 / 3.63	2.43 / 3.52	2.38 / 3.43	2.34 / 3.36	2.31 / 3.30	2.26 / 3.19	2.21 / 3.12	2.15 / 3.00	2.11 / 2.92	2.07 / 2.84	2.02 / 2.76	2.00 / 2.70	1.96 / 2.63	1.94 / 2.60	1.91 / 2.54	1.90 / 2.51	1.88 / 2.49	19
20	4.35 / 8.10	3.49 / 5.85	3.10 / 4.94	2.87 / 4.43	2.71 / 4.10	2.60 / 3.87	2.52 / 3.71	2.45 / 3.56	2.40 / 3.45	2.35 / 3.37	2.31 / 3.30	2.28 / 3.23	2.23 / 3.13	2.18 / 3.05	2.12 / 2.94	2.08 / 2.86	2.04 / 2.77	1.99 / 2.69	1.96 / 2.63	1.92 / 2.56	1.90 / 2.53	1.87 / 2.47	1.85 / 2.44	1.84 / 2.42	20
21	4.32 / 8.02	3.47 / 5.78	3.07 / 4.87	2.84 / 4.37	2.68 / 4.04	2.57 / 3.81	2.49 / 3.65	2.42 / 3.51	2.37 / 3.40	2.32 / 3.31	2.28 / 3.24	2.25 / 3.17	2.20 / 3.07	2.15 / 2.99	2.09 / 2.88	2.05 / 2.80	2.00 / 2.72	1.96 / 2.63	1.93 / 2.58	1.89 / 2.51	1.87 / 2.47	1.84 / 2.42	1.82 / 2.38	1.81 / 2.36	21
22	4.30 / 7.94	3.44 / 5.72	3.05 / 4.82	2.82 / 4.31	2.66 / 3.99	2.55 / 3.76	2.47 / 3.59	2.40 / 3.45	2.35 / 3.35	2.30 / 3.26	2.26 / 3.18	2.23 / 3.12	2.18 / 3.02	2.13 / 2.94	2.07 / 2.83	2.03 / 2.75	1.98 / 2.67	1.93 / 2.58	1.91 / 2.53	1.87 / 2.46	1.84 / 2.42	1.81 / 2.37	1.80 / 2.33	1.78 / 2.31	22
23	4.28 / 7.88	3.42 / 5.66	3.03 / 4.76	2.80 / 4.26	2.64 / 3.94	2.53 / 3.71	2.45 / 3.54	2.38 / 3.41	2.32 / 3.30	2.28 / 3.21	2.24 / 3.14	2.20 / 3.07	2.14 / 2.97	2.10 / 2.89	2.04 / 2.78	2.00 / 2.70	1.96 / 2.62	1.91 / 2.53	1.88 / 2.48	1.84 / 2.41	1.82 / 2.37	1.79 / 2.32	1.77 / 2.28	1.76 / 2.26	23
24	4.26 / 7.82	3.40 / 5.61	3.01 / 4.72	2.78 / 4.22	2.62 / 3.90	2.51 / 3.67	2.43 / 3.50	2.36 / 3.36	2.30 / 3.25	2.26 / 3.17	2.22 / 3.09	2.18 / 3.03	2.13 / 2.93	2.09 / 2.85	2.02 / 2.74	1.98 / 2.66	1.94 / 2.58	1.89 / 2.49	1.86 / 2.44	1.82 / 2.36	1.80 / 2.33	1.76 / 2.27	1.74 / 2.23	1.73 / 2.21	24
25	4.24 / 7.77	3.38 / 5.57	2.99 / 4.68	2.76 / 4.18	2.60 / 3.86	2.49 / 3.63	2.41 / 3.46	2.34 / 3.32	2.28 / 3.21	2.24 / 3.13	2.20 / 3.05	2.16 / 2.99	2.11 / 2.89	2.06 / 2.81	2.00 / 2.70	1.96 / 2.62	1.92 / 2.54	1.87 / 2.45	1.84 / 2.40	1.80 / 2.32	1.77 / 2.29	1.74 / 2.23	1.72 / 2.19	1.71 / 2.17	25
26	4.22 / 7.72	3.37 / 5.53	2.98 / 4.64	2.74 / 4.14	2.59 / 3.82	2.47 / 3.59	2.39 / 3.42	2.32 / 3.29	2.27 / 3.17	2.22 / 3.09	2.18 / 3.02	2.15 / 2.96	2.10 / 2.86	2.05 / 2.77	1.99 / 2.66	1.95 / 2.58	1.90 / 2.50	1.85 / 2.41	1.82 / 2.36	1.78 / 2.28	1.76 / 2.25	1.72 / 2.19	1.70 / 2.15	1.69 / 2.13	26

The function, $F = e$ with exponent $2z$, is computed in part from Fisher's table VI (7). Additional entries are by interpolation, mostly graphical.

TABLE 10.5.3—(Continued)

degrees of freedom (for greater mean square)

f^2	1	2	3	4	5	6	7	8	9	10	11	12	14	16	20	24	30	40	50	75	100	200	500	∞	f^2
27	4.21/7.68	3.35/5.49	2.96/4.60	2.73/4.11	2.57/3.79	2.46/3.56	2.37/3.39	2.30/3.26	2.25/3.14	2.20/3.06	2.16/2.98	2.13/2.93	2.08/2.83	2.03/2.74	1.97/2.63	1.93/2.55	1.88/2.47	1.84/2.38	1.80/2.33	1.76/2.25	1.74/2.21	1.71/2.16	1.68/2.12	1.67/2.10	27
28	4.20/7.64	3.34/5.45	2.95/4.57	2.71/4.07	2.56/3.76	2.44/3.53	2.36/3.36	2.29/3.23	2.24/3.11	2.19/3.03	2.15/2.95	2.12/2.90	2.06/2.80	2.02/2.71	1.96/2.60	1.91/2.52	1.87/2.44	1.81/2.35	1.78/2.30	1.75/2.22	1.72/2.18	1.69/2.13	1.67/2.09	1.65/2.06	28
29	4.18/7.60	3.33/5.42	2.93/4.54	2.70/4.04	2.54/3.73	2.43/3.50	2.35/3.33	2.28/3.20	2.22/3.08	2.18/3.00	2.14/2.92	2.10/2.87	2.05/2.77	2.00/2.68	1.94/2.57	1.90/2.49	1.85/2.41	1.80/2.32	1.77/2.27	1.73/2.19	1.71/2.15	1.68/2.10	1.65/2.06	1.64/2.03	29
30	4.17/7.56	3.32/5.39	2.92/4.51	2.69/4.02	2.53/3.70	2.42/3.47	2.34/3.30	2.27/3.17	2.21/3.06	2.16/2.98	2.12/2.90	2.09/2.84	2.04/2.74	1.99/2.66	1.93/2.55	1.89/2.47	1.84/2.38	1.79/2.29	1.76/2.24	1.72/2.16	1.69/2.13	1.66/2.07	1.64/2.03	1.62/2.01	30
32	4.15/7.50	3.30/5.34	2.90/4.46	2.67/3.97	2.51/3.66	2.40/3.42	2.32/3.25	2.25/3.12	2.19/3.01	2.14/2.94	2.10/2.86	2.07/2.80	2.02/2.70	1.97/2.62	1.91/2.51	1.86/2.42	1.82/2.34	1.76/2.25	1.74/2.20	1.69/2.12	1.67/2.08	1.64/2.02	1.61/1.98	1.59/1.96	32
34	4.13/7.44	3.28/5.29	2.88/4.42	2.65/3.93	2.49/3.61	2.38/3.38	2.30/3.21	2.23/3.08	2.17/2.97	2.12/2.89	2.08/2.82	2.05/2.76	2.00/2.66	1.95/2.58	1.89/2.47	1.84/2.38	1.80/2.30	1.74/2.21	1.71/2.15	1.67/2.08	1.64/2.04	1.61/1.98	1.59/1.94	1.57/1.91	34
36	4.11/7.39	3.26/5.25	2.86/4.38	2.63/3.89	2.48/3.58	2.36/3.35	2.28/3.18	2.21/3.04	2.15/2.94	2.10/2.86	2.06/2.78	2.03/2.72	1.98/2.62	1.93/2.54	1.87/2.43	1.82/2.35	1.78/2.26	1.72/2.17	1.69/2.12	1.65/2.04	1.62/2.00	1.59/1.94	1.56/1.90	1.55/1.87	36
38	4.10/7.35	3.25/5.21	2.85/4.34	2.62/3.86	2.46/3.54	2.35/3.32	2.26/3.15	2.19/3.02	2.14/2.91	2.09/2.82	2.05/2.75	2.02/2.69	1.96/2.59	1.92/2.51	1.85/2.40	1.80/2.32	1.76/2.22	1.71/2.14	1.67/2.08	1.63/2.00	1.60/1.97	1.57/1.90	1.54/1.86	1.53/1.84	38
40	4.08/7.31	3.23/5.18	2.84/4.31	2.61/3.83	2.45/3.51	2.34/3.29	2.25/3.12	2.18/2.99	2.12/2.88	2.07/2.80	2.04/2.73	2.00/2.66	1.95/2.56	1.90/2.49	1.84/2.37	1.79/2.29	1.74/2.20	1.69/2.11	1.66/2.05	1.61/1.97	1.59/1.94	1.55/1.88	1.53/1.84	1.51/1.81	40
42	4.07/7.27	3.22/5.15	2.83/4.29	2.59/3.80	2.44/3.49	2.32/3.26	2.24/3.10	2.17/2.96	2.11/2.86	2.06/2.77	2.02/2.70	1.99/2.64	1.94/2.54	1.89/2.46	1.82/2.35	1.78/2.26	1.73/2.17	1.68/2.08	1.64/2.02	1.60/1.94	1.57/1.91	1.54/1.85	1.51/1.80	1.49/1.78	42
44	4.06/7.24	3.21/5.12	2.82/4.26	2.58/3.78	2.43/3.46	2.31/3.24	2.23/3.07	2.16/2.94	2.10/2.84	2.05/2.75	2.01/2.68	1.98/2.62	1.92/2.52	1.88/2.44	1.81/2.32	1.76/2.24	1.72/2.15	1.66/2.06	1.63/2.00	1.58/1.92	1.56/1.88	1.52/1.82	1.50/1.78	1.48/1.75	44
46	4.05/7.21	3.20/5.10	2.81/4.24	2.57/3.76	2.42/3.44	2.30/3.22	2.22/3.05	2.14/2.92	2.09/2.82	2.04/2.73	2.00/2.66	1.97/2.60	1.91/2.50	1.87/2.42	1.80/2.30	1.75/2.22	1.71/2.13	1.65/2.04	1.62/1.98	1.57/1.90	1.54/1.86	1.51/1.80	1.48/1.76	1.46/1.72	46
48	4.04/7.19	3.19/5.08	2.80/4.22	2.56/3.74	2.41/3.42	2.30/3.20	2.21/3.04	2.14/2.90	2.08/2.80	2.03/2.71	1.99/2.64	1.96/2.58	1.90/2.48	1.86/2.40	1.79/2.28	1.74/2.20	1.70/2.11	1.64/2.02	1.61/1.96	1.56/1.88	1.53/1.84	1.50/1.78	1.47/1.73	1.45/1.70	48

TABLE 10.5.3—(Continued)

f degrees of freedom (for greater mean square)

f	∞	500	200	100	75	50	40	30	24	20	16	14	12	11	10	9	8	7	6	5	4	3	2	1
50	1.44/1.68	1.46/1.71	1.48/1.76	1.52/1.82	1.55/1.86	1.60/1.94	1.63/2.00	1.69/2.10	1.74/2.18	1.78/2.26	1.85/2.39	1.90/2.46	1.95/2.56	1.98/2.62	2.02/2.70	2.07/2.78	2.13/2.88	2.20/3.02	2.29/3.18	2.40/3.41	2.56/3.72	2.79/4.20	3.18/5.06	4.03/7.17
55	1.41/1.64	1.43/1.66	1.46/1.71	1.50/1.78	1.52/1.82	1.58/1.90	1.61/1.96	1.67/2.06	1.72/2.15	1.76/2.23	1.83/2.35	1.88/2.43	1.93/2.53	1.97/2.59	2.00/2.66	2.05/2.75	2.11/2.85	2.18/2.98	2.27/3.15	2.38/3.37	2.54/3.68	2.78/4.16	3.17/5.01	4.02/7.12
60	1.39/1.60	1.41/1.63	1.44/1.68	1.48/1.74	1.50/1.79	1.56/1.87	1.59/1.93	1.65/2.03	1.70/2.12	1.75/2.20	1.81/2.32	1.86/2.40	1.92/2.50	1.95/2.56	1.99/2.63	2.04/2.72	2.10/2.82	2.17/2.95	2.25/3.12	2.37/3.34	2.52/3.65	2.76/4.13	3.15/4.98	4.00/7.08
65	1.37/1.56	1.39/1.60	1.42/1.64	1.46/1.71	1.49/1.76	1.54/1.84	1.57/1.90	1.63/2.00	1.68/2.09	1.73/2.18	1.80/2.30	1.85/2.37	1.90/2.47	1.94/2.54	1.98/2.61	2.02/2.70	2.08/2.79	2.15/2.93	2.24/3.09	2.36/3.31	2.51/3.62	2.75/4.10	3.14/4.95	3.99/7.04
70	1.35/1.53	1.37/1.56	1.40/1.62	1.45/1.69	1.47/1.74	1.53/1.82	1.56/1.88	1.62/1.98	1.67/2.07	1.72/2.15	1.79/2.28	1.84/2.35	1.89/2.45	1.93/2.51	1.97/2.59	2.01/2.67	2.07/2.77	2.14/2.91	2.23/3.07	2.35/3.29	2.50/3.60	2.74/4.08	3.13/4.92	3.98/7.01
80	1.32/1.49	1.35/1.52	1.38/1.57	1.42/1.65	1.45/1.70	1.51/1.78	1.54/1.84	1.60/1.94	1.65/2.03	1.70/2.11	1.77/2.24	1.82/2.32	1.88/2.41	1.91/2.48	1.95/2.55	1.99/2.64	2.05/2.74	2.12/2.87	2.21/3.04	2.33/3.25	2.48/3.56	2.72/4.04	3.11/4.88	3.96/6.96
100	1.28/1.43	1.30/1.46	1.34/1.51	1.39/1.59	1.42/1.64	1.48/1.73	1.51/1.79	1.57/1.89	1.63/1.98	1.68/2.06	1.75/2.19	1.79/2.26	1.85/2.36	1.88/2.43	1.92/2.51	1.97/2.59	2.03/2.69	2.10/2.82	2.19/2.99	2.30/3.20	2.46/3.51	2.70/3.98	3.09/4.82	3.94/6.90
125	1.25/1.37	1.27/1.40	1.31/1.46	1.36/1.54	1.39/1.59	1.45/1.68	1.49/1.75	1.55/1.85	1.60/1.94	1.65/2.03	1.72/2.15	1.77/2.23	1.83/2.33	1.86/2.40	1.90/2.47	1.95/2.56	2.01/2.65	2.08/2.79	2.17/2.95	2.29/3.17	2.44/3.47	2.68/3.94	3.07/4.78	3.92/6.84
150	1.22/1.33	1.25/1.37	1.29/1.43	1.34/1.51	1.37/1.56	1.44/1.66	1.47/1.72	1.54/1.83	1.59/1.91	1.64/2.00	1.71/2.12	1.76/2.20	1.82/2.30	1.85/2.37	1.89/2.44	1.94/2.53	2.00/2.62	2.07/2.76	2.16/2.92	2.27/3.14	2.43/3.44	2.67/3.91	3.06/4.75	3.91/6.81
200	1.19/1.28	1.22/1.33	1.26/1.39	1.32/1.48	1.35/1.53	1.42/1.62	1.45/1.69	1.52/1.79	1.57/1.88	1.62/1.97	1.69/2.09	1.74/2.17	1.80/2.28	1.83/2.34	1.87/2.41	1.92/2.50	1.98/2.60	2.05/2.73	2.14/2.90	2.26/3.11	2.41/3.41	2.65/3.88	3.04/4.71	3.89/6.76
400	1.13/1.19	1.16/1.24	1.22/1.32	1.28/1.42	1.32/1.47	1.38/1.57	1.42/1.64	1.49/1.74	1.54/1.84	1.60/1.92	1.67/2.04	1.72/2.12	1.78/2.23	1.81/2.29	1.85/2.37	1.90/2.46	1.96/2.55	2.03/2.69	2.12/2.85	2.23/3.06	2.39/3.36	2.62/3.83	3.02/4.66	3.86/6.70
1000	1.08/1.11	1.13/1.19	1.19/1.28	1.26/1.38	1.30/1.44	1.36/1.54	1.41/1.61	1.47/1.71	1.53/1.81	1.58/1.89	1.65/2.01	1.70/2.09	1.76/2.20	1.80/2.26	1.84/2.34	1.89/2.43	1.95/2.53	2.02/2.66	2.10/2.82	2.22/3.04	2.38/3.34	2.61/3.80	3.00/4.62	3.85/6.66
∞	1.00/1.00	1.11/1.15	1.17/1.25	1.24/1.36	1.28/1.41	1.35/1.52	1.40/1.59	1.46/1.69	1.52/1.79	1.57/1.87	1.64/1.99	1.69/2.07	1.75/2.18	1.79/2.24	1.83/2.32	1.88/2.41	1.94/2.51	2.01/2.64	2.09/2.80	2.21/3.02	2.37/3.32	2.60/3.78	2.99/4.60	3.84/6.64

venient combinations of degrees of freedom. Across the top of the table is
found f_1 degrees of freedom corresponding to the number of samples:
$f_1 = a - 1$. At the left is f_2, the degrees of freedom for individuals,
$a(n - 1)$.

To find the 5% and 1% points for table 10.5.1, look in the column
headed by $f_1 = 9$ and down to the rows $f_2 = 80$ and 100. The required
points are 1.98 and 2.62, halfway between those in the table. To be
compared with these are the points experimentally obtained in table
10.5.2, 2.25 and 2.75; not bad estimates from a sample of 100 experiments. In order to check the sampling distribution more exactly, I went
back to the original calculations and found 8% of the F beyond the 5%
point and 2% beyond the 1%. This gives some idea of the variation to
be encountered in sampling.

For the doughnut experiment, the hypothesis set up—that the batches
are random samples from a common population—may be judged by
means of table 10.5.3. From the analysis of variance in table 10.4.2,

$$F = 545.5/100.9 = 5.41$$

For $f_1 = 3$ and $f_2 = 20$, the 1% point in the new table is 4.94. Thus
from the distribution specified in the hypothesis there is less than one
chance in 100 of drawing a sample having a larger value of F. Evidently
the samples come from populations with different μ. The conclusion is
that the fats have different capabilities for being absorbed by doughnuts.

EXAMPLE 10.5.1—Four tropical feedstuffs were each fed to a lot of 5 baby
chicks (24). The gains in weight were:

Lot					
1	55	49	42	21	52
2	61	112	30	89	63
3	42	97	81	95	92
4	169	137	169	85	154

Analyze the variance and test the equality of the μ. Ans. Mean squares: (i) lots, 8,745;
(ii) chicks, 722. $F = 12.1$. Since the sample F is far beyond the tabular 1% point,
there is little doubt that the feedstuff populations have different μ.

EXAMPLE 10.5.2—In the wool data of example 10.3.2, test the hypothesis that
the bags are all from populations with a common mean. Ans. $F = 1.35$, $F_{.05} = 2.85$.
There is not strong evidence against the hypothesis—the bags may all have the same
percentage of clean wool.

EXAMPLE 10.5.3—The sample means in the vitamin B_{12} experiment of example
10.3.1, like many of those in table 10.5.2, differ less than is to be expected from the
mean square for individuals. Although there is no reason for computing it, the value
of F is 0.54. There is, of course, no evidence of differences among the μ.

EXAMPLE 10.5.4—In example 10.4.1, test the hypothesis that the treatments
have no effect on the numbers of loopers. Ans. $F = 4.33$. What do you conclude?

*With this brief introduction to analysis of variance, the reader is prepared for
the earlier sections of chapter 11.*

10.6—Tests of all comparisons among means. In the doughnut experiment there was convincing evidence of differences among the μ. But the F-test gives no clue as to how many differences there are. In a group of a means there are in all $a(a - 1)/2$ potential differences; $(4)(3)/2 = 6$ among the fats. Does each μ differ from all the rest, or are some undifferentiated? If significant differences are evident, one proceeds to locate them.

There are several methods for testing hypotheses about these differences (4, 17, 22). I have adopted that of J. W. Tukey (with some modifications) partly because of its adaptability and partly because the experiment is the unit considered in tabbing up successes and failures (29).

The test is made by computing a difference, D, which is significant at the 5% level, then comparing it with the $a(a - 1)/2$ sample differences in the experiment. D is the product of $s_{\bar{x}}$ and a factor, Q, taken from table 10.6.1. Enter the table with the number of treatments as shown in the upper heading and degrees of freedom, f, for Batches (error) indicated at the left.

For the doughnuts, $s_{\bar{x}} = \sqrt{100.9/6} = 4.1$, $s^2 = 100.9$ being the estimate of σ^2. With 4 treatments and $f = 20$, Q is taken from the table as 3.96. So

$$D = Qs_{\bar{x}} = (3.96)(4.1) = 16.2$$

Referring to table 10.4.1, the experimental differences to be compared with D are:

Fat	$\bar{x}$	$\bar{x} - 162$	$\bar{x} - 172$	$\bar{x} - 176$
2	185	23	13	9
3	176	14	4	
1	172	10		
4	162			

Here the sample means are arrayed from high to low and each is subtracted from those above. Of the 6 differences, only one exceeds $D = 16.2$. The conclusion is that Fat 2 is absorbed in greater amounts than Fat 4 but that there are no detected differences among absorptions by the other fats.

If there are only 2 treatments, $Q = t\sqrt{2}$ and so $D = ts_{\bar{x}}\sqrt{2}$. This is the widely used *Least Significant Difference* or *LSD*. It is often incorrectly applied to all differences among 3 or more means, the result being that too many of the differences are adjudged significant. The *LSD* gives correct tests only if $a = 2$.

Tukey devised D as a confidence interval to be set on the sample differences. Thus, the difference, $\mu_2 - \mu_4$, is said with confidence to lie in the interval,

$$23 \pm 16.2; \text{ between 6.8 and 39.2 grams}$$

TABLE 10.6.1
UPPER 5% PERCENTAGE POINTS, Q, IN THE STUDENTIZED RANGE*

Number of Treatments, a

Degrees of Freedom, f	2	3	4	5	6	7	8	9	10	11	12	13	14	15	16	17	18	19	20
1	18.0	26.7	32.8	37.2	40.5	43.1	45.4	47.3	49.1	50.6	51.9	53.2	54.3	55.4	56.3	57.2	58.0	58.8	59.6
2	6.09	8.28	9.80	10.89	11.73	12.43	13.03	13.54	13.99	14.39	14.75	15.08	15.38	15.65	15.91	16.14	16.36	16.57	16.77
3	4.50	5.88	6.83	7.51	8.04	8.47	8.85	9.18	9.46	9.72	9.95	10.16	10.35	10.52	10.69	10.84	10.98	11.12	11.24
4	3.93	5.00	5.76	6.31	6.73	7.06	7.35	7.60	7.83	8.03	8.21	8.37	8.52	8.67	8.80	8.92	9.03	9.14	9.24
5	3.61	4.54	5.18	5.64	5.99	6.28	6.52	6.74	6.93	7.10	7.25	7.39	7.52	7.64	7.75	7.86	7.95	8.04	8.13
6	3.46	4.34	4.90	5.31	5.63	5.89	6.12	6.32	6.49	6.65	6.79	6.92	7.04	7.14	7.24	7.34	7.43	7.51	7.59
7	3.34	4.16	4.68	5.06	5.35	5.59	5.80	5.99	6.15	6.29	6.42	6.54	6.65	6.75	6.84	6.93	7.01	7.08	7.16
8	3.26	4.04	4.53	4.89	5.17	5.40	5.60	5.77	5.92	6.05	6.18	6.29	6.39	6.48	6.57	6.65	6.73	6.80	6.87
9	3.20	3.95	4.42	4.76	5.02	5.24	5.43	5.60	5.74	5.87	5.98	6.09	6.19	6.28	6.36	6.44	6.51	6.58	6.65
10	3.15	3.88	4.33	4.66	4.91	5.12	5.30	5.46	5.60	5.72	5.83	5.93	6.03	6.12	6.20	6.27	6.34	6.41	6.47
11	3.11	3.82	4.26	4.58	4.82	5.03	5.20	5.35	5.49	5.61	5.71	5.81	5.90	5.98	6.06	6.14	6.20	6.27	6.33
12	3.08	3.77	4.20	4.51	4.75	4.95	5.12	5.27	5.40	5.51	5.61	5.71	5.80	5.88	5.95	6.02	6.09	6.15	6.21
13	3.06	3.73	4.15	4.46	4.69	4.88	5.05	5.19	5.32	5.43	5.53	5.63	5.71	5.79	5.86	5.93	6.00	6.06	6.11
14	3.03	3.70	4.11	4.41	4.64	4.83	4.99	5.13	5.25	5.36	5.46	5.56	5.64	5.72	5.79	5.86	5.92	5.98	6.03
15	3.01	3.67	4.08	4.37	4.59	4.78	4.94	5.08	5.20	5.31	5.40	5.49	5.57	5.65	5.72	5.79	5.85	5.91	5.96
16	3.00	3.65	4.05	4.34	4.56	4.74	4.90	5.03	5.15	5.26	5.35	5.44	5.52	5.59	5.66	5.73	5.79	5.84	5.90
17	2.98	3.62	4.02	4.31	4.52	4.70	4.86	4.99	5.11	5.21	5.31	5.39	5.47	5.55	5.61	5.68	5.74	5.79	5.84
18	2.97	3.61	4.00	4.28	4.49	4.67	4.83	4.96	5.07	5.17	5.27	5.35	5.43	5.50	5.57	5.63	5.69	5.74	5.79
19	2.96	3.59	3.98	4.26	4.47	4.64	4.79	4.92	5.04	5.14	5.23	5.32	5.39	5.46	5.53	5.59	5.65	5.70	5.75
20	2.95	3.58	3.96	4.24	4.45	4.62	4.77	4.90	5.01	5.11	5.20	5.28	5.36	5.43	5.50	5.56	5.61	5.66	5.71
24	2.92	3.53	3.90	4.17	4.37	4.54	4.68	4.81	4.92	5.01	5.10	5.18	5.25	5.32	5.38	5.44	5.50	5.55	5.59
30	2.89	3.48	3.84	4.11	4.30	4.46	4.60	4.72	4.83	4.92	5.00	5.08	5.15	5.21	5.27	5.33	5.38	5.43	5.48
40	2.86	3.44	3.79	4.04	4.23	4.39	4.52	4.63	4.74	4.82	4.90	4.98	5.05	5.11	5.17	5.22	5.27	5.32	5.36
60	2.83	3.40	3.74	3.98	4.16	4.31	4.44	4.55	4.65	4.73	4.81	4.88	4.94	5.00	5.06	5.11	5.15	5.20	5.24
120	2.80	3.36	3.69	3.92	4.10	4.24	4.36	4.47	4.56	4.64	4.71	4.78	4.84	4.90	4.95	5.00	5.04	5.09	5.13
∞	2.77	3.32	3.63	3.86	4.03	4.17	4.29	4.39	4.47	4.55	4.62	4.68	4.74	4.80	4.84	4.89	4.93	4.97	5.01

* Reprinted from Biometrika, 39:192 (1952) by permission of the author, Joyce M. May, and the Editor.

Since this interval does not cover zero, the μ are evidently different. But the difference, $\mu_2 - \mu_1$, with confidence interval,

$$13 \pm 16.2; \text{ from } -2.2 \text{ to } 30.2 \text{ grams,}$$

does include zero, so that $\mu_2 - \mu_1$ may be zero. The advantage of the confidence interval is that the amount of overlap of zero is obvious; likewise the distance above or below zero in case there is no overlap.

In Tukey's test the experiment as a whole is the unit for assessing the risk of error. Use of table 10.6.1 fixes this risk at 5 experiments per 100 in which false conclusions will be reached. The number of false conclusions in any one experiment is not specified.

Hartley shows (13) that a sequential method of testing, like that of Keuls, is somewhat more powerful than the one just outlined. For this test, not one Q is taken from the table but several, one for each range of the treatment means. In the doughnut experiment, adjacent means in the array are tested with $Q = 2.95$ for $a = 2$; for two ranks apart in the array use $Q = 3.58$ for $a = 3$; use $Q = 3.96$ only for the extreme range where $a = 4$. The corresponding D are $(2.95)(4.1) = 12.1$, $(3.58)(4.1) = 14.7$, and the former $(3.96)(4.1) = 16.2$. These D are entered in the northeast-southwest diagonals of the table of differences:

Fat	$\bar{x}$	$\bar{x} - 162$	$\bar{x} - 172$	$\bar{x} - 176$
2	185	23 (16.2)	13 (14.7)	9 (12.1)
3	176	14 (14.7)	4 (12.1)	
1	172	10 (12.1)		
4	162			

Each difference is now compared with its own D, the difference being judged significant if it is larger than its D. A rule to be observed is that if any difference is less than its D then no further testing is to be done to the right of that difference in its row or below it in the column.

In the doughnut experiment the same conclusion follows the two forms of the test. Often the sequential test detects the greater number of differences.

Don't forget the *estimates* of the population differences. These are unbiased and, whether significant or not, do contain information about the real differences.

EXAMPLE 10.6.1—In the artificially constructed example 10.4.2 we know that the 4 μ are all different. But sampling variation conceals some of the differences. Calculate $D = 18.4$ and show that only 2 of the confidence intervals do not overlap zero. Note that the $\bar{x}$ are in the same order as the μ; this might not be so.

EXAMPLE 10.6.2—Calculate the least significant difference for $a = 2$, $s^2 = 100.9$, $n = 6$, $f = 20$, $t_{.05} = 2.086$ as in the doughnut experiment. Ans. $D = LSD = 12.1$. If this were mistakenly applied to the 6 differences among the doughnut means, 3 of them would be thought significant.

EXAMPLE 10.6.3—For the chicks of example 10.5.1, show that Lot 4 differs significantly from each of the other three.

At first reading, the person interested primarily in methods may skip to sections 10.14 and 10.16, then to chapter 11.

10.7—Short-cut computation using ranges. An easy method of testing all comparisons among means is based on the ranges of the samples (30). In the doughnut experiment, table 10.4.1, the 4 ranges are 39, 20, 30, 21; the sum is 110. This sum of ranges is multiplied by a factor taken from table 10.7.1. In the column for $a = 4$ and the row for $n = 6$, take the

TABLE 10.7.1
CRITICAL FACTORS FOR ALLOWANCES, 5% RISK *

Sample Size, n	Number of Samples, a								
	2	3	4	5	6	7	8	9	10
2	3.43	2.37	1.78	1.40	1.16	1.00	.87	.78	.70
3	1.91	1.44	1.13	.94	.80	.70	.62	.56	.51
4	1.63	1.25	1.01	.84	.72	.63	.57	.51	.47
5	1.53	1.19	.96	.81	.70	.61	.55	.50	.45
6	1.50	1.18	.95	.80	.69	.61	.55	.49	.45
7	1.49	1.17	.95	.80	.69	.61	.55	.50	.45
8	1.49	1.17	.96	.81	.70	.62	.55	.50	.46
9	1.50	1.18	.97	.82	.71	.62	.56	.51	.47
10	1.52	1.20	.98	.83	.72	.63	.57	.52	.47

* Extracted from table by Link and Wallace (18).

factor 0.95. Then $D' = \dfrac{(\text{Factor})(\text{Sum of Ranges})}{n} = \dfrac{(0.95)(110)}{6} = 17.4$.

D' is used like the D in the Tukey test of the foregoing section. Comparing it with the 6 differences among treatments, one concludes (as before) that only the largest is significant.

EXAMPLE 10.7.1—Using the short-cut method, examine all differences in the chick experiment of example 10.5.1. Ans. $D' = 49$. Same conclusions as in example 10.6.3.

10.8—Tests of designed comparisons among means. In many experiments the design includes a statement of the comparisons that are to be made; this decision is not delayed until after the results are seen. (Usually the number of designed comparisons is equal to the number of degrees of freedom among treatments.) Such foresight results in smaller differences detected at the same level of probability. The experiment is more *sensitive*. Planning the comparisons in advance of performing the experiment should be done whenever feasible.

The vitamin B_{12} experiment cited in example 10.3.1 included a check lot receiving no B_{12}. Some additional results are shown in table 10.8.1.

TABLE 10.8.1
AVERAGE DAILY GAINS IN 3 LOTS OF PIGS RECEIVING ANTIBIOTICS AND 3 LEVELS OF B_{12}

μg. of B_{12}	Average Daily Gains			Sums	Means
0	1.04	1.00	0.69	2.73	0.91
5	1.52	1.56	1.54	4.62	1.54
10	1.63	1.57	1.54	4.74	1.58

Source of Variation	Degrees of Freedom	Sum of Squares	Mean Squares
Levels of B_{12}	2	0.8474	0.4237
Individuals	6	0.0784	0.0131

$$F = 0.4237/0.0131 = 32, F_{.01} = 10.92$$

Often such experiments are planned to make 2 comparisons, one between the 2 levels and the other between check and treatment.

For the first comparison, that between $\bar{x}_{10} = 1.58$ and $\bar{x}_5 = 1.54$, the test is made by computing a sum of squares, conveniently by use of the sums:

$$\frac{(4.62)^2 + (4.74)^2}{3} - \frac{(4.62 + 4.74)^2}{6} = 0.0024$$

This sum of squares with a single degree of freedom is tested against error. Since it is less than the mean square, 0.0131, there is no convincing evidence of a population difference.

The second comparison is the difference between the mean of the 2 treatments, $(4.62 + 4.74)/6 = 1.56$ and the mean of check, 0.91. Since the means are based on different numbers of observations, the corresponding sum of squares is calculated thus (section 10.16):

$$\frac{(4.62 + 4.74)^2}{6} + \frac{(2.73)^2}{3} - \frac{(4.62 + 4.74 + 2.73)^2}{9} = 0.8450$$

Now, $F = 0.8450/0.0131 = 64$. Most of the sum of squares for the 3 means, 0.8474, has been segregated in this second comparison, only a negligible part of it in the first.

A notable fact is that the 2 single-degree-of-freedom sums of squares add to the total for Levels of B_{12}:

$$0.0024 + 0.8450 = 0.8474$$

This addition is a property of *orthogonal* comparisons to be discussed more extensively in chapter 12. If your experiment permits a set of orthogonal comparisons planned in advance, you will find it more efficient to use the method of this section than to resort to all comparisons among the means. See example 10.9.4 and chapter 12.

10.9—Analysis of variance with only two lots. Chapter 4 is a special case of the present one, so it is informative to analyze the variance of the two lots of chicks studied in that chapter. As has been noted, the pooling of the sample sums of squares is a common feature of the two chapters. For the chick data of table 4.3.2, this pooled sum of squares, 16,220, with $f = 20$ is entered in table 10.9.1. We shall complete the analysis of variance by computing the sum of squares for the two sample

TABLE 10.9.1
ANALYSIS OF VARIANCE OF CHICK COMB EXPERIMENT, TABLE 4.3.1

Source of Variation	Degrees of Freedom	Sum of Squares	Mean Square
Chicks	20	16,220	811
Lot means	1	9,245.5	9,245.5

$F = 9,245.5/811 = 11.4$ $\sqrt{F} = 3.38 = t$

means, 97 and 56 mg. It is perhaps clearest to calculate first the two sums, $97 \times 11 = 1,067$ and $56 \times 11 = 616$. Then, the sum of squares is, as usual,

$$\frac{(1,067)^2 + (616)^2}{11} - \frac{(1,683)^2}{22} = 9,245.5$$

This is entered in the table and the analysis then completed. F is greater than its 1% point, 8.10, just as t in table 4.3.2 was beyond its.

Here are two points of interest. (i) If there is only a single degree of freedom for lot means, then $\sqrt{F} = t$. The probability of F greater than 11.4 is identical with that of t greater than 3.38, so it is a matter of choice which one is used. (ii) With only two samples, the sum of squares for their means is easily calculated this way:

$$\frac{(\Sigma X_1 - \Sigma X_2)^2}{2n} = \frac{(1,067 - 616)^2}{(2)(11)} = 9,245.5,$$

as before.   Merely square the difference of the two sample sums, then divide by the total number of items.   Equally, the result may be got thus:

$$\frac{n(\bar{x}_1 - \bar{x}_2)^2}{2} = \frac{11(97 - 56)^2}{2} = 9{,}245.5$$

I think you will agree that the F test is easier to perform than the t.

EXAMPLE 10.9.1—Hansberry and Richardson (11) gave the percentages of wormy apples on two groups of 12 trees each. The trees of group A, sprayed with lead arsenate, had 19, 26, 22, 13, 26, 25, 38, 40, 36, 12, 16, and 8 per cent of apples wormy. Those of group B, sprayed with calcium arsenate and buffer materials, had 36, 42, 20, 43, 47, 49, 59, 37, 28, 49, 31, and 39 per cent wormy. Compute the mean square *within samples*, 111.41, with 22 *d.f.*; and that *between sample means*, 1,650.04, with 1 *d.f.*   Then

$$F = 1{,}650.04/111.41 = 14.8$$

Now, test the significance of the difference between the sample means in the manner of table 4.3.2. The value of t is 3.85 $= \sqrt{14.8}$.

EXAMPLE 10.9.2—Prove the identity of the three expressions for sum of squares given in the foregoing section.

EXAMPLE 10.9.3—Using the table of Q, set 95% confidence limits on the difference between the mean comb weights. Ans. 41 $\pm$ 25.3; from 15.7 to 66.3 mg.

EXAMPLE 10.9.4—Show that the test of the planned comparison, $\bar{x}_{10} - \bar{x}_6$, in the preceding section is equivalent to the t-test of the present section. Also that it is equivalent to use of the *LSD*.

10.10—Model I.   Fixed treatment effects.   It is time to make a more formal statement about the model of analysis of variance which has been used in section 10.4 and those following. The effects of the treatments have been assumed to fix the population means. The sample means estimate these fixed μ.

It is convenient to specify the population means by an over-all μ plus deviations therefrom. These deviations, characterizing the treatments, are denoted by a_i where i takes on values 1, 2, ... a. Since the a_i are deviations from μ, it follows that $\Sigma a_i = 0$. Corresponding to each a_i there are n observations or replications denoted by X_{ij} where $j = 1$, 2, ... n. The whole experiment is symbolized as in table 10.10.1.

The notation used is rather general in statistical papers. The first subscript specifies the treatment (or lot or sample) while the second refers to the individual observation receiving that treatment. A dot in the subscript indicates summation; $X_{i.}$ denotes the sum of the $j = 1 \ldots n$ observations in treatment i. Double dots indicate the sum over the entire experiment.

Model I for analysis of variance is expressed in words:

Any observed value is the sum of three parts: (i) an over-all mean, (ii) a treatment deviation, and (iii) a random element from a normally distributed population with mean zero and standard deviation σ.

In algebraic shorthand, this becomes,

$$X_{ij} = \mu + a_i + \epsilon_{ij}, i = 1 \ldots a, j = 1 \ldots n, \ \epsilon_{ij} \text{ is } N(0, \sigma)$$

The additive feature should be emphasized. If one treatment is related to another as a product or ratio, for example, analysis of variance is not appropriate. What to do about this will be discussed later.

The data in example 10.4.2 were made up according to the model above. The over-all mean was $\mu = 30$; the a_i were $a_1 = 15$, $a_2 = 0$,

TABLE 10.10.1

SYMBOLICAL REPRESENTATION OF AN EXPERIMENT WITH a FIXED TREATMENTS EACH
TRIED ON n INDIVIDUALS. OVER-ALL MEAN $= \mu$

Treatment Constants, $\mu + a_i$	Individual Observations					Total	Mean
	1	2	$\ldots j \ldots$		n		
$\mu + a_1$	X_{11}	X_{12}	$\ldots X_{1j} \ldots$		X_{1n}	$X_{1.}$	$\bar{x}_{1.}$
$\mu + a_2$	X_{21}	X_{22}	$\ldots X_{2j} \ldots$		X_{2n}	$X_{2.}$	$\bar{x}_{2.}$
.	.	.	.		.		
.	.	.	.		.		
.	.	.	.		.		
$\mu + a_i$	X_{i1}	X_{i2}	$\ldots X_{ij} \ldots$		X_{in}	$X_{i.}$	$\bar{x}_i$
.	.	.	.		.		
.	.	.	.		.		
.	.	.	.		.		
$\mu + a_a$	X_{a1}	X_{a2}	$\ldots X_{aj} \ldots$		X_{an}	$X_{a.}$	$\bar{x}_{a.}$
Total Mean	(Columns have no physical meaning because the X_{ij} are randomized in the rows)					$X_{..}$	$\bar{x}_{..}$

$a_3 = -6$, $a_4 = -9$. The ϵ_{ij} were drawn from the table of normally distributed pig weights, more clearly seen in table 10.2.1; $\epsilon_{11} = 40 - 30 = 10$, $\epsilon_{12} = 24 - 30 = -6$, $\epsilon_{21} = 29 - 30 = -1$, $\epsilon_{45} = 21 - 30 = -9$. These ϵ are $N(0, 10)$.

The validity of analysis of variance depends on the additive character of the treatment effects in the population. Confidence intervals and the F-test of significance are based on the random choice of the ϵ from some normally distributed population with mean equal to zero, but it has been found (23) that little bias is introduced if sampling is from moderately skewed distributions.

10.11—Components. Model I. In example 10.4.2 it was found that changes in the lot means made notable alterations in the corresponding mean square—it no longer estimated $\sigma^2 = 100$. Something had been added. We are now to learn that this addition is an estimate of $n\Sigma a_i^2/(a-1)$ which, for the pig gains, is $5(15^2 + 0^2 + 6^2 + 9^2)/3 = 5(114) = 570$. You will recognize this as the mean square of the a_i raised to the per-observation level by the factor, $n = 5$. Let $\kappa^2 = \Sigma a_i^2/(a - 1)$. This κ^2 is calculated exactly like s^2. The distinction is that s^2 is based on observations of a variable, whereas κ^2 is made up from the fixed a_i. So $n\kappa^2$ is the added *component*. The exact relations are shown in table 10.11.1.

It is perhaps startling to see how much the parameters are over-estimated: $n\kappa^2 = 570$ is estimated by 947 and $\kappa^2 = 114$ by 189.4. The sampling circumstances that led to this are explained in examples 10.4.3 and 10.4.4.

The parameters in the table throw light on the F-test of significance. It is now evident that

$$F \text{ estimates } \frac{\sigma^2 + n\kappa^2}{\sigma^2}$$

The null hypothesis is $H_0 : \kappa^2 = 0$, which is identical with $a_i = 0$. So, if H_0 is true, F estimates 1. If H_0 is false, F estimates a quantity greater

TABLE 10.11.1
ANALYSIS OF VARIANCE OF PIG GAINS IN EXAMPLE 10.4.2

Source of Variation	Degrees of Freedom	Mean Square	Parameters Estimated
Treatments	3	1,050	$\sigma^2 + n\kappa^2$
Individuals	16	103	σ^2

1,050 − 103 = 947 estimates $n\kappa^2 = 570$. 947/5 = 189.4 estimates $\kappa^2 = 114$

than one. As for sampling values of F, it was shown in table 10.5.2 that, if $\kappa^2 = 0$, F can vary over quite a range, from zero up. It is rare that small values of $F(F < 1)$ indicate anything but sampling variation. It is only large values of F that suggest treatment effects.

This relation of *component analysis* to the F-test will be increasingly useful as more complicated experiments are encountered. Other uses will be presented as they are needed.

EXAMPLE 10.11.1—Estimate $\kappa^2 = 114$ in example 10.4.3. Ans. 25.4.

EXAMPLE 10.11.2—Estimate κ^2 for the unknown a_i in the doughnut experiment, table 10.4.2. Ans. 74.1.

EXAMPLE 10.11.3—Because of the constant term, a mean square like that for Treatments in table 10.11.1 is not distributed like σ^2. The formulas of sections 2.14 and 3.5 do not apply (1, page 342).

10.12—Model II. Random effects. We have been discussing the effects of treatments which are associated with fixed parameters. We now turn to random effects evaluated by sampling normal populations.

Litter effects are of this kind if the litters are randomly selected. Interest may lie in estimating the *component of variance* among litters and in comparing it with that among individuals. Again, duplicate soil samples may be taken at a number of random positions in a field. While the primary object is to learn the average concentration of some element in the soil, yet the design provides for estimating a component for the positional effect as well as one for sampling variation within positions. Computationally, there is no distinction between this model and Model I. It is the interpretations (and the theory) which are different.

Model II is symbolized as

$$X_{ij} = \mu + A_i + \epsilon_{ij}, \quad i = 1 \ldots a, \quad j = 1 \ldots n, \quad A_i = \mathcal{N}(0, \sigma_A),$$
$$\epsilon_{ij} = \mathcal{N}(0, \sigma)$$

An example of random treatment effects is shown in table 10.12.1. These data are extracted from a larger and more complicated experiment (28). Four determinations were made on each of 4 leaves randomly selected from a plant.

TABLE 10.12.1
CALCIUM CONCENTRATION IN TURNIP GREENS
(Per cent of dry weight)

Leaf	Per Cent of Calcium				Sum	Mean
1	3.28	3.09	3.03	3.03	12.43	3.11
2	3.52	3.48	3.38	3.38	13.76	3.44
3	2.88	2.80	2.81	2.76	11.25	2 81
4	3.34	3.38	3.23	3.26	13.21	3.30

Source of Variation	Degrees of Freedom	Mean Square	Parameters Estimated
Leaf	3	0.2961	$\sigma^2 + 4\sigma_A^2$
Determinations	12	0.0066	σ^2

$s^2 = 0.0066$ estimates σ^2. $s_A^2 = (0.2961 - 0.0066)/4 = 0.0724$ estimates σ_A^2

In the component analysis the leaf *component of variance* is denoted by σ_A^2 instead of by κ^2 because we are now dealing with a variable whose variance is to be estimated, not with a set of constants, a_i. Notice that the sample estimates of σ^2 and σ_A^2 are, as usual, set equal to s^2 and s_A^2.

The null hypothesis usually tested is $\sigma_A^2 = 0$. For this,

$$F = \frac{0.2961}{0.0066} = 45 \text{ estimates } \frac{\sigma^2 + 4\sigma_A^2}{\sigma^2}$$

If the conclusion were less obvious, it would be well to make the test before separating the components, because if you should conclude that σ_A^2 may be zero, there would be little interest in estimating it.

It is evident that the leaf-to-leaf variation is far greater than that among determinations. Clearly, fewer determinations on each of more leaves would increase precision and save money—leaves are cheap and determinations expensive. To make these statements more definite, consider the mean square of the Leaf mean with $an = 16$ determinations,

$$s_{\bar{x}}^2 = \frac{0.2961}{16} = \frac{0.0066 + 4(0.0724)}{16} = \frac{0.0066}{16} + \frac{0.0724}{4}$$

Let us suppose the experiment is to be redesigned, changing n and a but keeping the components of variance as they are, the object being to get more information (that is, smaller $s_{\bar{x}}^2$) for the same cost. Then for the new experiment,

$$(s_{\bar{x}}^2)' = \frac{0.0066 + n'(0.0724)}{a'n'} = \frac{0.0066}{a'n'} + \frac{0.0724}{a'}$$

Since the larger numerator is 0.0724, it seems clear that a' should be increased and n' decreased without changing the total cost of the experiment. Try $n' = 1$ and $a' = 15$; since a determination costs perhaps 10 times as much as a leaf, the total outlay on the experiment will be little altered. For this new design, we may expect

$$(s_{\bar{x}}^2)' = \frac{0.0066}{15} + \frac{0.0724}{15} = 0.0053$$

With this smaller mean square, the "efficiency" of the proposed experiment is said to be

$$s_{\bar{x}}^2/(s_{\bar{x}}^2)' = 0.0185/0.0053 = 349\%$$

as compared to the original. This is because the expensive determinations with small variability have been extended to more leaves whose variation is large. More adequate treatment of this problem will be found in section 17.11.

The mean square of a component in Model II is made up of the mean squares, M_A and M, which enter its computation. Consider the component s_A^2 in table 10.12.1. It was calculated this way:

$$s_A^2 = \frac{M_A - M}{n} = \frac{0.2961 - 0.0066}{4}$$

The mean square of the component, then, is (section 3.5 and examples 3.9.5, 3.9.6)

$$\frac{1}{n^2}(s_{M_A}{}^2 + s_M{}^2) = \frac{1}{n^2}\left\{\frac{2M_A{}^2}{f_A+2} + \frac{2M^2}{f+2}\right\} = \frac{2}{16}\left\{\frac{0.2961^2}{5} + \frac{0.0066^2}{14}\right\} = 0.002192$$

From this, the sample standard deviation of $s_A{}^2$ is $\sqrt{0.002192} = 0.047$, more than half of $s_A{}^2 = 0.0724$. This gives a notion of the sampling variation in the component. I can make no exact statement about a confidence interval because the sampling distribution of the component is not known. For some approximations, see (1, page 231).

EXAMPLE 10.12.1—The following data were abstracted from records of performance of Poland China swine in a single inbred line at the Iowa Agricultural Experiment Station. Two boars were taken from each of 4 litters with common sire and fed a standard ration from weaning to about 225 pounds. Here are the average daily gains:

Litter	1	2	3	4
Gains	1.18	1.36	1.37	1.07
	1.11	1.65	1.40	0.90

Assuming that the litter variable is normally distributed, show that $\sigma_A{}^2$ differs significantly from zero ($F = 7.41$) and that 0.0474 estimates it.

EXAMPLE 10.12.2—Calculate the standard deviation of $s_A{}^2$ in the foregoing example. Ans. 0.035. If $s_A{}^2$ were normally distributed, this sample standard deviation would specify a confidence interval that would overlap zero. Yet $s_A{}^2$ is significant.

10.13—Structure of Model II illustrated by sampling. It is easy to construct a Model II experiment by sampling from known populations. One population can be chosen to represent the variable treatment effects with variance $\sigma_A{}^2$ and another the individuals with variance σ^2; then samples can be drawn from each and combined in any desired proportion. In table 10.13.1 is such a drawing. The components for the litters (random treatments) are from the pig gains of table 3.10.1 so that $\sigma_A{}^2 = 25$; there is one of these for each litter. Individual pig gains are taken from table 3.2.1 with $\sigma^2 = 100$, two of these per lot. The sum represents the observed gain in weight set down in column 4.

Forget for a moment how these gains came into being. Think of them as observations on 20 pigs taken from 10 litters chosen at random. The variance is analyzed in the usual manner, then the components of variance are separated.

Now look at the last line of the table and recover your memory. From the 20 observations we have estimated both $\sigma^2 = 100$ and $\sigma_A{}^2 = 25$, the two components that were put into the pig gains, with some sampling variation, of course.

This example was chosen because of its accurate estimates. An idea of ordinary variation can be got from examination of the records of 25 similar samples in table 10.13.2. One is struck immediately by the great variability in the estimates of σ_A^2, some of them being negative! These latter merely indicate that the mean square for lots is less than that for individuals; the lots vary less than random samples ordinarily do if drawn

TABLE 10.13.1

GAINS IN WEIGHT OF 20 PIGS IN 10 LITTERS OF 2 PIGS EACH

Each gain is the sum of 3 components. The component for litters is a sample from table 3.10.1 with $\sigma_A^2 = 25$, that for individuals is from table 3.2.1 with $\sigma^2 = 100$, each observation decreased by 30. The third component is $\mu = 30$.

Litter Number	Litter Component A_i	Pig Component ϵ_{ij}	Sample of Pig Gains $X_{ij} = \mu + A_i + \epsilon_{ij}$	Sample of Litter Gains
(1)	(2)	(3)	(4) = 30 + (2) + (3)	(5)
1	− 1	7	36	
		9	38	74
2	2	− 4	28	
		−23	9	37
3	− 1	0	29	
		19	48	77
4	0	2	32	
		2	32	64
5	− 4	3	29	
		12	38	67
6	−10	9	29	
		3	23	52
7	10	5	45	
		− 4	36	81
8	2	−19	13	
		−10	22	35
9	4	− 4	30	
		18	52	82
10	− 2	15	43	
		− 6	22	65

Source of Variation	Degrees of Freedom	Mean Square	Parameters Estimated
Litter means	9	144.6	$\sigma^2 + 2\sigma_A^2$
Individuals	10	96.5	σ^2

$s^2 = 96.5$ estimates 100. $s_A^2 = (144.6 - 96.5)/2 = 24.0$ estimates 25

TABLE 10.13.2
ESTIMATES OF $\sigma_A^2 = 25$ AND $\sigma^2 = 100$ MADE FROM 25 SAMPLES DRAWN LIKE
THAT OF TABLE 10.13.1

Sample Number	Estimate of $\sigma_A^2 = 25$	Estimate of $\sigma^2 = 100$	Sample Number	Estimate of $\sigma_A^2 = 25$	Estimate of $\sigma^2 = 100$
1	60	127	14	56	112
2	56	104	15	−33	159
3	28	97	16	67	54
4	6	91	17	−18	90
5	18	60	18	33	65
6	− 5	91	19	−21	127
7	7	53	20	−48	126
8	− 1	87	21	4	43
9	0	66	22	3	145
10	−78	210	23	49	142
11	14	148	24	75	23
12	7	162	25	77	106
13	68	76	Mean	17 0	102 6

from a single, normal population.   Clearly, one cannot hope for accurate estimates of σ^2 and σ_A^2 from such small samples.

I am sorry to have to warn you that one cannot measure the litter component; it is hidden behind the veil.   The only measurements that can be made are on pig gains.

10.14—Samples within samples.   Model II.   Each sample may be composed of *sub-samples* and these in turn may be sub-sampled, etc.   The repeated sampling and sub-sampling gives rise to *nested samples* or *heirarchal classifications*.   The several series of samples may be all Model II or mixed.

In table 10.14.1 is an example of Model II sub-sampling.   This is a part of the turnip greens experiment cited earlier (28).   The 4 plants were taken at random, then 3 leaves were randomly selected from each plant.   From each leaf were taken 2 samples of 100 mg. in which calcium was determined by microchemical methods.   The immediate objective is to separate the sums of squares due to the sources of variation, plants, leaves of the same plant, and determinations on the leaves.

As for calculations, the sums of squares for determinations, leaves, and plants follow the patterns now familiar.   The new feature is that there are now two Totals with corresponding Treatments to be subtracted: (i) The sum of squares for leaves is the total from which the sum of squares for plants is deducted to get the usual sum of squares for Individuals, that is *leaves of the same plant*, or *leaves in plants*, as it is often designated; (ii) the sum of squares for determinations is the total from which the sum of squares of the Treatment, *leaves*, is taken to get *determinations on the same leaf* or

TABLE 10.14.1

CALCIUM CONCENTRATION (PER CENT, DRY BASIS) IN $b = 3$ LEAVES FROM EACH OF $a = 4$ TURNIP PLANTS, $n = 2$ DETERMINATIONS PER LEAF. ANALYSIS OF VARIANCE

Plant, i $i = 1 \ldots a$	Leaf, ij $j = 1 \ldots b$	Determinations, X_{ijk}		$X_{ij.}$	$X_{i..}$	$X_{...}$
1	1	3.28	3.09	6.37		
	2	3.52	3.48	7.00		
	3	2.88	2.80	5.68	19.05	
2	1	2.46	2.44	4.90		
	2	1.87	1.92	3.79		
	3	2.19	2.19	4.38	13.07	
3	1	2.77	2.66	5.43		
	2	3.74	3.44	7.18		
	3	2.55	2.55	5.10	17.71	
4	1	3.78	3.87	7.65		
	2	4.07	4.12	8.19		
	3	3.31	3.31	6.62	22.46	72.29

Total Size $= abn = (4)(3)(2) = 24$ determinations

$C = (X...)^2/abn = (72.29)^2/24 = 217.7435$
Determinations: $\Sigma X_{ijk}^2 - C = 3.28^2 + \ldots + 3.31^2 - C = 10.2704$
Leaves: $\Sigma X_{ij.}^2/n - C = (6.37^2 + \ldots + 6.62^2)/2 - C = 10.1905$
Plants: $\Sigma X_{i..}^2/bn - C = (19.05^2 + \ldots + 22.46^2)/6 - C = 7.5603$
Leaves of the same plant = Leaves − Plants = $10.1905 - 7.5603 = 2.6302$
Determinations on same leaf = Determinations − Leaves = $10.2704 - 10.1905 = 0.0799$

Source of Variation	Degrees of Freedom	Sum of Squares	Mean Square
Plants	3	7.5603	2.5201
Leaves in plants	8	2.6302	0.3288
Determinations in leaves	12	0.0799	0.0067
Total	23	10.2704	

determinations in leaves. This process can be repeated with successive sub-sampling.

The model being used is,

$$X_{ijk} = \mu + A_i + B_{ij} + \epsilon_{ijk}, \quad i = 1 \ldots a, j = 1 \ldots b, k = 1 \ldots n, \quad A_i = \mathcal{N}(0, \sigma_A), B_{ij} = \mathcal{N}(0, \sigma_B), \epsilon_{ijk} = \mathcal{N}(0, \sigma),$$

where A refers to plants and B to leaves. Roman letters are used to denote plants and leaves because they are random variables, not constants.

In the completed analysis of variance, table 10.14.2, the components of variance are shown. Each component in a sub-sample is included among those in the sample above it. The estimates are calculated as indicated.

Null hypotheses which may be tested are:

1. $\sigma_A{}^2 = 0$; $F = \dfrac{2.5201}{0.3288} = 7.66$ estimates $\dfrac{\sigma^2 + n\sigma_B{}^2 + bn\sigma_A{}^2}{\sigma^2 + n\sigma_B{}^2}, f = 3, 8.$

2. $\sigma_B{}^2 = 0$; $F = \dfrac{0.3288}{0.0067} = 49$ estimates $\dfrac{\sigma^2 + n\sigma_B{}^2}{\sigma^2}, f = 8, 12.$

For the first, with degrees of freedom, $f_1 = 3$ and $f_2 = 8$, F is almost on its 1% point, 7.59; for the second, with degrees of freedom 8 and 12, F is

TABLE 10.14.2
COMPLETED ANALYSIS OF VARIANCE OF TURNIP GREENS DATA

Source of Variation	Degrees of Freedom	Mean Square	Parameters Estimated
Plants	3	2.5201	$\sigma^2 + n\sigma_B{}^2 + bn\sigma_A{}^2$
Leaves	8	0.3288	$\sigma^2 + n\sigma_B{}^2$
Determinations	12	0.0067	σ^2

$n = 2, b = 3, a = 4.$ $s^2 = 0.0067$ estimates σ^2. $s_B{}^2 = (0.3288 - 0.0067)/2 = 0.1610$ estimates $\sigma_B{}^2$. $s_A{}^2 = (2.5201 - 0.3288)/6 = 0.3652$ estimates $\sigma_A{}^2$.

far beyond its 1% point, 4.50. Evidently, in the sampled population the per cent calcium varies both from leaf to leaf and from plant to plant.

The mean square of the plant mean is

$$s_{\bar{x}}{}^2 = \frac{2.5201}{24} = 0.105 = \frac{0.0067 + n(0.1610) + bn(0.3652)}{nab}$$

$$= \frac{0.0067}{nab} + \frac{0.1610}{ab} + \frac{0.3652}{a}$$

As in section 10.12, more information per dollar may be got by decreasing the number of expensive determinations per leaf because they have a small component, then increasing the numbers of leaves or plants. Plants presumably cost more than leaves, but the component is also larger. How to balance these elements is the topic of section 17.12.

The utility of variance components is becoming increasingly apparent. Not only in planning experiments (as above) but, as has been remarked, in the testing program they are almost indispensable. Also in genetics they are being used effectively to evaluate hereditary contributions.

EXAMPLE 10.14.1—Calculate the standard deviation of $s_B{}^2$ in table 10.14.2. Ans. 0.074.

EXAMPLE 10.14.2—Show that the standard deviation of $s_A{}^2 = 0.27$.

10.15—Samples within samples. Mixed model. In repeated sub-sampling the major samples may have constants associated with them. An instance is the evaluation of the breeding value of sires, each mated to a random group of dams, some characteristic of the offspring being the criterion. The model is

$$X_{ijk} = \mu + a_i + B_{ij} + \epsilon_{ijk}, \quad i = 1 \ldots a, j = 1 \ldots b$$

The a_i are constants ($\Sigma a_i = 0$) associated with the sires but B and ϵ are variables corresponding to dams and offspring. Table 10.15.1 is an example. These are more data from records of performance of Poland

TABLE 10.15.1

AVERAGE DAILY GAIN OF TWO PIGS OF EACH LITTER

Sire	Dam	Pig Gains		Sums		
1	1	2.77	2.38	5.15		
	2	2.58	2.94	5.52	10.67	
2	1	2.28	2.22	4.50		
	2	3.01	2.61	5.62	10.12	
3	1	2.36	2.71	5.07		
	2	2.72	2.74	5.46	10.53	
4	1	2.87	2.46	5.33		
	2	2.31	2.24	4.55	9.88	
5	1	2.74	2.56	5.30		
	2	2.50	2.48	4.98	10.28	51.48

Source of Variation	Degrees of Freedom	Mean Square	Parameters Estimated
Sires	4	0.0249	$\sigma^2 + n\sigma_B^2 + nb\kappa^2$
Dams–Same Sire	5	0.1127	$\sigma^2 + n\sigma_B^2$
Pairs–Same Dam	10	0.0387	σ^2

$n = 2, b = 2, s^2 = 0.0387$ estimates σ^2, $s_B^2 = (0.1127 - 0.0387)/2 = 0.0370$ estimates σ_B^2, 0 estimates κ^2

To test $\sigma_B^2 = 0$, $F = 0.1127/0.0387 = 2.91$, $F_{.05} = 3.33$.

Chinas at the Iowa Agricultural Experiment Station. The calculations proceed as before. The only change in the model is that the mean square for the constants, a_i, is denoted by κ^2.

Here we have a situation which is not uncommon; the mean square for samples (sires) is less than that for sub-samples (dams). This cannot happen in the population even if $\kappa^2 = 0$. Sampling variation has either decreased the real mean square for sires, or increased that for dams, or both. But obviously there is no evidence against H_0: $\kappa^2 = 0$.

If the sire mean square were greater than that for dams, the null hypothesis $\kappa^2 = 0$ (that is, $a_i = 0$) would be tested by

$$F = \frac{\text{mean square for sires}}{\text{mean square for dams}}$$

10.16—Samples of unequal size. Sometimes it is not possible to provide samples of equal size, and at other times, not desirable. As an example of the latter case, suppose one is investigating the butterfat con-tent of the milk from cows of various breeds supplying the creameries of some district. He might wish to conduct the investigation so that the average butterfat yield per cow when multiplied by the total number of producing animals in the district would be an estimate of the total fat production. In that event, it would be desirable to sample the breeds by taking from each a number of cows proportional to the district population of that breed. Otherwise, the representatives of some rare, low-yielding breed would inordinately depress the average. It is just as important to choose samples representative of the population examined as it is to make quite random the taking of the ultimate experimental units. The two procedures are not incompatible, both being integral parts of good sampling designs (chapter 17). Incidentally, the criterion of representa-tiveness makes it imperative that the investigator confine his interpreta-tions to the sampled population, not broadcasting them over populations in general.

Another source of unequal-sized samples is that illustrated in table 10.16.1. Much experimental material has such natural groupings. Eight sows bore these litters, so that differences among the mean birth weights may be attributed partly to sow individualities and partly to litter size.

So far as method of computation is concerned, only a single minor alteration is required to adapt it to the inequality in sample sizes. This is in connection with the sum of squares between means of litters. Since n_i changes from litter to litter, each $X_i.^2$ must be divided by its own n_i in order to reduce it to the per-observation level. As for degrees of freedom, got by subtraction in the table, they may well be thought of as the sum of 8 sets, $n_i - 1$ from each litter:

$$\Sigma(n_i - 1) = 9 + 7 + \ldots + 3 = 48$$

This way of thinking is valuable because it brings to mind the fact that the corresponding sum of squares, 17.17, is itself the sum of 8 litter sums of squares each of which may be computed independently (table 10.2.1).

The model being used is a form of Model II:

$$X_{ij} = \mu + A_i + \epsilon_{ij}, \ i = 1 \ldots a, \ j = 1 \ldots n_i, \ \epsilon_{ij} = \mathcal{N}(0, \sigma)$$

The new feature is the value of j which varies among the samples. This

TABLE 10.16.1
BIRTH WEIGHTS (POUNDS) OF POLAND CHINA PIGS IN 8 LITTERS

Litter i	Birth Weights X_{ij}	Sums $X_{i.}$	Numbers n_i	Sum of Squares ΣX_{ij}^2
1	2.0 2.8 3.3 3.2 4.4 3.6 1.9 3.3 2.8 1.1	28.4	10	
2	3.5 2.8 3.2 3.5 2.3 2.4 2.0 1.6	21.3	8	
3	3.3 3.6 2.6 3.1 3.2 3.3 2.9 3.4 3.2 3.2	31.8	10	
4	3.2 3.3 3.2 2.9 3.3 2.5 2.6 2.8	23.8	8	
5	2.6 2.6 2.9 2.0 2.0 2.1	14.2	6	
6	3.1 2.9 3.1 2.5	11.6	4	
7	2.6 2.2 2.2 2.5 1.2 1.2	11.9	6	
8	2.5 2.4 3.0 1.5	9.4	4	
$a = 8$	$\Sigma X_{ij} = \Sigma X_{i.} = 152.4$		$n. = 56$	439.40

$C = X..^2/n. = (152.4)^2/56 = 414.75$

Total: $\Sigma X_{ij}^2 - C = 2.0^2 + 2.8^2 + \ldots + 1.5^2 - C = 439.40 - 414.75 = 24.65$

Litters: $\Sigma\dfrac{X_{i.}^2}{n_i} - C = \dfrac{(28.4)^2}{10} + \ldots + \dfrac{(9.4)^2}{4} - C = 422.23 - 414.75 = 7.48$

Source of Variation	Degrees of Freedom	Sum of Squares	Mean Square
Total	55	24.65	
Litters	7	7.48	1.07
Pigs in litters	48	17.17	0.36

$$F = 1.07/0.36 = 2.97, \quad F_{.01} = 3.04$$

gives rise to a difficulty in the component analysis. With equal $n_i(=n)$ the component for treatments is multiplied by n. Now it is necessary to make up an average of the n_i. Theory shows the correct average to be

$$n_0 = \frac{1}{a-1}\left(n. - \frac{\Sigma n_i^2}{n.}\right)$$

For the pigs, $\Sigma n_i^2 = 10^2 + 8^2 + \ldots + 4^2 = 432$ so that

$$n_0 = \frac{1}{8-1}\left(56 - \frac{432}{56}\right) = 6.90$$

The completed analysis of variance is shown in table 10.16.2. Here we have assumed a common σ^2 in the sampled populations. See section 10.20 for heterogeneous variance.

The test of H_0: $\sigma_A{}^2 = 0$ is done as before:

$$F = \frac{1.07}{0.36} = 2.97 \text{ estimates } \frac{\sigma^2 + n_0\sigma_A{}^2}{\sigma^2}$$

There is little doubt that the dams contribute additional variance to that of the pigs within litters. This may have two sources: (i) The dams may vary in their ability to nourish the fetuses, resulting in differences among litter birth weights even when other factors are identical; (ii) the size of the litter may affect the birth weight. The separation of these sources of variability will be the topic of the next section.

If the lot components are fixed (a_i instead of A_i), the computations are

TABLE 10.16.2
ANALYSIS OF VARIANCE OF PIG LITTERS OF TABLE 10.16.1

Source of Variation	Degrees of Freedom	Mean Square	Parameters Estimated
Litters	7	1.07	$\sigma^2 + n_0\sigma_A{}^2$
Pigs	48	0.36	σ^2

$n_0 = \dfrac{1}{a-1}\left[n. - \dfrac{\Sigma n_i{}^2}{n.} \right] = \dfrac{1}{7}\left[56 - \dfrac{432}{56} \right] = 6.90$, $s^2 = 0.36$ estimates σ^2,

$s_A{}^2 = (1.07 - 0.36)/6.90 = 0.103$ estimates $\sigma_A{}^2$

unchanged; but, to keep the record straight, the population mean square for treatments would be written, $\sigma^2 + n_0\kappa^2$.

A closing remark for this section on unequal sample numbers: As stated in section 4.5, it pays to keep the lots equal in size if this is feasible. Assuming a common σ^2 for all the lots, the most efficient use of resources goes with equal n_i.

EXAMPLE 10.16.1—Here is an easy example for practice:
Group 1: 18, 11, 16, 12, 14, 17, 18, 20
Group 2: 19
Group 3: 16, 18, 26
Group 4: 19, 15, 15, 10, 24, 17, 13, 17, 17, 13, 16
The total sum of squares, 307.65 with 22 degrees of freedom, is divided into 50.15 for group means, $f = 3$, and 257.50 for individuals. $F = 1.23$.

EXAMPLE 10.16.2—Applying analysis of variance to the two lots of rat gains in section 4.5, show that $\sqrt{F} = t = 1.89$. What portions of table 4.5.2 are used in the present computations?

EXAMPLE 10.16.3—Jenkins (16) and Snedecor (26) compared the yields of a number of varieties of corn, each variety being represented by several inbred lines. Six varieties, with yields (bushels per acre) of their inbred lines, are as follows:
1. Four County: 7.3, 4.5, 7.4, 7.4, 5.0, 5.9, 6.4, 6.3, 5.0, 6.1, 7.9, 5.7
2. Silver King: 7.7, 5.4, 5.2, 4.0
3. Iodent: 6.9, 6.8, 7.6, 8.1, 9.4, 12.0, 15.9, 7.4, 9.0, 5.2, 9.2, 8.6

4. Lancaster: 9.6, 7.8, 9.6, 7.7, 8.2, 7.3, 11.3, 9.5, 8.8, 8.4, 6.8
5. Osterland: 4.8, 9.2, 8.5, 8.8, 7.9, 5.9, 9.2
6. Clark: 4.3, 8.4, 6.6, 4.9, 5.8, 7.6, 3.7
Calculate $F = 17.55/3.38 = 5.19, f = 5$ and 47. Estimate the component of variance associated with the varieties of the preceding example. Ans. $n_0 = 8.63, \kappa_A^2 = 1.64$.

EXAMPLE 10.16.4—Among 224 mice inoculated with 3 strains of typhoid organisms, the days of survival are summarized in the following frequency distributions. In applying the method of section 8.2 it is perhaps easier not to code the days-to-death, X, but to use the recorded data. The column of totals is necessary only for verification. Calculate $F = 179.9/5.78 = 31.1, f = 2$ and 221.

	Numbers of Mice Inoculated With Indicated Strain			
Days to Death	9D	11C	DSC1	Total
2	6	1	3	10
3	4	3	5	12
4	9	3	5	17
5	8	6	8	22
6	3	6	19	28
7	1	14	23	38
8		11	22	33
9		4	14	18
10		6	14	20
11		2	7	9
12		3	8	11
13		1	4	5
14			1	1
Total	31	60	133	224
ΣX	125	442	1,037	1,604
ΣX^2	561	3,602	8,961	13,124

10.17—Samples within samples, unequal sizes. Both samples and sub-samples may be of unequal sizes. The situation is a bit complicated but some simplifying approximations seem adequate for most purposes.

To examine the question raised in the foregoing section, the litters are arranged in 4 size groups, 10, 8, 6, and 4 pigs per litter. The sums of birth weights are used to calculate Litters (within size groups) as shown in table 10.17.1. The corresponding mean square, along with the others, indicates that both dams and size of litter contributed to the total birth weight variation. The question of significance is postponed until after the component analysis is completed.

It is the coefficients of the variance components that are troublesome. Their calculation is shown in table 10.17.2 and the component analysis in table 10.17.3. The striking fact is that there are 2 different averages of litter size, neither calculated like that of table 10.16.2. But the average of the size groups $(nb)_0$, follows the earlier formula for n_0.

The model which seems relevant is

$$X_{ijk} = \mu + A_i + B_{ij} + \epsilon_{ijk}, i = 1 \ldots a, j = 1 \ldots b_i, k = 1 \ldots n_{ij}$$

TABLE 10.17.1
BIRTH WEIGHTS OF POLAND CHINA PIGS (TABLE 10.16.1) ARRANGED BY LITTER SIZE

Size i	Litter ij	Birth Weights X_{ijk}	Sum In Litter $X_{ij.}$	Sum In Size $X_{i..}$	Number In Litter n_{ij}	Number In Size $n_{i.}$	Number Of Litters b_i
1	1	2.0 ... 1.1	28.4		10		
	2	3.3 ... 3.2	31.8	60.2	10	20	2
2	1	3.5 ... 1.6	21.3		8		
	2	3.2 ... 2.8	23.8	45.1	8	16	2
3	1	2.6 ... 2.1	14.2		6		
	2	2.6 ... 1.2	11.9	26.1	6	12	2
4	1	3.1 ... 2.5	11.6		4		
	2	2.5 ... 1.5	9.4	21.0	4	8	2

$a = 4$ $\qquad \Sigma X_{ijk} = \Sigma X_{ij.} = \Sigma X_{i..} = 152.4 \qquad n.. = 56 \quad \Sigma b_i = 8$

Size: $\Sigma \dfrac{X_{i..}^2}{n_{i.}} = \dfrac{(60.2)^2}{20} + \ldots + \dfrac{(21.0)^2}{8} - C = 5.47$

Litters of same size: Litter $-$ Size $= 7.48 - 5.47 = 2.01$

Source of Variation	Degrees of Freedom	Sum of Squares	Mean Square
Size	3	5.47	1.82
Litters in size	4	2.01	0.50
Pigs in litter (table 10.16.1)	48	17.17	0.36

A consequence of the differing averages is that there is no exact test for $\sigma_A^2 = 0$ because the ratio one would expect to write from table 10.17.3,

$$\frac{\sigma^2 + 6.76 \, \sigma_B^2 + 13.52 \, \sigma_A^2}{\sigma^2 + 7.00 \, \sigma_B^2},$$

does not reduce to unity if $\sigma_A^2 = 0$. Anderson and Bancroft (1) propose an approximate test, but I suggest the following procedure for rough work.

Since the sample standard errors of the components are large, it would usually be accurate enough to compute both averages of litter size by the formula of table 10.16.2. The result, 6.90, is intermediate between the exact averages, 7.00 and 6.76. The same formula applied to the size groups gives $(nb)_0 = 13.52$ as in table 10.17.2. This approximate method yields the mean squares,

$$\begin{array}{ll} \text{Litter Size} & s^2 + 6.90 \, s_B^2 + 13.52 \, s_A^2 \\ \text{Litters} & s^2 + 6.90 \, s_B^2 \\ \text{Pigs} & s^2 \end{array}$$

Litter size is now tested against Litters, $F = 1.82/0.50 = 3.64$, $F_{.05} = 6.59$.

This is an exact test based on approximate values of the components. Finally, to 2 decimals, $s_B^2 = 0.02$ and $s_A^2 = 0.10$, as before.

Let us rescue ourselves from a welter of statistics to see what has been learned. In the preceding section it was evident that there is a litter component added to that of pig variation. Now it turns out that the 2 parts, s_B^2 and s_A^2, though both present, are neither one significant. The first concerns the ability of the dam to affect birth weights in litters of the same size. To see this performance, compare the X_{ij}. in table 10.17.1; 28.4 lbs.

TABLE 10.17.2

COMPUTATION OF AVERAGE FREQUENCIES IN HEIRARCHAL CLASSIFICATION
WITH SAMPLES OF UNEQUAL SIZES

n_{ij} (1)	$n_{i.}$ (2)	n_{ij}^2 (3)	Σn_{ij}^2 i (4)	$\dfrac{\Sigma n_{ij}^2}{n_{i.}}$ (5)	$n_{i.}^2$ (6)	$b_i - 1$ (7)
10		100				
10	20	100	200	10	400	1
8		64				
8	16	64	128	8	256	1
6		36				
6	12	36	72	6	144	1
4		16				
4	8	16	32	4	64	1
56		432		28	864	4

$$n_{0B} = \frac{\Sigma(1) - \Sigma(5)}{\Sigma(7)} = \frac{56-28}{4} = 7.00$$

$$n_{0A} = \frac{\Sigma(5) - \Sigma(3)/\Sigma(1)}{a - 1} = \frac{28 - 432/56}{4 - 1} = 6.76$$

$$(nb)_0 = \frac{\Sigma(1) - \Sigma(6)/\Sigma(1)}{a - 1} = \frac{56 - 864/56}{4 - 1} = 13.52$$

vs. 31.8, 21.3 vs. 23.8, etc. The second component relates to differences due to litter size. One would think that there would be limits to the total nutrients available to a litter so that pigs in small litters would tend to be large. This component, though small, does appear in the sample. But look at the means:

$$\text{For 10 pigs} \quad \bar{x}_1 = 60.2/20 = 3.01$$
$$8 \quad \bar{x}_2 = 45.1/16 = 2.82$$
$$6 \quad \bar{x}_3 = 26.1/12 = 2.18$$
$$4 \quad \bar{x}_4 = 21.0/8 = 2.62$$

TABLE 10.17.3

Component Analysis of Variance of Poland China Birth Weights

Source of Variation	Degrees of Freedom	Mean Square	Parameters Estimated
Size of Litter	3	1.82	$\sigma^2 + n_{0A}\,\sigma_B^2 + (nb)_0\sigma_A^2$
Litters	4	0.50	$\sigma^2 + n_{0B}\,\sigma_B^2$
Pigs	48	0.36	σ^2

For Litters, $F = 0.50/0.36 = 1.39$, $F_{.05} = 2.56$. $s^2 = 0.36$, $s_B^2 = 0.02$, $s_A^2 = 0.10$

If this component had been significant, interpretation would have been difficult. Further comment will be found in section 10.20.

If the sub-sampling process is extended, the exact formulas for the average sizes become more and more complicated (9). The approximate formula is easy to apply and may be sufficiently accurate for most purposes, especially in view of the large standard errors of the components.

EXAMPLE 10.17.1—Cochran (3) reports a sampling of commercial wheat yield in 6 districts of Great Britain. One or more farms were selected in each district, one or more fields per farm were chosen, and either 2 or 4 sampling areas per field were drawn at random. The analysis of variance of area means was:

Source of Variation	Degrees of Freedom	Mean Square
Districts	5	$10.284 = M_1$
Farms in districts	19	$6.591 = M_2$
Fields in farms	11	$3.026 = M_3$
Areas in fields	42	$0.825 = M_4$

The distribution of the sampling areas was as follows:

	Districts		Farms		Fields	
Serial No.	Areas Per District	Areas Per Farm	No. Farms	Areas Per Field	No Fields
1	8	4	2	2	4
2	6	4	1	2	2
		2	1	2	1
3	12	12	1	4	3
4	22	4	2⎫	2	11
		2	7⎭		
5	4	4	1	2	2
6	26	4	3⎫	2	13
		2	7⎭		
$P = 6$	78	78	25	78	36

Cochran makes it clear that this sampling is a mixed model, the districts being fixed and the farms not randomly selected. But for sake of the numerical illustration, Model II is assumed.

Anderson and Bancroft (1, page 328) worked out this component analysis using exact formulas:

Source of Variation	Mean Square	Parameters
Districts	10.284	$\sigma^2 + 2.34\,\sigma_C^2 + 4.90\,\sigma_B^2 + 11.96\,\sigma_A^2$
Farms	6.591	$\sigma^2 + 2.00\,\sigma_C^2 + 2.58\,\sigma_B^2$
Fields	3.026	$\sigma^2 + 2.36\,\sigma_C^2$
Areas	0.825	σ^2

$s^2 = 0.825$, $s_C^2 = 0.933$, $s_B^2 = 1.512$, $s_A^2 = -0.011$

Using the approximate formula, I got:

Districts	10.284	$\sigma^2 + 2.163\,\sigma_C^2 + 3.064\,\sigma_B^2 + 11.959\,\sigma_A^2$
Farms	6.591	$\sigma^2 + 2.163\,\sigma_C^2 + 3.064\,\sigma_B^2$
Fields	3.026	$\sigma^2 + 2.163\,\sigma_C^2$
Areas	0.825	σ^2

$s^2 = 0.825$, $s_C^2 = 1.018$, $s_B^2 = 1.164$, $s_A^2 = 0.309$

In comparing the two sets of estimates, remember the large standard deviations which you have calculated for some components. The standard deviation of s_B^2 may be in the neighborhood of 0.9. For critical investigations the exact formulas may be necessary, but the approximations are usually adequate and make testing easy.

10.18—Sample size. This problem was discussed in sections 2.15 and 4.7. With tables now available more realistic solutions can be given. These enable the experimenter to specify the security he wishes when he designs his experiment (29). Additional security is, of course, paid for by more replications.

As before, we assume the availability of an estimate of σ; call this s_c, with f_0 degrees of freedom. Now an experiment with a treatments is to be performed, n individuals per treatment. That will make the new degrees of freedom $f = a(n-1)$. We wish to know what difference, δ, will be detected. Specifying the probability of success is the new feature for which, in the earlier discussions, you were referred to this section. Unless otherwise stated, this probability will be taken as 0.75. This means that we are willing to take one chance in 4 of failing to detect δ if it exists. The formula is,

$$\delta = \frac{(Q_{a,f})(s_0)\sqrt{F_{f,f_0}}}{\sqrt{n}}$$

Table 10.6.1 gives $Q_{a,f}$ under a treatments in the line opposite f degrees of freedom. F_{f,f_0} is taken from table 10.18.1 with $f_1 = f$ and $f_2 = f_0$ in the line for $P = (1 - 0.75) = 0.25$. In each subscript the first letter designates a column, the second a row in the corresponding table.

For illustration, turn to examples 10.5.1 and 10.6.3. In the latter it

TABLE 10.18.1*

25%, 10%, 2.5%, AND 0.5% POINTS FOR THE DISTRIBUTION OF F*

f_1 Degrees of Freedom (for greater mean square)

f_2	P	1	2	3	4	5	6	7	8	9	10	12	15	20	24	30	40	60	120	∞
1	.250	5.83	7.50	8.20	8.58	8.82	8.98	9.10	9.19	9.26	9.32	9.41	9.49	9.58	9.63	9.67	9.71	9.76	9.80	9.85
	.100	39.86	49.50	53.59	55.83	57.24	58.20	58.91	59.44	59.86	60.20	60.70	61.22	61.74	62.00	62.26	62.53	62.79	63.06	63.33
	.025	648	800	864	900	922	937	948	957	963	969	977	985	993	997	1,001	1,006	1,010	1,014	1,018
	.005	16,211	20,000	21,615	22,500	23,056	23,437	23,715	23,925	24,091	24,224	24,426	24,630	24,836	24,940	25,044	25,148	25,253	25,359	25,465
2	.250	2.57	3.00	3.15	3.23	3.28	3.31	3.34	3.35	3.37	3.38	3.39	3.41	3.43	3.43	3.44	3.45	3.46	3.47	3.48
	.100	8.53	9.00	9.16	9.24	9.29	9.33	9.35	9.37	9.38	9.39	9.41	9.42	9.44	9.45	9.46	9.47	9.47	9.48	9.49
	.025	38.51	39.00	39.16	39.25	39.30	39.33	39.36	39.37	39.39	39.40	39.42	39.43	39.45	39.46	39.46	39.47	39.48	39.49	39.50
	.005	198	199	199	199	199	199	199	199	199	199	199	199	199	199	199	199	199	199	200
3	.250	2.02	2.28	2.36	2.39	2.41	2.42	2.43	2.44	2.44	2.44	2.45	2.46	2.46	2.46	2.47	2.47	2.47	2.47	2.47
	.100	5.54	5.46	5.39	5.34	5.31	5.28	5.27	5.25	5.24	5.23	5.22	5.20	5.18	5.18	5.17	5.16	5.15	5.14	5.13
	.025	17.44	16.04	15.44	15.10	14.88	14.74	14.62	14.54	14.47	14.42	14.34	14.25	14.17	14.12	14.08	14.04	13.99	13.95	13.90
	.005	55.55	49.80	47.47	46.20	45.39	44.84	44.43	44.13	43.88	43.69	43.39	43.08	42.78	42.62	42.47	42.31	42.15	41.99	41.83
4	.250	1.81	2.00	2.05	2.06	2.07	2.08	2.08	2.08	2.08	2.08	2.08	2.08	2.08	2.08	2.08	2.08	2.08	2.08	2.08
	.100	4.54	4.32	4.19	4.11	4.05	4.01	3.98	3.95	3.94	3.92	3.90	3.87	3.84	3.83	3.82	3.80	3.79	3.78	3.76
	.025	12.22	10.65	9.98	9.60	9.36	9.20	9.07	8.98	8.90	8.84	8.75	8.66	8.56	8.51	8.46	8.41	8.36	8.31	8.26
	.005	31.33	26.28	24.26	23.16	22.46	21.98	21.62	21.35	21.14	20.97	20.70	20.44	20.17	20.03	19.89	19.75	19.61	19.47	19.32
5	.250	1.69	1.85	1.88	1.89	1.89	1.89	1.89	1.89	1.89	1.89	1.89	1.89	1.88	1.88	1.88	1.88	1.87	1.87	1.87
	.100	4.06	3.78	3.62	3.52	3.45	3.40	3.37	3.34	3.32	3.30	3.27	3.24	3.21	3.19	3.17	3.16	3.14	3.12	3.10
	.025	10.01	8.43	7.76	7.39	7.15	6.98	6.85	6.76	6.68	6.62	6.52	6.43	6.33	6.28	6.23	6.18	6.12	6.07	6.02
	.005	22.78	18.31	16.53	15.56	14.94	14.51	14.20	13.96	13.77	13.62	13.38	13.15	12.90	12.78	12.66	12.53	12.40	12.27	12.14
6	.250	1.62	1.76	1.78	1.79	1.79	1.78	1.78	1.78	1.77	1.77	1.77	1.76	1.76	1.75	1.75	1.75	1.74	1.74	1.74
	.100	3.78	3.46	3.29	3.18	3.11	3.05	3.01	2.98	2.96	2.94	2.90	2.87	2.84	2.82	2.80	2.78	2.76	2.74	2.72
	.025	8.81	7.26	6.60	6.23	5.99	5.82	5.70	5.60	5.52	5.46	5.37	5.27	5.17	5.12	5.07	5.01	4.96	4.90	4.85
	.005	18.64	14.54	12.92	12.03	11.46	11.07	10.79	10.57	10.39	10.25	10.03	9.81	9.59	9.47	9.36	9.24	9.12	9.00	8.88
7	.250	1.57	1.70	1.72	1.72	1.71	1.71	1.70	1.70	1.69	1.69	1.68	1.68	1.67	1.67	1.66	1.66	1.65	1.65	1.65
	.100	3.59	3.26	3.07	2.96	2.88	2.83	2.78	2.75	2.72	2.70	2.67	2.63	2.59	2.58	2.56	2.54	2.51	2.49	2.47
	.025	8.07	6.54	5.89	5.52	5.29	5.12	4.99	4.90	4.82	4.76	4.67	4.57	4.47	4.42	4.36	4.31	4.25	4.20	4.14
	.005	16.24	12.40	10.88	10.05	9.52	9.16	8.89	8.68	8.51	8.38	8.18	7.97	7.75	7.64	7.53	7.42	7.31	7.19	7.08
8	.250	1.54	1.66	1.67	1.66	1.66	1.65	1.64	1.64	1.64	1.63	1.62	1.62	1.61	1.60	1.60	1.59	1.59	1.58	1.58
	.100	3.46	3.11	2.92	2.81	2.73	2.67	2.62	2.59	2.56	2.54	2.50	2.46	2.42	2.40	2.38	2.36	2.34	2.32	2.29
	.025	7.57	6.06	5.42	5.05	4.82	4.65	4.53	4.43	4.36	4.30	4.20	4.10	4.00	3.95	3.89	3.84	3.78	3.73	3.67
	.005	14.69	11.04	9.60	8.81	8.30	7.95	7.69	7.50	7.34	7.21	7.01	6.81	6.61	6.50	6.40	6.29	6.18	6.06	5.95

TABLE 10.18.1—*(Continued)* *

25%, 10%, 2.5%, AND 0.5% POINTS FOR THE DISTRIBUTION OF F*

f_1 Degrees of Freedom (for greater mean square)

f_2	P	1	2	3	4	5	6	7	8	9	10	12	15	20	24	30	40	60	120	∞
9	.250	1.51	1.62	1.63	1.63	1.62	1.61	1.60	1.60	1.59	1.59	1.58	1.57	1.56	1.56	1.55	1.54	1.54	1.53	1.53
	.100	3.36	3.01	2.81	2.69	2.61	2.55	2.51	2.47	2.44	2.42	2.38	2.34	2.30	2.28	2.25	2.23	2.21	2.18	2.16
	.025	7.21	5.71	5.08	4.72	4.48	4.32	4.20	4.10	4.03	3.96	3.87	3.77	3.67	3.61	3.56	3.51	3.45	3.39	3.33
	.005	13.61	10.11	8.72	7.96	7.47	7.13	6.88	6.69	6.54	6.42	6.23	6.03	5.83	5.73	5.62	5.52	5.41	5.30	5.19
10	.250	1.49	1.60	1.60	1.59	1.59	1.58	1.57	1.56	1.56	1.55	1.54	1.53	1.52	1.52	1.51	1.51	1.50	1.49	1.48
	.100	3.28	2.92	2.73	2.61	2.52	2.46	2.41	2.38	2.35	2.32	2.28	2.24	2.20	2.18	2.16	2.13	2.11	2.08	2.06
	.025	6.94	5.46	4.83	4.47	4.24	4.07	3.95	3.85	3.78	3.72	3.62	3.52	3.42	3.37	3.31	3.26	3.20	3.14	3.08
	.005	12.83	9.43	8.08	7.34	6.87	6.54	6.30	6.12	5.97	5.85	5.66	5.47	5.27	5.17	5.07	4.97	4.86	4.75	4.64
11	.250	1.47	1.58	1.58	1.57	1.56	1.55	1.54	1.53	1.53	1.52	1.51	1.50	1.49	1.49	1.48	1.47	1.47	1.46	1.45
	.100	3.23	2.86	2.66	2.54	2.45	2.39	2.34	2.30	2.27	2.25	2.21	2.17	2.12	2.10	2.08	2.05	2.03	2.00	1.97
	.025	6.72	5.26	4.63	4.28	4.04	3.88	3.76	3.66	3.59	3.53	3.43	3.33	3.23	3.17	3.12	3.06	3.00	2.94	2.88
	.005	12.23	8.91	7.60	6.88	6.42	6.10	5.86	5.68	5.54	5.42	5.24	5.05	4.86	4.76	4.65	4.55	4.44	4.34	4.23
12	.250	1.46	1.56	1.56	1.55	1.54	1.53	1.52	1.51	1.51	1.50	1.49	1.48	1.47	1.46	1.45	1.45	1.44	1.43	1.42
	.100	3.18	2.81	2.61	2.48	2.39	2.33	2.28	2.24	2.21	2.19	2.15	2.10	2.06	2.04	2.01	1.99	1.96	1.93	1.90
	.025	6.55	5.10	4.47	4.12	3.89	3.73	3.61	3.51	3.44	3.37	3.28	3.18	3.07	3.02	2.96	2.91	2.85	2.79	2.72
	.005	11.75	8.51	7.23	6.52	6.07	5.76	5.52	5.35	5.20	5.09	4.91	4.72	4.53	4.43	4.33	4.23	4.12	4.01	3.90
13	.250	1.45	1.55	1.55	1.53	1.52	1.51	1.50	1.49	1.49	1.48	1.47	1.46	1.45	1.44	1.43	1.42	1.42	1.41	1.40
	.100	3.14	2.76	2.56	2.43	2.35	2.28	2.23	2.20	2.16	2.14	2.10	2.05	2.01	1.98	1.96	1.93	1.90	1.88	1.85
	.025	6.41	4.97	4.35	4.00	3.77	3.60	3.48	3.39	3.31	3.25	3.15	3.05	2.95	2.89	2.84	2.78	2.72	2.66	2.60
	.005	11.37	8.19	6.93	6.23	5.79	5.48	5.25	5.08	4.94	4.82	4.64	4.46	4.27	4.17	4.07	3.97	3.87	3.76	3.65
14	.250	1.44	1.53	1.53	1.52	1.51	1.50	1.49	1.48	1.47	1.46	1.45	1.44	1.43	1.42	1.41	1.41	1.40	1.39	1.38
	.100	3.10	2.73	2.52	2.39	2.31	2.24	2.19	2.15	2.12	2.10	2.05	2.01	1.96	1.94	1.91	1.89	1.86	1.83	1.80
	.025	6.30	4.86	4.24	3.89	3.66	3.50	3.38	3.29	3.21	3.15	3.05	2.95	2.84	2.79	2.73	2.67	2.61	2.55	2.49
	.005	11.06	7.92	6.68	6.00	5.56	5.26	5.03	4.86	4.72	4.60	4.43	4.25	4.06	3.96	3.86	3.76	3.66	3.55	3.44
15	.250	1.43	1.52	1.52	1.51	1.49	1.48	1.47	1.46	1.46	1.45	1.44	1.43	1.41	1.41	1.40	1.39	1.38	1.37	1.36
	.100	3.07	2.70	2.49	2.36	2.27	2.21	2.16	2.12	2.09	2.06	2.02	1.97	1.92	1.90	1.87	1.85	1.82	1.79	1.76
	.025	6.20	4.76	4.15	3.80	3.58	3.41	3.29	3.20	3.12	3.06	2.96	2.86	2.76	2.70	2.64	2.58	2.52	2.46	2.40
	.005	10.80	7.70	6.48	5.80	5.37	5.07	4.85	4.67	4.54	4.42	4.25	4.07	3.88	3.79	3.69	3.58	3.48	3.37	3.26
16	.250	1.42	1.51	1.51	1.50	1.48	1.47	1.46	1.45	1.44	1.44	1.43	1.41	1.40	1.39	1.38	1.37	1.36	1.35	1.34
	.100	3.05	2.67	2.46	2.33	2.24	2.18	2.13	2.09	2.06	2.03	1.99	1.94	1.89	1.87	1.84	1.81	1.78	1.75	1.72
	.025	6.12	4.69	4.08	3.73	3.50	3.34	3.22	3.12	3.05	2.99	2.89	2.79	2.68	2.63	2.57	2.51	2.45	2.38	2.32
	.005	10.58	7.51	6.30	5.64	5.21	4.91	4.69	4.52	4.38	4.27	4.10	3.92	3.73	3.64	3.54	3.44	3.33	3.22	3.11
17	.250	1.42	1.51	1.50	1.49	1.47	1.46	1.45	1.44	1.43	1.43	1.41	1.40	1.39	1.38	1.37	1.36	1.35	1.34	1.33
	.100	3.03	2.64	2.44	2.31	2.22	2.15	2.10	2.06	2.03	2.00	1.96	1.91	1.86	1.84	1.81	1.78	1.75	1.72	1.69
	.025	6.04	4.62	4.01	3.66	3.44	3.28	3.16	3.06	2.98	2.92	2.82	2.72	2.62	2.56	2.50	2.44	2.38	2.32	2.25
	.005	10.38	7.35	6.16	5.50	5.07	4.78	4.56	4.39	4.25	4.14	3.97	3.79	3.61	3.51	3.41	3.31	3.21	3.10	2.98

TABLE 10.18.1—(Continued) *
25%, 10%, 2.5%, AND 0.5% POINTS FOR THE DISTRIBUTION OF F*

f_1 Degrees of Freedom (for greater mean square)

f_2	P	1	2	3	4	5	6	7	8	9	10	12	15	20	24	30	40	60	120	∞
18	.250	1.41	1.50	1.49	1.48	1.46	1.45	1.44	1.43	1.42	1.42	1.40	1.39	1.38	1.37	1.36	1.35	1.34	1.33	1.32
	.100	3.01	2.62	2.42	2.29	2.20	2.13	2.08	2.04	2.00	1.98	1.93	1.89	1.84	1.81	1.78	1.75	1.72	1.69	1.66
	.025	5.98	4.56	3.95	3.61	3.38	3.22	3.10	3.01	2.93	2.87	2.77	2.67	2.56	2.50	2.44	2.38	2.32	2.26	2.19
	.005	10.22	7.21	6.03	5.37	4.96	4.66	4.44	4.28	4.14	4.03	3.86	3.68	3.50	3.40	3.30	3.20	3.10	2.99	2.87
19	.250	1.41	1.49	1.49	1.47	1.46	1.44	1.43	1.42	1.41	1.41	1.40	1.38	1.37	1.36	1.35	1.34	1.33	1.32	1.30
	.100	2.99	2.61	2.40	2.27	2.18	2.11	2.06	2.02	1.98	1.96	1.91	1.86	1.81	1.79	1.76	1.73	1.70	1.67	1.63
	.025	5.92	4.51	3.90	3.56	3.33	3.17	3.05	2.96	2.88	2.82	2.72	2.62	2.51	2.45	2.39	2.33	2.27	2.20	2.13
	.005	10.07	7.09	5.92	5.27	4.85	4.56	4.34	4.18	4.04	3.93	3.76	3.59	3.40	3.31	3.21	3.11	3.00	2.89	2.78
20	.250	1.40	1.49	1.48	1.47	1.45	1.44	1.43	1.42	1.41	1.40	1.39	1.37	1.36	1.35	1.34	1.33	1.32	1.31	1.29
	.100	2.97	2.59	2.38	2.25	2.16	2.09	2.04	2.00	1.96	1.94	1.89	1.84	1.79	1.77	1.74	1.71	1.68	1.64	1.61
	.025	5.87	4.46	3.86	3.51	3.29	3.13	3.01	2.91	2.84	2.77	2.68	2.57	2.46	2.41	2.35	2.29	2.22	2.16	2.09
	.005	9.94	6.99	5.82	5.17	4.76	4.47	4.26	4.09	3.96	3.85	3.68	3.50	3.32	3.22	3.12	3.02	2.92	2.81	2.69
21	.250	1.40	1.48	1.48	1.46	1.44	1.43	1.42	1.41	1.40	1.39	1.38	1.37	1.35	1.34	1.33	1.32	1.31	1.30	1.28
	.100	2.96	2.57	2.36	2.23	2.14	2.08	2.02	1.98	1.95	1.92	1.88	1.83	1.78	1.75	1.72	1.69	1.66	1.62	1.59
	.025	5.83	4.42	3.82	3.48	3.25	3.09	2.97	2.87	2.80	2.73	2.64	2.53	2.42	2.37	2.31	2.25	2.18	2.11	2.04
	.005	9.83	6.89	5.73	5.09	4.68	4.39	4.18	4.01	3.88	3.77	3.60	3.43	3.24	3.15	3.05	2.95	2.84	2.73	2.61
22	.250	1.40	1.48	1.47	1.45	1.44	1.42	1.41	1.40	1.39	1.39	1.37	1.36	1.34	1.33	1.32	1.31	1.30	1.29	1.28
	.100	2.95	2.56	2.35	2.22	2.13	2.06	2.01	1.97	1.93	1.90	1.86	1.81	1.76	1.73	1.70	1.67	1.64	1.60	1.57
	.025	5.79	4.38	3.78	3.44	3.22	3.05	2.93	2.84	2.76	2.70	2.60	2.50	2.39	2.33	2.27	2.21	2.14	2.08	2.00
	.005	9.73	6.81	5.65	5.02	4.61	4.32	4.11	3.94	3.81	3.70	3.54	3.36	3.18	3.08	2.98	2.88	2.77	2.66	2.55
23	.250	1.39	1.47	1.47	1.45	1.43	1.42	1.41	1.40	1.39	1.38	1.37	1.35	1.34	1.33	1.32	1.31	1.30	1.28	1.27
	.100	2.94	2.55	2.34	2.21	2.11	2.05	1.99	1.95	1.92	1.89	1.84	1.80	1.74	1.72	1.69	1.66	1.62	1.59	1.55
	.025	5.75	4.35	3.75	3.41	3.18	3.02	2.90	2.81	2.73	2.67	2.57	2.47	2.36	2.30	2.24	2.18	2.11	2.04	1.97
	.005	9.63	6.73	5.58	4.95	4.54	4.26	4.05	3.88	3.75	3.64	3.47	3.30	3.12	3.02	2.92	2.82	2.71	2.60	2.48
24	.250	1.39	1.47	1.46	1.44	1.43	1.41	1.40	1.39	1.38	1.38	1.36	1.35	1.34	1.33	1.32	1.31	1.30	1.29	1.26
	.100	2.93	2.54	2.33	2.19	2.10	2.04	1.98	1.94	1.91	1.88	1.83	1.78	1.73	1.70	1.67	1.64	1.61	1.57	1.53
	.025	5.72	4.32	3.72	3.38	3.15	2.99	2.87	2.78	2.70	2.64	2.54	2.44	2.33	2.27	2.21	2.15	2.08	2.01	1.94
	.005	9.55	6.66	5.52	4.89	4.49	4.20	3.99	3.83	3.69	3.59	3.42	3.25	3.06	2.97	2.87	2.77	2.66	2.55	2.43
25	.250	1.39	1.47	1.46	1.44	1.42	1.41	1.40	1.39	1.38	1.37	1.36	1.34	1.33	1.32	1.31	1.29	1.28	1.27	1.25
	.100	2.92	2.53	2.32	2.18	2.09	2.02	1.97	1.93	1.89	1.87	1.82	1.77	1.72	1.69	1.66	1.63	1.59	1.56	1.52
	.025	5.69	4.29	3.69	3.35	3.13	2.97	2.85	2.75	2.68	2.61	2.51	2.41	2.30	2.24	2.18	2.12	2.05	1.98	1.91
	.005	9.48	6.60	5.46	4.84	4.43	4.15	3.94	3.78	3.64	3.54	3.37	3.20	3.01	2.92	2.82	2.72	2.61	2.50	2.38
26	.250	1.38	1.46	1.45	1.44	1.42	1.41	1.39	1.38	1.37	1.37	1.35	1.34	1.32	1.31	1.30	1.29	1.28	1.26	1.25
	.100	2.91	2.52	2.31	2.17	2.08	2.01	1.96	1.92	1.88	1.86	1.81	1.76	1.71	1.68	1.65	1.61	1.58	1.54	1.50
	.025	5.66	4.27	3.67	3.33	3.10	2.94	2.82	2.73	2.65	2.59	2.49	2.39	2.28	2.22	2.16	2.09	2.03	1.95	1.88
	.005	9.41	6.54	5.41	4.79	4.38	4.10	3.89	3.73	3.60	3.49	3.33	3.15	2.97	2.87	2.77	2.67	2.56	2.45	2.33

TABLE 10.18.1—*(Continued)* *

25%, 10%, 2.5%, AND 0.5% POINTS FOR THE DISTRIBUTION OF F*

f_2	P	\multicolumn{19}{c}{f_1 Degrees of Freedom (for greater mean square)}																		
		1	2	3	4	5	6	7	8	9	10	12	15	20	24	30	40	60	120	∞
27	.250	1.38	1.46	1.45	1.43	1.42	1.40	1.39	1.38	1.37	1.36	1.35	1.33	1.32	1.31	1.30	1.28	1.27	1.26	1.24
	.100	2.90	2.51	2.30	2.17	2.07	2.00	1.95	1.91	1.87	1.85	1.80	1.75	1.70	1.67	1.64	1.60	1.57	1.53	1.49
	.025	5.63	4.24	3.65	3.31	3.08	2.92	2.80	2.71	2.63	2.57	2.47	2.36	2.25	2.19	2.13	2.07	2.00	1.93	1.85
	.005	9.34	6.49	5.36	4.74	4.34	4.06	3.85	3.69	3.56	3.45	3.28	3.11	2.93	2.83	2.73	2.63	2.52	2.41	2.29
28	.250	1.38	1.46	1.45	1.43	1.41	1.40	1.39	1.38	1.37	1.36	1.34	1.33	1.31	1.30	1.29	1.28	1.27	1.25	1.24
	.100	2.89	2.50	2.29	2.16	2.06	2.00	1.94	1.90	1.87	1.84	1.79	1.74	1.69	1.66	1.63	1.59	1.56	1.52	1.48
	.025	5.61	4.22	3.63	3.29	3.06	2.90	2.78	2.69	2.61	2.55	2.45	2.34	2.23	2.17	2.11	2.05	1.98	1.91	1.83
	.005	9.28	6.44	5.32	4.70	4.30	4.02	3.81	3.65	3.52	3.41	3.25	3.07	2.89	2.79	2.69	2.59	2.48	2.37	2.25
29	.250	1.38	1.45	1.45	1.43	1.41	1.40	1.38	1.37	1.36	1.35	1.34	1.32	1.31	1.30	1.29	1.27	1.26	1.25	1.23
	.100	2.89	2.50	2.28	2.15	2.06	1.99	1.93	1.89	1.86	1.83	1.78	1.73	1.68	1.65	1.62	1.58	1.55	1.51	1.47
	.025	5.59	4.20	3.61	3.27	3.04	2.88	2.76	2.67	2.59	2.53	2.43	2.32	2.21	2.15	2.09	2.03	1.96	1.89	1.81
	.005	9.23	6.40	5.28	4.66	4.26	3.98	3.77	3.61	3.48	3.38	3.21	3.04	2.86	2.76	2.66	2.56	2.45	2.33	2.21
30	.250	1.38	1.45	1.44	1.42	1.41	1.39	1.38	1.37	1.36	1.35	1.34	1.32	1.30	1.29	1.28	1.27	1.26	1.24	1.23
	.100	2.88	2.49	2.28	2.14	2.05	1.98	1.93	1.88	1.85	1.82	1.77	1.72	1.67	1.64	1.61	1.57	1.54	1.50	1.46
	.025	5.57	4.18	3.59	3.25	3.03	2.87	2.75	2.65	2.57	2.51	2.41	2.31	2.20	2.14	2.07	2.01	1.94	1.87	1.79
	.005	9.18	6.35	5.24	4.62	4.23	3.95	3.74	3.58	3.45	3.34	3.18	3.01	2.82	2.73	2.63	2.52	2.42	2.30	2.18
40	.250	1.36	1.44	1.42	1.40	1.39	1.37	1.36	1.35	1.34	1.33	1.31	1.30	1.28	1.26	1.25	1.24	1.22	1.21	1.19
	.100	2.84	2.44	2.23	2.09	2.00	1.93	1.87	1.83	1.79	1.76	1.71	1.66	1.61	1.57	1.54	1.51	1.47	1.42	1.38
	.025	5.42	4.05	3.46	3.13	2.90	2.74	2.62	2.53	2.45	2.39	2.29	2.18	2.07	2.01	1.94	1.88	1.80	1.72	1.64
	.005	8.83	6.07	4.98	4.37	3.99	3.71	3.51	3.35	3.22	3.12	2.95	2.78	2.60	2.50	2.40	2.30	2.18	2.06	1.93
60	.250	1.35	1.42	1.41	1.38	1.37	1.35	1.33	1.32	1.31	1.30	1.29	1.27	1.25	1.24	1.22	1.21	1.19	1.17	1.15
	.100	2.79	2.39	2.18	2.04	1.95	1.87	1.82	1.77	1.74	1.71	1.66	1.60	1.54	1.51	1.48	1.44	1.40	1.35	1.29
	.025	5.29	3.93	3.34	3.01	2.79	2.63	2.51	2.41	2.33	2.27	2.17	2.06	1.94	1.88	1.82	1.74	1.67	1.58	1.48
	.005	8.49	5.80	4.73	4.14	3.76	3.49	3.29	3.13	3.01	2.90	2.74	2.57	2.39	2.29	2.19	2.08	1.96	1.83	1.69
120	.250	1.34	1.40	1.39	1.37	1.35	1.33	1.31	1.30	1.29	1.28	1.26	1.24	1.22	1.21	1.19	1.18	1.16	1.13	1.10
	.100	2.75	2.35	2.13	1.99	1.90	1.82	1.77	1.72	1.68	1.65	1.60	1.55	1.48	1.45	1.41	1.37	1.32	1.26	1.19
	.025	5.15	3.80	3.23	2.89	2.67	2.52	2.39	2.30	2.22	2.16	2.05	1.94	1.82	1.76	1.69	1.61	1.53	1.43	1.31
	.005	8.18	5.54	4.50	3.92	3.55	3.28	3.09	2.93	2.81	2.71	2.54	2.37	2.19	2.09	1.98	1.87	1.75	1.61	1.43
∞	.250	1.32	1.39	1.37	1.35	1.33	1.31	1.29	1.28	1.27	1.25	1.24	1.22	1.19	1.18	1.16	1.14	1.12	1.08	1.00
	.100	2.71	2.30	2.08	1.94	1.85	1.77	1.72	1.67	1.63	1.60	1.55	1.49	1.42	1.38	1.34	1.30	1.24	1.17	1.00
	.025	5.02	3.69	3.12	2.79	2.57	2.41	2.29	2.19	2.11	2.05	1.94	1.83	1.71	1.64	1.57	1.48	1.39	1.27	1.00
	.005	7.88	5.30	4.28	3.72	3.35	3.09	2.90	2.74	2.62	2.52	2.36	2.19	2.00	1.90	1.79	1.67	1.53	1.36	1.00

*Reprinted from "Tables of percentage points of the inverted beta (F) distribution," by Maxine Merrington and Catherine M. Thompson, Biometrika, 33:73 (1943) by permission of the authors and the editor.

was found that $Qs_{\bar{x}} = 48.7$ so that only treatment 4 differed from the others. Now 48.7 is 57% of the experimental mean, 84.8; the experiment has low precision. How much would it be increased if 20 chicks were assigned at random to each lot?

From the original experiment, $s_0 = \sqrt{722} = 26.9$ with $f_0 = 16$. For the proposed one, $a = 4$, $n = 20$, $f = 76$; whence $Q_{4,76} = 3.72$ and $F_{76,16} = 1.36$. (Hint about interpolation: plot Q against reciprocals of f.) From these data,

$$\delta = \frac{(3.72)(26.9)\sqrt{1.36}}{\sqrt{20}} = 26$$

With 20 chicks per lot, the prospective experiment should $(P = 0.75)$ detect any difference so large as $26/84.8 = 31\%$ of the mean. Other lot sizes may be tried until satisfactory sensitivity is indicated

More directly, we may ask how to determine n so as to attain a specified precision, say $\delta = 20\%$ of $84.8 = 17$. Solving the equation for n, we have

$$n = \frac{(Q_{a,f})^2 (s_0^2) F_{f,f_0}}{\delta^2}$$

Since both Q and F depend on n, an iterative method of solution is required. This is made easy by the small changes in Q and F over the parts of the tables used. Take what you consider a too-large value of n and make a first approximation. For example, $n = 121$ seems beyond reasonable lot sizes. For this n, $f = (120)(4) = 480$. Interpolation yields $Q_{4,480} = 3.65$, $F_{480,16} = 1.34$. Substituting these values in the formula,

$$\text{1st approximation to } n = \frac{(3.65)^2 (722)(1.34)}{17^2} = 45$$

This approximation is now tried in the formula for δ. With $f = (44)(4) = 176$ $Q_{4,176} = 3.67$ and $F_{176,16} = 1.35$,

$$\delta = \frac{(3.67)(26.9)\sqrt{1.35}}{\sqrt{45}} = 17.1$$

Since this is somewhat larger than the specified $\delta = 17$, increase the approximate n by unity. You will find that $n = 46$ gives $\delta = 17$ closely enough. If the experimenter increases each lot size to 46 chicks, he has a good chance $(P = 0.75)$ of detecting any difference so large as 17.

It pays to make f_0 as large as the available information warrants. The experimental errors from several similar experiments may be combined. In some laboratories the variability of their colonies of animals is often so well known that f_0 can be increased to ∞.

But if no definite information is available, the experimenter may have to estimate s_0 and f_0 from general knowledge of his experimental material.

He is familiar with the range of weights or yields which may be encountered. He may use table 2.2.2 for translating range to standard deviation. Known coefficients of variation may be helpful. From this kind of information he may make estimates of upper and lower limits on σ such that he thinks it an even bet that the true value lies between them. That is, he attempts to fix a 50% confidence interval on σ. Let g and h be these upper and lower limits. Then s_0 is estimated as $(g + h)/2$. For f_0, use a number from this table (14):

Ratio, g/h	3.6	2.2	1.84	1.67	1.58	1.51	1.46	1.42	1.39	1.36
Degrees of Freedom, f_0	1	2	3	4	5	6	7	8	9	10

The extensive table 10.18.1 calls for further comment. In addition to its usefulness in estimating sample size at the 25% and 10% points, it allows greater range for testing homogeneity of variance in 2 samples. Comparison with table 4.8.1 shows that the latter table contains a portion of the 2.5% points of the new table, the two-tailed test being required because always the larger mean square was divided by the smaller. With the new table, the 0.5% points allow the testing of homogeneity at the 1% level. Again, one may wish to make a test of significance at other points than 5% and 1%. If consequences are not serious, testing at 10% may be reasonable. In any case the tester may wish to know how far his sample F is outside the 5%–1% range.

For estimating probabilities between those given in the tables, linear interpolation is usually adequate. More nearly accurate results can be got by plotting the tabular values of F against the logarithms of the probabilities (use of percentages is simpler), then interpolating graphically.

There is often need for interpolating between tabular degrees of freedom, especially in table 10.18.1. Linear interpolation is usually sufficient. If greater accuracy is needed, plot the tabular F against the reciprocals of the degrees of freedom. The resulting graph is almost linear, allowing easy evaluation of F corresponding to the desired degree of freedom.

EXAMPLE 10.18.1—In the period from 1941 to 1947, there were selected 4 reports of the percentages of albumin in plasma proteins of normal subjects as determined by electrophoresis (27):

Number of Subjects	Mean Percentage	Degrees of Freedom	s	s^2	Σx^2
12	62.3	11	3.60	12.96	142.56
15	60.3	14	2.80	7.84	109.76
7	59.5	6	5.78	33.41	200.46
16	61.5	15	4.30	18.49	277.35
50 Weighted $\bar{x} = 61.05$		46			730.13

By methods to be presented in section 10.20, the hypothesis of homogeneity of variance was tested and accepted. So the common σ^2 was estimated as $730.13/46 = 15.87$; from which $s_0 = 3.98$ with $f_0 = 46$. The weighted mean percentage is 61.05 ($C = 6.5\%$). An investigator plans to use this technique to test 4 treatments. He wishes to detect, at the 5% level, any difference so large as three per cent of albumin, with 3:1 odds of being successful.   How many subjects for each treatment should he provide? Ans. 29. Note: 3% of albumin is about 5% of the mean.

EXAMPLE 10.18.2—An investigator has no reliable estimate of σ but, from his knowledge of the range, he estimates it as being between $g = 18$ and $h = 13$ with 1:1 odds of being correct. Estimate $s_0 = 15.5$, $f_0 = 9$. He estimates μ as 120. With 4 treatments he wishes to detect any difference so large as 12. What size of lots will be required? Ans. 35.

EXAMPLE 10.18.3—In the preceding example, estimate the size of lot that will give the investigator 9:1 odds of being successful. Ans. 49.

EXAMPLE 10.18.4—In the third-to-last paragraph of section 2.15, verify the sample size required for 3:1 odds.

EXAMPLE 10.18.5—In section 4.7, last paragraph, verify the sample size, 25.

10.19—Intraclass correlation. It has been shown that the mean square for "treatments" may be separated into two parts, one reflecting the natural variation of individuals treated alike, and the other arising from genetic or environmental conditions peculiar to the samples. The former is an estimate of σ^2, which may be assumed equal in the sampled populations, while the latter is an estimate of σ_A^2, the added portion related to differences among the population means. The sum, $\sigma^2 + \sigma_A^2$, is the variance of individuals picked at random from the entire universe made up of the sampled populations. The ratio of the two variances,

$$\frac{\sigma_A^2}{\sigma^2 + \sigma_A^2},$$

is known as the *intraclass correlation*, ρ_I. In the numerator is the variance which, in a sample or lot, is common to all individuals because all of them are affected alike by the variation which pertains to the lot as a whole. This is $\sigma_A^2 = 25$ in the illustrative sampling of table 10.13.1. In the denominator is an average variance that would apply to individuals if they were picked at random from the universe without attention to population boundaries.

The justification for calling this "correlation" may be understood by reference to section 7.4 where it was shown that r is the ratio of two variances. The numerator in both correlations is associated with the variance that is common to individuals: the *covariance* in one case, and σ_A^2 in the other. The denominator is an average of the variation that would affect individuals if they were not classified—into X_1 and X_2, or into sub-samples.

If all samples are from the same population, as in the pig gains of tables 10.2.1 and 10.5.2, then $\sigma_A^2 = 0$ and consequently $\rho_I = 0$: the entire variation, both individual and group, arises from the random sampling of a single population. Of course, in any particular sample from $\rho_I = 0$ the value of the intraclass correlation r_I, is not usually zero. Thus, in table 10.5.1, $s^2 = 114.0$, $s_A{}^2 = (172.3 - 114.0)/10 = 5.83$, and

$$r_I = \frac{5.83}{114.0 + 5.83} = 0.049$$

The hypothesis that $\rho_I = 0$ is identical with the hypothesis, $\sigma_A{}^2 = 0$, and

$$F = 172.3/114.0 = 1.51,$$

a nonsignificant value, is the appropriate test of both of them.

Large intraclass correlation indicates relatively small variation among the individuals of the sub-samples. Indeed, in the limiting situation, $\sigma^2 = 0$ and

$$\rho_I = \frac{\sigma_A{}^2}{0 + \sigma_A{}^2} = 1$$

Since this could happen only if all the individuals in each group had exactly the same measurement, it is of only theoretical interest. However, the data on identical twins in table 10.19.1 illustrate a striking approach to perfect correlation. The totals of finger ridges are much the same for the two members of each pair but differ markedly among pairs. Since these counts are presumably unaffected by age, the high twin correlation, $r_I = 0.966$, measures the similarity of their inheritance of this character.

TABLE 10.19.1

NUMBER OF FINGER RIDGES ON BOTH HANDS OF INDIVIDUALS IN 12 PAIRS
OF FEMALE IDENTICAL TWINS

Data from Newman, Freeman, and Holzinger (21)

Pair	Finger Ridges of Individuals		Pair	Finger Ridges of Individuals		Pair	Finger Ridges of Individuals	
1	71,	71	5	76,	70	9	114,	113
2	79,	82	6	83,	82	10	94,	91
3	105,	99	7	114,	113	11	75,	83
4	115,	114	8	57,	44	12	76,	72

Analysis of Variance

Source of Variation	Degrees of Freedom	Mean Square
Twin pairs	11	817 31
Individuals	12	14.29

$$s^2 = 14.29, \quad s_A{}^2 = 401.51, \quad r_I = 0.966$$

One can get a good idea of the variation of r_I in small samples by computing its values from the random samples of pig variance in table 10.13.2. In sample 1, for example,

$$r_I = 60/(60 + 127) = 0.321$$

Among the 25 samples the smallest intraclass correlation is -0.615 in number 20, the largest, 0.765 in number 24. This is ordinary sampling variation from the population value,

$$\rho_I = 25/(25 + 100) = 0.2$$

If $n = 2$, intraclass correlations may be averaged and may have confidence limits set as in section 7.6 (7, chapter 7). The value of z has a negative bias which may be corrected approximately by the addition of $1/(2a - 1)$, where a is the number of pairs. Thus in sample 1, table 10.13.2,

$$r_I = 0.321$$
$$z = 0.333$$
$$1/(2a - 1) = 0.053$$
$$\overline{}$$
$$\text{Unbiased } z = 0.386$$

In order to calculate intraclass correlation directly from a table of analysis of variance, it is convenient to put the formula thus:

$$r_I = \frac{M_A - M}{M_A + (n - 1)M},$$

where M_A and M denote mean squares for Treatment (lot) and Individuals. In the twin data, $M_A = 817.31$, $M = 14.29$, $n = 2$, whence

$$r_I = \frac{817.31 - 14.29}{817.31 + (2 - 1)14.29} = 0.97 \text{ (as before)}$$

If the sub-samples differ in size, the average, n_0, is used. For example, in the pig data of table 10.16.1,

$$r_I = \frac{1.07 - 0.36}{1.07 + (6.90 - 1)(0.36)} = 0.222$$

The F-test in the table shows that this small correlation is significant.

A negative r_I occurs if the sample means vary less than is to be expected from the individual variation, M_A being less than M. If this happens, $s_A{}^2$ appears to be a negative number. The hypothesis, $\sigma_A{}^2 = 0$ (or $\kappa^2 = 0$) is not rejected, but the alternative conclusion is not $a_i \neq 0$ but this: *Some control has made the sampling non-random.* Either the observations within the lots have been spread artificially or the lot means have been compressed into a range smaller than that ordinarily found in sampling. The first could occur in balanced lots of animals where the individuals are assigned in such a way as to keep the ranges (standard deviations) in all lots about equal. The second could be brought about by adjusting the rations from time to time, maintaining equal mean gains.

If one attempts to graph the twin data, he will not know, in any one pair, which number of finger ridges is X_1 and which, X_2. The solution is to locate 2 points for each pair: the second pair in table 10.19.1, for example, determines the points (79, 82) and (82, 79), symmetrically located with respect to a 45° line through the origin (45°, that is, if the scales for X_1 and X_2 are equal). If there were triplets instead of twins, each set of observations, a, b, and c, would specify 6 points, (a, b), (b, a), (a, c), (c, a), (b, c), and (c, b). The number of points per sub-sample rises rapidly with n; 12 for $n = 4$, 20 for $n = 5$, etc. For large n, the job of computing r_I directly from all these pairs was discouraging until Harris (12) discovered a shortened process similar to the later-developed analysis of variance (7).

EXAMPLE 10.19.1—In the wool sampling of example 10.3.2, now assuming Model II, $M_A = 11.11$ and $M = 8.22$. Calculate $r_I = 0.105$. $F = 1.35$ shows that r_I is not significant. In the sampled population, the batches from the same bag may be no more alike than batches from different bags.

EXAMPLE 10.19.2—There are 2 intraclass correlations in the turnip green data of table 10.14.1. Calculate the intra-leaf-in-plant correlation among determinations, 0.960, and the intraplant correlation among leaves, 0.690. According to the F-test, each is significant.

10.20—Tests of homogeneity of variance. From time to time we have raised the question as to whether two or more mean squares might differ significantly. For two samples an answer was given in section 4.8. For more than two samples Bartlett's original test of homogeneity (2) seems adequate.

If the samples are equal in size, the test involves the comparison of a times the logarithm of the average mean square with the sum of logarithms of the separate mean squares. In table 10.20.1 the method is applied to the 4 sub-samples of s^2 in table 10.2.1—sub-samples known to have been drawn from a common source. The factor, 2.3026, is a constant ($\log_e 10$) necessary because common logarithms are used. Chi-square, as first calculated, is slightly biased upwards. In this example, even the biased value shows less than average sampling variation in s^2 (table 1.14.1). It is necessary to make the correction only if χ^2 lies close above one of the critical tabular values, and then only if one wishes to get an accurate evaluation of P.

For samples of differing size, the computation of chi-square is more complicated though following the same pattern. In table 10.20.2 the test of homogeneity is applied to the pig birth weights of table 10.16.1.

Each Σx^2 is calculated from the corresponding ΣX^2 by deducting the usual $(\Sigma X)^2/n$. The table requires no further explanation.

Another anomaly in the pig birth weights now stands out: the differing variances do not seem to have any physiological explanation. Both the largest and the smallest were in the 10-pig litters, and the others appear to occur at random. Coupled with the unexplained sizes of the birth weights (section 10.17), this leads to the conclusion that this sample contains little information.

In addition to these biological peculiarities, there is a statistical feature that modifies some of the assumptions made in section 10.16. The

TABLE 10.20.1
COMPUTATION OF BARTLETT'S TEST OF HOMOGENEITY OF VARIANCE.
SAMPLE EQUAL IN SIZE
Data from table 10.2.1: $a = 4$, $n = 5$

Sample	Sum of Squares, Σx^2	Mean Square, s^2	log s^2
1	472	118	2.07188
2	396	99	1.99564
3	616	154	2.18752
4	164	41	1.61278

$$\Sigma s^2 = 412 \qquad \Sigma \log s^2 = 7.86782$$

Mean: $\bar{s}^2 = \Sigma s^2/a = 412/4 = 103 \qquad \log \bar{s}^2 = 2.01284$

$$a \log \bar{s}^2 = 4(2.01284) = 8.05136$$
$$\Sigma \log s^2 \qquad\qquad = 7.86782$$

Difference $\qquad\qquad 0.18354$

$$\chi^2 = 2.3026\ (n-1)\ (a \log \bar{s}^2 - \Sigma \log s^2)$$
$$= 2.3026\ (5-1)\ (0.18354)$$
$$= 1.69, f = a - 1 = 3$$

Correction factor: $C = 1 + \dfrac{a+1}{3a(n-1)} = 1 + \dfrac{4+1}{3(4)(5-1)} = 1.1042$

Corrected $\chi^2 = \chi^2/C = 1.69/1.1042 = 1.53$

estimate of mean square within lots, 0.36, is evidently an average of mean squares in samples from populations with differing σ^2. If so, the ratio,

$$\frac{s^2 + n_0 s_A{}^2}{s^2},$$

does not follow the usual F-distribution and the test in table 10.16.1 lacks validity.

As for the pig litter data, the matter is unimportant; there was no understandable trend in either the birth weights or the mean squares, so that the sample appears uninformative.   In other experiments there would be several considerations of interest.   The first question that should be answered is, "What is the meaning of the different variances?"   Pursuit of that lead might be more profitable than any findings about the means. If not, the natural conclusion would seem to be that differences among mean squares are only sampling phenomena, the ordinary test of the hypothesis, $\sigma_A = 0$, being valid.

If there is evidence (including Bartlett's test) that the σ^2 differ, one may still test the hypothesis that the means are the same even in the

TABLE 10.20.2

COMPUTATION OF BARTLETT'S TEST OF HOMOGENEITY OF VARIANCE.
SAMPLES DIFFERING IN SIZE
Pig birth weights from table 10.16.1

Sample	Σx^2	Degrees of Freedom, $n-1$	Reciprocal, $1/(n-1)$	Mean Square, s^2	$\log s^2$	$(n-1)\log s^2$
1	8.18	9	0.11111	0.9089	-0.04148	-0.3733
2	3.48	7	0.14286	0.4972	-0.30347	-2.1243
3	0.68	9	0.11111	0.0756	-1.12148	-10.0933
4	0.72	7	0.14286	0.1029	-0.98758	-6.9131
5	0.73	5	0.20000	0.1460	-0.83565	-4.1782
6	0.24	3	0.33333	0.0800	-1.09691	-3.2907
7	1.97	5	0.20000	0.3940	-0.40450	-2.0225
8	1.17	3	0.33333	0.3900	-0.40894	-1.2268

$a = 8$ 17.17   48   1.5746 $\Sigma(n-1)(\log s^2) = -30.2222$
      $= \Sigma x^2$ $= \Sigma(n-1)$ $= \Sigma 1/(n-1)$

$$\bar{s}^2 = \Sigma x^2 / \Sigma(n-1) = 17.17/48 = 0.3577$$
$$(\log \bar{s}^2)\Sigma(n-1) = (-0.44648)(48) = -21.4310$$
$$\chi^2 = 2.3026\left[(\log \bar{s}^2)\Sigma(n-1) - \Sigma(n-1)(\log s^2)\right]$$
$$= 2.3026\left[-21.4310 - (-30.222)\right]$$
$$= 20.24$$

Correction factor, $C = 1 + \dfrac{1}{3(a-1)}\left(\Sigma\dfrac{1}{n-1} - \dfrac{1}{\Sigma(n-1)}\right)$

$$= 1 + \frac{1}{(3)(7)}\left(1.5746 - \frac{1}{48}\right) = 1.074$$

Corrected $\chi^2 = 20.24/1.074 = 18.85**$ $f = a - 1 = 7$

presence of heterogeneous variance (15, 31, 10).   The method is to calculate a pair of weighted mean squares, then test their ratio against the F-distribution.   (The test is not exact, but I think you needn't worry about that.)   The calculations are laid out in table 10.20.3.

F' is distributed approximately as F with f_1 and f_2 degrees of freedom. Table 10.18.1 shows that P is close to 0.005: H_0 is rejected with very small

TABLE 10.20.3

Calculation of Test of $H_0: \mu_i = \mu$ if Variance is Heterogeneous

Birth weights of table 10.16.1

Size of Sample, n_i (1)	Mean, $\bar{x}_i$ (2)	Mean Square, s_i^2 (3)	Weight, $w_i = n_i/s_i^2$ (4)	Deviations, $\bar{x}_i - \bar{x}_w$ (5)	$(\bar{x}_i - \bar{x}_w)^2$ (5)^2 (6)	$\frac{w_i}{\Sigma w_i} = \frac{(4)}{\Sigma(4)}$ (7)	$\frac{(1 - \frac{w_i}{\Sigma w_i})^2}{[1 - (7)]^2}$ (8)	$\frac{(1 - \frac{w_i}{\Sigma w_i})^2}{n_i - 1} = \frac{(8)}{(1) - 1}$ (9)
10	2.84	0.9089	11.00	−0.05	0.0025	0.03110	0.9388	0.1043
8	2.66	0.4972	16.09	−0.23	0.0529	0.04549	0.9111	0.1302
10	3.18	0.0756	132.28	0.29	0.0841	0.37398	0.3919	0.0435
8	2.98	0.1029	77.75	0.09	0.0081	0.21981	0.6087	0.0870
6	2.37	0.1460	41.10	−0.52	0.2704	0.11620	0.7811	0.1562
4	2.90	0.0800	50.00	0.01	0.0001	0.14136	0.7373	0.2458
6	1.98	0.3940	15.23	−0.91	0.8281	0.04306	0.9157	0.1831
4	2.35	0.3900	10.26	−0.54	0.2916	0.02901	0.9428	0.3143
$a = 8$ $\bar{x}_w = 2.89$			$\Sigma(4) = 353.71$					$\Sigma(9) = 1.2644$

Weighted mean: $\bar{x}_w = \dfrac{\Sigma(2)(4)}{\Sigma(4)} = \dfrac{(2.84)(11.00) + \ldots + (2.35)(10.26)}{353.71} = 2.89$ pounds

Weighted sum of squares: $\Sigma(4)(6) = (11.00)(0.0025) + \ldots + (10.26)(0.2916) = 39.36$

$$F' = \frac{\Sigma(4)(6)/(a-1)}{1 + \dfrac{2(a-2)}{a^2-1}\Sigma(9)} = \frac{39.36/(8-1)}{1 + \dfrac{2(8-2)}{8^2-1}(1.2644)} = 4.53$$

$$f_1 = a - 1 = 7. \quad f_2 = \frac{1}{\dfrac{3}{a^2-1}\Sigma(9)} = \frac{1}{\dfrac{3}{63}(1.2644)} = 16.6$$

probability of error. Rejection is even more strongly indicated than it was by the questionable test of table 10.16.1. Sometimes the opposite is true. One does not select the test according to the size of P but according to his hypothesis about the σ^2.

REFERENCES

1. R. L. Anderson and T. A. Bancroft. Statistical Theory in Research. McGraw-Hill Book Company, Inc., New York (1952).

2. M. S. Bartlett. Supplement to the Journal of the Royal Statistical Society, 4:137 (1937).

3. W. G. Cochran. Journal of the American Statistical Association, 34:492 (1939)

4. David B. Duncan Biometrics, 11:1 (1955).

5. F. L. Engledow and G. Udny Yule. The Principles and Practice of Field Trials. Empire Cotton Growing Corporation, London (1926).

6. R. A. Fisher International Mathematical Conference, Toronto (1924).

7. R. A. Fisher. Statistical Methods for Research Workers. Oliver and Boyd Edinburgh (1925–1950).

8. R. A. Fisher and F. Yates. Statistical Tables. Oliver and Boyd, Edinburgh (1938–1953).

9. M. Ganguli. Sankhya, 5:449 (1941).

10. John Gurland. Queries in Biometrics, 11: (December, 1955).

11. T. Roy Hansberry and Charles H. Richardson. Iowa State Journal of Science 10:27 (1935).

12. J. A. Harris. Biometrika, 9:446 (1913).

13. H. O. Hartley. Communications on Pure and Applied Mathematics, 8:47 (1955).

14. Marilyn Harris, D. G. Horvitz, and A. M. Mood. Journal of the American Statistical Association, 43:391 (1948).

15. G. S. James. Biometrika, 38:324 (1951).

16. M. T. Jenkins. Journal of Agricultural Research, 39:677 (1929).

17. M. Keuls. Euphytica, 1:112 (1952).

18. R. F. Link and D. L. Wallace. Ditto, Princeton University, March, 1952.

19. Belle Lowe. Data from Iowa Agricultural Experiment Station (1935).

20. P. C. Mahalanobis. Indian Journal of Agricultural Science, 2:694 (1932).

21. Horatio H. Newman, Frank N. Freeman, and Karl J. Holzinger. Twins. The University of Chicago Press (1937).

22. D. Newman. Biometrika, 31:20 (1939).

23. E. S. Pearson. Biometrika, 23:114 (1931).

24. Query in Biometrics, 5:250 (1949).

25. D. Richardson, D. V. Catron, L. A. Underkofler, H. M. Maddock, and W. C Frieland, The Journal of Nutrition, 44:371 (1951).

26. GEORGE W. SNEDECOR. Analysis of Variance and Covariance. Iowa State University Press, Ames, Iowa (1934).

27. GEORGE W. SNEDECOR. Annals of the New York Academy of Sciences, 52:792 (1950).

28. Studies of Sampling Techniques and Chemical Analyses of Vegetables. Southern Cooperative Series Bulletin No. 10 (1951).

29. J. W. TUKEY. The Problem of Multiple Comparisons. Mimeographed for limited circulation (1953).

30 J W. TUKEY. New York Academy of Science Transactions, Series II, 16:88 (1953).

31 B. L. WELCH. Biometrika, 38:330 (1951).

CHAPTER 11

Two-Way Experiments. Analysis of Variance

11.1—The use of knowledge about outcome. The investigator often acquires the ability to predict roughly the behavior of his experimental material. He knows that young male rats will gain weight faster than females in identical environments. Plants in one section of a greenhouse, even on the same bench, may produce more flowers than will plants in another section. Such knowledge can be used to increase the value of an experiment. It could not be used in the designs of the foregoing chapter. There the units were assigned at random to the lots; the experimental error contained not only the unpredictable variation due to sampling but also any variation that might be predicted. The 2-way design now to be described enables the experimenter to take advantage of his knowledge of outcome. For 2 treatments this was done in chapter 2. Now the methods will be expanded to provide for comparisons among 3 or more treatments.

11.2—An experiment with two criteria of classification. In nutritional experiments with swine, it is known that one litter may react differently from another. Richardson *et al.* (20) planned to eliminate from error this anticipated source of variation by trying every treatment on the pigs of a single litter, replicating the litters. Each individual is classified by 2 criteria, the litter of which he is a member and the treatment he receives. The pigs of each litter are assigned at random to the treatments.

The data in table 11.2.1 are selected from a larger experiment already cited (example 10.3.1, where litters were ignored). Omitted are the zero level of the vitamin B_{12} and the treatments with antibiotics.

With one exception, the computations follow the form already familiar. In addition to sums of squares for Total and Treatments, there is now one for Litters. The remainder, Discrepance, will be shown later to be an estimate of experimental error. It, along with its degrees of freedom, is got by applying the addition theorem appropriate to orthogonal effects. Notice also that degrees of freedom for Discrepance is the product of those for the main effects.

A characteristic of analysis of variance is the partition of the total sum of squares and degrees of freedom into parts, each associated with a feature of the experimental design. The separation of the litter effect from error enables the experimenter to use his knowledge of animal behavior to decrease s^2, thus increasing the precision of his experiment.

Before discussing the relative sizes of the mean squares, it is desirable to observe the kind of results that are expected in random sampling from a common population. Table 11.2.2 differs from the vitamin B_{12} experi-

TABLE 11.2.1
AVERAGE DAILY GAIN TO 75 POUNDS LIVE WEIGHT OF 3 PIGS
From each of 3 litters. Pounds per day. No antibiotics

Levels of B_{12} (μg/lb ration)	Litter 1	Litter 2	Litter 3	Sum	Mean
5	1.26	1.21	1.19	3.66	1.22
10	1.29	1.23	1.23	3.75	1.25
15	1.38	1.27	1.22	3.87	1.29
Sum	3.93	3.71	3.64	11.28	1.25

Correction Term: $(11.28)^2/9 = 14.1376$
Total: $1.26^2 + 1.29^2 + \ldots + 1.22^2 - C = 14.1634 - 14.1376 = 0.0258$

Litters: $\dfrac{3.93^2 + 3.71^2 + 3.64^2}{3} - C = 14.1529 - 14.1376 = 0.0153$

Treatments: $\dfrac{3.66^2 + 3.75^2 + 3.87^2}{3} - C = 14.1450 - 14.1376 = 0.0074$

Discrepance = Remainder = $0.0258 - (0.0153 + 0.0074) = 0.0031$

Source of Variation	Degrees of Freedom	Sum of Squares	Mean Square
Litters	2	0.0153	0.0076
Treatments	2	0.0074	0.0037
Discrepance (Error)	4	0.0031	0.0008
Total	8	0.0258	

ment only in this: the pig gains are all drawn at random from the normal distribution of table 3.2.1. The advantage is that we know the variance, $\sigma^2 = 100$, in the population sampled. We can observe the fact that, when all observations are from a common population, the 4 mean squares are all estimates of the common σ^2; in this example, very close estimates.

If there are real treatment and litter effects, the corresponding mean squares will be inflated, but Discrepance is still expected to estimate σ^2, ordinarily called *experimental error*. Evidence on this point will be presented later.

Returning to the vitamin B_{12} experiment, the significance of the main effects is tested by F. For Litters, $F = 0.0076/0.0008 = 9.5$; $f = 2, 4$; $P = 0.04$; for Treatments, $F = 4.6$, $P > 0.05$. Clearly it was worth while to eliminate litter differences from error—the efficiency of this design, relative to the completely random one of chapter 10, is discussed in section 11.6. The treatments may have no effect; $5\mu g$. of the vitamin is known to increase gains, but additional amounts are questionable. For additional information, see examples 11.3.1 and 11.3.2.

TABLE 11.2.2
DUMMY EXPERIMENT WITH 5 TREATMENTS REPLICATED ON 4 LITTERS
Observations are from the pig gains of table 3.2.1
$\sigma^2 = 100$

| Treatments | Litters | | | | Sum | Mean |
	1	2	3	4		
A	15	31	20	30	96	24
B	22	11	45	26	104	26
C	33	37	30	44	144	36
D	18	31	49	34	132	33
E	37	30	36	21	124	31
Sum	125	140	180	155	600	

Source of Variation	Degrees of Freedom	Sum of Squares	Mean Square
Treatment	4	392	98
Litter	3	330	110
Discrepance	12	1,212	101
Total	19	1,934	101.8

EXAMPLE 11.2.1—In 3 species of citrus trees the ratio of leaf area to dry weight was determined for 3 conditions of shading (17).

Shading	Shamouti Orange	Marsh Grapefruit	Clementine Mandarin
Sun	112	90	123
Half shade	86	73	89
Shade	80	62	81

Compute the analysis of variance. Ans. Mean squares for shading and error, 942.1 and 21.8. The shading was clearly effective in decreasing the variable measured. But see example 11.14.3.

EXAMPLE 11.2.2—The experiment with mosaic virus, section 2.9, is a 2-way design with 8 replications of 2 treatments. Analyze the variance as follows:

Treatments	1	64	64
Replications	7	575	82.2
Error	7	65	9.29

The treatment components are clearly significant ($F = 6.89$; $f = 1, 7$; $P = 0.04$).

The replication components were anticipated. Note that, with $f_1 = 1$, $\sqrt{F} = \sqrt{6.89} = 2.63 = t$.

EXAMPLE 11.2.3—Calculate the mean square for treatments by each of the special 2-sample formulas given in section 10.9.

EXAMPLE 11.2.4—Calculate the mean square for discrepance from the mean square of differences, $s^2 = 18.57$, in table 2.9.1.

11.3—Comparisons among means. There is little to add to the discussion in sections 10.6 and 10.8. Both kinds of comparisons might be required in an experiment conducted by the South Carolina Truck Experiment Station (19) as part of a cooperative seed treatment trial, table 11.3.1. The designed comparison between treated and untreated seeds,

TABLE 11.3.1

NUMBER OF PLANTS EMERGING FROM 100 PLANTED SOYBEAN SEEDS, KANRO VARIETY

Treatment	Replication					Sum	Mean
	1	2	3	4	5		
Check	92	90	88	87	89	446	89.2
Arasan	98	94	93	89	95	469	93.8
Spergon	96	90	91	92	90	459	91.8
Semesan Jr.	97	95	91	90	94	467	93.4
Fermate	91	93	95	95	97	471	94.2
Sum	474	462	458	453	465	2,312	

Correction: $(2,312)^2/25 = 213,813.76$

Treatments: $\dfrac{(446)^2 + \ldots + (471)^2}{5} - C = 83.84$

Check vs. Chemicals: $\dfrac{(446)^2}{5} + \dfrac{(469 + \ldots + 471)^2}{20} - C = 67.24$

Among Chemicals: $83.84 - 67.24 = 16.60$

Source of Variation	Degrees of Freedom	Sum of Squares	Mean Square
Replication	4	49.84	
Treatments:			
Check vs. Chemicals	1	67.24	67.24
Among Chemicals	3	16.60	5.53
Error	16	86.56	5.41

For Check vs. Chemicals: $F = 67.24/5.41 = 12.43$, $F_{.01} = 8.53$

chemicals vs. check, is calculated in the way required for samples of un-equal size (section 10.16).

A feature of this comparison is the additive relation of its sum of squares with that among Chemicals, $67.24 + 16.60 = 83.84$. These comparisons are said to be *orthogonal*. You may remember that those made in section 10.8 had this property.

It is notable that designed comparisons are tested regardless of over-all significance. One or more such comparisons may be significant in an experiment whose treatments do not as a whole show a significant F.

There is no evidence of differential effects among the 4 chemicals, so it is not realistic to seek significant differences among the 6 comparisons that might be made. But to illustrate the method again, the 5% significant difference D is calculated.

$$s_{\bar{x}} = \sqrt{5.41/5} = 1.04 \text{ plants}, \ Q_{16,4} = 4.05,$$
$$D = Q s_{\bar{x}} = 4.21 \text{ plants}$$

As suspected, none of the differences among means of chemical treatments is so large. The experiment is convincing that chemical seed treatments are effective in increasing emergence of Kanro soybean plants under the conditions of the experiment but is not convincing that the chemicals differ in effectiveness.

EXAMPLE 11.3.1—In table 11.2.1, test the hypothesis that the highest level of B_{12} is as effective as the lowest. Ans. Mean square $= 0.00735$, $P = 0.04$. This is additional information not available in the earlier handling of the data.

EXAMPLE 11.3.2—Complete the foregoing by testing the hypothesis that the population mean for the middle level is the same as the mean of the other 2 levels combined. The easiest way is to compare the sum, $3.66 + 3.87$, with $2(3.75)$. Ans. Mean square $= 0.00005$. That the two comparisons are orthogonal is shown by the fact the $0.00375 + 0.00005 = 0.0074$, the Treatment sum of squares in table 11.2.1.

EXAMPLE 11.3.3—Test all differences among the shading treatments of example 11.2.1. Ans. $D = 13.5$.

At first reading, sections 11.4 and 11.5 may be omitted.

11.4—Symbolism in two-way table. The dot notation has become standard in mathematical statistics, the subscript dot representing summation. It will be used to a limited extent in what follows. For the benefit of those who prefer literal symbols, table 11.4.1 is inserted.

It is not by accident that this book is written so that the reader is largely independent of literal symbols. The results of most experiments are recorded in numbers and it is to these numbers that the experimenter must look for the information acquired. I have tried to keep the reader close to the numerical records, diverting him as little as possible with other symbolical shorthand.

TABLE 11.4.1

SYMBOLICAL REPRESENTATION OF A 2-WAY TABLE WITH a TREATMENTS AND b BLOCKS
Computing instructions and analysis of variance

Treatments, $i = 1 \ldots a$	Blocks, $j = 1 \ldots b$					Sum	Mean
	1	$\ldots$	j	$\ldots$	b		
1	X_{11}	$\ldots$	X_{1j}	$\ldots$	X_{1b}	$X_1.$	$\bar{x}_1.$
2	X_{21}	$\ldots$	X_{2j}	$\ldots$	X_{2b}	$X_2.$	$\bar{x}_2.$
.	.		.		.	.	.
.	.		.		.	.	.
i	X_{i1}	$\ldots$	X_{ij}	$\ldots$	X_{ib}	$X_i.$	$\bar{x}_i.$
.	.		.		.	.	.
.	.		.		.	.	.
a	X_{a1}	$\ldots$	X_{aj}	$\ldots$	X_{ab}	$X_a.$	$\bar{x}a.$
Sum	$X._1$	$\ldots$	$X._j$	$..$	$X._b$	$X..$	
Mean	$\bar{x}._1$	$\ldots$	$\bar{x}._j$	$\ldots$	$\bar{x}._b$		$\bar{x}..$

Correction: $C = (\Sigma X_{ij})^2/ab = X..^2/ab$

Total: $\Sigma X_{ij}^2 - C$

Treatments: $A = \dfrac{X_1.^2 + \ldots + X_a.^2}{b} - C$

Blocks: $B = \dfrac{X._1^2 + \ldots + X._b^2}{a} - C$

Discrepance: $D =$ Total $-$ (Treatments $+$ Blocks)

Source of Variation	Degrees of Freedom	Sum of Squares	Mean Square
Treatments	$a - 1$	A	$A/(a-1)$
Blocks	$b - 1$	B	$B/(b-1)$
Discrepance	$(a-1)(b-1)$	D	$D/(a-1)(b-1)$
Total	$ab - 1$	$A+B+D$	

11.5—Structure of two-way experiment. The model being used
(Model I) is
$$X_{ij} = \mu + a_i + \beta_j + \epsilon_{ij}, \; i = 1 \ldots a, j = 1 \ldots b, \; \epsilon_{ij} = N(0, \sigma),$$
$$\Sigma a_i = \Sigma \beta_j = 0,$$
where a_i stands for treatment effects, β_j for replication (litter or block)
effects, and ϵ_{ij} is a random variable representing sampling variation.

The best way to understand the model is to construct an experiment
by its use.

Let $\mu = 30$ pounds
$a_1 = 10, a_2 = 3, a_3 = 0, a_4 = -13; \Sigma a_i = 0$
$\beta_1 = 1, \beta_2 = -4, \beta_3 = 3; \Sigma \beta_j = 0$
  ϵ_{ij} drawn at random from table 3.10.1, each gain decreased by
    $\mu = 30$ pounds

In each cell of table 11.5.1, $\mu = 30$ is entered first. Next is the treatment component, differing from row to row. Following this is the block component, one in each column. In each cell, the sum of these three parts is fixed by μ, the a_i, and the β_j. Sampling variation is introduced by the fourth entry, a deviation drawn at random from table 3.10.1. These elements are normally distributed with mean zero and variance 25. According to the model, X_{ij} is the sum of the 4 entries just described.

Some features of the model are now apparent. (i) The *main effects* of the treatments are not affected by the β_j because their sum in each row

TABLE 11.5.1

EXPERIMENT CONSTRUCTED ACCORDING TO MODEL I. $\mu = 30$

Treatment	$\beta_1 = 1$	Block $\beta_2 = -4$	$\beta_3 = 3$	$X_{i.}$	$\bar{x}_{i.}$
$a_1 = 10$	30 10 1 -11	30 10 -4 -7	30 10 3 3		
	$X_{11} = 30$	$X_{12} = 29$	$X_{13} = 46$	105	35
$a_2 = 3$	30 3 1 1	30 3 -4 5	30 3 3 -3		
	$X_{21} = 35$	$X_{22} = 34$	$X_{23} = 33$	102	34
$a_3 = 0$	30 0 1 0	30 0 -4 4	30 0 3 -1		
	$X_{31} = 31$	$X_{32} = 30$	$X_{33} = 32$	93	31
$a_4 = -13$	30 -13 1 -2	30 -13 -4 -2	30 -13 3 1		
	$X_{41} = 16$	$X_{42} = 11$	$X_{43} = 21$	48	16
$X_{.j}$	112	104	132	348	
$\bar{x}_{.j}$	28	26	33		29

Source of Variation	Degrees of Freedom	Sum of Squares	Mean Square
Blocks	2	104	52
Treatments	3	702	234
Error	6	132	22

is zero; aside from the ϵ_{ij}, the sum for treatment 1 is $41 + 36 + 43 = 120$, the mean being $40 = \mu + a_1$. It is the unusual pair of small ϵ_{ij}, -11 and -7, that reduces the observed mean to 35.   (ii) In block 3, not only is $\Sigma a_i = 0$ but it happens that $\Sigma \epsilon_{i3}$ is also zero. Consequently the mean has the value fixed by the constants, $\mu + \beta_3 = 33$.   (iii) Since $\Sigma \epsilon_{ij} = -12$, the experiment mean is less than $\mu = 30$ by the mean of the ϵ_{ij}: $-12/12 = -1$.   (iv) The main point to be remembered is that the a_i balance out in each block and the β_j in each row, leaving each main effect unaffected by the other (though both are affected by the ϵ_{ij}): (v) Again additivity is emphasized. The model would not apply if the treatment constants were modified percentagewise (for example) by the blocks.

The analysis of variance has two features of interest.   (i) The mean square for Error, 22, is the sample estimate of $\sigma^2 = 25$.   (ii) The mean squares for Blocks and Treatments are inflated by the β_j and a_i; how much is shown by the component analysis of table 11.5.2, where the parametric values of the mean squares and of the components are calculated so that they may be compared with the sample estimates.

TABLE 11.5.2

COMPONENT ANALYSIS OF THE CONSTRUCTED EXPERIMENT

Source of Variation	Degrees of Freedom	Mean Square	Parameters Estimated
Block	2	52	$\sigma^2 + a\kappa_B^2$
Treatment	3	234	$\sigma^2 + b\kappa_A^2$
Error	6	22	σ^2

$$\kappa_B^2 = \frac{\Sigma \beta_j^2}{b-1} = \frac{(1)^2 + (-4)^2 + (3)^2}{2} = 13$$

$$\kappa_A^2 = \frac{\Sigma a_i^2}{a-1} = \frac{(10)^2 + (3)^2 + (0)^2 + (-13)^2}{3} = 92\frac{2}{3}$$

$s_B^2 = (52 - 22)/4 = 8$ estimates 13. $s_A^2 = (234 - 22)/3 = 71$ estimates $92\frac{2}{3}$

Error Mean Square $= 22$ estimates 25
Block Mean Square $= 52$ estimates $25 + 4(13) = 77$
Treatment Mean Square $= 234$ estimates $25 + 3(93) = 304$

In striking contrast to the analysis in chapter 10, neither component appears in the other main effect. This is true also for Model II and for mixed models; indeed, the only change would be the replacement of one or both kappas by the corresponding sigma.

Summarizing: We have constructed a Model I experiment with two sets of fixed components and a random error. Analysis of the data gives estimates of both the fixed and random parts and these are compared with the known parameters. The whole process leads to an appreciation

of the kind of approximations furnished by a real experiment whose
parameters are estimated but (due to the ϵ_{ij}) are never known.

Analogous to the foregoing is the fitting of the linear model to experimental data. The parameters are now only estimated. The process has
later uses, but the chief advantage at present is to show the make-up of
discrepance.

The data in table 11.5.3 are from a greenhouse experiment on the
growth of soybeans. Slight modifications were made for ease in computation. The table is bordered with sums, means, and deviations of the means
from the experimental mean, $\bar{x}.. = 24$ centimeters.

In table 11.5.4 is fitted the linear model,

$$\hat{X}_{ij} = \bar{x}.. + (\bar{x}_i. - \bar{x}..) + (\bar{x}._j - \bar{x}..)$$

That is, to the over-all mean, 24, in each cell is added the deviation of the
row mean and the deviation of the column mean. The sum, $\hat{X}_{ij}$, is entered directly under the observed height, X_{ij}.

TABLE 11.5.3

HEIGHTS (CENTIMETERS) OF SOYBEAN PLANTS IN 5 WEEKS
FOUR BLOCKS OR REPLICATIONS

Block	Week					Sum $X_i.$	Mean $\bar{x}_i.$	Deviation $\bar{x}_i. - \bar{x}..$
	1	2	3	4	5			
1	4	18	26	38	44	130	26	2
2	3	19	25	35	43	125	25	1
3	6	18	24	28	39	115	23	− 1
4	7	13	21	31	38	110	22	− 2
Sum, $x._j$	20	68	96	132	164	480		
Mean, $\bar{x}._j$	5	17	24	33	41	$\bar{x}.. = 24$		
Deviation, $\bar{x}._j - \bar{x}..$	−19	− 7	0	9	17			

Source of Variation	Degrees of Freedom	Sum of Squares	Mean Square
Total	19	3,250	
Weeks	4	3,120	780
Blocks	3	50	16.67
Remainder (discrepance)	12	80	6.67

The sums, $\hat{X}_{ij}$, are the heights which, under the linear model, the
plants would have if there were no further chance variation. If you
should analyze the variance of the $\hat{X}_{ij}$, you would find the discrepance
equal to zero. The difference between the $\hat{X}_{ij}$ in any pair of columns is
the same for every row. For example, in columns 1 and 3,

$$\hat{X}_{11} - \hat{X}_{13} = 7 - 26 = -19 = \hat{X}_{21} - \hat{X}_{23} = \hat{X}_{31} - \hat{X}_{33} = \hat{X}_{41} - \hat{X}_{43}$$

TABLE 11.5.4
LINEAR MODEL FITTED TO SAMPLE DATA.   SOYBEAN HEIGHTS

Block		Week 1		Week 2		Week 3		Week 4		Week 5	
1	X_{1j}		4		18		26		38		44
	$\bar{x}_{..}$	24		24		24		24		24	
	$\bar{x}_{1.} - \bar{x}_{..}$	2		2		2		2		2	
	$\bar{x}_{.j} - \bar{x}_{..}$	−19	7*	−7	19	0	26	9	35	17	43
	d_{1j}	−3		−1		0		3		1	
2	X_{2j}		3		19		25		35		43
	$\bar{x}_{..}$	24		24		24		24		24	
	$\bar{x}_{2.} - \bar{x}_{..}$	1		1		1		1		1	
	$\bar{x}_{.j} - \bar{x}_{..}$	−19	6	−7	18	0	25	9	34	17	42
	d_{2j}	−3		1		0		1		1	
3	X_{3j}		6		18		24		28		39
	$\bar{x}_{..}$	24		24		24		24		24	
	$\bar{x}_{3.} - \bar{x}_{..}$	−1		−1		−1		−1		−1	
	$\bar{x}_{.j} - \bar{x}_{..}$	−19	4	−7	16	0	23	9	32	17	40
	d_{3j}	2		2		1		−4		−1	
4	X_{4j}		7		13		21		31		38
	$\bar{x}_{..}$	24		24		24		24		24	
	$\bar{x}_{4.} - \bar{x}_{..}$	−2		−2		−2		−2		−2	
	$\bar{x}_{.j} - \bar{x}_{..}$	−19	3	−7	15	0	22	9	31	17	39
	d_{4j}	4		−2		−1		0		−1	

* $\hat{X}_{11} = \bar{x}_{..} + (\bar{x}_{1.} - \bar{x}_{..}) + (\bar{x}_{.1} - \bar{x}_{..}) = 24 + 2 - 19 = 7.$

A similar statement holds for pairs of rows. This fact has a useful practical application. One can easily assess the magnitude of the discrepance in a 2-way table by looking across the pairs of rows and down the pairs of columns, observing the failure of the differences to be alike.

In the last line of each block are the differences,

$$d_{ij} = X_{ij} - \hat{X}_{ij}$$

These discrepancies between observed and calculated heights have this notable property:

$$\Sigma d_{ij}^2 = \text{Sum of squares for discrepance}$$

In verification, $(-3)^2 + (-1)^2 + \ldots + (-1)^2 = 80$, which checks with the discrepance in table 11.5.3. This emphasizes the manner in which the mean square for discrepance estimates σ^2 in a table like 11.5.1. Notice that the d_{ij} in the sample are the analogs of the ϵ_{ij} in the population.

11.6—Randomized blocks in a field trial. The foregoing design is widely used in field plot experimentation. The agronomist capitalizes his knowledge that fertility differences increase with distance. He tries all treatments on a block of plots lying as closely together as possible, then replicates such blocks. Differences between blocks do not enter the estimate of error.

Each block is divided into a number of plots equal to the number of treatments. Now comes a vital step in the design. Since adjacent plots tend to have the same fertility, this similarity decreasing with distance, the yields of adjacent plots are not independent. To overcome this difficulty, randomization is necessary. The random arrangement also serves other purposes among which is the equalization of error over all treatment differences. In each block the position of the treatments must be left to chance.

To get an estimate of experimental error, two or more blocks (replications) are required. Precision increases with the number of replications.

BLOCK I		BLOCK II		BLOCK V	
D	29.3	B	33.0	D	28.8
B	33.3	A	34.0	C	35.8
C	30 8	C	34 3	B	34.5
A	32 3	D	26.0	A	36.5

BLOCK III		BLOCK IV	
D	29 8	B	36.8
A	34 3	A	35.0
B	36.3	D	28.0
C	35.3	C	32 3

FIG. 11.6.1—Field plan of an experiment with four strains, *A*, *B*, *C*, and *D*, of Gallipoli wheat. Yields are in pounds per plot.

Figure 11.6.1 is the plan of a field layout for testing 4 strains of Gallipoli wheat in each of 5 blocks (13). Narrow plots extending the length of the block increase the precision of the experiment. The reason is that there may be considerable variation in fertility from one end of the block to the other; the long, narrow plots tend to share and equalize such differences among themselves. Many experimenters do not follow this practice. If the plots lie across the blocks, two plots in one block tend to differ more than the corresponding plots in adjacent blocks. The result is that the randomized blocks design is often less efficient than a random arrangement like that of chapter 10. The object of the present design is to make the plots within a block as much alike as possible. The differences should be from block to block where they will be eliminated from error. If square plots are desirable, see the next section.

The data, together with the analysis of variance, are recorded in table 11.6.1. Differences among strains are convincing. Applying the method of section 10.6, $D = 2.8$ pounds, showing that it is the fourth strain which is poor, the other three being undifferentiated.

Note the coefficient of variation, $C = \sqrt{2.19}/32.8$, only 4.5%, indicating unusually precise field plot technique. This is reflected in the small significant difference, 2.7 pounds, only 8% of the mean.

The efficiency of a randomized blocks experiment as compared to a completely random arrangement of the plots is the inverse ratio of their estimates of error; the less the error, the more efficient is the design.

TABLE 11.6.1

YIELDS OF FOUR STRAINS OF GALLIPOLI WHEAT PLANTED IN FIVE RANDOMIZED BLOCKS
Pounds per plot

Strain	Block 1	2	3	4	5	Sum	Mean
A	32.3	34.0	34.3	35.0	36.5	172.1	34.4
B	33.3	33.0	36.3	36.8	34.5	173.9	34.8
C	30.8	34.3	35.3	32.3	35.8	168.5	33.7
D	29.3	26.0	29.8	28.0	28.8	141.9	28.4
Sum	125.7	127.3	135.7	132.1	135.6	656.4	32.8

Source of Variation	Degrees of Freedom	Sum of Squares	Mean Square
Blocks	4	21.46	5.36
Strains	3	134.45	44.82
Error	12	26.26	2.19

For Strains: $F = 44.82/2.19 = 20$, $F_{.01} = 5.95$

Assuming that the two designs are laid out on the same plots, the relative efficiency of the blocks is (8, 14)

$$\frac{(b-1)M_B + b(a-1)M_E}{(ab-1)M_E},$$

the mean squares, M_B and M_E, being taken from the data of a randomized blocks experiment which has been performed. Using table 11.6.1 as illustration, $M_B = 5.36$, $M_E = 2.19$, $b = 5$, $a = 4$,

$$\text{Relative Efficiency} = \frac{s_R^2}{s_B^2} = \frac{(5-1)(5.36) + (5)(4-1)(2.19)}{(20-1)(2.19)} = 130\%$$

That is, $s_R^2/s_B^2 = 1.30$, where R and B refer to random and blocks arrangements. To get the same standard error of the mean, one must choose n and b so that

$$\frac{s_B^2}{b} = \frac{s_R^2}{n}$$

Solving for n, we got the number of completely randomized replications necessary to match the efficiency of b blocks:

$$n = \frac{b s_R^2}{s_B^2} = 1.30 \, b$$

For the wheat, $n = (1.30)(5) = 6.5$, the number of replications in the completely random layout to equal the 5 randomized blocks. This means 30% extra plots or 30% additional cost of the random experiment.

The efficiency is increased at the expense of a loss in degrees of freedom, from 16 for the random arrangement to 12 in the blocks. This is taken into consideration in a formula due to Fisher (10):

$$\text{Relative Amount of Information} = \frac{(f_B + 1)(f_R + 3) \, s_R^2}{(f_B + 3)(f_R + 1) \, s_B^2}$$

$$= \frac{(12 + 1)(16 + 3)}{(12 + 3)(16 + 1)}(1.30) = 126\%$$

The formula consists of a factor, made up entirely from degrees of freedom, applied to the ratio, s_R^2/s_B^2. The latter factor is got from the relative efficiency formula.

EXAMPLE 11.6.1—At Hudson, Iowa, in 1949 the yields (bushels per acre) of 7 lines of soybeans were abstracted from a larger experiment (9):

Lines	Block			
	1	2	3	4
A	21.3	19.7	28.7	27.3
B	27.7	15.9	28.1	29.0
C	22.0	22.1	22.0	26.9
D	28.3	20.7	26.0	34.1
E	25.1	20.1	24.9	29.8
F	28.1	19.4	31.5	28.7
G	32.7	26.7	34.2	35.6

Calculate the analysis of variance:

Source of Variation	Degrees of Freedom	Sum of Squares	Mean Square
Replications	3	347.78	
Treatments	6	215.47	35.91
Error	18	111.75	6.21

EXAMPLE 11.6.2—In the soybean experiment, show that strain G differs significantly from A, B, C, and E. Ans. $D = 5.8$.

EXAMPLE 11.6.3—Set 95% confidence limits on the difference, δ, between strains G and F. Ans. $-0.4 \leq \delta \leq 11.2$. If it seems reasonable, I would not hesitate to accept this difference as a population characteristic.

EXAMPLE 11.6.4—Calculate the coefficient of variation in the soybean experiment.   Ans. 9.5%.

11.7—Latin square. In randomized blocks designs the plots in a block should be as nearly alike as possible, each plot partaking of all the variability in the block. Often this cannot be arranged. Some treatments require almost square plots so that fertility changes within the block decrease the sensitivity of the experiment. For this and other reasons it may be advantageous to put the plots in columns across the blocks, assigning every treatment once to each column as well as to each block. This requires as many columns and blocks as treatments. Such a design is called a Latin square. For 4 treatments *A*, *B*, *C*, *D* it may be like this:

A	*B*	*C*	*D*
B	*C*	*D*	*A*
C	*D*	*A*	*B*
D	*A*	*B*	*C*

Blocks and columns contribute equally to the estimate of every treatment mean. In the analysis of variance, fertility differences between columns as well as rows (blocks) are eliminated from error. In agronomic experiments the Latin square tends to increase efficiency, which means that less replications are required for the same precision, or greater precision for the same number of replications.

The model for a Latin square experiment (Model I) is

$$X_{ijk} = \mu + \alpha_i + \beta_j + \gamma_k + \epsilon_{ijk}; i, j, \text{ and } k = 1 \ldots a; \epsilon_{ijk} = \mathcal{N}(0, \sigma),$$

where α, β, and γ indicate treatment, row, and column effects with the usual restrictions.

Table 11.7.1 shows the field layout as well as the yields of an experiment involving the spacing of millet plants (15). The sums for rows and columns are supplemented by a summary for treatments. One additional effect (Columns) is calculated and entered in the analysis of variance. The estimate of error is got by subtracting the sums of squares of the three main effects from Total.

The component analysis involves only one addition to that of randomized blocks. I have assumed in table 11.7.2 that columns and rows are variables but treatments fixed, a mixed model, the only distinction being in the use of σ^2 and κ^2.

In numerous situations other than field tests the Latin square is effective in controlling 2 independent variables of which the experimenter has predictive knowledge. In animal nutrition, the effects of both litter and condition or breed and condition may be removed from the estimates of Treatment and Error. Some of the difficulties arising from successive treatments of the same individual may be avoided by use of the Latin square as a device for randomizing the sequence of treatments. It insures

TABLE 11.7.1

YIELDS (GRAMS) OF PLOTS OF MILLET ARRANGED IN A LATIN SQUARE
Spacings: A, 2-inch; B, 4; C, 6; D, 8; E, 10

Row	Column					Sum
	1	2	3	4	5	
1	B: 257	E: 230	A: 279	C: 287	D: 202	1,255
2	D: 245	A: 283	E: 245	B: 280	C: 260	1,313
3	E: 182	B: 252	C: 280	D: 246	A: 250	1,210
4	A: 203	C: 204	D: 227	E: 193	B: 259	1,086
5	C: 231	D: 271	B: 266	A: 334	E: 338	1,440
Sum	1,118	1,240	1,297	1,340	1,309	6,304

	Summary by Spacing					
	A: 2″	B: 4″	C: 6″	D: 8″	E: 10″	
Sum	1,349	1,314	1,262	1,191	1,188	6,304
Mean	269.8	262.8	252.4	238.2	237.6	252.2

Correction: $(6,304)^2/25 = 1,589,617$

Total: $(257)^2 + \ldots + (338)^2 - 1,589,617 = 36,571$

Rows: $\dfrac{(1,255)^2 + \ldots + (1,440)^2}{5} - 1,589,617 = 13,601$

Columns: $\dfrac{(1,118)^2 + \ldots + (1,309)^2}{5} - 1,589,617 = 6,146$

Spacings: $\dfrac{(1,349)^2 + \ldots + (1,188)^2}{5} - 1,589,617 = 4,156$

Remainder: 12,668

Source of Variation	Degrees of Freedom	Sum of Squares	Mean Square
Total	24	36,571	
Rows	4	13,601	3,400
Columns	4	6,146	1,536
Spacings	4	4,156	1,039
Error	12	12,668	1,056

TABLE 11.7.2

COMPONENT ANALYSIS IN LATIN SQUARE

Source of Variation	Degrees of Freedom	Mean Square	Components
Rows, B	$a - 1$	M_B	$\sigma^2 + a\sigma_B^2$
Columns, G	$a - 1$	M_G	$\sigma^2 + a\sigma_G^2$
Treatments, A	$a - 1$	M_A	$\sigma^2 + a\kappa_A^2$
Error	$(a - 1)(a - 2)$	M_E	σ^2

balance of both treatments and individuals in the succession of periods (example 11.7.3). As in the field, one may cope with 2-way positional differences in a chamber or on a greenhouse bench.

A rough rule for randomization of Latin squares is this: Having written down any systematic arrangement of the letters, rearrange at random the rows and columns; then assign the treatments at random to the letters. For refinements, see Fisher and Yates (12).

From the mean squares in table 11.7.1 one concludes that the spacing effect is negligible, the variation being just that to be expected in sampling from a single normal population of yields. But the design of the experiment included a feature not yet brought into the analysis—the regression of yield on spacing. The summary by spacing in table 11.7.1 shows mean plot yield decreasing with wider spacing. It appears, then, that the sum

TABLE 11.7.3
ANALYSIS OF REGRESSION OF SPACING MEAN ON WIDTH OF SPACING.
MILLET EXPERIMENT

Source of Variation	Degrees of Freedom	Sum of Squares	Mean Square
Regression	1	3,960	3,960
Deviations	3	196	65 7
Error (table 11.7.1)	12		1,056

For regression, $F = 3,960/1,056 = 3.75$, $F_{05} = 4.75$

of squares for spacings, 4,156, contains a considerable portion attributable to linear regression, and that it will be informative to subdivide this sum accordingly. We shall need Σx^2, Σxy, and Σy^2 in the manner of chapter 6. The latter is already calculated, 4,156. The other two are conveniently computed from means, then expanded to the item basis (characteristic of sums of squares and mean squares) through multiplication by $a = 5$.

$$\Sigma x^2/5 = (2)^2 + \ldots + (10)^2 - (30)^2/5 = 40$$

$$\Sigma xy/5 = (2)(269.8) + \ldots + (10)(237.6) - \frac{(30)(1,260.8)}{5} = -178$$

The desired sums of squares and products, therefore, are 200 and -890. Finally, Σy^2 is separated into the two parts: (i) attributable to regression, $(\Sigma xy)^2/\Sigma x^2 = (-890)^2/200 = 3,960$; and (ii) deviations from regression, $4,156 - 3,960 = 196$. The revised analysis of variance (omitting rows and columns) is in table 11.7.3.

It now appears that most of the variation in yield is associated with regression, deviations from regression being trivial. To put it another way, the major portion of the sum of squares for spacings belongs to the single degree of freedom for regression. Even so, this regression is not significant so that there might be no relation between spacing and yield in the population. It is interesting, however, that in the sample the notable increase of yield per plant due to freedom from competition in the wider spacings failed to compensate for the fewer plants. Notice the sizable coefficient of variation, $C = \sqrt{1{,}056}/252.2 = 13\%$, which may explain the non-significance of the rather reasonable sample regression.

Since the number of replications in the Latin square is equal to the number of treatments, the experimenter is ordinarily limited to 8 or 10 treatments if he uses this design. For 4 or less treatments, the degrees of freedom for error are fewer than desirable, $(a - 1)(a - 2) = (3)(2) = 6$ for the 4 × 4. This difficulty can be remedied by replicating the squares (example 11.7.4).

The relative efficiency of a Latin square experiment as compared to complete randomization is

$$\frac{M_B + M_G + (a - 1)\, M_E}{(a + 1)\, M_R}$$

Substituting the millet data:

$$\text{Relative Efficiency} = \frac{s_R^2}{s_L^2} = \frac{3{,}400 + 1{,}536 + (5 - 1)(1{,}056)}{(5 + 1)(1{,}056)} = 145\%,$$

a gain of 45% over complete randomization.

There may be some interest in knowing the relative efficiency as compared to a randomized blocks experiment in which either rows or columns were lacking. In the millet experiment, since the column mean square was small (this may have been an accident of sampling), it might have been omitted and the rows retained as blocks. The relative efficiency of the Latin square is

$$\frac{M_G + (a - 1)M_E}{aM_E} = \frac{1{,}536 + (5 - 1)\,1{,}056}{(5)(1{,}056)} = 109\%$$

Kempthorne (14) reminds us that this may not be a realistic comparison. For the blocks experiment the shape of the plots would presumably have been changed, improving the efficiency of that experiment. In this millet experiment, appropriately shaped plots in randomized blocks might well have compensated for the column control.

In experiments where the comparisons have not been planned, all comparisons among means may be made as in section 10.6.

EXAMPLE 11.7.1—Here is a Latin square for easy computation. Treatments are indicated by A, B, and C.

| | Columns | | |
Rows	1	2	3
1	B: 23	A: 17	C: 29
2	A: 16	C: 25	B: 16
3	C: 24	B: 18	A: 12

The mean squares are: rows, 21; columns, 3; treatments, 93; remainder, 3.

EXAMPLE 11.7.2—Fit the linear model for Latin squares to the data of example 11.7.1. Verify the fitting by the relation, $\Sigma d_{ijk}^2 = 6$.

EXAMPLE 11.7.3—In experiments affecting the milk yield of dairy cows the great variation among individuals requires large numbers of animals for evaluating moderate differences. Efforts to apply several treatments successively to the same cow are complicated by the decreasing milk flow, by the shapes of the lactation curves, by carry-over effects, and by presumed correlation among the errors, ϵ_{ijk}. The effort was made to control these difficulties by the use of several pairs of orthogonal Latin squares (7), the columns representing cows, the rows successive periods during lactation, the treatments being A = roughage, B = limited grain, C = full grain.

For this example, a single square is presented, no effort being made to deal with carry-over effects. The entries are pounds of milk for a 6-week period.

| | Cow | | |
Period	1	2	3
I	A: 608	B: 885	C: 940
II	B: 715	C: 1087	A: 766
III	C: 844	A: 711	B: 832

Source of Variation	Degrees of Freedom	Sum of Squares	Mean Square
Periods	2	5,900	2,950
Cows	2	47,214	23,607
Treatments	2	103,436	51,718
Error	2	4,843	2,422

In some late researches by Patterson (18) and by Lucas (16) nonlinear carry-over effects are examined. If carry-over effects are present, the error for direct effects is biased downward. Corrections for nonlinearity may be calculated, but Lucas considers them of no practical importance in work with dairy cows.

EXAMPLE 11.7.4—One 3 × 3 square, with only 2 degrees of freedom for error, is low in sensitivity. With 5 such squares, Cochran *et al.* reported an analysis of the total digestible nutrients consumed, presumably unaffected by carry over:

Source of Variation	Degrees of Freedom	Mean Square
Squares or Groups	4	39,484
Rows (Periods) within Squares	10	4,053
Columns (Cows) within Squares	10	10,534
Rations	2	266,934
Combined Error	10	1,410
Remainder	8	1,503

The Remainder is the interaction between Rations and Groups, an effect to be explained in chapter 12.

11.8—Size of experiment. The methods of section 10.18 are directly applicable to randomized blocks and Latin squares. An illustration may be drawn from the soybean data of example 11.6.2. The difference detected was $D/\bar{x}.. = 5.8/26.3 = 22\%$. Suppose it were decided worth while to try the first 6 lines in a new randomized blocks experiment which would $(P = .75)$ detect $(P = 0.05)$ differences as small as 10% of the mean; 10% of 25.3 = 2.5 bushels per acre. So $\delta = 2.5$. Also, for treatments, $a = 6$, $s_0 = \sqrt{6.21} = 2.49$ bushels per acre and $f_0 = 18$. Try the too-large number of blocks, $b = 31$. Then $f = (6 - 1)(31 - 1) = 150$, $Q_{6,150} = 4.09$, $F_{150,18} = 1.33$. As a preliminary estimate,

$$b = \frac{(4.09)^2(6.21)(1.33)}{(2.5)^2} = 23$$

This number of replications, $f = (6 - 1)(23 - 1) = 110$, $Q_{6,110} = 4.11$, $F_{110,18} = 1.33$, would likely detect

$$\delta = \frac{(4.11)(2.49)\sqrt{1.33}}{\sqrt{23}} = 2.5$$

as specified.

Few would think of putting in 23 replications at any one time or place. Instead, if the varieties are promising they will be tried in smaller experiments at a number of localities for several years.

Suppose it is planned to try the 6 varieties in randomized blocks at 4 places over a number of seasons. At each place in the next season, 3 replications are decided upon. Two questions are of interest. First, what per cent difference (coefficient of variation) is likely (3 in 4) to be detected $(P = 0.05)$ at each place during the first season? It may seem reasonable to assume a common σ_0 and to use $s_0 = 2.49/25.3 = 9.8\%$ with $f_0 = 18$. In the prospective experiment, $f = 10$; so $Q_{6,10} = 4.91$ and $F_{10,18} = 1.42$. The formula gives δ as per cent of mean:

$$\delta = \frac{(4.91)(9.8)\sqrt{1.42}}{\sqrt{3}} = 33\%$$

The next question is, "What per cent difference is likely to be detected in the 4 places combined?" If we make the rather optimistic assumption that $s_0 = 9.8\%$ is a reasonable estimate of the per cent error for all places, then $f = (4)(10) = 40$, $Q_{6,40} = 4.23$, $F_{40,18} = 1.35$, and

$$\delta = \frac{(4.23)(9.8)\sqrt{1.35}}{\sqrt{12}} = 14\%$$

Admittedly these are rough forecasts, but they are helpful in planning an experimental program. (Zero variety-place interaction is being assumed. For the analysis of variance of such a group of experiments see chapter 12.)

EXAMPLE 11.8.1—A Latin square is planned to test 6 varieties. From experience the investigator is willing to set lower and upper 50% limits on σ as 6 and 8 bushels per acre. Then $s_0 = 7$ bushels per acre and (from section 10.18) $f_0 = 11$. For the prospective experiment, $f = 20$, $Q_{6,20} = 4.45$ and $F_{20,11} = 1.49$. Calculate $\delta = 16$ bu./acre.

11.9—Missing data. Accidents often result in the loss of data in one or more of the cells of a 2-way table. Crops may be destroyed, animals may die, or errors may be made in recording. A missing item nullifies the addition theorem for sums of squares. Consequently, one cannot use the calculational methods which have been presented. But the theory behind these methods can be applied, giving correct analysis of experimental data with missing items (section 12.17). Fortunately for the user of statistical methods, it turns out that the missing data can be estimated from the theory and entered in the vacant cells of the table. For only one missing item, application of the usual methods (with modification of degrees of freedom) gives an approximate analysis of variance which can be made exact by correction of a bias in the sum of squares for treatments.

In randomized blocks, a single missing datum is estimated by the formula (1, 26),

$$X = \frac{aT + bB - S}{(a - 1)(b - 1)},$$

where
   $a =$ number of treatments
   $b =$ number of blocks
   $T =$ sum of items with same treatment as missing item
   $B =$ sum of items in same block as missing item
   $S =$ sum of all observed items.

As an example, suppose the datum 29.3 pounds were missing from table 11.6.1, block 1, strain D. Deducting this yield from the sums for the block, strain, and total, we get what these quantities would have been had the plot yield been lost:

$$B = 125.7 - 29.3 = 96.4, \ T = 141.9 - 29.3 = 112.6, \ S = 656.4 - 29.3$$
$$= 627.1, \ b = 5, \ a = 4$$

Then

$$X = \frac{(4)(112.6) + (5)(96.4) - 627.1}{(4 - 1)(5 - 1)} = 25.4 \text{ pounds}$$

This value is entered in the table as the yield of the missing plot. The analysis of variance then proceeds as usual with 2 modifications; the degrees of freedom for Total and Error are each decreased by unity, and the sum of squares for Treatment is decreased by

$$\text{Correction for Bias} = \frac{\{B - (a-1)X\}^2}{a(a-1)} = \frac{\{96.4 - (4-1)(25.4)\}^2}{4(4-1)} = 34.00$$

The analysis of the wheat data, with 25.4 pounds substituted for the supposed missing value, is

Blocks	4	35.39	
Strains	3	171.36 − 34.00 = 137.36	45.79
Error	12 − 1 = 11	17.33	1.58

Comparison of this with table 11.6.1 is both consoling and a warning: Despite the loss of the plot yield we have an unbiased analysis of the remaining data, but the lost information is not recovered. The loss of 1 plot in 20 means the loss of one-twentieth of the money invested in the experiment. The best that can be done is to cash in on the remainder.

For the Latin square, the formulas are:

$$X = \frac{a(R + C + T) - 2S}{(a - 1)(a - 2)}$$

Deduction for Bias $= \dfrac{[S - R - C - (a - 1)T]^2}{[(a - 1)(a - 2)]^2}$,

where a is the number of treatments, rows, or columns.

To illustrate, suppose that in example 11.7.3 the first item, 608 pounds, were missing. Then

$$R = 885 + 940 = 1,825$$
$$C = 715 + 844 = 1,559$$
$$T = 711 + 766 = 1,477$$
$$S = 715 + \ldots + 832 = 6,780$$

$$X = \frac{3(1,825 + 1,559 + 1,477) - 2(6,780)}{(3 - 1)(3 - 2)} = 512 \text{ pounds}$$

$$\text{Bias} = \frac{[6,780 - 1,825 - 1,559 - (3 - 1)(1,477)]^2}{[(3 - 1)(3 - 2)]^2} = 48,841$$

After putting the estimated missing yield, 512 pounds, in the table, the analysis of variance gives

Treatment Sum of Squares	129,655
Less Bias	48,841
Unbiased Treatment	80,814

The final analysis is

Rows	2	9,847	
Columns	2	68,185	
Treatments	2	80,814	40,407
Error	1		2,773

Comparison with the original analysis gives some idea of the numerical changes due to the loss of the yield of one cow. No worth-while conclusions are likely to flow from a single 3 × 3 square. Example 11.7.4 shows how to analyze the data from several such squares.

Two or more missing data require more complicated methods. The direct least squares solution of section 12.17 may be applied to randomized blocks. But for a few missing values an iterative scheme may be used for estimation, followed by special methods for calculating unbiased estimates of the sums of squares for treatments.

For ease of illustration the simple data in table 11.9.1 seem adequate. Start by entering a reasonable value for one of the missing data, say

TABLE 11.9.1
RANDOMIZED BLOCKS EXPERIMENT WITH 2 MISSING DATA

Treatments	Blocks			Sums
	1	2	3	
A	6	5	4	15
B	15	X_{22}	8	23
C	X_{31}	15	12	27
Sums	21	20	24	65

$X_{22} = 10.5$. This could be $x_{..} = 9$, but both the block and treatment means are above average, so 10.5 seems better. From the formula, X_{31} is now estimated as

$$X_{31} = \frac{(3)(27) + (3)(21) - 75.5}{(3-1)(3-1)} = 17.1$$

Substituting $X_{31} = 17.1$ in the table, try for a better estimate of X_{22} by using the formula for X_{22} missing:

$$X_{22} = \frac{(3)(23) + (3)(20) - 82.1}{4} = 11.7$$

With this revised estimate of X_{22}, re-estimate X_{31}:

$$X_{31} = \frac{(3)(27) + (3)(21) - 76.7}{4} = 16.8$$

Finally, with this new value of X_{31} in the table, calculate $X_{22} = 11.8$. One stops because, with $X_{22} = 11.8$, no change occurs when X_{31} is recalculated.

The 2 estimated data are put in the table and the analysis of variance calculated. Only one result is useful, the sum of squares for error with $4 - 2 = 2$ degrees of freedom (one deducted for each missing plot). This sum of squares is 6.40.

Returning to the original table, ignoring the empty cells, calculate the total sum of squares,

$$\text{Total: } \Sigma X_{ij}^2 - C = 735 - (65)^2/7 = 131.43$$

Also calculate the sum of squares for blocks, using the original data:

$$\text{Blocks: } \frac{(21)^2 + (20)^2}{2} + \frac{(24)^2}{3} - C = 8.93$$

The unbiased estimate of the treatment sum of squares is got as follows:

		Sum of Squares
Total, Original Data		131.43
Blocks, Original Data	8.93	
Error, Completed Data	6.40	15.33
Treatment Sum of Squares		116.10

The final analysis of variance is

Treatments	2	116.10	58.05
Error	2	6.40	3.20

The complete analysis of variance of the augmented table (including estimates of the missing data) would have given the biased sum of squares for treatments as 144. The difference, $144 - 116.1 = 27.9$, is the bias, not now needed.

For the Latin square with two or more missing data, Kempthorne (14, page 198) outlines a method for making an unbiased test. Never having seen a Latin square with 2 missing plots, I constructed a 4×4 by the linear model (section 11.7). I took

$$\mu = 12$$
$$a_i = -5, -1, 2, 4; \kappa_A^2 = \Sigma a_i^2/(4-1) = 15.3$$
$$\beta_j = -2, -1, 0, 3$$
$$\gamma_k = -4, 0, 2, 2$$
$$\epsilon_{ijk} = \mathcal{N}(0, 1)\text{(from table 3.2.1, each deviation divided by 10)}$$

After eliminating 2 plots at random, I had the data of table 11.9.2. (The values eliminated were $X_{111} = 1$ and $X_{324} = 18$.)

The first step is to supply estimates of the missing values. The recursion method described above is now applied to the missing plot formula for the Latin square. Results: $X_{111} = 2.2$, $X_{324} = 12.3$.

Next, analyze the variance of the augmented square (that is, including the two X). The only part needed is the sum of squares for error, $SSE_s = 5.33$.

Third, treating table 11.9.2 as randomized blocks in rows and columns,

TABLE 11.9.2

FOUR-BY-FOUR LATIN SQUARE WITH 2 MISSING PLOTS

Rows	Columns				Sum
	1	2	3	4	
1	A X_{111}	B 8	C 17	D 15	40
2	B 6	C 14	D 16	A 9	45
3	C 10	D X_{324}	A 7	B 12	29
4	D 15	A 9	B 16	C 19	59
Sum	31	31	56	55	173

ignoring the letters, supply a new pair of X by use of the formula for missing plots in randomized blocks: $X_{11} = 11.7$, $X_{32} = 6.1$.

Fourth, analyze the variance of the augmented randomized blocks. What is needed is the sum of squares for error, $SSE_B = 119.49$.

Finally, analyze the variance of the Latin square, using $SSE_B - SSE_S = 119.49 - 5.33 = 114.16$ as the sum of squares for Treatments, table 11.9.3.

TABLE 11.9.3

ANALYSIS OF VARIANCE OF LATIN SQUARE WITH 2 MISSING PLOTS

Source of Variation	Degrees of Freedom	Sum of Squares	Mean Square	Parameters Estimated
Treatments	3	114.16	38.05	$\sigma^2 + 4\kappa^2$ *
Error	4	5.33	1.33	σ^2

$5.33 = SSE_S$, $114.16 = SSE_B - SSE_S = 119.49 - 5.33$
1.33 estimates $\sigma^2 = 1$, $(38.05 - 1.33)/4 = 9.18$ estimates $\kappa^2 = 15.3$

*Ignoring modifications due to missing plots.

You will see that we have been moderately successful in estimating the known parameters. The method applies to more than 2 missing values, one degree of freedom being deducted from Error for each item supplied.

This is the last of these signposts for the reader pursuing a short course. He will be able to read the earlier sections in most following chapters.

11.10—Non-conformity to model. Transformations. We have been using a model which specifies additivity of the effects together with normal and independent distribution of the errors with constant variance, $e = N(0, \sigma)$. It is not unusual to encounter samples from populations in which this model is violated. One way to meet the situation is to change the model; a variety of nonparametric methods have been proposed (sections 5.7–5.10, 7.12). Another way is to change the scale of measurement by a *transformation*. In samples from certain specified populations exact solutions may be attained (11) but usually the sample is a mixture. Ordinarily there are approximate solutions which seem to be satisfactory (3). Three of these will be described below.

Anormality, non-additivity, and heterogeneity of variance ordinarily appear together. It would be ideal if a transformation could remedy all the difficulties, but that doesn't often happen. Additivity is the most essential requirement and homogeneity of variance next.

Theoretically it is in the population that the model must be satisfied. If the sampling is from binomial or Poisson populations, the variance is known to be related to the mean (chapter 16). For such cases, the appropriate transformation can be specified. But often one has to look at the sample for guidance. Sometimes widely differing ranges within the treatments give a clue. Also, see (23).

Additivity in a sample can be tested (section 11.14) by a method due to Tukey (21). The test is applied if there is doubt about the necessity for a transformation or about the success of one.

11.11—Square root trnsformation for enumeration data. Counts of variables, such as weeds per plot or insects caught in traps, tend to be distributed in Poisson fashion with variance proportional to the mean and non-additive effects. A transformation to $\sqrt{X}$ (or to $\sqrt{(X + 1)}$ if some counts are small) is often effective. An example is the record of poppy plants in oats (2) shown in table 11.11.1. The differing ranges would lead to the suspicion of heterogeneous variance. If the error mean square were calculated, it would be an average, too large for testing differences among C, D, and E and too small for A and B.

In table 11.11.2 the square roots of the numbers are recorded and analyzed. The ranges in the several treatments are now similar. Additivity will be evidenced in section 11.14.

That there are differences among treatments is obvious in either table; it is unnecessary to look at F. For making all comparisons, the confidence interval for the mean differences (section 10.6) is

$$D = 4.51 \ \sqrt{4.06/4} = 4.54$$

TABLE 11.11.1
NUMBER OF POPPY PLANTS IN OATS
Plants per 3¾ square feet

Block	Treatment				
	A	B	C	D	E
1	438	538	77	17	18
2	442	422	61	31	26
3	319	377	157	87	77
4	380	315	52	16	20
Mean	395	413	87	38	35
Range	123	223	105	71	59

TABLE 11.11.2
SQUARE ROOTS OF THE POPPY NUMBERS IN TABLE 11.11.1

Block	A	B	C	D	E
1	20.9	23.2	8.8	4.1	4.2
2	21.0	20.5	7.8	5.6	5.1
3	17.9	19.4	12.5	9.3	8.8
4	19.5	17.7	7.2	4.0	4.5
Mean	19.8	20.2	9.1	5.8	5.6

Source of Variation	Degrees of Freedom	Sum of Squares	Mean Square
Blocks	3	22.65	
Treatments	4	865.44	216.36
Error	12	48.69	4.06

This shows that there may be no differences among the three effective treatments and no difference between the two that are ineffective (A was check), but that C, D, and E differ significantly from A and B.

After a test or comparison is made, retransformation to the original units gives interpretable information. The correct estimates of the mean counts are: $\bar{x}_A = (19.8)^2 = 392$ plants, $\bar{x}_B = 408$, $\bar{x}_C = 83$, $\bar{x}_D = 34$, and $\bar{x}_E = 31$ plants. Comparison with the original estimates shows the effects of non-additivity and heterogeneous variance.

EXAMPLE 11.11.1—The numbers of wireworms counted in the plots of a Latin square (6) following soil fumigations in the previous year were:

		Columns			
Rows	1	2	3	4	5
1	P 3	O 2	N 5	K 1	M 4
2	M 6	K 0	O 6	N 4	P 4
3	O 4	M 9	K 1	P 6	N 5
4	N 17	P 8	M 8	O 9	K 0
5	K 4	N 4	P 2	M 4	O 8

Since these are such small numbers, transform to $\sqrt{(X + 1)}$. The first number, 3, becomes $\sqrt{(3 + 1)} = 2$, etc.

Analyze the variance. Ans. Mean square for Treatments, 1.4457; for Error, 0.3259.

EXAMPLE 11.11.2—Treatment O was "check," but it is otherwise not distinguished. Calculate $D = 1.15$ and show that K is followed by significantly less wireworms than M, N, and O.

EXAMPLE 11.11.3—Estimate the average numbers of wireworms per plot for the several treatments. Ans. K, 0.99; M, 6.08; N, 6.40; O, 5.55; P, 4.38.

11.12—Arcsin transformation for proportions. If the variable consists of the proportion of individuals affected, the distribution tends to be binomial in form. The transformation is to the angle whose sine is the square root of the proportion or percentage, table 11.12.1.

This table weights more heavily the small percentages which have small variance.   Its application is shown in table 11.12.2, the proportion of plants infested with stem canker (9).

TABLE 11.12.2

PROPORTION OF SOYBEAN PLANTS INFECTED WITH STEM CANKER, HUDSON, IOWA, 1949

| Block | Varieties | | | | | |
	A	B	C	D	E	F
1	19.3	10.1	25.2	14.0	3.3	3.1
2	29.2	34.7	36.5	30.2	35.8	9.6
3	1.0	14.0	23.4	7.2	1.1	1.0
4	6.4	5.6	12.9	8.9	2.0	1.0

Arcsin $\sqrt{\text{Proportion}}$

	A	B	C	D	E	F
1	26.1	18.5	30.1	22.0	10.5	10.1
2	32.7	36.1	37.2	33.3	36.8	18.0
3	5.7	22.0	28.9	15.6	6.0	5.7
4	14.6	13.7	21.0	17.4	8.1	5.7
Mean	19.8	22.6	29.3	22.1	15.4	9.9
% Plants	11.5	14.8	24.0	14.0	7.1	3.0

Source of Variation	Degrees of Freedom	Sum of Squares	Mean Square
Blocks	3	1,392.85	
Varieties	5	885.72	177.14
Error	15	364.15	24.28

If most of the percentages were above 50%, some computational time could be saved by working with the other of the two conjoint events, free instead of infested, for example.

The application of $D = 11.3$ indicates that variety F is more resistent than B, C, and D and that E is more resistent than C.   The retranslation to percentages infected is shown in the line above the analysis of variance.

EXAMPLE 11.12.1—To control boll weavils, four dusts were applied by J. C. Gaines of the Texas Agricultural Experiment Station.   With an untreated plot E in each replication, a 5 × 5 Latin square was used.   In each plot 200 squares were examined for punctures.   The percentages of punctured squares were:

C	27	E	42	A	18	D	34	B	17
A	18	D	27	E	42	B	14	C	12
D	23	B	14	C	17	E	25	A	14
E	24	A	10	B	8	C	12	D	26
B	9	C	11	D	15	A	11	E	22

TABLE 11.12.1

ANGLES CORRESPONDING TO PERCENTAGES, ANGLE = ARCSIN $\sqrt{\text{PERCENTAGE}}$, AS GIVEN BY C. I. BLISS (4)

%	0	1	2	3	4	5	6	7	8	9
0.0	0	0.57	0.81	0.99	1.15	1.28	1.40	1.52	1.62	1.72
0.1	1.81	1.90	1.99	2.07	2.14	2.22	2.29	2.36	2.43	2.50
0.2	2.56	2.63	2.69	2.75	2.81	2.87	2.92	2.98	3.03	3.09
0.3	3.14	3.19	3.24	3.29	3.34	3.39	3.44	3.49	3.53	3.58
0.4	3.63	3.67	3.72	3.76	3.80	3.85	3.89	3.93	3.97	4.01
0.5	4.05	4.09	4.13	4.17	4.21	4.25	4.29	4.33	4 37	4.40
0.6	4.44	4.48	4.52	4.55	4.59	4.62	4.66	4.69	4.73	4.76
0.7	4.80	4.83	4.87	4.90	4.93	4.97	5.00	5.03	5.07	5.10
0.8	5.13	5.16	5.20	5.23	5.26	5.29	5.32	5.35	5.38	5.41
0.9	5.44	5.47	5.50	5.53	5.56	5.59	5.62	5.65	5.68	5.71
1	5.74	6.02	6.29	6.55	6.80	7.04	7.27	7.49	7.71	7.92
2	8.13	8.33	8.53	8.72	8.91	9.10	9.28	9.46	9.63	9.81
3	9.98	10.14	10.31	10.47	10.63	10.78	10.94	11.09	11.24	11.39
4	11.54	11.68	11.83	11.97	12.11	12.25	12.39	12.52	12.66	12.79
5	12.92	13.05	13.18	13.31	13.44	13.56	13.69	13.81	13.94	14.06
6	14.18	14.30	14.42	14.54	14.65	14.77	14.89	15.00	15.12	15.23
7	15.34	15.45	15.56	15.68	15.79	15.89	16.00	16.11	16.22	16.32
8	16.43	16.54	16.64	16.74	16.85	16.95	17.05	17.16	17.26	17.36
9	17.46	17.56	17.66	17.76	17.85	17.95	18.05	18.15	18.24	18.34
10	18.44	18.53	18.63	18.72	18.81	18.91	19.00	19.09	19.19	19.28
11	19.37	19.46	19.55	19.64	19.73	19.82	19.91	20.00	20.09	20.18
12	20.27	20.36	20.44	20.53	20.62	20.70	20.79	20.88	20.96	21.05
13	21.13	21.22	21.30	21.39	21.47	21.56	21.64	21.72	21.81	21.89
14	21.97	22.06	22.14	22.22	22.30	22.38	22.46	22.55	22.63	22.71
15	22.79	22.87	22.95	23.03	23.11	23.19	23.26	23.34	23.42	23.50
16	23.58	23.66	23.73	23.81	23.89	23.97	24.04	24.12	24.20	24.27
17	24.35	24.43	24.50	24.58	24.65	24.73	24.80	24.88	24.95	25.03
18	25.10	25.18	25.25	25.33	25.40	25.48	25.55	25.62	25.70	25.77
19	25.84	25.92	25.99	26.06	26.13	26.21	26.28	26.35	26.42	26.49
20	26.56	26.64	26.71	26.78	26.85	26.92	26.99	27.06	27.13	27.20
21	27.28	27.35	27.42	27.49	27.56	27.63	27.69	27.76	27.83	27.90
22	27.97	28.04	28.11	28.18	28.25	28.32	28.38	28.45	28.52	28.59
23	28.66	28.73	28.79	28.86	28.93	29.00	29.06	29.13	29.20	29.27
24	29.33	29.40	29.47	29.53	29.60	29.67	29.73	29.80	29.87	29.93
25	30.00	30.07	30.13	30.20	30.26	30.33	30.40	30.46	30.53	30.59
26	30.66	30.72	30.79	30.85	30.92	30.98	31.05	31.11	31.18	31.24
27	31.31	31.37	31.44	31.50	31.56	31.63	31.69	31.76	31.82	31.88
28	31.95	32.01	32.08	32.14	32.20	32.27	32.33	32.39	32.46	32.52
29	32.58	32.65	32.71	32.77	32.83	32.90	32.96	33.02	33.09	33.15
30	33.21	33.27	33.34	33.40	33.46	33.52	33.58	33.65	33.71	33.77
31	33.83	33.89	33.96	34.02	34.08	34.14	34.20	34.27	34.33	34.39
32	34.45	34.51	34.57	34.63	34.70	34.76	34.82	34.88	34.94	35.00
33	35.06	35.12	35.18	35.24	35.30	35.37	35.43	35.49	35.55	35.61
34	35.67	35.73	35.79	35.85	35.91	35.97	36.03	36.09	36.15	36.21
35	36.27	36.33	36.39	36.45	36.51	36.57	36.63	36.69	36.75	36.81
36	36.87	36.93	36.99	37.05	37.11	37.17	37.23	37.29	37.35	37.41
37	37.47	37.52	37.58	37.64	37.70	37.76	37.82	37.88	37.94	38.00
38	38.06	38.12	38.17	38.23	38.29	38.35	38.41	38.47	38.53	38.59
39	38.65	38.70	38.76	38.82	38.88	38.94	39.00	39.06	39.11	39.17
40	39.23	39.29	39.35	39.41	39.47	39.52	39.58	39.64	39.70	39.76
41	39.82	39.87	39.93	39.99	40.05	40.11	40.16	40.22	40.28	40.34
42	40.40	40.46	40.51	40.57	40.63	40.69	40.74	40.80	40.86	40.92
43	40.98	41.03	41.09	41.15	41.21	41.27	41.32	41.38	41.44	41.50
44	41.55	41.61	41.67	41.73	41.78	41.84	41.90	41.96	42.02	42.07
45	42.13	42.19	42.25	42.30	42.36	42.42	42.48	42.53	42.59	42.65
46	42.71	42.76	42.82	42.88	42.94	42.99	43.05	43.11	43.17	43.22
47	43.28	43.34	43.39	43.45	43.51	43.57	43.62	43.68	43.74	43.80
48	43.85	43.91	43.97	44.03	44.08	44.14	44.20	44 25	44.31	44.37
49	44.43	44.48	44.54	44.60	44.66	44.71	44.77	44.83	44.89	44.94

(Continued next page)

TABLE 11.12.1—(*Continued*)

ANGLES CORRESPONDING TO PERCENTAGES, ANGLE = ARCSIN $\sqrt{\text{PERCENTAGE}}$, AS GIVEN BY C. I. BLISS

%	0	1	2	3	4	5	6	7	8	9
50	45.00	45.06	45.11	45.17	45.23	45.29	45.34	45.40	45.46	45.52
51	45.57	45.63	45.69	45.75	45.80	45.86	45.92	45.97	46.03	46.09
52	46.15	46.20	46.26	46.32	46.38	46.43	46.49	46.55	46.61	46.66
53	46.72	46.78	46.83	46.89	46.95	47.01	47.06	47.12	47.18	47.24
54	47.29	47.35	47.41	47.47	47.52	47.58	47.64	47.70	47.75	47.81
55	47.87	47.93	47.98	48.04	48.10	48.16	48.22	48.27	48.33	48.39
56	48.45	48.50	48.56	48.62	48.68	48.73	48.79	48.85	48.91	48.97
57	49.02	49.08	49.14	49.20	49.26	49.31	49.37	49.43	49.49	49.54
58	49.60	49.66	49.72	49.78	49.84	49.89	49.95	50.01	50.07	50.13
59	50.18	50.24	50.30	50.36	50.42	50.48	50.53	50.59	50.65	50.71
60	50.77	50.83	50.89	50.94	51.00	51.06	51.12	51.18	51.24	51.30
61	51.35	51.41	51.47	51.53	51.59	51.65	51.71	51.77	51.83	51.88
62	51.94	52.00	52.06	52.12	52.18	52.24	52.30	52.36	52.42	52.48
63	52.53	52.59	52.65	52.71	52.77	52.83	52.89	52.95	53.01	53.07
64	53.13	53.19	53.25	53.31	53.37	53.43	53.49	53.55	53.61	53.67
65	53.73	53.79	53.85	53.91	53.97	54.03	54.09	54.15	54.21	54.27
66	54.33	54.39	54.45	54.51	54.57	54.63	54.70	54.76	54.82	54.88
67	54.94	55.00	55.06	55.12	55.18	55.24	55.30	55.37	55.43	55.49
68	55.55	55.61	55.67	55.73	55.80	55.86	55.92	55.98	56.04	56.11
69	56.17	56.23	56.29	56.35	56.42	56.48	56.54	56.60	56.66	56.73
70	56.79	56.85	56.91	56.98	57.04	57.10	57.17	57.23	57.29	57.35
71	57.42	57.48	57.54	57.61	57.67	57.73	57.80	57.86	57.92	57.99
72	58.05	58.12	58.18	58.24	58.31	58.37	58.44	58.50	58.56	58.63
73	58.69	58.76	58.82	58.89	58.95	59.02	59.08	59.15	59.21	59.28
74	59.34	59.41	59.47	59.54	59.60	59.67	59.74	59.80	59.87	59.93
75	60.00	60.07	60.13	60.20	60.27	60.33	60.40	60.47	60.53	60.60
76	60.67	60.73	60.80	60.87	60.94	61.00	61.07	61.14	61.21	61.27
77	61.34	61.41	61.48	61.55	61.62	61.68	61.75	61.82	61.89	61.96
78	62.03	62.10	62.17	62.24	62.31	62.37	62.44	62.51	62.58	62.65
79	62.72	62.80	62.87	62.94	63.01	63.08	63.15	63.22	63.29	63.36
80	63.44	63.51	63.58	63.65	63.72	63.79	63.87	63.94	64.01	64.08
81	64.16	64.23	64.30	64.38	64.45	64.52	64.60	64.67	64.75	64.82
82	64.90	64.97	65.05	65.12	65.20	65.27	65.35	65.42	65.50	65.57
83	65.65	65.73	65.80	65.88	65.96	66.03	66.11	66.19	66.27	66.34
84	66.42	66.50	66.58	66.66	66.74	66.81	66.89	66.97	67.05	67.13
85	67.21	67.29	67.37	67.45	67.54	67.62	67.70	67.78	67.86	67.94
86	68.03	68.11	68.19	68.28	68.36	68.44	68.53	68.61	68.70	68.78
87	68.87	68.95	69.04	69.12	69.21	69.30	69.38	69.47	69.56	69.64
88	69.73	69.82	69.91	70.00	70.09	70.18	70.27	70.36	70.45	70.54
89	70.63	70.72	70.81	70.91	71.00	71.09	71.19	71.28	71.37	71.47
90	71.56	71.66	71.76	71.85	71.95	72.05	72.15	72.24	72.34	72.44
91	72.54	72.64	72.74	72.84	72.95	73.05	73.15	73.26	73.36	73.46
92	73.57	73.68	73.78	73.89	74.00	74.11	74.21	74.32	74.44	74.55
93	74.66	74.77	74.88	75.00	75.11	75.23	75.35	75.46	75.58	75.70
94	75.82	75.94	76.06	76.19	76.31	76.44	76.56	76.69	76.82	76.95
95	77.08	77.21	77.34	77.48	77.61	77.75	77.89	78.03	78.11	78.32
96	78.46	78.61	78.76	78.91	79.06	79.22	79.37	79.53	79.69	79.86
97	80.02	80.19	80.37	80.54	80.72	80.90	81.09	81.28	81.47	81.67
98	81.87	82.08	82.29	82.51	82.73	82.96	83.20	83.45	83.71	83.98
99.0	84.26	84.29	84.32	84.35	84.38	84.41	84.44	84.47	84.50	84.53
99.1	84.56	84.59	84.62	84.65	84.68	84.71	84.74	84.77	84.80	84.84
99.2	84.87	84.90	84.93	84.97	85.00	85.03	85.07	85.10	85.13	85.17
99.3	85.20	85.24	85.27	85.31	85.34	85.38	85.41	85.45	85.48	85.52
99.4	85.56	85.60	85.63	85.67	85.71	85.75	85.79	85.83	85.87	85.91
99.5	85.95	85.99	86.03	86.07	86.11	86.15	86.20	86.24	86.28	86.33
99.6	86.37	86.42	86.47	86.51	86.56	86.61	86.66	86.71	86.76	86.81
99.7	86.86	86.91	86.97	87.02	87.08	87.13	87.19	87.25	87.31	87.37
99.8	87.44	87.50	87.57	87.64	87.71	87.78	87.86	87.93	88.01	88.10
99.9	88.19	88.28	88.38	88.48	88.60	88.72	88.85	89.01	89.19	89.43
100.0	90.00	—	—	—	—	—	—	—	—	—

Transform these percentages to angles then analyze the variance as follows:

Rows	4	311.3	
Columns	4	6.0	
Treatments	4	637.5	159.38
Error	12	108.8	9.07

EXAMPLE 11.12.2—Show that $D = 6.1$ and that dusts A, B, and C gave significantly smaller percentages than D or control E.

11.13—The logarithmic transformation. Logarithms are used if effects are known to be proportional instead of additive; also, if the standard deviation varies directly as the mean. Proportional effects are common in economic data and, in the opinion of C. B. Williams (24), are prevalent in counts of insects caught in traps. Logarithms may correct more serious cases of non-additivity where the square root fails (see Bartlett's article, 3).

The plankton catches (25) of table 11.13.1 yielded nicely to the

TABLE 11.13.1
ESTIMATED NUMBERS OF FOUR KINDS OF PLANKTON CAUGHT IN SIX HAULS
WITH EACH OF TWO NETS

Count	Estimated Numbers				Logarithms			
	I	II	III	IV	I	II	III	IV
1	895	1,520	43,300	11,000	2.95	3.18	4.64	4.04
2	540	1,610	32,800	8,600	2.73	3.21	4.52	3.93
3	1,020	1,900	28,800	8,260	3.01	3.28	4.46	3.92
4	470	1,350	34,600	9,830	2.67	3.13	4.54	3.99
5	428	980	27,800	7,600	2.63	2.99	4.44	3.88
6	620	1,710	32,800	9,650	2.79	3.23	4.52	3.98
7	760	1,930	28,100	8,900	2.88	3.29	4.45	3.95
8	537	1,960	18,900	6,060	2.73	3.29	4.28	3.78
9	845	1,840	31,400	10,200	2.93	3.26	4.50	4.01
10	1,050	2,410	39,500	15,500	3.02	3.38	4.60	4.19
11	387	1,520	29,000	9,250	2.59	3.18	4.46	3.97
12	497	1,685	22,300	7,900	2.70	3.23	4.35	3.90
Mean	671	1,701	30,775	9,396	2.802	3.221	4.480	3.962
Range	663	1,480	24,400	9,440	0.43	0.39	0.36	0.41

Analysis of Variance of Logarithms

Source of Variation	Degrees of Freedom	Sum of Squares	Mean Square
Kind of plankton	3	20.2070	6.7357
Haul	11	0.3387	0.0308
Discrepance	33	0.2300	0.0070

logarithmic transformation. The original ranges and means were nearly proportional—the ratios of mean to range being 1.01, 1.15, 1.26, 1.00. This is another way of saying that the coefficients of variation were approximately the same. After transformation the ranges are almost equal and uncorrelated with the means.

In terms of numbers caught, the correctly estimated means for the four kinds are antilog 2.802 = 634; 1,663; 30,200; and 9.162. These are *geometric means*.

After calculating $D = 0.092$, the means of the logarithms (and consequently the geometric means of the numbers) are all seen to differ significantly.

The standard deviation of the logarithms is $\sqrt{0.0070} = 0.084$, that of the numbers being the antilogarithm, 1.21. Quoting Winsor and Clarke (page 5), "Now a deviation of 0.084 in the logarithms of the catch means that the catch has been multiplied (or divided) by 1.21. Hence we may say that one standard deviation in the logarithm corresponds to a percentage standard deviation, or coefficient of variation, of 21% in the catch."

EXAMPLE 11.13.1—The following data were abstracted from an experiment (24) which was somewhat more complicated in design. The entries are geometric means of trap catches in 3 successive nights, one night at each of 3 locations. The insects are macrolepidoptera. The place, Rothamsted Experimental Station.

Trap	3-Night Periods. August, 1950				
	16–18	19–21	22–24	25–27	28–30
1	19.1	23.4	29.5	23.4	16.6
2	50.1	166.0	223.9	58.9	64.6
3	123.0	407.4	398.1	229.1	251.2

There is no doubt about significance, but correct estimates require a transformation. Williams used logarithms though one might expect counts to be distributed in Poisson fashion. Transform to logarithms and analyze their variance. Ans. Mean square for traps = 1.4455; for error, 0.0172.

Show that all differences are significant and that the geometric means for traps are 21.9, 93.3, and 257.0 insects. This example is discussed further in the next section.

11.14—Tukey's test of additivity. This is useful in a variety of ways: (i) to learn if a transformation is successful; (ii) to get evidence about aberrant observations; (iii) to help decide if a transformation is necessary; (iv) to indicate a suitable transformation. The reader is referred to Tukey's articles for justification of the process (21, 23) and for further illustrations.

Non-additivity occurs if the main effects are formed by some such process as multiplication; that is, percentagewise. Also if some observation has accidentally intruded from a population different from those being investigated. Again if heterogeneous variance calls for weighted means. Finally if there are effects (interactions) in addition to the main effects and error (chapter 12).

In randomized blocks, the method of testing the hypothesis of additivity is explained by means of the logarithms of macrolepidoptera catches, table 11.14.1. The original numbers are quoted in example 11.13.1.

TABLE 11.14.1

Logarithms (X_{ij}) of Macrolepidoptera Catches, Example 11.13.1
Calculations for test of additivity

Period	Trap 1	2	3	Sum $X_{i.}$	Mean $\bar{x}_{i.}$	Deviation*, $d_i = \bar{x}_{i.} - \bar{x}_{..}$	Product, $p_i = \Sigma X_{ij} d_j$
1	1.28	1.70	2.09	5.07	1.69	−0.22	0.4344
2	1.37	2.22	2.61	6.20	2.07	0.16	0.6795
3	1.47	2.35	2.60	6.42	2.14	0.23	0.6266
4	1.37	1.77	2.36	5.50	1.83	−0.07	0.5230
5	1.22	1.81	2.40	5.43	1.81	−0.10	0.6313
Sum, $X_{.j}$	6.71	9.85	12.06	28.62		$\Sigma p_i = 2.8948$	
Mean, $\bar{x}_{.j}$	1.34	1.97	2.41		$\bar{x}_{..} = 1.91$		
*Dev., d_j	−0.57	0.07	0.50				

1. Products: $p_1 = \Sigma X_{1j} d_j = (1.28)(-0.57)+(1.70)(0.07)+(2.09)(0.50) = 0.4344$

.
.
.

$\quad\quad\quad p_5 = \Sigma X_{5j} d_j = (1.22)(-0.57)+(1.81)(0.07)+(2.40)(0.50) = 0.6313$

2. $P = \Sigma d_i p_i = (-0.22)(0.4344)+ \ldots + (-0.10)(0.6313) = 0.05753$

3. $\Sigma d_i^2 = (-0.22)^2 + \ldots + (-0.10)^2 = 0.1418$

4. $\Sigma d_j^2 = (-0.57)^2 + (0.07)^2 + (0.50)^2 = 0.5798$

5. Sum of squares for non-additivity $= \dfrac{P^2}{(\Sigma d_i^2)(\Sigma d_j^2)} = \dfrac{(0.05753)^2}{(0.1418)(0.5798)} = 0.0403$

Analysis of Variance of Logarithms of Catches			
Period	4	0.4251	
Trap	2	2.8910	1.4455
Error	8	0.1381	0.0172

* Sum of d must be 0.

The new computational features are shown in steps 1 and 2 of the list of calculations. The first, p_i, entered in the right-hand column, is made up of sums of products of the logarithms in a row by the deviations in the last line below. The second, P, is the sum of products of the entries in the two columns at the right.

Step 5 gives a sum of squares (with a single degree of freedom) due to non-additivity. This is part of the Error sum of squares in the analysis of variance. The test of the hypothesis of additivity is made as follows:

Error	8	0.1381	
Non-additivity	1	0.0403	0.0403
	—	———	
For Testing	7	0.0978	0.0140

$F = 0.0403/0.0140 = 2.88$, $f = 1, 7$. Since $F_{.05} = 5.59$, there is little doubt of additivity. In this respect, at least, the logarithmic transformation has been successful.

If F were large, non-additivity would be indicated and a decision would have to be made about procedure. Help in making the decision comes from the graph of p_i as ordinate against the mean, $\bar{x}_{i.}$ (figure 11.14.1). The mean of the $p_i, \bar{p}_i = 2.8948/5 = 0.58$, is plotted as a horizontal line. Similar lines show the 95% confidence interval,

$$\bar{p}_i \pm 2\sqrt{(\Sigma d_j^2)} \text{ (Mean square for testing additivity)}$$
$$= 0.58 \pm 2\sqrt{(0.58)(0.0140)}$$
$$= 0.58 \pm 0.18; \text{ that is, from } 0.40 \text{ to } 0.76$$

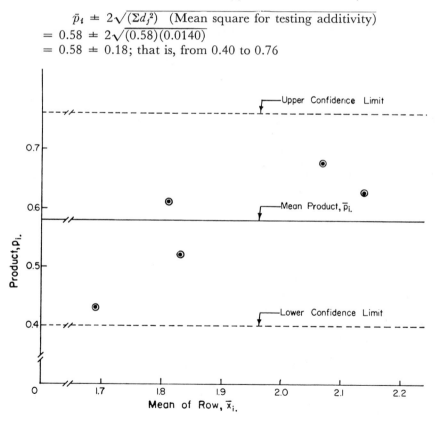

Fig. 11.14.1—Product p_i as function of row mean $\bar{x}_{i.}$. Mean of p_i is shown with confidence limits.

The fact that all points lie within the confidence limits corresponds with the nonsignificance of the one degree of freedom for non-additivity. If non-additivity were present, one or more of the plotted points would be expected to lie outside the confidence lines.

If the original insect catches (example 11.13.1) are tested for additivity, the single degree of freedom for non-additivity will be highly significant and the points in the graph will slope upward to the right (positive regression) with several lying beyond the confidence lines both above and below. This is the manner in which the graph shows the need of a square root or logarithmic transformation. The logarithm is the more strenuous of the two, correcting the more strongly non-additive effects.

It may be that most of the points in the graph will show no trend but that one or two will lie beyond the confidence lines. This suggests that these points are due to aberrant observations, observations from some unrelated population. Errors in recording or abnormal experimental material should be sought (example 11.14.1) and, if feasible, corrected or eliminated. If no ready explanation is found, the experimenter is faced with a difficult decision. The discrepant observations may be set aside as being from a foreign population, vitiating the information furnished by the experiment, or they may be accepted as unusual members of the populations sampled.

Further information about treating non-additive data is to be found in (3).

For the Latin square the test of additivity (22) requires fitting of the linear model, carrying the fitting process further than was necessary in randomized blocks. The data in table 11.14.2 are from an experiment on monkeys (5). Recorded were the numbers of responses to auditory and/or visual stimuli administered under 5 conditions. In order to avoid the effects of correlated errors (ϵ_{ijk}), the periods of application of the stimuli were randomized over 5 weeks, each of 5 pairs of monkeys receiving one stimulus per week.

It was discovered that the standard deviation of the number of responses was almost directly proportional to the mean, so the counts were transformed to logarithms. Each entry in the table is the logarithm of the geometric mean of the counts for the members of a pair. The question is: Has additivity been attained?

First, the table is bordered with means and deviations from mean, those for the treatments being entered at the bottom.

Next, the linear model is applied,

$$\hat{X}_{ijk} = \bar{x}_{...} + (\bar{x}_{i..} - \bar{x}_{...}) + (\bar{x}_{.j.} - \bar{x}_{...}) + (\bar{x}_{..k} - \bar{x}_{...})$$

That is, a regression estimate is the sum of (i) the experiment mean, $\bar{x}_{...}$; the row deviation, $(\bar{x}_{i..} - \bar{x}_{...})$; the column deviation, $(\bar{x}_{.j.} - \bar{x}_{...})$; and a treatment deviation, $(\bar{x}_{..k} - \bar{x}_{...})$. For example, the first entry is

$$2.215 + 0.007 - 0.131 - 0.069 = 2.02$$

TABLE 11.14.2
LOGARITHMS OF GEOMETRIC MEANS OF NUMBERS OF RESPONSES BY PAIRS OF MONKEYS
UNDER 5 STIMULI
Test of additivity in the Latin square

| Monkey Pair | Week | | | | | Sum, $X_{i..}$ | Mean, $\bar{x}_{i..}$ | $\bar{x}_{i..} - \bar{x}_{...}$ |
	1	2	3	4	5			
1	B 1.99 2.02	D 2.25 2.27	C 2.18 2.22	A 2.18 2.08	E 2.51 2.52	11.11	2.222	0.007
	−0.03	−0.02	−0.04	0.10	−0.01			
2	D 2.00 1.95	B 1.85 1.93	A 1.79 1.85	E 2.14 2.15	C 2.31 2.21	10.09	2.018	−0.197
	0.05	−0.08	−0.06	−0.01	0.10			
3	C 2.17 2.13	A 2.10 2.08	E 2.34 2.35	B 2.20 2.18	D 2.40 2.47	11.21	2.242	0.027
	0.04	0.02	−0.01	0.02	−0.07			
4	E 2.41 2.45	C 2.47 2.46	B 2.44 2.37	D 2.53 2.53	A 2.44 2.48	12.29	2.458	0.243
	−0.04	0.01	0.07	0.00	−0.04			
5	A 1.85 1.87	E 2.32 2.25	D 2.21 2.17	C 2.05 2.16	B 2.25 2.23	10.68	2.136	−0.079
	−0.02	0.07	0.04	−0.11	0.02			

Sum, $X_{.j.}$ 10.42   10.99   10.96   11.10   11.91 $X_{...} = 55.38$
Mean, $\bar{x}_{.j.}$ 2.084   2.198   2.192   2.220   2.382 $\bar{x}_{...} = 2.215$
$\bar{x}_{.j.} - \bar{x}_{...}$ −0.131   −0.017   −0.023   0.005   0.167

Treatment	Sum, $X_{..k}$	Mean, $\bar{x}_{..k}$	Deviation, $\bar{x}_{..k} - \bar{x}_{...}$
A	10.36	2.072	−0.143
B	10.73	2.146	−0.069
C	11.18	2.236	0.021
D	11.39	2.278	0.063
E	11.72	2.344	0.129

These regression values, following exactly the linear model, have this characteristic; if their variance is analyzed, the error sum of squares is zero.

Third, the differences in lines 3 are calculated. These have the following properties:

1. The sum in each row, in each column, and in each treatment is zero. If rounding errors have crept in, changes must be made to force the sums to zero.

2 The sum of their squares is the sum of squares for Error in the analysis of variance, $SSE = 0.0706$. If the variance is analyzed directly, avoiding rounding errors, the more accurate result is found to be 0.0725 (example 11.14.6).

Fourth, calculate the 25 differences, $\hat{X}_{ijk} - \bar{x}...$, square each, code by multiplying by 1,000, and enter in table 11.14.3. As an example,

TABLE 11.14.3

SQUARES OF DEVIATIONS OF REGRESSION ESTIMATES FROM THE EXPERIMENT MEAN, EACH MULTIPLIED BY 1,000

B	38	D	3	C	0	A	18	E	93
D	70	B	81	A	133	E	4	C	0
C	7	A	18	E	18	B	1	D	65
E	55	C	60	B	24	D	99	A	70
A	119	E	1	D	2	C	3	B	0

Discrepance = 22,216

$$1,000 \, (\hat{X}_{112} - \bar{x}...)^2 = 1,000 \, (2.02 - 2.215)^2 = 38$$

Coding may be any convenient multiplication or division; the coded squares occur in both numerator and denominator of the formula below.

Fifth, in this new table calculate the Discrepance sum of squares, $SSD = 22,216$, either by analyzing variance or by fitting the linear model and summing the squares of the deviations.

Sixth, sum the products of the entries in table 11.14.3 by the deviations in 11.14.2:

$$P = (-0.03)(38) + (-0.02)(3) + \ldots + (0.02)(0) = -20.68$$

Seventh, calculate the sum of squares (with a single degree of freedom) for non-additivity,

$$SSN = P^2/SSD = (-20.68)^2/22,216 = 0.0192$$

Finally, analyze the variance,

Error, SSE	12	0.0725	
Non-additivity, SSN	1	0.0192	0.0192
For Testing	11	0.0533	0.0048

Since $F = 4.00$ is short of the 5% point, $F = 4.84$, additivity may be accepted. The interpretations are not critical (examples 11.14.6–11.14.8) so that the presence of slight non-additivity may not affect them.

EXAMPLE 11.14.1—In section 2.9 and in example 11.2.2 we examined the numbers of lesions on pairs of half leaves inoculated with two concentrations of tobacco virus. A question was raised about the assumption of normality. Anormality is relatively unimportant but is usually associated with non-additivity. Test the virus counts for additivity putting the treatments in 2 columns and the replications in 8 rows. You will get

Discrepance	7	65	
Non-additivity	1	38	38
For Testing	6	27	4.5

The graph will show 7 points without trend, but one transcending the upper confidence line. This one corresponds to the pair of observations 31, 18. The graph is shown in Tukey's article.

EXAMPLE 11.14.2—Apply $\sqrt{(X + 1)}$ to the virus data. While F is not significant, the single point in the new graph is still outstanding. The original count of 31 still appears unusual. If you apply the logarithmic transformation to the tobacco virus data, you will find complete control of non-additivity.

EXAMPLE 11.14.3—In example 11.2.1 no estimate of error was provided, so the additive model for randomized blocks was assumed. For evidence, apply the test of additivity. Ans. For non-additivity, $F = 5.66$.

EXAMPLE 11.14.4—Using the deviations, $\bar{x}_{i.} - \bar{x}_{..}$ and $\bar{x}_{.j} - \bar{x}_{..}$, together with the mean, $\bar{x}_{..}$, calculate regression estimates in the 15 cells of table 11.14.1, then the deviations, $X_{ij} - \hat{X}_{ij}$. The sum of squares of the latter should be $0.1381 = SSE$ (except for rounding errors).

EXAMPLE 11.14.5—After augmenting table 11.9.2 with the 2 missing data, calculate the 16 regression estimates and the deviations therefrom. The deviations in cells 111 and 324 should each be zero (except for rounding) and the sum of squares in the other 14 cells should be equal to $5.33 = SSE_S$. The 2 zero deviations correspond with the 2 degrees of freedom deducted from Error.

EXAMPLE 11.14.6—Analyze the variance of the logarithms of the monkey responses. You will get,

Monkey Pairs	4	0.5244	0.1311
Weeks	4	0.2294	0.0574
Stimuli	4	0.2313	0.0578
Error	12	0.0725	0.00604

EXAMPLE 11.14.7—Test all differences among the means in table 11.14.2, using the sequential method of section 10.6. Ans. E and D are larger than A and B; C is larger than A.

EXAMPLE 11.14.8—In table 11.14.2, convert the logarithms of the treatment means to the original counts. Ans. $\bar{x}_E = 220.8$ responses, etc.

EXAMPLE 11.14.9—Calculate the sum of squares due to the regression of log response on weeks. It is convenient to code the weeks as $\bar{x} = -2, -1, 0, 1, 2$. Then, taking the weekly means as Y, $\Sigma xy = 0.618$ and $(\Sigma xy)^2/\Sigma x^2 = 0.03819$. On the per item basis, the sum of squares due to regression is $5(0.03819) = 0.1910$. The line for weeks in example 11.14.6 may now be separated into 2 parts:

Linear Regression	1	0.1910	0.1910
Deviations from Regression	3	0.0384	0.0128

Comparing the mean squares with error, it is seen that deviations are not significant, most of the sum of squares for Weeks being due to the regression.

REFERENCES

1. F. E. ALLEN and J. WISHART. Journal of Agricultural Science, 20:399 (1930).

2. M. S. BARTLETT. Supplement to the Journal of the Royal Statistical Society, 3:68 (1936).

3. M. S. BARTLETT. Biometrics, 3:39 (1947).

4. C. I. BLISS. Plant Protection, No. 12, Leningrad (1937).

5. R. A. BUTLER. Journal of Experimental Psychology, 48:19 (1954).

6. W. G. COCHRAN. The Empire Journal of Experimental Agriculture, 6:157 (1938).

7. W. G. COCHRAN, K. M. AUTREY, and C. Y. CANNON. Journal of Dairy Science, 24:937 (1941).

8. WILLIAM G. COCHRAN and GERTRUDE M. COX. Experimental Designs. John Wiley and Sons, Inc., New York (1950).

9. JAMES M. CRALL. Data from the Iowa Agricultural Experiment Station (1949).

10. R. A. FISHER. The Design of Experiments. Oliver and Boyd, Edinburgh (1935–1951).

11. R. A. FISHER. Biometrics, 10:130 (1954).

12. R. A. FISHER and F. YATES. Statistical Tables. Oliver and Boyd, Edinburgh (1938–1953).

13. H. C. FORSTER and A. J. VASEY. Journal of the Department of Agriculture of Victoria, Australia, 30:35 (1932).

14. OSCAR KEMPTHORNE. Design and Analysis of Experiments. John Wiley and Sons, Inc., New York (1952).

15. H. W. LI, C. J. MENG, and T. N. LIU. Journal of the American Society of Agronomy, 28:1 (1936).

16. H. L. LUCAS. Quoted in (18).

17. S. P. MONSELISE. Palestine Journal of Botany, 8:1 (1951).

18. H. D. PATTERSON. Journal of Agricultural Science, 40:375 (1950).

19. R. H. PORTER. Cooperative Soybean Seed Treatment Trials, Iowa State University Seed Laboratory (1936).

20. D. RICHARDSON *et al.* See reference 25, chapter 10.

21. J. W. TUKEY. Biometrics, 5:232 (1949).

22. J. W. TUKEY. Queries in Biometrics, 10:562 (1954).

23. J. W. TUKEY. Queries in Biometrics, 11:111 (1955).

24. C. B. WILLIAMS. Bulletin of Entomological Research, 42:513 (1951).

25. C. P. WINSOR and G. L. CLARKE. Sears Foundation: Journal of Marine Research, 3:1 (1940).

26. F. YATES. The Empire Journal of Experimental Agriculture, 1:129 (1933).

CHAPTER 12

Comparisons. Factorial
Arrangements of Treatments

12.1—Comparisons. Comparisons are differences between 2 means or groups of means. We have made them many times, both the designed type and those where all differences are assessed. It is the designed types that will occupy our attention in this chapter. In the first 3 sections some properties of these comparisons will be presented along with efficient methods of calculation.

Let us review some of the designed comparisons which we have made. In the vitamin B_{12} experiment of table 10.8.1, we first compared the means of the treated lots,

$$\bar{x}_{10} - \bar{x}_5 = 1.58 - 1.54 = 0.04 \text{ lb /day}$$

This was done by using the sums,

$$S_{10} - S_5 = 4.74 - 4.62 = 0.12$$

Sums avoid the rounding often present in means and lead to more convenient formulas.

The second comparison was between check and treatment,

$$\frac{S_{10} + S_5}{2} - S_0 = \frac{4.74 + 4.62}{2} - 2.73 = 1.95$$

This comparison is ordinarily made by doubling both quantities,

$$S_{10} + S_5 - 2S_0 = 4.74 + 4.62 - 2(2.73) = 3.90$$

In the soybean seed treatment experiment of table 11.3.1, a comparison was made between check and the mean of 4 chemicals. In present terms, the comparison is

$$S_1 + S_2 + S_3 + S_4 - 4S_0 = 469 + 459 + 467 + 471 - 4(446) = 82$$

To keep the record straight, this is 4 times the difference you would have got had you compared the mean of 4 treatment sums with the check sum; also, since there are 5 replications, 82 is (4)(5) times the result of comparing the mean of the treatments with check, $(93.8 + 91.8 + 93.4 + 94.2)/4 - 89.2 = 4.1$ plants.

Before going further, it is convenient to learn some rules governing comparisons and sums of squares based on them.

12.2—Rules for making comparisons, constant number of replications. In this section and in most of those to follow it is assumed that all sums are based on the same number of replications, n. We shall be concerned with linear relations among the sums,

$$c = \lambda_1 S_1 + \ldots + \lambda_a S_a,$$

where a is the number of treatments in the comparison and the λ_i are coefficients of the sums making up the comparison. As examples, in the vitamin B_{12} comparison, $S_{10} - S_5$, $\lambda_1 = 1$ and $\lambda_2 = -1$; in $S_{10} + S_5 - 2S_0$, $\lambda_1 = 1$, $\lambda_2 = 1$ and $\lambda_3 = -2$.

Rule 12.2.1. The quantity, $c = \Sigma \lambda_i S_i$, is a comparison if $\Sigma \lambda_i = 0$.

This means that there is no interest in comparing $S_1 + S_2$ with S_3, for example; the interest is in comparing $S_1 + S_2$ with $2S_3$ or with $S_3 + S_4$. In terms of the coefficients, λ_i, the last 2 comparisons are

+1	+1	−2		$\Sigma \lambda_i = 0$
+1	+1	−1	−1	$\Sigma \lambda_i = 0$

Rule 12.2.2. If c is any comparison among the S, then

$$\frac{c^2}{n\Sigma\lambda^2}$$

is a part of the sum of squares for treatments, associated with a single degree of freedom.

Contrast this rule with that applied in section 10.8. For the sum of squares between the 2 levels of vitamin B_{12}, we now have

$$\frac{(4.74 - 4.62)^2}{(3)(2)} = 0.0024$$

The comparison between treatment and check becomes

$$\frac{[4.74 + 4.62 - 2(2.73)]^2}{(3)(6)} = 0.8450$$

In each denominator, 3 is the number of replications. The second factor is $\Sigma\lambda^2$; this is $(1)^2 + (-1)^2$ in the first comparison and $(1)^2 + (1)^2 + (-2)^2$ in the second.

Rule 12.2.3. Two comparisons,

$$c_1 = \lambda_{11}S_1 + \lambda_{12}S_2 + \ldots + \lambda_{1a}S_a$$
$$c_2 = \lambda_{21}S_1 + \lambda_{22}S_2 + \ldots + \lambda_{2a}S_a,$$

are *orthogonal* if

$$\lambda_{11}\lambda_{21} + \lambda_{12}\lambda_{22} + \ldots + \lambda_{1a}\lambda_{2a} = 0$$

In applying this rule, if a sum, S_i, does not enter into the comparison, its coefficient is taken to be zero.

That the 2 comparisons in the vitamin B_{12} experiment are orthogonal is shown by the coefficients:

	S_{12}	S_t	S_ℓ
c_1	$+1$	-1	0
c_2	$+1$	$+1$	-2

whence, $(+1)(+1) + (-1)(+1) + (0)(-2) = 0$.

Rule 12.2.4. Among a treatments, if $a - 1$ comparisons are mutually orthogonal, then

$$\frac{c_1^2}{n\Sigma\lambda_1^2} + \frac{c_2^2}{n\Sigma\lambda_2^2} + \ldots + \frac{c_{a-1}^2}{n\Sigma\lambda_{a-1}^2} = \text{Sum of Squares for Treatments}$$

This rule is illustrated by the sums of squares for the 2 orthogonal comparisons among average daily gains in the vitamin B_{12} experiment,

$$0.0024 + 0.8450 = 0.8474,$$

which is the Treatment sum of squares in table 10.8.1.

A convenient way of applying the rules to a set of orthogonal comparisons, like those in the pig experiment, is this:

Levels of B_{12}	0	5	10			
Sums	2.73	4.62	4.74	Comparison	Denominator	Sum of Squares
B_{12} vs. None	-2	$+1$	$+1$	3.90	18	0.8450
5µg. vs. 10	0	-1	$+1$	0.12	6	0.0024
Sum						0.8474

Rule 12.2.5. If there are k comparisons, c_i, of the same kind (for example, linear comparisons), the sum, Σc_i, is equal to the comparison, c_S, in the sum of the treatments. Also, the sum of squares for c_S is

$$\frac{(\Sigma c_i)^2}{kn\Sigma\lambda^2}$$

and the sum of squares for the interactions among the k comparisons is

$$\frac{\Sigma c_i{}^2}{n\Sigma\lambda^2} - \frac{(\Sigma c_i)^2}{kn\Sigma\lambda^2}$$

The use of this rule and the next will be illustrated in section 12.8.

Rule 12.2.6. After one comparison, c_i, has been made, a second comparison, c_j, may be made on the c_i. The sum of squares for the second comparison is

$$\frac{c_j{}^2}{n(\Sigma\lambda_i{}^2)(\Sigma\lambda_j{}^2)}$$

EXAMPLE 12.2.1—In table 11.3.1, verify the sum of squares for Check vs. Chemicals, 67.24, by the methods of the present section.

EXAMPLE 12.2.2—The gains in weight (grams) of 6 lots of male rats in a completely randomized experiment are shown in this table:

	High Protein			Low Protein	
Beef	Cereal	Pork	Beef	Cereal	Pork
73	98	94	90	107	49
102	74	79	76	95	82
118	56	96	90	97	73
104	111	98	64	80	86
81	95	102	86	98	81
107	8?	102	51	74	97
100	82	108	72	74	106
87	77	91	90	67	70
117	86	120	95	89	61
111	92	105	78	58	82

Source of Variation	Degrees of Freedom	Sum of Squares	Mean Square
Treatments	5	4,613	923
Individuals	54	11,586	214.6

The following comparisons might be made:

	High Protein			Low Protein		
	Beef	Cereal	Pork	Beef	Cereal	Pork
Sum of Weights	1,000	859	995	792	839	787
1. High Protein vs. Low	+1	+1	+1	−1	−1	−1
2. Beef vs. Pork, High Protein	+1	0	−1	0	0	0
3. Beef vs. Pork, Low Protein	0	0	0	+1	0	−1
4. Animal vs. Vegetable, High Protein	+1	−2	+1	0	0	0
5. Animal vs. Vegetable, Low Protein	0	0	0	+1	−2	+1

Verify the fact that these comparisons are mutually orthogonal. Calculate the 5 comparisons. Ans. 436, 5, 5, 277, and −99. Compute the sum of squares for each comparison, then verify by comparing the sum of the five with the sum of squares for Treatment, 4,613. More informative sets of comparisons will be made in examples 12.4.2 and 12.5.1.

12.3—Rules for making comparisons, differing numbers of replications.

Rule 12.3.1. The quantity, $c = \Sigma\lambda_i S_i$, is a comparison if $\Sigma n_i \lambda_i = 0$.

Rule 12.3.2. If c is any comparison among the S, then

$$\frac{c^2}{\Sigma n_i \lambda_i^2}$$

is the sum of squares for the comparison.

Rule 12.3.3. Two comparisons, c_1 and c_2, are orthogonal if $\Sigma n_i \lambda_{1i}\lambda_{2i} = 0$.

The fourth rule is unchanged.

12.4—Factorial arrangement of treatments. 2 × 2 or 2². Two or more series of treatments may be tried in all combinations. Each series is called a *factor* and the arrangement is known as *factorial*. *Factorial experiment* is a term commonly used (34).

The factorial experiment is contrasted with the type in which all factors but one are controlled; that is, held constant. In the controlled experiment, one learns the behavior of a single factor in some predetermined environment. If this behavior is suspected of changing with environment, the factor may be tried in several of them. The series of environments becomes a second factor. Thus a series of varieties (factor one) may be tried at several locations (factor two) and the two-factor arrangement may be repeated during a series of years (factor three). This factorial arrangement gives information not only about the performance of each variety in each place and season but also about contrasts in its performance from place to place and from season to season. One variety may excel in one location but be poor in another. Some varieties may produce uniformly over a range of seasonal conditions while others may be unduly sensitive to weather.

Each factor may be tried at two or more levels; in a fertilizer experiment, the factor nitrogen could be tried at levels zero (check), 20, and 40 pounds per acre. In this technical sense, varieties and seasons may be called *levels*. Two factors, each at 2 levels, form a 2 × 2 or 2² factorial. If there are f factors each at k levels, the designation is k^f, the number of factors being the exponent. For differing numbers of levels the arrangement is described by their product; a 3 × 4 factorial means 2 factors, one at 3 levels, the other at 4.

Table 12.4.1 contains the somewhat modified results of a 2^2 factorial experiment tried in a completely randomized design, already quoted several times (20). With no antibiotics the vitamin had practically no effect, apparently because intestinal flora utilized the B_{12}; but with the antibiotics to control the flora, the effect of the vitamin was marked. Looking at the table the other way, the antibiotics alone decreased gain,

TABLE 12.4.1
FACTORIAL EXPERIMENT WITH ANTIBIOTICS AND VITAMIN B_{12}.
AVERAGE DAILY GAIN OF SWINE (POUNDS)

Level of Antibiotics (mg.)		Level of B_{12} (μg.)		Total for Antibiotics
		0	5	
0		1.30	1.26	
		1.19	1.21	
		1.08	1.19	
	Sum	3.57	3.66	7.23
	Mean	1.19	1.22	
40		1.05	1.52	
		1.00	1.56	
		1.05	1.55	
	Sum	3.10	4.63	7.73
	Mean	1.03	1.54	
Total for B_{12}		6.67	8 29	14.96

Analysis of Variance *

Source of Variation	Degrees of Freedom	Sum of Squares	Mean Square
Treatments	3	0.4124	
Error	8	0.0293	0.00366

* By the methods of chapter 10, completely randomized design, 4 lots with 3 observations in each.

perhaps by suppressing intestinal flora that synthesize B_{12}; but with B_{12} added, the antibiotics being present to decrease the activities of unfavorable flora, the effect was striking.

This is the type of effect which the factorial experiment is designed to detect. It is called *interaction*. Its presence destroys the additivity of the main effects; what is added by one factor at the first level of the other is different from what is added at another level.

Interaction is measured by the difference between two differences; that is, by the failure of the two differences to be the same. For the pigs, at the 2 levels of B_{12},

Difference for 40 mg. Antibiotics, $1.54 - 1.03$ = 0.51
Difference for no Antibiotics, $1.22 - 1.19$ 0.03
Interaction equals Difference   = 0.48

Equally, at the 2 levels of antibiotics,

Difference for 5 μg. B_{12}, $1.54 - 1.22$	=	0.32
Difference for no B_{12}, $1.03 - 1.19$	=	-0.16
Interaction equals Difference		0.48

As will be seen later, the interaction in this experiment is not attributable to sampling variation.

Interaction means different things to different people. To the chemist, it is much the same as reaction. The physiologist working with hormones thinks of mutual stimulation among the glandular activities. The agronomist may be interested in the effect of one plant nutrient as conditioned by the availability of a second. To the statistician interaction is measured by the failure of effects to be additive.

Arithmetically, interaction in the 2^2 table is a comparison of the following sums:

High Levels + Low Levels of Both Factors, $1.54 + 1.19 =$	2.73
High-Low + Low-High, $\qquad\qquad\qquad 1.03 + 1.22 =$	2.25
Interaction = Difference,	0.48

The sum of squares for this comparison is calculated, as usual, by the use of corresponding sums:

$$\frac{(4.63 + 3.57 - 3.66 - 3.10)^2}{(3)\,(4)} = \frac{(1.44)^2}{12} = 0.1728$$

where $n = 3$ and $\Sigma\lambda^2 = 4$. The difference in the numerator is n times the interaction; $(3)(0.48) = 1.44$.

The mean square, 0.1728, with $f = 1$, is now tested against the error mean square in table 12.4.1:

$$F = 0.1728/0.00366 = 47, \quad f = 1, 8$$

Clearly the two substances have a combined effect which is different from the sum of the effects when the two are applied separately.

In the presence of interaction, it is rarely useful to ask about the main effect of either factor. There is no single Effect of Vitamin B_{12}. Instead there are two *separate* effects; one without antibiotics,

$$1.22 - 1.19 = 0.03,$$

and another with antibiotics,

$$1.54 - 1.03 = 0.51$$

The sum or an average of the two effects applies to neither situation.

Each separate effect may be tested against experimental error. For the effect of the vitamin with antibiotics,

$$\frac{(4.63 - 3.10)^2}{(3)(2)} = 0.3902$$

F is then $0.3902/0.00366 = 106.6$, $f = 1, 8$. This is beyond the 0.5% level, $F_{.005} = 14.69$. It should be observed that there are 4 of these effects associated with only 2 degrees of freedom (one has gone with interaction). The 4 comparisons cannot be independent or orthogonal; the tests are not exact.

Despite questionable meaning, mean squares for the main effects are commonly reported even when interaction is present. This is a routine

TABLE 12.4.2

APPARENT RIBOFLAVIN CONCENTRATION (mcg/g.) IN COLLARD LEAVES FOR 2 SAMPLE SIZES WITH AND WITHOUT TREATMENT WITH PERMANGANATE PEROXIDE

Replication	With Permanganate		Without Permanganate				
	0.25 g. Sample	1.00 g. Sample	0.25 g. Sample	1.00 g. Sample			
1	27.2	24.6	39.5	38.6			
2	23.2	24.2	43.1	39.5			
3	24.8	22.2	45.2	33.0			
Sum	75.2	71.0	127.8	111.1	Comparison	Denominator	Sum of Squares
Permanganate	−1	−1	+1	+1	92.7	12	716.11
Sample Size	+1	−1	+1	−1	20.9	12	36.40
Interaction	−1	+1	+1	−1	12.5	12	13.02
Total							765.53

Source of Variation	Degrees of Freedom	Sum of Squares	Mean Square
Replication	2	3.76	
Treatments:	(3)	(765.53)	
Permanganate	1	716.11	716.11**
Sample Size	1	36.40	36.40
Interaction	1	13.02	13.02
Error	6	49.08	8.18

** Indicates $P \leq 0.01$. The other effects are not significant at the 5% level.

practice which is open to criticism, but it is almost unavoidable (see below). The reader must learn to discriminate.

Detection of a possible interaction often has to be provided as insurance. It may turn out that there is no interaction. But even so, the factorial arrangement is at least as effective as 2 experiments on the vitamin would be, one at each level of antibiotics. Combination of the two decreases the hazard of extraneous environmental variation.

The case where no interaction appears is illustrated by an experiment

(28) to learn the effect of a permanganate-peroxide treatment on the apparent concentration of riboflavin in the leaves of the collard, table 12.4.2. This was a randomized blocks design replicated on 3 successive days. The 2 factors were Permanganate and Size of Sample.   The initial analysis follows the methods of chapter 11.

Following the experimental data in the table is the calculation of 3 orthogonal comparisons among the 4 treatments.   The 3 sums of squares add to the Treatment sum of squares in the initial analysis of variance. N.B.   Each coefficient for interaction is the product of the 2 coefficients immediately above.

There is no convincing evidence of interaction so one proceeds to investigate the main effects.   Notice that each of these is a comparison got by adding two separate effects.   For example, the main effect of permanganate is calculated from

$$(127.8 - 75.2) + (111.1 - 71.0) = 92.7$$

Thus, in the absence of interaction, the Permanganate comparison is made from the whole of the experimental data, 6 determinations vs. 6. The Sample Size comparison is likewise calculated from 12 observations. "No interaction" means that the additive property applies to the main effects; that they are independent.

The conclusion from this experiment was that "In the fluorometric determination of riboflavin of the standard dried collard sample, the permanganate-hydrogen peroxide clarification step is essential.   Without this step, the mean value is 39.8 mcg. per gram, while with it the more reasonable mean of 24.4 is obtained."

EXAMPLE 12.4.1—From a randomized blocks experiment on sugar beets in Iowa the numbers of surviving plants per plot were counted as follows:

			Block	
Treatment	1	2	3	4
None	183	176	291	254
Superphosphate, P	356	300	301	271
Potash, K	224	258	244	217
P + K	329	283	308	326

These are such large counts that no transformation seems necessary.   Compute the mean square for error.   Ans. 1,494.   Also the following mean squares: P, 24,570; K, 203; PK (interaction), 28.   It is not known why superphosphate affected plant numbers so strongly.   Perhaps vigorous growth or early growth enabled them to escape the more destructive phase of some soil organism.   (Compare section 13.6.)

EXAMPLE 12.4.2—Examine the completely random experiment of example 12.2.2, using only the beef and cereal treatments at high and low levels.   You will find the mean square for error is 223.6, with that for the interaction of level with source, 884, just beyond the 5% level.   Evidently the rats could utilize the high level of beef to increase their gains in weight but could not utilize additional cereal.

EXAMPLE 12.4.3—Despite the presence of interaction, it is customary to complete the analysis of an experiment like that of table 12.4.1 as follows:

	Degrees of Freedom	Mean Square
Antibiotics	1	0.0208
Vitamin	1	0.2187
Interaction	1	0.1728
Error	8	0.00366

Verify the mean squares for the 2 main effects.

EXAMPLE 12.4.4—Hoblyn and Palmer (14), working with root cuttings from Common Mussel plum, tried 2 lengths (6, 12 cm.) each with 2 diameters (3–6, 9–12 mm.) planting 240 of each type at the time of making the cutting and preserving 240 to be planted the following spring.

	Planted at Once			Planted in Spring		
	Alive	Dead	Total	Alive	Dead	Total
Long	156	84	240	84	156	240
Short	107	133	240	31	209	240

As indicated in section 9.10, it is the percentages living that are of interest:

65.0	35.0
44.6	12.9

Transform these percentages to angles (table 11.12.1) and analyze the variance remembering that the angles are means, not sums, and that the squares must be multiplied by 240, not divided. Ans. Mean squares: time of planting, 88,059; length of cutting, 43,902; interaction, 690.

For the arcsin transformation applied to binomial data there is a theoretically determined error variance, always 821 with infinite degrees of freedom (17, page 156). Examples: For length, $F = 43,902/821$; for interaction, $F = 690/821$.

EXAMPLE 12.4.5—In the foregoing example, it is easier to refrain from multiplying the squares by 240. Instead, use as error $821/240$.

12.5—The two-factor experiment. Leaving the special case of 2 treatments per factor, let us consider the more general arrangement with a treatments in the first factor and b in the second, the $a \times b$ factorial. As before, the design may be any of those heretofore presented or a wide assortment of others.

Model I (constants), using the completely randomized design, is

$$X_{ijk} = \mu + \alpha_i + \beta_j + (\alpha\beta)_{ij} + \epsilon_{ijk},$$

where $i = 1 \ldots a, j = 1 \ldots b, k = 1 \ldots n, \Sigma\alpha_i = \Sigma\beta_j = 0, \epsilon_{ijk} = \mathcal{N}(0, \sigma)$. The restrictions on the interactions, $(\alpha\beta)_{ij}$, are quite severe; they must add to zero in both rows and columns of the $a \times b$ table. That is, $\Sigma(\alpha\beta)_{i.} = \Sigma(\alpha\beta)_{.j} = 0$. The model allows as many interactions as there are cells in the table.

The presence of interactions eliminates the additive character of the main effects, α_i and β_j. This will be clear in what follows.

The best understanding of a model is got by constructing an experiment based on it. It is convenient to utilize the construction of table 11.5.1, replacing Blocks by the second factor. To do this, add the first 3 numbers in each cell of that table, entering the sum in the corresponding cell of table 12.5.1; for the first cell, $\mu + a_1 + \beta_1 = 30 + 10 + 1 = 41$. Next, put down interaction constants in every cell. These may be any numbers you please, but the sum in each row and each column must be zero. Third, add a pair of random ϵ_{ijk} in each cell. For the first of these (on the left) I copied the ϵ_{ij} from table 11.5.1; the second was taken from table 3.10.1 by the same random process used for the first. The 2 sums in each cell represent a pair of random observations on one of the ab treatment combinations. For convenience the sum of the two, the treatment sum, is entered as the last item in each cell, then these are added for the marginal totals.

We now have a 4×3 experiment with 2 random observations making up each of the 12 treatment sums. Factor 1 has 4 treatments, a_t, while factor 2 has 3, b_j; they occur in all combinations.

The first step in the analysis utilizes the method of chapter 10. The total sum of squares is separated into 2 parts:

Treatments, $ab - 1 = 11$ 2,468

Individuals (error)   12   305   25

The next step is to separate the Treatment sum of squares into parts for 2 main effects, A and B, and the interaction, AB. The latter is calculated by subtracting from Treatments the sums of squares for A and B.

You now have evidence about a fact not widely understood, the relation of the main effects to the interactions. If you add

$$X_{111} + X_{121} + X_{131} = 26 + 30 + 49 = 105,$$

then compare this with the corresponding sum in table 11.5.1, you will emphasize the fact that the interactions do not alter the main effect because $\Sigma(\alpha\beta)_i = 0$. The natural impulse is to think that additivity of all effects is preserved. There are two reasons against this. First, biological interactions do not accommodate themselves to the model—consider the one in table 12.4.1 which is chiefly in the 4th cell of the table, then follow through again the argument against additivity. The mathematical model is perfect for its purposes; setting up the analysis of variance, estimating components, and testing. But it doesn't describe the kinds of interaction that are usually interesting. The second reason is less obvious. To explain it, let us think of the first factor in table 12.5.1 as 4 levels of a fertilizer and the second as 3 varieties. With no interaction, the effects of the levels of fertilizer are the same for every variety; if a_1 increases yield 10 bushels per acre with variety b_1, then it gives the same increase (aside from error) with b_2 and b_3. The main effect applies equally to each separate effect. On the contrary, with interaction the effects of a_1 on the variety yields are different; in the table, they are shown as increasing the yield b_1 by $10 - 4$

bushels but increasing the yield b_3 by $10 + 3$ bushels. On account of the requirement $\Sigma(\alpha\beta)_i = 0$, the main effect is unchanged but it no longer reflects the facts about the separate effects.

With evidence of interaction there is ordinarily no reason for calculating mean squares for the main effects though it is usually done routinely. (I did it for use in table 12.5.3.) Instead, an $a \times b$ table of the treatment sums (or means) should be written down and studied for mean-

TABLE 12.5.1
TWO-FACTOR EXPERIMENT CONSTRUCTED FROM MODEL I. COMPLETELY RANDOM DESIGN

Treatment a_i Factor A	Treatment b_j: Factor B						$X_{i..}$
	b_1		b_2		b_3		
a_1	41 / −4		36 / 1		43 / 3		
	37		37		46		
	−11	1	−7	2	3	1	
	26	38	30	39	49	47	
	64		69		96		229
a_2	34 / 8		29 / −5		36 / −3		
	42		24		33		
	1	−2	5	4	−3	2	
	43	40	29	28	30	35	
	83		57		65		205
a_3	31 / −3		26 / −1		33 / 4		
	28		25		37		
	0	5	4	−13	−1	0	
	28	33	29	12	36	37	
	61		41		73		175
a_4	18 / −1		13 / 5		20 / −4		
	17		18		16		
	−2	0	−2	−1	1	−4	
	15	17	16	17	17	12	
	32		33		29		94
$X_{.j.}$	240		200		263		703

TABLE 12.5.1—(*Continued*)

Correction: $(\Sigma X_{ijk})^2/nab = (703)^2/24 = 20{,}592$

Total: $\Sigma X_{ijk}^2 - C = 26^2 + 38^2 + \ldots + 12^2 - C = 2{,}773$

Treatments: $\dfrac{\Sigma X_{ij.}^2}{n} - C = \dfrac{64^2 + 69^2 + \ldots + 29^2}{2} - C = 2{,}468$

Error: $2{,}773 - 2{,}468 = 305$

A: $\dfrac{\Sigma X_{i..}^2}{nb} - C = \dfrac{229^2 + \ldots + 94^2}{(2)(3)} - C = 1{,}729$

B: $\dfrac{\Sigma X_{.j.}^2}{na} - C = \dfrac{240^2 + 200^2 + 263^2}{(2)(4)} - C = 254$

AB: Treatments $- A - B = 2{,}468 - 1{,}729 - 254 = 485$

Source of Variation	Degrees of Freedom	Sum of Squares	Mean Square
Treatment Effects:			
A	3	1,729	(576)
B	2	254	(127)
AB	6	485	81*
Error	12	305	25
Total	23	2,773	

ing. To emphasize this point, I calculated the treatment means from table 12.5.1 and entered them in table 12.5.2. As an example of method, consider the means in the first 2 rows. If there were no interaction or error, the differences, $a_1 - a_2$, should all be $a_1 - a_2 = 10 - 3 = 7$ (table 11.5.1). Contrast this with the facts:

$$32 - 42 = -10, \qquad 34 - 28 = 6, \qquad 48 - 32 = 16$$

If this were a real experiment, the failure of these differences to be the same (aside from error) would form the basis for the experimenter's interpretation of interaction.

A more effective way to study interactions is to fit the linear model (table 11.5.4) to the 4×3 table above. Deviations measure interaction plus error.

TABLE 12.5.2
TREATMENT MEANS SHOWING INTERACTION, FROM TABLE 12.5.1

Factor A	Factor B		
	b_1	b_2	b_3
a_1	32	34	48
a_2	42	28	32
a_3	30	20	36
a_4	16	16	14

For Model I, constant effects, the *components* are set out in table 12.5.3. In our constructed experiment, where the constants are known, the expected values (parameters) of the components can be calculated, as in the table. The sample estimates are unusually close, especially $s^2 = 25.4$ (rounded to 25), estimating 25.

TABLE 12.5.3

COMPONENT ANALYSIS OF A TWO-FACTOR EXPERIMENT, MODEL I. COMPLETELY RANDOM DESIGN. DATA FROM TABLE 12.5.1

Source of Variation	Mean Square	Parameter Estimated
Treatment Effects: A	576	$\sigma^2 + nb\kappa_A^2$
B	127	$\sigma^2 + na\kappa_B^2$
AB	81	$\sigma^2 + n\kappa_{AB}^2$
Error	25	σ^2

$$n = 2, \qquad a = 4, \qquad b = 3$$

$$\kappa_{AB}^2 = \frac{\Sigma(\alpha\beta)_{ij}^2}{(a-1)(b-1)} = \frac{(-4)^2 + (1)^2 + \ldots + (-4)^2}{(3)(2)} = 32.$$

$\kappa_A^2 = 92\tfrac{2}{3}$, $\kappa_B^2 = 13$ (table 11.5.2)

$s_{AB}^2 = (81 - 25)/2 = 28$ estimates 32. $s_B^2 = (127 - 25)/8 = 12.8$ estimates 13.
$s_A^2 = (576 - 25)/6 = 92$ estimates $92\tfrac{2}{3}$

The testing is easy, the error mean square being the denominator for every F.

If the 2-factor experiment is tried in randomized blocks, the model includes a term for blocks:

$$X_{ijk} = \mu + \alpha_i + \beta_j + (\alpha\beta)_{ij} + \rho_k + \epsilon_{ijk}$$

The preliminary analysis follows the methods of chapter 11. After that is completed, the main effects and interaction are separated in the Treatment sum of squares as shown in table 12.5.1. The block effect is of no interest in the component analysis.

For Model II and mixed models the component analysis is shown in table 12.5.4. It is evident in Model II that the significance of the main effects is tested with the mean square for AB in the denominator of F. The same is true for the fixed effect in mixed models, the random effect being tested as before with the Error mean square as denominator. In the present chapter this is the first case encountered where a mean square other than Error has been the denominator of F. As in chapter 10, the criterion for choosing the denominator is not its estimation of error but this: it must contain all components in the numerator except the one (or more) being tested.

In section 12.10 there are rules for writing down the component analyses for the various models. Meanwhile it is well to notice 3 facts: (i) The

TABLE 12.5.4
COMPONENT ANALYSIS OF A TWO-FACTOR EXPERIMENT MODEL II AND MIXED MODELS

	Parameters Estimated	
	Model II	Mixed Model, A Fixed*
Treatment Effects:		
A	$\sigma^2 + n\sigma_{AB}^2 + nb\sigma_A^2$	$\sigma^2 + n\sigma_{AB}^2 + nb\sigma_A^2$
B	$\sigma^2 + n\sigma_{AB}^2 + na\sigma_B^2$	$\sigma^2 + na\sigma_B^2$
AB	$\sigma^2 + n\sigma_{AB}^2$	$\sigma^2 + n\sigma_{AB}^2$
Error	σ^2	σ^2

* If B is fixed and A variable, $n\sigma_{AB}^2$ is a component of B but not of A.

main effect for the random factor does not include the interaction component because it adds to zero. (ii) Attached to each σ^2 (except that for error) there are both coefficients and subscripts, the total number of which is constant, 3 in this case. (iii) Capital letters represent factors; small letters, numbers of treatments or replications. If a capital letter is put in the subscript, the corresponding small letter is omitted from the coefficient.

Note: There is some chance of confusion about the notation because I have used a_i and b_j to denote treatments along with a and b (without subscripts) to represent numbers of treatments. The notation is so convenient and easy to remember that I think it worth while to risk the confusion.

EXAMPLE 12.5.1—For the rat data of example 12.2.2, a more realistic set o comparisons is now available. Verify the sums of squares in the last column and check the sum against the Treatment sum of squares in the original example.

	High Protein			Low Protein			
Comparison	Beef 1,000	Cereal 859	Pork 995	Beef 792	Cereal 839	Pork 787	Sum of Squares
Protein	+1	+1	+1	−1	−1	−1	3,168.3
Beef vs. Pork	+1	0	−1	+1	0	−1	2.5
Interaction with Protein	+1	0	−1	−1	0	+1	0.0
Animal vs. Vegetable	+1	−2	+1	+1	−2	+1	264.0
Interaction with Protein	+1	−2	+1	−1	+2	−1	1,178.1

The significant interaction of Protein with Animal vs. Vegetable is worth looking at. Multiply the sums by the indicated coefficients and make this 2×2 table:

	Animal	Vegetable
High Protein	1,995	1,718
Low Protein	1,579	1,678

It is evident that the high level of animal protein was more available to the rats than that of vegetable protein, perhaps because the amino acids were better balanced.

12.6—Randomized blocks experiment with sampling of plots.
Formally, randomized blocks experiments are factorial, treatments being

one factor and blocks the other. If there is sampling of the plots instead of complete measurement, the analysis of variance is arithmetically the same as that in the foregoing section. The model, however, has no interaction but contains 2 random sampling components:

$$X_{ijk} = \mu + \tau_i + \beta_i + \epsilon_{ij} + \delta_{ijk}$$

The δ_{ijk} are sampling units in the plots. Both ϵ_{ij} and δ_{ijk} are $\mathcal{N}(0, \sigma)$, but the σ are ordinarily different.

An example is taken from a cooperative experiment on the effect of fertilizer applied to broadcast oats grown on Carrington loam. The yields are in decagrams per quadrat, a $36'' \times 36''$ square, 4 of which, randomly selected, were harvested from each $21' \times 52'$ plot, table 12.6.1.

As in table 12.5.1, the first calculation, using the quadrat yields and the plot sums, gives

$$\text{Total} - \text{Plots} = \text{Sampling Error}$$

The second calculation is the usual one for randomized blocks, except for the divisors. For example, ΣX_{ij}^2 for plots must be divided by 4 before the correction is subtracted.

Experimental error is much larger than can be accounted for by sampling variation of the quadrats. To appreciate this, examine the plot sums as though you were studying interaction. This large discrepance makes

$$C = \sqrt{31.77/4}/\bar{x} = 14.7\% \text{ per plot}$$

(division by 4 is to convert experimental error to the plot basis). The component analysis shows the part added, beyond quadrat variation, to be

$$(31\ 77 - 7\ 46)/4 = 6.08$$

If you attempt to calculate the component for Treatment, you will find it negative. Now the treatments applied are not expected to keep the yields more nearly alike than can be expected in random sampling. It is more likely that accidents of sampling have increased Experimental Error and/or decreased the Treatment mean square. So far as this experiment is competent, the conclusion is that the component for Treatment is zero.

The provision of the Sampling Error allows an assessment of the adequacy of the sampling rate, the kind of problem that will be discussed in section 17.11. If you estimate the experimental error with 8 quadrats per plot, you will get $7.46 + 8(6.08) = 56.10$ instead of 31.77. So, $s_{\bar{x}}^2$ is now $56.10/32 = 1.753$ instead of $31.77/16 = 1.986$, a trivial decrease to compensate for doubling the sampling rate. Any material decrease in the standard error of the mean would have to be sought by increasing the replication.

In the preceding section there were some rules about coefficients and subscripts of σ^2. To apply them, think of Experimental Error, E, in terms of its arithmetical equal, TB.

TABLE 12.6.1

Yɪᴇʟᴅ (Dᴇᴄᴀɢʀᴀᴍs ᴘᴇʀ Qᴜᴀᴅʀᴀᴛ) ᴏꜰ Oᴀᴛs ᴏɴ Cᴀʀʀɪɴɢᴛᴏɴ Lᴏᴀᴍ. Fᴏᴜʀ
36″ × 36″ Qᴜᴀᴅʀᴀᴛs Pᴇʀ Pʟᴏᴛ

Block	Check	N	P	NP	Sum
1	19	18	16	13	
	16	16	22	27	
	18	17	18	28	
	18	14	18	28	
	71	65	74	96	306
2	15	22	19	15	
	16	24	20	14	
	16	22	20	18	
	17	20	24	14	
	64	88	83	61	296
3	21	20	24	25	
	19	21	15	20	
	18	20	19	24	
	22	20	20	20	
	80	81	78	89	328
4	18	20	20	20	
	20	22	20	18	
	20	18	17	12	
	18	19	20	18	
	76	79	77	68	300
Sum	291	313	312	314	1,230

Source of Variation	Degrees of Freedom	Mean Square	Parameter Estimated
Block	3		
Treatment	3	7.61	$\sigma_S^2 + 4\sigma_E^2 + 16\kappa_T^2$
Experimental Error	9	31.77	$\sigma_S^2 + 4\sigma_E^2$
Sampling Error	48	7.46	σ_S^2

$$s_E^2 = (31.77 - 7.46)/4 = 6.08$$

EXAMPLE 12.6.1—The efficiency of two sizes of quadrats for sampling plots of oats was studied by Homeyer and Black (15). The data from one field are copied in the table.

P–K	Block 1	Block 2	Block 3	Treatment Total
0–0	160	140	100	
	149	157	120	
	205	150	156	
	514	447	376	1,337
0–10	160	80	143	
	215	170	62	
	253	192	170	
	628	442	375	1,445
20–0	208	221	232	
	235	205	141	
	240	242	211	
	683	668	584	1,935
20–10	185	265	122	
	204	243	225	
	207	132	189	
	596	640	536	1,772
Block Total	2,421	2,197	1,871	6,489

Treatments		3	25,892	8,631
Blocks		2	12,749	6,374
Error		6	5,595	932
Sampling		24	42,987	1,791

These are yields (grams) from three 3′ × 3′ quadrats in each fortieth-acre plot. The fertilizers were applied at the rate of 300 lbs. per acre. Calculate the analysis of variance.

Sampling error is here larger than Experimental Error. Increased sampling seems called for; either larger quadrats or more of them or both.

EXAMPLE 12.6.2—Subdivide the sum of squares for treatments as follows:

Phosphorus	1	23,767
Potassium	1	84
Interaction	1	2,040
Total	3	25,891

For phosphorus, $F = 23,767/932 = 25.5$, $f = 1, 6$.

12.7—Regression in single factor experiments. Treatments are often applied at more than 2 levels, bringing into prominence some problems of regression. If the levels, X, are equally spaced, they may be coded to a succession of integers such as -1, 0, $+1$; this makes computations easy. An example is taken from a randomized blocks experiment to learn the effect of spacing in rows 3 feet apart, the crop being cowpea hay (22). Table 12.7.1 contains the data for one variety.

Preliminary analysis gives a Spacing sum of squares of 204.17. This is to be separated into 2 parts, one being due to linear regression, the other to deviations from regression.

TABLE 12.7.1
Yield of Cowpea Hay (Pounds Per 1/100 Morgen Plot)

| Spacing (inches) | Block | | | | Sum | Mean |
	1	2	3	4		
4	65	61	60	63	249	62
8	60	58	56	60	234	58
12	53	53	48	55	209	52
Sum	178	172	164	178	692	

Blocks	3	44.00	
Spacings:	(2)	(204.17)	
Linear Regression	1	200.00	200.00**
Deviation	1	4.17	4.17
Error	6	8.50	1.42

Setting $x = -1, 0, 1$, $\Sigma x^2 = 2$ and $\Sigma xy = (-1)(249) + (0)(234) + (1)(209) = -40$. The regression coefficient is then

$$b = \frac{\Sigma xy}{(n)(\Sigma x^2)} = \frac{-40}{(4)(2)} = -5 \text{ pounds per coded } X$$

The factor, $n = 4$, in the denominator is necessary to convert from sums to means. (Note: In terms of inches, the regression is $-5/4 = -1.25$ pounds per inch.)

The reduction in sum of squares is

$$\frac{(\Sigma xy)^2}{(n)(\Sigma x^2)} = \frac{(-40)^2}{(4)(2)} = 200$$

This is entered in the table of analysis of variance as the sum of squares for linear regression. The remainder of the Spacing sum of squares, $204.17 - 200 = 4.17$ is entered as Deviation from regression.

The conclusion is that the wider the spacing the less the yield, the yield decreasing 1.25 pounds per inch of spacing. Most of the variation in yield is attributable to linear regression.

I have assumed that the 2 parts of the Spacing sum of squares are additive. Table 12.7.2 shows that these parts correspond to a pair of

TABLE 12.7.2
ORTHOGONAL COMPARISONS IN REGRESSION OF YIELD ON SPACING

Spacings (inches)	4	8	12	Comparisons	Divisor	Sum of Squares
Sums	249	234	209			
Linear	−1	0	+1	−40	8	200.00
Deviations	+1	−2	+1	−10	24	4.17
Total						204.17

orthogonal comparisons. The first is the total decrease in yield, $209 - 249$ $= -40$. The second is twice the deviation of the middle yield from the mean of the other two:

$$2\left(\frac{249 + 209}{2} - 234\right) = 2(229 - 234) = -10$$

If you draw a graph with the spacings as X and sums as Y, then connect the end points by a straight line, you will see that the midpoint of this line is 229 units above the X-axis and 5 units below the middle yield. The coefficients are arranged to produce the correct sums of squares with the least effort.

TABLE 12.7.3
COEFFICIENTS AND DIVISORS FOR SETS OF ORTHOGONAL COMPARISONS IN REGRESSION IF
X IS SPACED AT EQUAL INTERVALS

Degree of Polynomial	Comparison	Number of Treatments							Divisor $\Sigma\lambda^2$
		1	2	3	4	5	6	7	
1	Linear	−1	+1						2
2	Linear	−1	0	+1					2
	Quadratic	+1	−2	+1					6
3	Linear	−3	−1	+1	+3				20
	Quadratic	+1	−1	−1	+1				4
	Cubic	−1	+3	−3	+1				20
4	Linear	−2	−1	0	+1	+2			10
	Quadratic	+2	−1	−2	−1	+2			14
	Cubic	−1	+2	0	−2	+1			10
	Quartic	+1	−4	+6	−4	+1			70
5	Linear	−5	−3	−1	+1	+3	+5		70
	Quadratic	+5	−1	−4	−4	−1	+5		84
	Cubic	−5	+7	+4	−4	−7	+5		180
	Quartic	+1	−3	+2	+2	−3	+1		28
	Quintic	−1	+5	−10	+10	−5	+1		252
6	Linear	−3	−2	−1	0	+1	+2	+3	28
	Quadratic	+5	0	−3	−4	−3	0	+5	84
	Cubic	−1	+1	+1	0	−1	−1	+1	6
	Quartic	+3	−7	+1	+6	+1	−7	+3	154
	Quintic	−1	+4	−5	0	+5	−4	+1	84
	Sextic	+1	−6	+15	−20	+15	−6	+1	924

Notice that the experiment has furnished little evidence as to the spacing that would give the greatest yield. Clearly it is less than 4 inches. The experimenter tries to select spacings that will include the optimum, but weather conditions make this uncertain. If he were completely successful, the linear regression might be horizontal with all of the Spacing sum of squares in Deviations.

The two sets of orthogonal coefficients used above are to be found in the second group of lines in table 12.7.3. They are guides to the 2 components into which one can separate the curved regression through 3 points. This is called a *second degree* or *parabolic* regression; a second degree polynomial or parabola can be fitted exactly to any 3 points. At the right of each row of coefficients is $\Sigma\lambda^2$, the factor to be multiplied by n to make up the proper divisor for

$$\frac{c^2}{n\Sigma\lambda^2}$$

As another illustration of the use of the table, the 5 spacings and sums of the millet experiment, table 11.7.1, are copied into table 12.7.4 along

TABLE 12.7.4
REGRESSION COMPARISONS AMONG MILLET YIELDS OF TABLE 11.7.1

Spacings Sums	2 1,349	4 1,314	6 1,262	8 1,191	10 1,188	Comparisons	Divisors	Sum of Squares
Linear	−2	−1	0	+1	+2	−445	50	3,960
Quadratic	+2	−1	−2	−1	+2	45	70	29
Cubic	−1	+2	0	−2	+1	85	50	144
Quartic	+1	−4	+6	−4	+1	89	350	23
Sum								4,156

with the coefficients for 5 treatments from table 12.7.3. The $\Sigma\lambda^2$ are multiplied by $n = 5$ to make the divisors. The first sum of squares, for the linear comparison, verifies the 3,960 of table 11.7.3. The sum of the other three, $29 + 144 + 23 = 196$, agrees with the sum of squares for Deviations. But the deviations are now separated into 3 parts. The first new part is the additional reduction in sum of squares, over and above that due to fitting the straight line, attributable to fitting the parabola. That is, $3,960 + 29 = 3,989$ is the reduction in sum of squares that would have been made if a parabola had been fitted initially to the original treatment means. Similar statements apply to the other comparisons. The quartic will pass exactly through the 5 points, so that, after it is fitted, there is no remaining sum of squares.

Of course, this fitting of curved regressions to the millet data is merely an exercise because most of the variation in treatment yields is explained by the linear regression; and even that is not significant.

It surprises some people to get a significant comparison from a non-significant set of treatments. One often encounters some such analysis as this:

Treatments	10	(400)	(40)
Linear	1	350	350
Deviations	9	50	
Error	30	1,200	40

The over-all test of Treatments would give $F = 1$, but the test of Linear Regression, $F = 350/40 = 8.75$ shows $P < 0.01$. Most of the Treatment sum of squares belongs to the single comparison, Linear Regression. This emphasizes the distinction between designed and undesigned comparisons; it is only for the latter that the preliminary over-all test must be significant.

12.8—Regression in two-factor experiments. Either one or more factors may contain regressions. As an example of the one-factor regression I have taken some additional data from the cowpea spacing experiment of the foregoing section. In table 12.8.1, variety II is repeated. There are now 2 factors, each at 3 levels—a 3^2 factorial with 9 treatments.

The striking feature of this experiment is the upward trend of yield in varieties I and III as compared to the opposite trend which was observed in II. This accounts for the large interaction mean square and warns that no useful over-all statement can be made about the main effects.

To examine the trends of yield on spacing, the linear and quadratic comparisons are calculated for each variety, table 12.8.2. The negative linear comparison of variety II is contrasted with the positive in I and III. The mean squares for each variety emphasize the linear trends and the absence of curvilinearity. Observe that the sum of the six mean squares is identical with the sums of squares for Spacings and Interaction combined, 6 degrees of freedom. In the presence of interaction, there is little or no interest in the mean square for Variety.

If varieties I and III are compared, the difference between their upward linear trends will be found significant.

In case the interaction had been small, the calculations in the lower part of the table would be substituted for those above. Rule 12.2.5 is used. For the over-all Spacing comparisons, $kn = 12$, the number of plots planted to each spacing. The interactions involve differences among the 3 variety comparisons; hence $n = 4$, the number of replications.

We now have a test of significance for the outstanding feature of this experiment; the varieties have linear trends which are not the same. Since there is no significant curvature, there is no evidence as to what might be

TABLE 12.8.1

Y<small>IELD OF</small> C<small>OWPEA</small> H<small>AY</small> (P<small>OUNDS</small> P<small>ER</small> 1/100 M<small>ORGEN</small> P<small>LOT</small>) F<small>ROM</small> 3 V<small>ARIETIES</small>

Variety	Spacing (In.)	Block				Sum
		1	2	3	4	
I	4	56	45	43	46	190
	8	60	50	45	48	203
	12	66	57	50	50	223
II	4	65	61	60	63	249
	8	60	58	56	60	234
	12	53	53	48	55	209
III	4	60	61	50	53	224
	8	62	68	67	60	257
	12	73	77	77	65	292
Sum		555	530	496	500	2,081

Varieties	Spacings			
	4	8	12	
I	190	203	223	616
II	249	234	209	692
III	224	257	292	773
Sum	663	694	724	2,081

Block		3	255.64	
Variety,	V	2	1,027.39	513.70
Spacing,	S	2	155.06	77.53
Interaction,	VS	4	765.44	191.36**
Error		24	424.11	17.67

the optimum spacing for the varieties. Apparently I and III have heavy vegetative growth which requires more than 12″ spacing for maximum yield. Another experiment seems called for; the spacings tried for varieties I and III should be different from those for II.

You may ask why the 9 treatment sums were not put in a row with coefficients applied as in the 2^2 factorial of table 12.4.2. The reason lies in the undesigned variety comparisons. In a formal manner, some orthogonal comparisons could easily be devised, but they would not be realistic.

We turn now to a 3 × 4 experiment in which there is regression in each factor. The data are from the Foods and Nutrition Section of the Iowa Agricultural Experiment Station (25). The object was to learn about losses of ascorbic acid in snapbeans stored at 3 temperatures for 4 periods, each 2 weeks longer than the preceding. The beans were all harvested under uniform conditions before eight o'clock one morning. They were prepared and quick-frozen before noon of the same day. Three

TABLE 12.8.2
LINEAR AND QUADRATIC COMPARISONS FOR EACH VARIETY IN COWPEA EXPERIMENT

	4″	8″	12″	Comparisons, c	
Linear	−1	0	+1		
Quadratic	+1	−2	+1	Linear	Quadratic
Variety I	190	203	223	33	7
Variety II	249	234	209	−40	−10
Variety III	224	257	292	68	2
Sum	663	694	724	61	− 1

Variety I: Linear, $\dfrac{(33)^2}{(4)(2)} = 136.12**$ Quadratic, $\dfrac{(7)^2}{(4)(6)} = 2.04$

II: $\dfrac{(-40)^2}{(4)(2)} = 200.00**$ $\dfrac{(-10)^2}{(4)(6)} = 4.17$

III: $\dfrac{(68)^2}{(4)(2)} = 578.00**$ $\dfrac{(2)^2}{(4)(6)} = 0.17$

Total $\overline{914.12}$ $\overline{6.38}$

Verification: $914.12 + 6.38 = 155.06 + 765.44 (= S + SV), f = 6$

Spacings: Linear, $\dfrac{(\Sigma c_i)^2}{kn(\Sigma\lambda^2)} = \dfrac{(61)^2}{(3)(4)(2)} = 155.04$

Quadratic, $\dfrac{(-1)^2}{(3)(4)(6)} = 0.01$

Interaction: Linear, $\dfrac{\Sigma c_i^2}{(n)(\Sigma\lambda^2)} - S_L = \dfrac{(33)^2 + (-40)^2 + (68)^2}{(4)(2)} - 155.05 = 759.08$

Quadratic, $\dfrac{\Sigma c_i^2}{(n)(\Sigma\lambda^2)} - S_Q = \dfrac{(7)^2 + (-10)^2 + (2)^2}{(4)(6)} - 0.01 = 6.37$

Spacing:	(2)	(155.06)	
Linear, S_L	1		155.04
Quadratic, S_Q	1		.01
Interaction:	(4)	(765.44)	
Linear, $S_L V$	2	759.08	379.54**
Quadratic, $S_Q V$	2	6.37	3.18
Error	24		17.67

packages were assigned at random to each of the 12 treatments and all packages were stored at random positions in the locker, a completely randomized design. The sums of 3 ascorbic acid determinations are recorded in table 12.8.3.

It is plain that the concentration of ascorbic acid decreases with higher storage temperatures and, except at 0°, with storage time. It seems that

TABLE 12.8.3

SUM OF 3 ASCORBIC ACID DETERMINATIONS (MG./100 G.) FOR EACH OF 12 TREATMENTS
IN A 3 × 4 FACTORIAL EXPERIMENT ON SNAPBEANS

Temperature, F.°	Weeks of Storage				Sum
	2	4	6	8	
0	45	47	46	46	184
10	45	43	41	37	166
20	34	28	21	16	99
Sum	124	118	108	99	449

Temperature, T	2	334.39	
Two-week Period, P	3	40.53	
Interaction, TP	6	34.05	
Error*	24		0.706

* Error (packages of same treatment) was calculated from original data not recorded here.

the rate of decrease with temperature is not linear and not the same for the several storage periods. These observations are to be numeralized and supplied with suitable tests.

One can look first at either temperature or period; I chose temperature. At each period the linear and quadratic temperature comparisons $(-1, 0, +1; +1, -2, +1)$ are calculated:

Weeks of Storage	2	4	6	8	Sum
Linear, T_L	−11	−19	−25	−30	−85
Quadratic, T_Q	−11	−11	−15	−12	−49

The downward slopes of the linear regressions get steeper with time. This will be examined later. At present, calculate sums of squares as follows:

$$T_L = \frac{(-85)^2}{(12)(2)} = 301.04**$$

$$T_Q = \frac{(-49)^2}{(12)(6)} = 33.35**$$

The sum is the sum of squares for T, $301.04 + 33.35 = 334.39$. Significance in each effect is tested by comparison with the Error mean square, 0.706. Evidently the regressions are curved because the parabolic comparison is significant; quality decreases with accelerated rapidity as the temperature increases. (Note the number of replications in each temperature sum, 4 periods times 3 packages.)

Are the regressions the same for all periods? To answer this, calculate the interactions with period (Rule 12.2.5):

$$T_L P: \frac{(-11)^2 + \ldots + (-30)^2}{(3)(2)} - T_L = 33.46**$$

$$T_Q P: \frac{(-11)^2 + \ldots + (-12)^2}{(3)(6)} - T_Q = 0.59$$

The sum is equal to the sum of squares for TP. The linear regressions decrease significantly with period but the curved population increments may be the same for all periods.

Turning now to the sums for the 4 periods, calculate the 3 comparisons:

Sums	124	118	108	99	Comparison	Sum of Squares
Linear, P_L	-3	-1	$+1$	$+3$	-85	40.14**
Quadratic, P_Q	$+1$	-1	-1	$+1$	-3	0.25
Cubic, P_C	-1	$+3$	-3	$+1$	5	0.14
Sum = Sum of Squares for Periods						40.53

This indicates that the population regressions on period may be linear.

We come now to the new feature of this section, the regressions of T_L and T_Q on period. T_L, the downward slope of the vitamin with temperature, has been calculated for each period; the question is, in what manner does T_L change with period?

To T_L calculated above, apply the orthogonal coefficients for 4 treatments. Example:

$$T_L P_L: (-3)(-11) + (-1)(-19) + (1)(-25) + (3)(-30) = -63$$

For this comparison the sum of squares is

$$T_L P_L = \frac{(-63)^2}{(3)(2)(20)} = 33.08**$$

The new feature is the use of Rule 12.2.6 for successive application of the coefficients. The factor 2 is $\Sigma \lambda_i^2$ in the first application (to temperature), while 20 is $\Sigma \lambda_j^2$ in the second. Similarly:

$$T_L P_Q = \frac{(3)^2}{(3)(2)(4)} = 0.38$$

$$T_L P_C = \frac{(-1)^2}{(3)(2)(20)} = 0.01$$

The sum of these 3 regression sums of squares is 33.47 which is equal to T_LP. Now it is evident that, in the population, the linear regression on temperature decreases linearly with period, as was inferred above from examining the T_L.

Proceeding in the same way with T_Q:

$$T_QP_L = \frac{(-7)^2}{(3)(6)(20)} = 0.14$$

$$T_QP_Q = \frac{(3)^2}{(3)(6)(4)} = 0.12$$

$$T_QP_C = \frac{(11)^2}{(3)(6)(20)} = 0.34$$

The sum is $T_QP = 0.60$. Clearly there is no change in T_Q with period. The results are collected in table 12.8.4. A regression on a regression is by nature an interaction.

Ordinarily one would not report all the nonsignificant comparisons, merely grouping them into batches as Remainder.

In summary, it is learned that the regression of ascorbic acid on temperature is parabolic in form, the linear part sloping downward more steeply with period. The regression on period is linear, sloping downward more rapidly as temperature increases. Based on these conclusions, a ruled surface was fitted to the data, allowing the estimation of ascorbic acid after any period of storage at any temperature (within the limits of the data). This was reported in the reference cited.

TABLE 12.8.4

ANALYSIS OF VARIANCE OF ASCORBIC ACID IN SNAPBEANS

Source of Variation	Degrees of Freedom	Sum of Squares	Mean Square
Temperature:	(2)	(334.39)	
T_L	1		301.04**
T_Q	1		33.35**
Period:	(3)	(40.53)	
P_L	1		40.14**
P_Q	1		0.25
P_C	1		0.14
Interaction:	(6)	(34.05)	
T_LP_L	1		33.08**
T_LP_Q	1		0.38
T_LP_C	1		0.01
T_QP_L	1		0.14
T_QP_Q	1		0.12
T_QP_C	1		0.34
Error	24		0.706

EXAMPLE 12.8.1—Since there is interaction in table 12.8.1, examine separately the two Spacing comparisons in each variety.

EXAMPLE 12.8.2—In an experiment like that of table 12.8.3, many prefer to lay out the treatment sums in a row, then use the coefficients for making all comparisons.

	0°				10°				20°			
	2	4	6	8	2	4	6	8	2	4	6	8
T_L	−1	−1	−1	−1	0	0	0	0	+1	+1	+1	+1
T_Q	+1	+1	+1	+1	−2	−2	−2	−2	+1	+1	+1	+1
S_L	−3	−1	+1	+3	−3	−1	+1	+3	−3	−1	+1	+3
S_Q	+1	−1	−1	+1	+1	−1	−1	+1	+1	−1	−1	+1
S_C	−1	+3	−3	+1	−1	+3	−3	+1	−1	+3	−3	+1
T_LS_L	+3	+1	−1	−3	0	0	0	0	−3	−1	+1	+3

etc.

Complete the table, compute the sums of squares ($n = 3$), and check their total against the Treatment sum of squares ($334.39 + 40.53 + 34.05 = 408.97$) in table 12.8.3.

12.9—Three-factor experiments; the 2^3.

The experimenter often requires evidence about the effects of 3 or more factors in a common environment. The simplest arrangement is that of 3 factors each at 2 levels, the $2 \times 2 \times 2$ or 2^3 experiment. The 8 treatment combinations may be tried in any of the common experimental designs.

The data in table 12.9.1 are extracted from an unpublished randomized blocks experiment (16) to learn the effect of supplementing a corn ration with soybean meal. Corn is deficient in lysine, so 0.6% of this amino acid was added. Lysine is present in the soybean meal. In the last column of the table it is suggested that the added protein in the form of soybean meal increased the rate of gain in the absence of the lysine additive but was not needed when the amino acid was added directly.

TABLE 12.9.1

AVERAGE DAILY GAINS OF SWINE IN 2^3 FACTORIAL ARRANGEMENT OF TREATMENTS. RANDOMIZED BLOCKS EXPERIMENT

Ly-sine %	Pro-tein %	Sex	Replications (Blocks)								Treat-ment Sum	Sum for 2 Sexes
			1	2	3	4	5	6	7	8		
0	12	M	1.11	0.97	1.09	0.99	0.85	1.21	1.29	0.96	8.47	
		F	1.03	0.97	0.99	0.99	0.99	1.21	1.19	1.24	8.61	17.08
	14	M	1.52	1.45	1.27	1.22	1.67	1.24	1.34	1.32	11.03	
		F	1.48	1.22	1.53	1.19	1.16	1.57	1.13	1.43	10.71	21.74
0.6	12	M	1.22	1.13	1.34	1.41	1.34	1.19	1.25	1.32	10.20	
		F	0.87	1.00	1.16	1.29	1.00	1.14	1.36	1.32	9.14	19.34
	14	M	1.38	1.08	1.40	1.21	1.46	1.39	1.17	1.21	10.30	
		F	1.09	1.09	1.47	1.43	1.24	1.17	1.01	1.13	9.63	19.93
Replication Sum			9.70	8.91	10.25	9.73	9.71	10.12	9.74	9.93		78.09

Replications	7		0.1411	
Treatments	7		0.7986	0.1141**
Error	49		1.0994	0.0224

This interaction indicates that main effects have little interest, but for illustrative purposes the analysis will be carried through.

For separating the Treatment sum of squares into 7 comparisons, each corresponding to one degree of freedom, the scheme in table 12.9.2 is

TABLE 12.9.2

SEVEN COMPARISONS IN 2^3 FACTORIAL EXPERIMENT ON SWINE

Effects	Lysine = 0				Lysine = 0.6%				Compari-son	Sum of Squares
	$P = 12\%$		$P = 14\%$		$P = 12\%$		$P = 14\%$			
	M	F	M	F	M	F	M	F		
	8.47	8.61	11.03	10.71	10.20	9.14	10.30	9.63		
Sex, S	−1	+1	−1	+1	−1	+1	−1	+1	−1.91	0.0570
Protein, P	−1	−1	+1	+1	−1	−1	+1	+1	5.25	0.4307
SP	+1	−1	−1	+1	+1	−1	−1	+1	−0.07	0.0001
Lysine, L	−1	−1	−1	−1	+1	+1	+1	+1	0.45	0.0032
SL	+1	−1	+1	−1	−1	+1	−1	+1	−1.55	0.0375
PL	+1	+1	−1	−1	−1	−1	+1	+1	−4.07	0.2588**
SPL	−1	+1	+1	−1	+1	−1	−1	+1	0.85	0.0113
Total										0.7986

effective. The treatment sums are copied from the next-to-last column in table 12.9.1. The coefficients for the main effects are first set down; afterwards those for the interactions are got by multiplication. There are now three 2-factor interactions and one 3-factor. For the latter, the coefficients come from multiplying those of any main effect by those of the interaction of the other 2 factors; conveniently, SP by L. The fact that the 7 comparisons are mutually orthogonal is tested by Rule 12.2.3.

To calculate the comparisons, apply the coefficients to the treatment sums. For example, for Sex = Female − Male:

$$c = +8.61 + 10.71 + 9.14 + 9.63 - 8.47 - 11.03 - 10.20 - 10.30$$
$$= -1.91$$

The sums of squares result from applying Rule 12.2.2 with $n = 8$ and $\Sigma\lambda^2 = 8$, the denominator being 64 in every case.

Rule 12.2.4 furnishes a check on the computations. The total of the 7 sums of squares must be the same as the Treatment sum of squares in the analysis of variance.

There is no evident effect of sex, either in the main effect or the interactions. This warrants combining the sex sums for a study of the significant protein-lysine interaction. The sums from the last column of table 12.9.1 are entered in the following 2 × 2 table:

	L_0	$L_{0.6}$
P_{12}	17.08	19.34
P_{14}	21.74	19.93

With corn protein alone the addition of 0.6% of lysine was effective but with added protein in the form of soybean meal, rich in lysine, the added amino acid was without effect.

It will be remembered that the interaction comparison is the difference between two differences:

$$\text{Effect of Lysine at } P_{14}: 19.93 - 21.74 = -1.81$$
$$\text{Effect of Lysine at } P_{12}: 19.34 - 17.08 = 2.26$$
$$\text{Interaction} = \text{Difference} = -\overline{4.07}$$

as in table 12.9.2. To calculate the sum of squares for this condensed table, it is convenient to think of replication in the combined sexes, $n = 16$. This is compensated by the reduction in coefficients to $+1\ -1\ -1\ +1$ so that $\Sigma\lambda^2 = 4$. The result is the same as before

$$\frac{c^2}{n\Sigma\lambda^2} = \frac{(-4.07)^2}{(16)(4)} = 0.2588$$

There is no particular interest in the significant main effect of protein. Certainly one would not recommend the addition of soybean protein both with and without lysine. The amino acid is valuable in the absence of soybean meal but not with it. The experimenter now has the data to decide which source of the amino acid is the cheaper.

If the 3-factor interaction were significant, its meaning could be examined by comparing two 2-factor interactions, thus:

	Males		Females	
	L_0	$L_{0.6}$	L_0	$L_{0.6}$
P_{12}	8.47	10.20	8.61	9.14
P_{14}	11.03	10.30	10.71	9.63
$P_{14} - P_{12}$	2.56	0.10	2.10	0.49
PL		-2.46		-1.61

The interaction among females is not so strongly marked as that among males. The difference,

$$-1.61 - (-2.46) = 0.85,$$

is the 3-factor interaction of table 12.9.2.

If one were calculating the sum of squares from the comparison, $-1.61 + 2.46$, he would have $n = 32$, $\Sigma\lambda^2 = 2$. It is instructive to identify all the coefficients in the 2 tables above with those in the last comparison of table 12.9.2.

In my experience, experiments are seldom sufficiently sensitive to detect 3-factor interactions even if they exist in the populations.

12.10—Three-factor experiments; a 2 × 3 × 4. This section will be used to summarize some of the more general methods applying to factorial experiments, including the 2-factor. Component analyses of Models I, II, and mixed will be explained, together with rules for testing significance. We shall begin with a numerical example, then pass to the general case.

As an example, I have again made a selection of data from the experiment drawn on in the foregoing section. A fourth factor consisted of levels of methionine, from which I have taken three. Four levels of lysine are now included. Only the males in 2 replications are used. This makes a $2 \times 3 \times 4$ factorial arrangement of treatments in randomized blocks design. Table 12.10.1 contains the data. The computations are self-explanatory.

The model being used is

$$X_{tjkm} = \mu + R_t + L_j + M_k + P_m + (LM)_{jk} + (LP)_{jm} + (MP)_{km} + (LPM)_{jkm} + \epsilon_{tjkm}$$

This is a Model I experiment with the values of the factors considered fixed. The analysis and components of variance are shown in table 12.10.2. Rules for writing components will be given in the following paragraphs. In examples 12.10.1, 2, 3, interpretations will be suggested.

We turn now to the general case. In preparation for component analysis and testing hypotheses, it is convenient to start with Model II, completely random design. This may be written,

$$X_{tjkm} = \mu + A_t + B_j + C_k + (AB)_{tj} + (AC)_{tk} + (BC)_{jk} + (ABC)_{tjk} + \epsilon_{tjkm}$$

$i = 1 \ldots a, \quad j = 1 \ldots b, k = 1 \ldots c, m = 1 \ldots n, \epsilon_{tjkm} = N(0, \sigma)$

Since all the effects are now random, consider them as normally distributed with variances $\sigma_A^2 \ldots \sigma_{ABC}^2$. The components for each effect are laid out in table 12.10.3.

Two rules are helpful (23). The second was anticipated in section 12.5. The first applies only if the sources of variation are listed in the order indicated, main effects first, followed by interactions.

Rule 12.10.1—The components in any mean square (above the last) are determined by the capital letter (or letters) designating the corresponding source of variation. The final component has the designating letter (or letters) as subscript. Each parameter contains all components having in their subscripts the letter (or letters) designating the corresponding source of variation.

Rule 12.10.2—Attached to each σ^2 (except that for Error) there are both coefficients and subscripts, the total number being constant. Capital letters represent factors; the corresponding small letters, numbers of treatments or replications. If a capital letter is put in the subscript, the corresponding small letter is omitted from the coefficient.

The testing of interactions is straightforward, but in the main effects a difficulty is encountered. If the hypothesis, $\sigma_A^2 = 0$, is to be tested, there

TABLE 12.10.1

THREE-FACTOR EXPERIMENT ($2 \times 3 \times 4$) IN RANDOMIZED BLOCKS. AVERAGE DAILY GAINS OF SWINE FED VARIOUS PERCENTAGES OF SUPPLEMENTARY LYSINE, METHIONINE, AND PROTEIN

Lysine, L	Methionine, M	Protein, P	Replications, R (Blocks) 1	Replications, R (Blocks) 2	Treatment Total
0	0	12	1.11	0.97	2.08
		14	1.52	1.45	2.97
	0.025	12	1.09	0.99	2.08
		14	1.27	1.22	2.49
	0.050	12	0.85	1.21	2.06
		14	1.67	1.24	2.91
0.05	0	12	1.30	1.00	2.30
		14	1.55	1.53	3.08
	0.025	12	1.03	1.21	2.24
		14	1.24	1.34	2.58
	0.050	12	1.12	0.96	2.08
		14	1.76	1.27	3.03
0.10	0	12	1.22	1.13	2.35
		14	1.38	1.08	2.46
	0.025	12	1.34	1.41	2.75
		14	1.40	1.21	2.61
	0.050	12	1.34	1.19	2.53
		14	1.46	1.39	2.85
0.15	0	12	1.19	1.03	2.22
		14	0.80	1.29	2.09
	0.025	12	1.36	1.16	2.52
		14	1.42	1.39	2.81
	0.050	12	1.46	1.03	2.49
		14	1.62	1.27	2.89
Total			31.50	28.97	60.47

Computations:
1. $C = (60.47)^2/48 = 76.1796$
2. Total: $1.11^2 + 0.97^2 + \ldots + 1.62^2 + 1.27^2 - C = 2.0409$
3. Treatments: $(2.08^2 + 2.97^2 + \ldots + 2.89^2)/2 - C = 1.2756$
4. Replications: $(31.50^2 + 28.97^2)/24 - C = 0.1334$
5. Error: $2.0409 - (1.2756 + 0.1334) = 0.6319$

Summary Table *A*

Methionine	Lysine 0	Lysine 0.05	Lysine 0.10	Lysine 0.15	Total
0	5.05	5.38	4.81	4.31	19.55
0.025	4.57	4.82	5.36	5.33	20.08
0.050	4.97	5.11	5.38	5.38	20.84
Total	14.59	15.31	15.55	15.02	60.47

Computations (continued):
6. Entries are sums of 2 levels of protein; $5.05 = 2.08 + 2.97$, etc.

TABLE 12.10.1—(*Continued*)

7. Total in A: $(5.05^2 + \ldots + 5.38^2)/4 - C = 0.3496$
8. Lysine, L: $(14.59^2 + \ldots + 15.02^2)/12 - C = 0.0427$
9. Methionine, M: $(19.55^2 + 20.08^2 + 20.84^2)/16 - C = 0.0526$
10. LM, $0.3496 - (0.0427 + 0.0526) = 0.2543$

SUMMARY TABLE B

Methionine	Protein 12	Protein 14	Total
0	8.95	10.60	19.55
0.025	9.59	10.49	20.08
0.050	9.16	11.68	20.84
Total	27.70	32.77	60.47

Computations (continued):

11. Entries are sums of 4 levels of lysine; $8.95 = 2.08 + 2.30 + 2.35 + 2.22$, etc.
12. Total in B: $(8.95^2 + \ldots + 11.68^2)/8 - C = 0.6702$
13. Protein, P: $(27.70^2 + 32.77^2)/24 - C = 0.5355$
14. MP: $0.6702 - (0.5355 + 0.0526) = 0.0821$

Summary Table C

Protein	Lysine 0	0.05	0.10	0.15	Total
12	6.22	6.62	7.63	7.23	27.70
14	8.37	8.69	7.92	7.79	32.77
Total	14.59	15.31	15.55	15.02	60.47

Computations (continued):

15. Entries are sums of 3 levels of methionine; $6.22 = 2.08 + 2.08 + 2.06$, etc.
16. Total in C: $(6.22^2 + \ldots + 7.79^2)/6 - C = 0.8181$
17. LP: $0.8181 - (0.5355 + 0.0427) = 0.2399$
18. LMP: $1.2756 - (0.0427 + 0.0526 + 0.5355 + 0.2543 + 0.0821 + 0.2399)$
    $= 0.0685$

is no apparent denominator for F. But approximate tests have been devised (21, 8). The parameter for A contains components for both AB and AC, suggesting the addition of the corresponding mean squares. In terms of components, this gives a mean square,

$$MS_2 = 2\sigma^2 + 2n\sigma_{ABC}^2 + nc\sigma_{AB}^2 + nb\sigma_{AC}^2$$

To match MS_2, add the components for A and ABC:

$$MS_1 = 2\sigma^2 + 2n\sigma_{ABC}^2 + nc\sigma_{AB}^2 + nb\sigma_{AC}^2 + nbc\sigma_A^2$$

The ratio, $F' = MS_1/MS_2$, is of the form to test $\sigma_A^2 = 0$ but it does not follow the F-distribution. However, the probability of its being exceeded

TABLE 12.10.2

ANALYSIS OF VARIANCE OF 3-FACTOR SWINE EXPERIMENT. COMPONENTS OF VARIANCE
FOR MODEL I. RANDOMIZED BLOCKS DESIGN

Source of Variation	Degrees of Freedom	Sum of Squares	Mean Square	Components Estimated by Mean Square
Replications	1	0.1334		
Lysine, L $(l = 4)$	3	0.0427	0.0142	$\sigma^2 + rmp\kappa_L^2$
Methionine, $M(m = 3)$	2	0.0526	0.0263	$\sigma^2 + rlp\kappa_M^2$
Protein, P $(p = 2)$	1	0.5355	0.5355**	$\sigma^2 + rlm\kappa_P^2$
LM	6	0.2543	0.0424	$\sigma^2 + rp\kappa_{LM}^2$
LP	3	0.2399	0.0800	$\sigma^2 + rm\kappa_{LP}^2$
MP	2	0.0821	0.0410	$\sigma^2 + rl\kappa_{MP}^2$
LMP	6	0.0685	0.0114	$\sigma^2 + r\kappa_{LMP}^2$
Error $(r = 2)$	23	0.6319	0.0275	σ^2

TABLE 12.10.3

COMPONENT ANALYSIS OF 3-FACTOR EXPERIMENT, MODEL II, COMPLETELY
RANDOMIZED DESIGN

Source of Variation	Parameter Estimated by Mean Square
A	$\sigma^2 + n\sigma_{ABC}^2 + nc\sigma_{AB}^2 + nb\sigma_{AC}^2 + nbc\sigma_A^2$
B	$\sigma^2 + n\sigma_{ABC}^2 + nc\sigma_{AB}^2 + na\sigma_{BC}^2 + nac\sigma_B^2$
C	$\sigma^2 + n\sigma_{ABC}^2 + nb\sigma_{AC}^2 + na\sigma_{BC}^2 + nab\sigma_C^2$
AB	$\sigma^2 + n\sigma_{ABC}^2 + nc\sigma_{AB}^2$
AC	$\sigma^2 + n\sigma_{ABC}^2 + nb\sigma_{AC}^2$
BC	$\sigma^2 + n\sigma_{ABC}^2 + na\sigma_{BC}^2$
ABC	$\sigma^2 + n\sigma_{ABC}^2$
Replication	σ^2

can be approximated from the F-table by calculating degrees of freedom
as follows:

$$n_1 = \frac{MS_1^2}{\dfrac{MS_A^2}{f_A} + \dfrac{MS_{ABC}^2}{f_{ABC}}}$$

$$n_2 = \frac{MS_2^2}{\dfrac{MS_{AB}^2}{f_{AB}} + \dfrac{MS_{AC}^2}{f_{AC}}}$$

where MS designates a mean square and f the corresponding degrees of
freedom.

Despite the fact that the nutrition experiment of table 12.10.2 is not
of type II, the numbers may be used to illustrate the foregoing test of

significance. Suppose Protein is to be tested under the assumption that all effects are random. The mean squares in the formulas are those with P in the subscripts.

$$MS_1 = MS_P + MS_{LMP} = 0.5355 + 0.0114 = 0.5469$$
$$MS_2 = MS_{LP} + MS_{MP} = 0.0800 + 0.0410 = 0.1210$$
$$F' = 0.5469/0.1210 = 4.52$$

$$n_1 = \frac{(0.5469)^2}{\dfrac{(0.5355)^2}{1} + \dfrac{(0.0114)^2}{6}} = 1.04$$

$$n_2 = \frac{(0.1210)^2}{\dfrac{(0.0800)^2}{3} + \dfrac{(0.0410)^2}{2}} = 4.9$$

Usually it is sufficiently accurate to round to the nearest integral degrees of freedom. In this case there is no doubt that F is short of the 5% point. Contrast this with the correct test (Model I) showing the protein effect to be highly significant.

For mixed models, one starts by writing down the components for Model II, then applying this simple rule:

Rule 12.10.3—Look at the subscripts of each component of an effect. Ignore the subscript letters which are the same as those designating the effect. If any of the other subscript letters correspond to a fixed effect, mark out the component. This rule does not affect either the first component in any line (σ^2) or the last.

For illustration, assume that A, table 12.10.3, is a fixed effect. Look first at the component, σ_{ABC}^2 in the first line. Ignoring A, both B and C correspond to random effects, so keep this component. In like manner, keep components σ_{AB}^2 and σ_{AC}^2. The last component, κ_A^2, is always kept; it is not affected by the rule.

In the second line, ignoring B in the subscript of σ_{ABC}^2, since A corresponds to a fixed effect, mark out the component. Delete also σ_{AB}^2 but retain σ_{BC}^2.

In AB, the only component affected by the rule is σ_{ABC}^2. Ignoring the subscripts AB, designating the effect, retain the component because C is random. But in the line for BC, this component is deleted because A is fixed. The resulting component analysis is that of table 12.10.4.

The testing offers no difficulties except in the main effect A. Here the approximate method is applied.

If A and B are both fixed effects, only C random, application of the

TABLE 12.10.4

COMPONENT ANALYSIS OF 3-FACTOR EXPERIMENT, MIXED MODEL, A FIXED, B AND C
RANDOM. COMPLETELY RANDOM DESIGN

A	$\sigma^2 + n\sigma_{ABC}^2 + nc\sigma_{AB}^2 + nb\sigma_{AC}^2 + nbc\kappa_A^2$
B	$\sigma^2 + na\sigma_{BC}^2 + nac\sigma_B^2$
C	$\sigma^2 + na\sigma_{BC}^2 + nab\sigma_C^2$
AB	$\sigma^2 + n\sigma_{ABC}^2 + nc\sigma_{AB}^2$
AC	$\sigma^2 + n\sigma_{ABC}^2 + nb\sigma_{AC}^2$
BC	$\sigma^2 + na\sigma_{BC}^2$
ABC	$\sigma^2 + n\sigma_{ABC}^2$
R	σ^2

rule to table 12.10.4 (or table 12.10.3) results in deletion of the following
additional effects:

$$\text{In } A: \sigma_{ABC}^2, \sigma_{AB}^2$$

$$\text{In } C: \sigma_{BC}^2$$

$$\text{In } AC: \sigma_{ABC}^2$$

If A, B, and C are all fixed, further application of the rule produces
the component analysis of table 12.10.2.

EXAMPLE 12.10.1—In table 12.10.2, for L, M, MP, and LMP the sums of
squares are all so small that no single degree of freedom isolated from them could
reach significance. But LM and LP deserve further study.

In the LM summary table A in table 12.10.1, there is some evidence of interaction
though the over-all test on 6 degrees of freedom doesn't detect it. Let us look at the
linear effects. First, calculate M_L (-1, 0, $+1$) for each level of lysine:

$$-0.08, \quad -0.27, \quad 0.57, \quad 1.07$$

Next, take the linear effect of lysine (-3, -1, $+1$, $+3$) in these M_L; the result, 4.29
Finally, application of Rule 12.2.6 yields the sum of squares,

$$L_L M_L = \frac{(4.29)^2}{(4)(2)(20)} = 0.1150,$$

which is just short of significance at the 5% level. None of the other 5 comparisons is
significant. In the larger experiment of which this is a part, $L_L M_L$ was significant.
What interpretation do you suggest?

EXAMPLE 12.10.2—In the LP summary table C, the differences between 14%
and 12%,

$$2.15, \quad 2.07, \quad 0.29, \quad 0.56,$$

suggest an interaction. The linear effects of lysine (-3, -1, 1, 3) at the 2 levels of
Protein are 4.04 and -2.51. Taking the difference as the linear effect of Protein
(-1, $+1$) we have $4.04 - (-2.51) = 6.55$. By Rule 12.2.6,

$$L_L P_L = \frac{(6.55)^2}{(6)(2)(20)} = 0.1788$$

$F = 0.1788/0.0275 = 6.50$, $P = 0.025$. This corresponds to the highly significant
effect observed in table 12.9.2, where an interpretation was given.

Deducting $L_L P_L$ from the LP sum of squares in table 12.10.2, $0.2399 - 0.1788 =
0.0611$, shows that neither of the other 2 comparisons can be significant.

EXAMPLE 12.10.3—The investigator is often interested in estimates of differences rather than in tests of significance. Because of the LP interaction he might wish
to estimate the effect of protein with no lysine. Summary table C shows this mean
difference: $(8.37 - 6.22)/6 = 0.36$ lb./day. (The justification for using all levels of
methionine is that there is little evidence of either main effect or interaction with protein.) Confidence interval $= 2.069 \sqrt{(2)(0.0275)/6} = 0.20$ lb./day. So the 95%
interval is from 0.16 to 0.56 lb./day.

EXAMPLE 12.10.4—Some experiments combine the completely randomized design with two-way designs like randomized blocks. In the following table are data extracted from a report which has already been referred to (28). Three plants were picked at random and from each were randomly selected 4 leaves. From the wet ash solution of each leaf two 2-ml. aliquots were analyzed for calcium. A second set of analyses was run on a subsequent day. The model is

$$X_{ijkm} = \mu + P_i + L_{ij} + A_k + (PA)_{ik} + (LA)_{ijk} + \epsilon_{ijkm}$$

$i = 1 \ldots 3, j = 1 \ldots 4, k = 1, 2, m = 1, 2, \epsilon = N(0, \sigma)$. All effects may be considered random so that $\sigma_P^2 \ldots \sigma_{LA}^2$ are taken as variances from normal populations.

The distinquishing feature of this design is that a leaf has its number designation, j, for *each plant*, i, as in chapter 10.

The data with the analysis of variance are in the accompanying tables. The symbol, $L(P)$ "leaves within plants," is necessary for application of the rules for components.

THREE-FACTOR EXPERIMENT ($2 \times 3 \times 4$), COMPLETELY RANDOMIZED DESIGN.
CALCIUM CONCENTRATION (PER CENT DRY BASIS) IN TURNIP GREENS

Plant	Leaf	Ashing 1			Ashing 2			Leaf Sum	Plant Sum
		R_1	R_2	Sum	R_1	R_2	Sum		
1	1	3.28	3.09	6.37	3.03	3.03	6.06	12.43	
	2	3.52	3.48	7.00	3.38	3.38	6.76	13.76	
	3	2.88	2.80	5.68	2.81	2.76	5.57	11.25	
	4	3.34	3.38	6.72	3.23	3.26	6.49	13.21	
		13.02	12.75	25.77	12.45	12.43	24.88		50.65
2	1	2.63	2.66	5.29	2.54	2.59	5.13	10.42	
	2	3.74	3.44	7.18	3.58	3.64	7.22	14.40	
	3	2.55	2.55	5.10	2.49	2.49	4.98	10.08	
	4	2.77	2.66	5.43	2.86	2.80	5.66	11.09	
		11.69	11.31	23.00	11.47	11.52	22.99		45.99
3	1	3.78	3.87	7.65	3.88	3.82	7.70	15.35	
	2	4.31	4.40	8.71	3.99	4.05	8.04	16.75	
	3	3.31	3.31	6.62	3.19	3.13	6.32	12.94	
	4	4.07	4.12	8.19	4.00	4.08	8.08	16.27	
		15.47	15.70	31.17	15.06	15.08	30.14		61.31
Sum				79.94			78.01		157.95

ANALYSIS OF VARIANCE OF CALCIUM EXPERIMENT, MODEL II

Source of Variation	Degrees of Freedom	Mean Square	Parameters Estimated by Mean Square
Plant, P ($p = 3$)	2	3.8548 *	$\sigma^2 + 2\sigma_{AL(P)}^2 + 8\sigma_{AP}^2 + 4\sigma_{L(P)}^2 + 16\sigma_P^2$
Leaves in Plant, $L(P)(l = 4)$	9	0.6646 **	$\sigma^2 + 2\sigma_{AL(P)}^2 + 4\sigma_{L(P)}^2$
Ashing, A ($a = 2$)	1	0.0776	$\sigma^2 + 2\sigma_{AL(P)}^2 + 8\sigma_{AP}^2 + 24\sigma_A^2$
AP	2	0.0191	$\sigma^2 + 2\sigma_{AL(P)}^2 + 8\sigma_{AP}^2$
$AL(P)$	9	0.0112 *	$\sigma^2 + 2\sigma_{AL(P)}^2$
Replications, R ($n = 2$)	24	0.00412	σ^2

Rule 12.10.1 puts this among the components of P, a peculiarity of the design. Rule 12.10.2 makes its coefficient $an = 4$. P is put in parentheses to distinguish the symbol from that of an interaction. Using the rules given, verify the analysis.

EXAMPLE 12.10.5—Verify the indicated tests of significance in the calcium experiment. For plants, $F' = 5.65, f' = 2.0, 9.5$.

EXAMPLE 12.10.6—What components would be deleted from the calcium experiment if Ashings were assumed fixed? Ans. From $L(P)$, $\sigma_{AL(P)}{}^2$; from P, $\sigma_{AL(P)}{}^2$ and $\sigma_{AP}{}^2$. What effects would this have on the tests of significance?

EXAMPLE 12.10.7—What additional components would be deleted if P as well as A were fixed? Ans. From A, $\sigma_{AL(P)}{}^2$ and $\sigma_{AP}{}^2$. How would this affect the testing?

12.11—The split-plot design. It is often desirable to get rather precise information on one factor and on the interaction of this factor with a second, but to forego such precision on the second factor. For example, 3 sources of vitamin might be compared by trying them on 3 males of the same litter, replicating the experiment on 20 litters. This would be a randomized blocks design with high precision, 38 degrees of freedom for error. Superimposed on this could be some experiment with the litters as units. Four types of housing could be tried, one litter to each type, thus allowing 5 replications with 12 degrees of freedom for error. The main treatments (housings) would not be compared so accurately as the sub-treatments (sources of vitamin) for two reasons; less replication is provided, and litter differences are included in the error for evaluating the housing effects. Nevertheless, some information about housing may be got at little extra expense, and any interaction between housing and vitamin will be accurately evaluated.

In experiments on varieties or fertilizers on small plots, cultural practices with large machines may be tried on whole groups of the smaller plots, each group containing all the varieties. (Irrigation is one such practice that demands fairly large areas per treatment.) The series of cultural practices is usually replicated only a small number of times but the varieties are repeated on every cultural plot. Experiments of this type are called *split-plot*, the cultural *main plot* being split into smaller varietal *sub-plots*. This design is remarkably popular.

The essential feature of the split-plot experiment is that the sub-plot

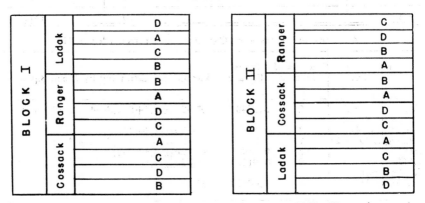

Fig. 12.11.1—First 2 blocks of split-plot experiment on alfalfa, illustrating random arrangement of main and sub-plots.

treatments are not randomized over the whole large block but only over the main plots. Randomization of the sub-treatments is newly done in each main plot and the main treatments are randomized in the large blocks. A consequence is that the experimental error for sub-treatments is different (characteristically smaller) than that for main treatments.

Figure 12.11.1 shows the field layout of a split-plot design with 3 varieties of alfalfa, the sub-treatments being 4 dates of final cutting (31). The first 2 harvests were common to all plots, the second on July 27, 1943. The third harvests were: A, none; B, September 1; C, September 20; D, October 7. Yields in 1944 are recorded in table 12.11.1. Such an experi-

TABLE 12.11.1

YIELDS OF 3 VARIETIES OF ALFALFA (TONS PER ACRE) IN 1944 FOLLOWING 4 DATES
OF FINAL CUTTING IN 1943

Variety	Date	Block					
		1	2	3	4	5	6
Ladak	A	2.17	1.88	1.62	2.34	1.58	1.66
	B	1.58	1.26	1.22	1.59	1.25	0.94
	C	2.29	1.60	1.67	1.91	1.39	1.12
	D	2.23	2.01	1.82	2.10	1.66	1.10
		8.27	6.75	6.33	7.94	5.88	4.82
Cossack	A	2.33	2.01	1.70	1.78	1.42	1.35
	B	1.38	1.30	1.85	1.09	1.13	1.06
	C	1.86	1.70	1.81	1.54	1.67	0.88
	D	2.27	1.81	2.01	1.40	1.31	1.06
		7.84	6.82	7.37	5.81	5.53	4.35
Ranger	A	1.75	1.95	2.13	1.78	1.31	1.30
	B	1.52	1.47	1.80	1.37	1.01	1.31
	C	1.55	1.61	1.82	1.56	1.23	1.13
	D	1.56	1.72	1.99	1.55	1.51	1.33
		6.38	6.75	7.74	6.26	5.06	5.07
Total		22.49	20.32	21.44	20.01	16.47	14.24

Variety	Date of Cutting				
	A	B	C	D	Total
Ladak	11.25	7.84	9.98	10.92	39.99
Cossack	10.59	7.81	9.46	9.86	37.72
Ranger	10.22	8.48	8.90	9.66	37.26
Total	32.06	24.13	28.34	30.44	114.97
Mean (tons per acre)	1.78	1.34	1.57	1.69	

ment is, of course, not evaluated by a single season's yields; statistical methods for perennial crops are referred to below.

The analysis of variance reflects the essential feature of the design; the main plot analysis is that of randomized blocks with 3 varieties replicated in 6 blocks, the sub-plot analysis being that of 4 dates of cutting randomized in each of 18 main plots (table 12.11.2).

TABLE 12.11.2
ANALYSIS OF VARIANCE OF SPLIT-PLOT EXPERIMENT ON ALFALFA

Source of Variation	Degrees of Freedom	Sum of Squares	Mean Square
Main plots:			
Varieties	2	0.1781	0.0890
Blocks	5	4.1499	0.8300
Main plot error	10	1.3622	0.1362
Sub-plots:			
Dates of cutting	3	1.9625	0.6542**
Date × variety	6	0.2105	0.0351
Sub-plot error	45	1.2586	0.0280

1. Correction: $C = (114.9)^2/72 = 183.5847$
2. Total: $(2.17)^2 + \ldots + (1.33)^2 - C = 9.1218$
3. Main plot: $\dfrac{(8.27)^2 + \ldots + (5.07)^2}{4} - C = 5.6902$
4. Variety: $\dfrac{(39.99)^2 + \ldots + (37.26)^2}{24} - C = 0.1781$
5. Block: $\dfrac{(22.49)^2 + \ldots + (14.24)^2}{12} - C = 4.1499$
6. Main plot error: $5.6902 - (0.1781 + 4.1499) = 1.3622$
7. Sub-classes in variety-date table: $\dfrac{(11.25)^2 + \ldots + (9.66)^2}{6} - C = 2.3511$
8. Date: $\dfrac{(32.06)^2 + \ldots + (30.44)^2}{18} - C = 1.9625$
9. Variety × date: $2.3511 - (0.1781 + 1.9625) = 0.2105$
10. Sub-plot error: $9.1218 - (5.6902 + 1.9625 + 0.2105) = 1.2586$

The significant differences among dates of cutting were not unexpected, nor were the smaller yields following B and C. The last harvest should be either early enough to allow renewed growth and restoration of the consequent depletion of root reserves, or so late that no growth and depletion will ensue. The surprising features of the experiment were two: the yield following C being greater than B, since late September is usually considered a poor time to cut alfalfa in Iowa; and the absence of interaction between date and variety—Ladak is slow to renew growth after cutting and might have reacted differently from the other varieties. These are probably seasonal peculiarities.

The model for the split-plot experiment in randomized blocks is

$$X_{ijk} = \mu + B_i + M_j + \epsilon_{ij} + T_k + (MT)_{jk} + \delta_{ijk}$$
$$i = 1 \ldots b, j = 1 \ldots m, k = 1 \ldots t, \ \epsilon_{ij} = \mathcal{N}(0, \sigma_M), \ \delta_{ijk} = \mathcal{N}(0, \sigma_I)$$

Here, M stands for main plot treatment and T for that in the sub-plot.

The component analyses for the split-plot experiment in randomized blocks are summarized in table 12.11.3. The Model II analysis is easily got from the full 3-factor structure of table 12.10.3 by combining into the 2 error terms all "interactions" with blocks.

TABLE 12.11.3

COMPONENT ANALYSES FOR SPLIT-PLOT DESIGNS; m MAIN TREATMENTS, t SUB-TREATMENTS, b BLOCKS. BLOCKS RANDOM

Source of Variation	M and T Random	M Random, T Fixed
Main Treatment, M	$E_a + b\sigma_{MT}^2 + bt\sigma_M^2$	$E_a + bt\sigma_M^2$
Error (a)	E_a	E_a
Sub-treatment, T	$E_b + b\sigma_{MT}^2 + bm\sigma_T^2$	$E_b + b\sigma_{MT}^2 + bm\kappa_T^2$
MT	$E_b + b\sigma_{MT}^2$	$E_b + b\sigma_{MT}^2$
Error (b)	E_b	E_b

	M Fixed, T Random	M and T Fixed
	$E_a + b\sigma_{MT}^2 + bt\kappa_M^2$	$E_a + bt\kappa_M^2$
	E_a	E_a
	$E_b + bm\sigma_T^2$	$E_b + bm\kappa_T^2$
	$E_b + b\sigma_{MT}^2$	$E_b + b\kappa_{MT}^2$
	E_b	E_b

If T is fixed, the testing is straightforward; but if T is random, for testing the main treatments one must use the approximate method described in the preceding section.

Anderson and Bancroft (2, page 347), suggest that there may be occasions for separating Error (b) into the 2 components, BT and BNT. Ordinarily the two are expected to be much the same and are taken to estimate the same σ^2.

If there is no interaction, comparisons planned for either or both of the two factors are made as usual, with degrees of freedom and error (a) or (b) corresponding to the factor being studied. If F is significant for either factor, tests of all differences may be made in accord with section 10.6.

In case of interaction between the main and sub-plot factors, the 2-way table like that at the bottom of table 12.11.1 is studied for interpretations.

There may be wholly different recommendations for two varieties, the main effects being without interest.

Missing plots in a split-plot experiment have been studied by Anderson (1). For a single missing sub-plot,

$$X_{ijk} = \frac{b(X_{ij.}) + t(X_{.jk}) - X_{.j.}}{(b-1)(t-1)}$$

where there are b blocks (replications) and t sub-treatments. The other symbols are, as usual, the totals of the *remaining yields* in the main plot $(X_{ij.})$, in the sub-treatment $(X_{.jk})$, and in the main treatment $(X_{.j.})$ containing the missing datum

Example: Assume $X_{111} = 2.17$ is missing from table 12.11.1 in which $b = 6$ and $t = 4$. $X_{11.} = 8.27 - 2.17 = 6.10$, the sum of the remaining yields in main plot Ladak, block 1; $X_{.11} = 1.88 + 1.62 + \ldots + 1.66 = 9.08$, the sum of the remaining yields in Ladak, cutting A; and $X_{.1.} = 39.99 - 2.17 = 37.82$, the sum of the remaining yields for Ladak. Substituting:

$$X_{111} = \frac{6(6.10) + 4(9.08) - 37.82}{(6-1)(4-1)} = 2.34 \text{ tons/acre}$$

Except in Error (b), there will be an upward bias in all the mean squares. These are presumably small, but Anderson gives methods for correcting them.

Experimenters often split the sub-plot and even the sub-sub-plot. The statistical methods offer no great additional complexity. For the split-split-plot experiment, the structure of Model II is given in table 12.11.4. As usual, the small letters, b, m, etc., stand for the numbers of treatments in the factors denoted by the corresponding capitals. The mixed models and Model I are got by applying the rule given in the preceding section. In Model I there are only 2 components for each effect, the first and the last in the table. The calculations follow those of the randomized blocks,

TABLE 12.11.4

STRUCTURE OF SPLIT-SPLIT-PLOT EXPERIMENT, MODEL II

Block, B	
Main Plot, M	$E_a + b\sigma_{MNT}^2 + bn\sigma_{MT}^2 + bt\sigma_{MN}^2 + bnt\sigma_M^2$
Error (a), E_a	E_a
Sub-Plot, N	$E_b + b\sigma_{MNT}^2 + bm\sigma_{NT}^2 + bt\sigma_{MN}^2 + bmt\sigma_N^2$
MN	$E_b + b\sigma_{MNT}^2 + bt\sigma_{MN}^2$
Error (b), E_b	E_b
Sub-Sub-Plot, T	$E_c + b\sigma_{MNT}^2 + bm\sigma_{NT}^2 + bn\sigma_{MT}^2 + bmn\sigma_T^2$
MT	$E_c + b\sigma_{MNT}^2 + bn\sigma_{MT}^2$
NT	$E_c + b\sigma_{MNT}^2 + bm\sigma_{NT}^2$
MNT	$E_c + b\sigma_{MNT}^2$
Error (c), E_c	E_c

the 2-factor experiment, and the 3-factor experiment, successively.   Each error term comes from subtraction.

EXAMPLE 12.11.1—A split-split-plot experiment on corn was conducted to try 3 rates of planting (stands) with 3 levels of fertilizer in irrigated and non-irrigated plots (4).   The design was randomized blocks with 4 replications.   The main plots carried the irrigation treatments.   On each there were sub-plots with 3 stands, 10,000, 13,000, and 16,000 plants per acre.   Finally, each sub-plot was divided into 3 parts respectively fertilized with 60, 120, and 180 pounds of nitrogen.   The yields are in bushels per acre. Calculate the analysis of variance.

					Block			
					1	2	3	4
Not Irrigated	Stand	1	Fertilizer	1	90	83	85	86
				2	95	80	88	78
				3	107	95	88	89
		2		1	92	98	112	79
				2	89	98	104	86
				3	92	106	91	87
		3		1	81	74	82	85
				2	92	81	78	89
				3	93	74	94	83
Irrigated		1		1	80	102	60	73
				2	87	109	104	114
				3	100	105	114	114
		2		1	121	99	90	109
				2	110	94	118	131
				3	119	123	113	126
		3		1	78	136	119	116
				2	98	133	122	136
				3	122	132	136	133

Source of Variation	Degrees of Freedom	Mean Square
Main Plots:		
Blocks	3	
Irrigation, I	1	8,277.56
Error (a)	3	470.59
Sub-plots:		
Stand, S	2	879.18
IS	2	1,373.51 *
Error (b)	12	232.33
Sub-sub-plots:		
Fertilizer, F	2	988.72
IF	2	476.72 **
SF	4	76.22
ISF	4	58.68
Error (c)	36	86.36

EXAMPLE 12.11.2—Attention is attracted to the 2 significant interactions, *IS* and *IF*. Now, *ISF* is less than error. This means that the *IS* interaction is much the same at all levels of *F*; or, alternatively, that the *IF* interaction is similar at all levels of *S*. Hence, each 2-way table gives information.

	F_1	F_2	F_3	S_1	S_2	S_3
Not Irrigated	1,047	1,058	1,099	1,064	1,134	1,006
Irrigated	1,183	1,356	1,437	1,162	1,353	1,461

It is clear that neither fertilizer nor stand affected yield on the non-irrigated plots. With irrigation, the effect of each was pronounced. So it is necessary to examine separately the split-plot experiment on the irrigated plots. Verify the following mean squares:

Stand:		
Linear	1	3,725 **
Deviations	1	96
Error (*a*)	6	316

Fertilizer:		
Linear	1	2,688 **
Deviations	1	118
SF	4	92
Error (*b*)	18	137

EXAMPLE 12.11.3—Notice that the planting and fertilizer rates were well chosen for the unirrigated plots, but on the irrigated plots they were too low to allow any evaluation of the optima. This suggests that irrigation should not be a factor in such experiments. But in order to compare costs and returns over a number of years, two experiments (one with and one without irrigation) should be randomly interplanted to control fertility differences.

12.12—Series of experiments. A series of experiments may extend over several places or over several seasons or over both. The places and seasons become added factors to be included in the analysis. Either factor may be planned as fixed or random. I never encountered an experiment in which the seasons were actually selected at random, and random selection of places is rare in any but survey-type experiments; but the *effects* of seasons and places are often taken as random.

It is not much of an overstatement to say that every series of experiments is a unique problem for both the statistician and the experimenter. The size and design of the experiment may vary from place to place or from year to year. The treatment-place or treatment-season interactions may complicate the analysis. The experimental error may differ in place and time. Unless an experimenter is unusually expert in statistical theory he would be well advised to seek the cooperation of a competent mathematical statistician before undertaking a series of experiments. My observation is that much time and money are wasted in ill-considered series of experiments.

There are excellent presentations of the difficulties involved (7, 33, 10, 17, 9) with directions for attacking the less complicated. The methods presented in this book will enable the reader to follow the references cited.

It may be well to warn the reader of a difficulty which arises when a perennial crop is investigated over a number of years. The yields from a plot in successive years are probably correlated; the experimental error one season is not independent of that in another season. For these reasons the primary analysis is based on the sum of the plot yields over the lifetime of the experiment.

For illustration, the data in table 12.12.1 are taken from an experiment by Haber (12) to compare the effects of various cutting treatments on asparagus. Planting was in 1927 and cutting began in 1929. One plot in each block was cut till June 1 each year, others to June 15, July 1, and July 15. The yields are the weights cut to June 1 in every plot, irrespective of later cuttings in some of them. This weight, then, is a measure of

TABLE 12.12.1

WEIGHT (OUNCES) OF ASPARAGUS CUT BEFORE JUNE 1 FROM PLOTS WITH VARIOUS CUTTING TREATMENTS

Block	Year	Cutting Ceased				Total
		June 1	June 15	July 1	July 15	
1	1930	230	212	183	148	773
	1931	324	415	320	246	1,305
	1932	512	584	456	304	1,856
	1933	399	386	255	144	1,184
		1,465	1,597	1,214	842	5,118
2	1930	216	190	186	126	718
	1931	317	296	295	201	1,109
	1932	448	471	387	289	1,595
	1933	361	280	187	83	911
		1,342	1,237	1,055	699	4,333
3	1930	219	151	177	107	654
	1931	357	278	298	192	1,125
	1932	496	399	427	271	1,593
	1933	344	254	239	90	927
		1,416	1,082	1,141	660	4,299
4	1930	200	150	209	168	727
	1931	362	336	328	226	1,252
	1932	540	485	462	312	1,799
	1933	381	279	244	168	1,072
		1,483	1,250	1,243	874	4,850
Total		5,706	5,166	4,653	3,075	18,600

Blocks	3	30,170	
Cuttings:	(3)	(241,377)	
Linear	1		220,815**
Quadratic	1		16,835*
Remainder	1		3,727
Error	9		2,429

vigor, and the experiment is to learn the relative effectiveness of the harvesting plans.

To avoid the effects of correlation, the annual plot yields are added and the analysis made on the sums. Certainly there is no doubt that the cuttings affected the vigor of the plants as measured by yields to June 1.

The cutting totals are separated into linear, quadratic, and cubic effects and the corresponding sums of squares entered in the table. The significant quadratic component indicates that the yields fall off more and more rapidly as the severity of the cutting increases. A graph of the cutting means (or totals) against dates will show this clearly. Since Remainder is little larger than Error, deviations from a parabolic curve are attributable to sampling variation.

In this experiment there is much more information than has been extracted by the analysis given. Correlated errors can be avoided to a great extent by taking differences between the years. For example, the linear component on years for one block should be independent from that in the other blocks. Features of this experiment have been discussed by Snedecor and Haber (13, 27) as well as in the 4th edition of this text. The necessary statistical methods are given in the foregoing sections so need not be repeated here.

EXAMPLE 12.12.1—The following data illustrate a series of experiments over 5 places (19). Four treated lots of 100 Mukden soybean seeds, together with one lot untreated, were planted in 5 randomized blocks at each participating station. The total numbers of emerging plants (from 500 seeds) are shown for the 5 locations. Also shown are the analyses of variance at the several stations.

NUMBER OF EMERGING PLANTS (500 SEEDS) IN 5 PLOTS. COOPERATIVE SEED TREATMENT TRIALS WITH MUKDEN SOYBEANS, 1943

Location	Untreated	Arasan	Spergon	Semesan, Jr.	Fermate	Total
Michigan	360	356	362	350	373	1,801
Minnesota	302	354	349	332	332	1,669
Wisconsin	408	407	391	391	409	2,006
Virginia	244	267	293	235	278	1,317
Rhode Island	373	387	406	394	375	1,935
Total	1,687	1,771	1,801	1,702	1,767	8,728

Mean Squares From Original Analyses of Variance

Source of Variation	Degrees of Freedom	Location				
		Michigan	Minnesota	Wisconsin	Virginia	Rhode Island
Treatment	4	14.44	82.84*	17.44	114.26*	37.50
Block	4	185.14	54.64	5.64	70.76	4.80
Error	16	42.29	26.67	30.64	26.34	13.05

Test the hypothesis of homogeneity of error variance. Ans. Corrected $\chi^2 = 5.22, f = 4$.

EXAMPLE 12.12.2—For the entire soybean data, analyze the variance as follows:

Source of Variation	Degrees of Freedom	Sum of Squares	Mean Square
Treatment	4	380.29	95.07
Location	4	11,852.61	2,963.15
Interaction	16	685.63	42.85
Blocks in Location	20	1,283.92	. . . .
Experimental Error	80	2,223.68	27.80

Blocks and Experimental Error are pooled from the analyses of all the 5 places.

EXAMPLE 12.12.3—Write out the component analysis, assuming treatments fixed with locations and blocks random.

Treatment, T	$\sigma^2 + 5\sigma_{TL}^2 + 25\kappa_T^2$
Location, L	$\sigma^2 + 5\sigma_{B(L)}^2 + 25\sigma_L^2$
TL	$\sigma^2 + 5\sigma_{TL}^2$
Blocks in Location, $B(L)$	$\sigma^2 + 5\sigma_{B(L)}^2$
Pooled error	σ^2

For Treatments, $F = 95.07/42.85 = 2.22$, $F_{.05} = 3.01$.

EXAMPLE 12.12.4—Isolate the sum of squares for the planned comparison Treatment vs. Check. Ans. 171.70, $F = 4.01$, $F_{.05} = 4.49$.

12.13—Proportional sub-class numbers. For one reason or another the numbers of observations in the treatments of a table like 12.4.1 may not be equal. When through accident, or under the limitations of an experimental technique, erratic losses of data occur, the addition theorem for sums of squares is annulled and the analysis of variance must be modified. Appropriate methods are described in following sections. Occasionally, however, the sub-class numbers are proportional, as in some of the foregoing tables, causing no injury to the analysis of variance.

In table 12.13.1 the numbers of dressing percentages (each decreased by 70%) for the breeds and sexes represent approximately the proportions in which the animals were brought in for slaughter at the College Meats Laboratory (5). For illustration we have chosen only a small sample from the original data. All the pigs represented have weights between 200 and 219 pounds; with such large denominators, transformation of these percentages seems unnecessary. Let me emphasize the fact that the sub-class numbers for breeds are representative of population proportions. The picture would be distorted by equality of numbers. The only modification introduced into the original data has been to make the numbers proportional; that is,

both   12:6 = 30:15 = 4:2, etc.

and   12:30:4:6:10 = 6:15:2:3:5

While proportional sub-class numbers do not disturb the analysis of variance, the computations must be modified slightly because of unequal

TABLE 12.13.1

DRESSING PERCENTAGES (LESS 70%) OF 93 SWINE CLASSIFIED BY BREED AND SEX.
LIVE WEIGHTS 200–219 POUNDS

Number	Breed 1 Male	Breed 1 Female	Breed 2 Male	Breed 2 Female	Breed 3 Male	Breed 3 Female	Breed 4 Male	Breed 4 Female	Breed 5 Male	Breed 5 Female
1	13.3	18.2	10.9	14.3	13.6	12.9	11.6	13.8	10.3	12.8
2	12.6	11.3	3.3	15.3	13.1	14.4	13.2	14.4	10.3	8.4
3	11.5	14.2	10.5	11.8	4.1		12.6	4.9	10.1	10.6
4	15.4	15.9	11.6	11.0	10.8		15.2		6.9	13.9
5	12.7	12.9	15.4	10.9			14.7		13.2	10.0
6	15.7	15.1	14.4	10.5			12.4		11.0	
7	13.2		11.6	12.9					12.2	
8	15.0		14.4	12.5					13.3	
9	14.3		7.5	13.0					12.9	
10	16.5		10.8	7.6					9.9	
11	15.0		10.5	12.9						
12	13.7		14.5	12.4						
13			10.9	12.8						
14			13.0	10.9						
15			15.9	13.9						
16			12.8							
17			14.0							
18			11.1							
19			12.1							
20			14.7							
21			12.7							
22			13.1							
23			10.4							
24			11.9							
25			10.7							
26			14.4							
27			11.3							
28			13.0							
29			12.7							
30			12.6							
ΣX	168.9	87.6	362.7	182.7	41.6	27.3	79.7	33.1	110.1	55.7

Total: $N = 93$, $\Sigma X = 1{,}149.4$, $\Sigma X^2 = 14{,}785.62$
Breed Sums: 1; 256.5, 2; 545.4, 3; 68.9, 4; 112.8, 5; 165.8
Sex Sums: Male, 763.0; Female, 386.4

1. Correction: $C = (\Sigma X)^2/n = (1{,}149.4)^2/93 = 14{,}205.60$
2. Total: $\Sigma X^2 - C = 14{,}785.62 - 14{,}205.60 = 580.02$

3. Sub-classes: $\dfrac{(168.9)^2}{12} + \dfrac{(87.6)^2}{6} + \ldots + \dfrac{(55.7)^2}{5} - C = 122.83$

4. Within sub-classes: $580.02 - 122.83 = 457.19$

5. Sex: $\dfrac{(763.0)^2}{62} + \dfrac{(386.4)^2}{31} - C = 0.52$

6. Breed: $\dfrac{(256.5)^2}{18} + \ldots + \dfrac{(165.8)^2}{15} - C = 97.38$

7. Interaction: $122.83 - (97.38 + 0.52) = 24.93$

TABLE 12.13.1—(*Continued*)

Sex	1	0.52	0.52
Breed	4	97.38	24.34**
Breed-Sex Interaction	4	24.93	6.23
Within Sub-classes	83	457.19	5.51

sample sizes (section 10.16). The appropriate method is shown in the table. Since the sample chosen for illustration represents only a small fraction of the original data, conclusions should be only tentative.

With unequal sub-class numbers the component analysis is complicated as it was in sections 10.16 and 10.17. Different coefficients must be calculated for each component in each effect (24).

Wilk and Kempthorne (30) have developed general formulas applying to all models of 3-factor arrangements; the sub-class members may be equal or proportional. I shall report only the 2-factor parts. Let the proportions in factor A be $u_1:u_2: \ldots :u_a$ and those in B, $v_1:v_2: \ldots :v_b$. Also let:

$$U = \Sigma u, \ V = \Sigma v, \ U^* = \frac{\Sigma u^2}{(\Sigma u)^2}, \ V^* = \frac{\Sigma v^2}{(\Sigma v)^2}$$

Then the population components are:

A:
$$\sigma^2 + \frac{nUV(1 - U^*)}{a - 1} \left\{ (V^* - \frac{1}{B}) \sigma_{AB}^2 + \sigma_A^2 \right\}$$

B:
$$\sigma^2 + \frac{nUV(1 - V^*)}{b - 1} \left\{ (U^* - \frac{1}{A}) \sigma_{AB}^2 + \sigma_B^2 \right\}$$

AB:
$$\sigma^2 + \frac{nUV(1 - U^*)(1 - V^*)}{(a - 1)(b - 1)} \sigma_{AB}^2$$

As usual, n is the number of replications in the completely random design; it represents number of blocks in randomized blocks. A and B have the following values:

In Model I, $A = a$, $B = b$

In Model II, $\frac{1}{A} = 0, \frac{1}{B} = 0$

If A is fixed, B random, $A = a, \frac{1}{B} = 0$

If A is random, B fixed, $\frac{1}{A} = 0, B = b$

For the swine, if A denotes sex and B, breed:

$$n = 1; a = 2, b = 5; u_1 = 2, u_2 = 1; v_1 = 6, v_2 = 15, v_3 = 2, v_4 = 3, v_5 = 5.$$

$$U = 2 + 1 = 3, V = 6 + \ldots + 5 = 31,$$

$$U^* = \frac{2^2 + 1^2}{3^2} = 0.556. \qquad V^* = \frac{6^2 + \ldots + 5^2}{31^2} = 0.311$$

Finally, since sex and breed involve fixed parameters, $A = a = 2, B = b = 5$.   Substituting, the components are:

$$A: \quad \sigma^2 + 4.58 \; \kappa_{AB}^2 + 41.3 \kappa_A^2$$

$$B: \quad \sigma^2 + 0.90 \; \kappa_{AB}^2 + 16.0 \; \kappa_B^2$$

$$AB: \; \sigma^2 + 7.11 \; \kappa_{AB}^2$$

In the swine data, the estimates are:

$$s^2 \quad = 5.51$$

$$s_{AB}^2 = \frac{6.23 - 5.51}{7.11} = 0.101$$

$$s_B^2 = \frac{24.34 - 5.51 - (0.90)(0.101)}{16.0} = 1.17$$

The sample furnishes no estimate of s_A^2, so take it as zero.

For testing, one may not be far off if he uses the Satterthwaite-Cochran approximation, section 12.10.   To get comparable mean squares for testing breed, start with the mean square for Breed-Sex Interaction,

$$6.23 = s^2 + 7.11 \; s_{AB}^2$$

Multiply by the ratio of the coefficients of s_{AB}^2 in B and AB, $0.90/7.11$:

$$\frac{0.90}{7.11} (6.23) = \frac{0.90}{7.11} s^2 + 0.90 s_{AB}^2$$

Or $0.79 = 0.13 s^2 + 0.90 s_{AB}^2$

Now add $\underline{5.51 = \quad s^2 \qquad\qquad}$

Denominator mean square $6.30 = 1.13 s^2 + 0.90 s_{AB}^2$

For the numerator of F, start with

$$\frac{0.90}{7.11} (5.51) = \frac{0.90}{7.11} s^2$$

Or $\qquad\qquad\qquad 0.70 = 0.13\ s^2$

Breed mean square, $24.34 = \dfrac{s^2 + 0.90\ s_{AB}^2 + 16.0 s_B^2}{}$

Sum, $\qquad\qquad\qquad 25.04 = 1.13 s^2 + 0.90\ s_{AB}^2 + 16.0\ s_B^2$

Then, $\qquad F' = \dfrac{1.13\ s^2 + 0.90\ s_{AB}^2 + 16.0\ s_B^2}{1.13\ s^2 + 0.90\ s_{AB}^2} = \dfrac{25.04}{6.30} = 3.97$

Since both terms of F' are sums of combinations of mean squares, degrees of freedom must be estimated.

$$n_1' = \frac{(25.04)^2}{\dfrac{(0.70)^2}{83} + \dfrac{(24.34)^2}{4}} = 4.2$$

$$n_1' = \frac{(6.30)^2}{\dfrac{(0.79)^2}{4} + \dfrac{(5.51)^2}{83}} = 76$$

For $f = 4$ and 76, $F_{.01} = 3.58$ to be compared with the sample value, $F' = 3.97$. Doubtless there are breed differences in dressing percentage. The means are: 84.2, 82.1, 81.5, 82.5, 81.1%.

If unequal frequencies occur by chance, not representing real population differences in size, it may be well to analyze the unweighted means of the 2-way table. The method is given in section 12.16 and applied to the swine data in example 12.16.2.

12.14—Disproportionate sub-class numbers. The 2 × 2 table Neither equality nor proportionality in sub-class numbers is always attainable. For example, one can't control the proportion of the sexes of chicks hatched from differently treated batches of eggs. The consequences may be serious if the character measured, such as growth rate, is different in the sexes. A lot of chicks with a predominance of males will likely gain faster than one with extra females even though the treatment of the second lot is more favorable to growth. Much the same effect may be observed in table 12.14.1 (26). The weighted mean of the 2 lots injected with hormone B is the smaller, whereas the unweighted mean (ignoring sub-class numbers) is the greater. As we shall learn, neither pair gives an unbiased estimate of the effect of B.

Another startling characteristic of disproportionality in a 2-way table is the failure of the addition theorem for sums of squares. While this is not evident in table 12.14.1, it shows up in the analysis of the rat data of table 12.15.1, the two sums of squares, sex and generation, adding to more than the total sum of squares. Clearly, no proper estimate of interaction is given in such a table. In fact, all estimates and tests of significance may be biased by the disproportion of sub-class numbers, and the

TABLE 12.14.1

COMB WEIGHTS (MILLIGRAMS) OF LOTS OF CHICKS INJECTED WITH 2 SEX HORMONES
SEPARATELY AND IN COMBINATION

	Untreated			Hormone B		
	Number	ΣX	$\bar{x}$	Number	ΣX	$\bar{x}$
Untreated	3	240	80	12	1,200	100
Hormone A	12	1,440	120	6	672	112
	15	1,680		18	1,872	
Weighted mean	1,680/15 = 112			104		
Unweighted mean	(80 + 120)/2 = 100					106

Preliminary Analysis of Variance, Ignoring Disproportion Among Sub-class Numbers

Source of Variation	Degrees of Freedom	Sum of Squares	Mean Square
Hormone A	1	3,724	
Hormone B	1	524	
Individuals	29	23,519	811

appropriate statistical methods are thereby complicated (32). Missing data in randomized blocks and Latin square experiments constituted special cases of the more general one now to be explained.

In the problems of this section and the next, there is required a preliminary analysis of variance in which the disproportion of sub-class numbers is ignored. The analysis follows the pattern for proportional numbers in the preceding section. We are to learn how unbiased estimates and tests of significance may be attained for the main effects (means of rows and columns) and interactions. But it should be noted that there is no bias in the sums of squares for sub-classes, either among or within them. In table 12.14.1, for example, the sums of squares among sub-classes,

$$\frac{(240)^2}{3} + \frac{(1,440)^2}{12} + \frac{(1,200)^2}{12} + \frac{(672)^2}{6} - \frac{(3,552)^2}{33} = 4{,}940$$

and for individuals, 23,519, are correctly estimated in the manner of section 10.16.

The calculations of table 12.14.2 require little explanation. Weights, W, are made up from the numbers of chicks, n, and these lead to a weighted sum of squares (1,216) of the mean differences. A correction term yields the interaction mean square which is little greater than sampling expectation. Therefore, the interaction in the population may be assumed negligible.

It turns out that the correction term, $(\Sigma WD)^2/\Sigma W = 40$, is an unbiased estimate of the mean square between the column means (hormone

TABLE 12.14.2

INTERACTION NEGLIGIBLE IN A 2×2 TABLE WITH DISPROPORTIONATE SUB-CLASS NUMBERS. COMPUTATIONS FOLLOWING TABLE 12.14.1. CHICK HORMONE DATA

	Untreated		Hormone B		$\dfrac{n_1 n_2}{n_1 + n_2}$ $= W$	$\bar{x}_2 - \bar{x}_1$ $= D$	WD	WD^2
	n_1	$\bar{x}_1$	n_2	$\bar{x}_2$				
Untreated	3	80	12	100	2.4	20	48	960
Hormone A	12	120	6	112	4.0	−8	−32	256
					6.4		16	1,216

Sum of squares for interaction
$$= \Sigma WD^2 - (\Sigma WD)^2/\Sigma W = 1,216 - (16)^2/6.4 = 1,216 - 40 = 1,176$$
$$F = 1,176/811 = 1.45, f = 1 \text{ and } 29, \text{ not significant}$$

Correction for disproportion = (sum of squares for hormone B) − $(\Sigma WD)^2/\Sigma W = 524 - 40 = 484$

(see preliminary analysis, table 12.14.1)

Completed Analysis of Variance

Source of Variation	Degrees of Freedom		Mean Square
Hormone A	1	$(3,724 - 484)$	3,240
Hormone B	1		40
Interaction	1		1,176
Individuals	29		811

For A, $F = 3,240/811 = 4.00$; For B, $F = 40/811 = 0.05$

B); hence, the preliminary value in table 12.14.1 must be reduced by a

Correction for disproportion = $524 - 40 = 484$

The same correction for hormone A results in the completed analysis at the bottom of the table.

There is now available an unbiased estimate of the mean difference due to hormone B acting both with and without A: this weighted mean difference is:

$$\Sigma WD/\Sigma W = 16/6.4 = 2.5 \text{ mg.}$$

It is notable that this is not the difference between either the weighted or unweighted means of table 12.14.1. A similar estimate for the difference due to A may be calculated from the columns. In this table the weights happen to be the same as those in the rows so that

$$\Sigma WD/\Sigma W = [(2.4)(40) + (4.0)(12)]/6.4 = 22.5 \text{ mg.}$$

It is the significance of these weighted differences that is tested by the F-values in the table.

If interaction appears, there is usually no point in pursuing the analysis. Main effects would have little or no meaning. The existence and interpretation of the interaction usually ends the investigation. If further comparison among the groups is indicated, separate effects for hormone A and hormone B may be examined as in section 4.5 or section 10.16.

EXAMPLE 12.14.1—In studying the isolating mechanisms of two species of Drosophila, Mayr and Dobzhansky (18) confined males of *D. persimilis* for several days with females of the same species, proconditioning them, then gave them access to females of both their own species and of *D. pseudoobscura*. They then confined *persimilis* males with *pseudoobscura* females, counterconditioning them, following this with multiple choice as before. The numbers of females inseminated were:

	Proconditioned		Counterconditioned	
	Inseminated	Not	Inseminated	Not
Persimilis	18	14	41	6
Pseudoobscura	5	32	20	32

Recalling section 9.10, transform the percentages inseminated to angles (table 11.12.1), the frequencies and angles being as follows:

32	48.59	47	69.06
37	21.57	52	38.33

Analyze the variance as follows (mean squares given):

Conditioning	1	13,910
Species	1	35,701
Interaction	1	139
Error (see example 12.4.4)		821

How do you interpret these results?

12.15—Disproportionate sub-class numbers. The R × 2 table. This type of table is of rather common occurrence, ordinarily involving the two sexes. The data in table 12.15.1 first brought to our attention some

TABLE 12.15.1

Interaction Negligible in $R \times 2$ Table With Disproportionate Sub-class Numbers. Number and Mean Gain in Weight (Grams) of 149 Wistar Rats During 1928–29. Four Successive Generations. Gains During 6 Weeks Beginning at 28 Days of Age. 100 Grams Subtracted From Each Gain

Generation	Male		Female		$\dfrac{n_1 n_2}{n_1 + n_2}$ $= W$	$\bar{x}_1 - \bar{x}_2$ $= D$	WD
	n_1	$\bar{x}_1$	n_2	$\bar{x}_2$			
1	21	76.952	27	9.518	11.8125	67.434	796.564
2	15	61.467	25	14.080	9.3750	47.387	444.253
3	12	55.667	23	8.522	7.8857	47.145	371.771
4	7	71.000	19	6.790	5.1154	64.210	328.460
					34.1886		1,941.048

TABLE 12.15.1—(*Continued*)

Preliminary Analysis of Variance of Original Data

Source of Variation	Degrees of Freedom	Sum of Squares	Mean Square
Sub-class means	7	119,141	
Sexes	1	114,287	
Generations	3	5,756	
Individuals	141		409

Interaction sum of squares: $*\Sigma WD^2 - (\Sigma WD)^2/\Sigma W = 113{,}385 - 110{,}202 = 3{,}183$
Correction for disproportion $= 114{,}287 - 110{,}202 = 4{,}085$

Completed Analysis

Sexes	1		110,202	110,202
Generations	3	$(5{,}756-4{,}085)$	1,671	557
Interaction	3		3,183	1,061
Individuals	141			409

* ΣWD^2 is run up on the machine: $(67.434)(796.564) + \ldots$

of the peculiarities of disproportionate sub-class numbers (6). In the preliminary analysis of variance the two sums of squares, for sex and generation, add to more than the total for sub-classes, emphasizing the non-orthogonal feature introduced by irregularities in the cell frequencies.

The interaction, though large, falls short of significance. Since there is no reason to believe that the difference in the sex rates of gain would change with generation, so far as the population is concerned, negligible interaction may be assumed.

The remaining computations proceed as in table 12.14.2.

This method is applicable to tables in which the data are missing entirely from a sub-class. Zero may be entered instead of n and $\bar{x}$ with no disturbance of the computations. From the degrees of freedom for interaction deduct 1 for each cell with no entry.

The unbiased estimate of the sex difference in mean gain is

$$\Sigma WD/\Sigma W = 1{,}941.048/34.1886 = 56.77 \text{ grams}$$

That is the mean difference tested by $F = 110{,}202/409$.

Unbiased estimates of generation mean differences will be made available by the method of fitting constants to be explained in section 12.17. Very good approximations can be got by applying the method of table 12.14.2. As an example, the weighted mean difference between generations 1 and 2 is calculated in table 12.15.2, and a test of significance is provided.

TABLE 12.15.2

APPROXIMATE METHOD OF CALCULATING THE WEIGHTED MEAN DIFFERENCE BETWEEN
GENERATIONS 1 AND 2. FOR EXACT METHOD, SEE SECTION 12.17

	Generation 1		Generation 2		W	D	WD
	n_1	$\bar{x}_1$	n_2	$\bar{x}_2$			
Male	21	76.952	15	61.467	8.75	15.485	135.49
Female	27	9.518	25	14.080	12.98	−4.562	−59.21
					21.73		76.28

Weighted mean difference = $\Sigma WD / \Sigma W$ = 3.51 grams
Mean square of mean difference = 409/21.73 = 18.82, $s_{\bar{d}}$ = 4.34,
$t = 3.51/4.34 = 0.81, f = 141$

EXAMPLE 12.15.1—Becker and Hall (3) determined the number of oocysts produced by rats of 5 strains during immunization with *Eimeria miyairii*. The unit of
measurement is 10^6 oocysts

		Strain				
Sex		Lambert	Lo	Hi	W.E.L.	Wistar (A)
Male	n	8	14	20	8	9
	$\bar{x}$	36.1	94.9	194.4	64.1	175.7
Female	n	7	14	21	10	8
	$\bar{x}$	31.9	68.6	187.3	89.2	148.4

Verify the completed analysis of variance quoted from the original article.

Sex	1	2,594.6	2,594.6
Strain	4	417,565.6	104,391.4
Interaction	4	8,805.3	2,201.3
Error	109	332,962.9	3,054.7

You will not be able to duplicate these numbers exactly because the means are reported
to only 3 significant digits. Your results should approximate the first 3 figures in the
mean squares, and no more are necessary for testing.

EXAMPLE 12.15.2—Many investigators have studied the effect of site (cervix
and uterus) on the success of artificial insemination of dairy cows. From 3 reports I
compiled this 3-way contingency table (section 9.10):

	Cervix		Uterus	
Investigator	Success	Failure	Success	Failure
1	64	39	97	53
2	123	70	121	72
3	292	208	324	176

Calculate the percentages of success, transform to angles and analyze the variance (mean squares given):

Site	1	2,357
Investigator	2	174.5
Interaction	2	688
Error	∞	821

The argument is advanced that less time and less chance of infection are involved in the cervical method. What decision would you make about site?

12.16—Disproportionate sub-class numbers in R × C table. Approximate methods. The general method for fitting constants, to be given in the next section, is a bit tedious. The approximate *method of unweighted means,* now to be explained, has several advantages, including a familiar form of calculation. If interaction becomes obvious, no further computation need be done. If interaction is clearly negligible, the main effects may be so obviously present or absent that the exact method of the next section is not needed. This approximate method allows the use of planned comparisons (section 12.2) or of all comparisons as in section 10.6. If the sub-class numbers are only slightly unequal, especially if they are fairly large (say, 10 or more), this approximation to the method of fitting constants is close.

The method is illustrated by an experiment in which the disproportion of the sub-class numbers is considerable. The same data will be used in the next section so that comparisons may be made.

Three strains of mice were inoculated with 3 isolations of the typhoid organism (11). Days-to-death was recorded for each mouse. From the original data, not given here, there is required only the estimate of error, the variation among mice receiving the same treatment. This is 5.015 with $f = 774$. Sub-class numbers and means are shown in table 12.16.1. The former are ignored in the analysis of variance, only the means being used in a simple 2-way computation like that of table 11.2.1.

For comparison with error, the mean squares for means must be multiplied by the number of mice in a sub-class. Since this varies, an average is used, the harmonic mean. This is the reciprocal of the mean of the reciprocals of the sub-class numbers, calculated at the bottom of the table. The product of n_0 by the mean square for Interaction is recorded in the last column. (Alternatively, 5.015 may be divided by n_0 to get an estimate of error for the mean squares of means. Result, 0.0841.)

As would be assumed from scanning the data, interaction is evident. Strains RI and Z were resistent to isolations 11C and DSC1 but Ba was susceptible to all. No comparisons among main effects would seem appropriate. Some separate comparisons might be made among the 4 large means and among the 5 small; but these would be biased comparisons because they are selected on the basis of a previous test and after examination of the data themselves. However, I tried the 4 large means in a

TABLE 12.16.1

Sub-class Numbers and Mean Days-to-Death in 3 Strains of Mice Inoculated
With 3 Isolations of the Typhoid Bacillus

| Isolation | Strain of Mice | | | Sum |
	RI	Z	Ba	
9D	34	31	33	
	4.0000	4.0323	3.7576	11.7899
11C	66	78	113	
	6.4545	6.7821	4.3097	17.5463
DSC 1	107	133	188	
	6.6262	7.8045	4.1277	18.5584
Sum	17.0807	18.6189	12.1950	47.8946

Analysis of Variance of Unweighted Means				Individual Basis
Isolation	2	8.8859		
Strain	2	7.5003		
Interaction	4	3.2014	0.8004 **	47.71 **
Individuals	774		0.0841	5.015

$$\frac{1}{n_0.} = \frac{1}{9}\left(\frac{1}{34} + \ldots + \frac{1}{188}\right) = 0.0167754. \quad n_0 = 59.6111$$

2 × 2 table like 12.14.1 and found the interaction not quite significant at the 5% point.

Instead of the method of unweighted means, there is a second approximate method occasionally useful if it is evident that the sample frequencies are representative of those in the sampled population. The border totals may be used to calculate cell frequencies which are proportional so that the method of *proportional sub-class numbers*, section 12.13, becomes applicable. This was the case in a survey of farm tenancy (29) used as illustration in section 9.8. There it was shown that the sub-class numbers might follow the pattern of the border totals independently of soil or tenure. It seems reasonable, then, to use proportional numbers instead of the disproportionate sample numbers.

Table 12.16.2 contains sub-class means of acres in corn, calculated from the survey data. This mean in each cell is multiplied by the proportional sub-class number to get a new estimate of ΣX in that cell. The new ΣX along with the proportional numbers are combined in the analysis of variance.

The advantage of this analysis is that it is orthogonal and that it allows the components to be estimated as in section 12.13.

There is no evidence of interaction in the population, while the tenure means are doubtless different. If it seems necessary to make a more critical test of the soil effects, the method of the next section is appropriate.

TABLE 12.16.2

FARM ACRES IN CORN CLASSIFIED BY TENURE AND SOIL PRODUCTIVITY.
AUDUBON COUNTY, IOWA

Soil Class		Owner		Renter		Mixed		Σn	ΣX
		Ob-served	Propor-tional	Ob-served	Propor-tional	Ob-served	Propor-tional		
I	n	36	36.75	67	62 92	49	52.33	152	
	$\bar{x}$	32.7		55.2		50.6			
	ΣX		1,202		3,473		2,684		7,323
II	n	31	33.85	60	57.95	49	48.20	140	
	$\bar{x}$	36.0		53.4		47.1			
	ΣX		1,219		3,095		2,270		6,584
III	n	58	54.40	87	93.13	80	77.47	225	
	$\bar{x}$	30.1		46.8		40.1			
	ΣX		1,637		4,358		3,107		9,102
Σk		125		214		178		517	
ΣX			4,058		10,926		8,025		23,009

Analysis of Variance Using Proportional Numbers

Source of Variation	Degrees of Freedom	Sum of Squares	Mean Square
Soils	2	6,635	3,318*
Tenure	2	27,367	13,684**
Interaction	4	883	221
Error (from original data)	508		830

EXAMPLE 12.16.1—To the mean farm acres in table 12.16.2 apply the method of unweighted means. You will get

Soils	2	2,436*
Tenancy	2	14,490**
Interaction	4	255
Error	508	830

There is no change in conclusions though the effect of soils seems less pronounced. See example 12.17.1.

EXAMPLE 12.16.2—In table 12.13.1, the sizes of the breed samples are assumed proportional to the population of these breeds in the region, but the proportion of sexes arises from marketing practices. If the estimates are to apply to the local population of swine, it may be as well to analyze the unweighted means in an ordinary 2 × 5 table, one mean per cell:

Sex	1	1.3
Breed	4	15.5*
Interaction	4	10.1
Error	83	5.51

12.17—Fitting constants in a two-factor table. This is a general method for analyzing 2-factor experiments; most of the methods which have been given, including the supplying of missing data, are special cases. *Fitting constants* leads to an unbiased estimate and test of interaction if it is present. If there is no interaction in the population, the estimates and tests of the main effects are unbiased.

For comparison with the method of unweighted means, constants

TABLE 12.17.1

THE METHOD OF FITTING CONSTANTS. DAYS-TO-DEATH IN 3 STRAINS OF MICE INOCULATED WITH 3 ISOLATIONS OF THE TYPHOID BACILLUS

Organ-ism		Strain of Mice			$\Sigma n_{i.}$	ΣX	$\bar{x}_w$	$b + \bar{x}$
		RI	Z	Ba				
9D	n	34	31	33	98	385		3.9490
	$n/\Sigma n_i$	0.34694	0.31633	0.33673			3.9286	
11C	n	66	78	113	257	1,442		5.8600
	$n/\Sigma n_{i.}$	0.25681	0.30350	0.43969			5.6109	
DSC 1	n	107	133	188	428	2,523		6.1375
	$n/\Sigma n_{i.}$	0.25000	0.31075	0.43925			5.8949	
$\Sigma n_{.j}$		207	242	334	783			
ΣX		1,271	1,692	1,387		4,350		
a		0.4506	1.2240	−1.6746			$\bar{x} =$	5.3155

Preliminary Analysis of Variance

Source of Variation	Degrees of Freedom	Sum of Squares	Mean Square
Sub-classes	8	1,785.58	
Organisms	2	309.47 ⎫	1,536.66
Strains	2	1,227.19 ⎭	
Individuals	774		5.015

a_1: $[(34)(0.34694) + \ldots + (107)(0.25000) - 207]a_1$
$+ [(34)(0.31633) + \ldots + (107)(0.31075)]a_2$
$+ [(34)(0.33673) + \ldots + (107)(0.43925)]a_3$
$= (34)(3.9286) + \ldots + (107)(5.8949) - 1,271$

(and so on to the last a)

a_3: $[(33)(0.34694) + \ldots + (188)(0.2500)]a_1$
$+ [(33)(0.31633) + \ldots + (188)(0.31075)]a_2$
$+ [(33)(0.33673) + \ldots + (188)(0.43925) - 334]a_3$
$= (33)(3.9286) + \ldots + (188)(5.8949) - 1,387$

are fitted to the mouse data of table 12.16.1 augmented by the original values of ΣX. The constants are the values of α and β in the model,

$$X_{ijk} = \mu + a_i + \beta_j + e_{ijk},$$

where α and β correspond to the 2 factors, A and B. The estimates are a_i and b_i, $\Sigma a_i = \Sigma b_i = 0$.

In each cell, the ratio of n to $\Sigma n_{i.}$ is entered; the sum in each row is necessarily unity. In each row is the weighted mean, $\bar{x}_w = \Sigma X / \Sigma n_{i.}$. If the table were rectangular instead of square, it should be arranged so that R is large and C small; the fewer the columns the easier the calculations.

The computations are quite systematic. Corresponding to each column an a-equation is written as outlined at the bottom of the table. In a_1 the sub-class numbers in column 1 are used over and over, each time with successive columns of ratios; and in the right member, with the column of means. In a_2 the numbers in column 2 are applied in the same pattern of ratios and means. The only irregularity in the pattern is the subtraction of $\Sigma n_{.j}$ from one of the terms in each equation.

The coefficients of the a's, easily calculated with a machine, are set down in the following set of simultaneous linear equations:

$$-151.505\, a_1 + 64.036\, a_2 + 87.468\, a_3 = -136.35$$
$$64.036\, a_1 - 167.191\, a_2 + 103.155\, a_3 = -348.54$$
$$87.468\, a_1 + 103.155\, a_2 - 190.624\, a_3 = 484.92$$

In verification of the computations, observe that the coefficients occur in pairs symmetrically arranged with respect to the principal diagonal, and that the sum of the coefficients in each of the 3 columns, as well as the sum of the right-hand members, is zero (except for rounding errors).

Since $\Sigma a = 0$, the first step is to substitute $a_3 = -a_1 - a_2$ in each equation. This is easily done: simply subtract 87.468 from each of the preceding coefficients in the first equation, and 103.155 from each in the second, the results being

$$-238.973\, a_1 - 23.432\, a_2 = -136.35$$
$$-39.119\, a_1 - 270.346\, a_2 = -348.54$$

The third equation is merely the sum of these two and may be discarded. The solution is

$$a_1 = 0.4506$$
$$a_2 = 1.2240$$

and, therefore, $$a_3 = -1.6746$$

Verify by substitution in one or more of the original equations It is convenient to enter the a's in the last row of the table.

A quantity, $b + \bar{x}$, in each row is now calculated from the a's together with $\bar{x}_w$ and the ratios in the same row. As an example, in row 1,

$$b_1 + \bar{x} = 3.9286 - (0.34694)(0.4506) - \ldots - (0.33673)(-1.6746)$$

$$= \quad 3.9490$$

Similarly, $\qquad b_2 + \bar{x} = \quad 5\ 8600$

$$b_3 + \bar{x} = \quad 6.1375$$

Adding, $\qquad 3\bar{x} = \quad 15.9465 \text{ (because } \Sigma b = 0)$

$$\bar{x} = \quad 5.3155$$

Finally, $\qquad b_1 = -1.3665, b_2 = 0.5445, b_3 = 0.8220$

The "reduction in sum of squares due to fitting constants" is now calculated from the constants and the original ΣX in the borders of the table by this process:

$$(0.4506)(1{,}271) + (1.2240)(1{,}692) + \cdots$$
$$+ (6.1375)(2{,}523) - (4{,}350)^2/783 = 1{,}609.78$$

Deducting this from the sum of squares for sub-classes, the interaction sum of squares is attained,

$$1.785.58 - 1{,}609.78 = 175.80$$

Since there are 4 degrees of freedom for interaction, we have

$$\text{Mean square for interaction} = 175.80/4 = 43.95$$

$$F = 43.95/5.015 = 8.76, \quad f = 4 \text{ and } 774, F_{.01} = 3.35$$

As before, interaction is shown to be present in the population so that ordinarily the analysis would not be carried further; the data would be interpreted as in the foregoing section. But as an illustration of the calculational procedure, we proceed as though there were no interaction.

Estimates of sub-class means and treatment means, $\bar{x} + a_i + b_j$, are made in table 12.17.2. If interaction in the population were zero, these would be unbiased estimates of population parameters. Clearly there is no interaction among the sub-class means made up from fitted constants (there was none provided in the model). Consequently these means cannot represent those in the mouse population where interaction is present.

The method of fitting constants is not dependent on the presence of data in all cells of the table. If cells are empty, zeros for n and $n/\Sigma n_i$. do not disturb the calculations. Degrees of freedom for Sub-classes and Interaction in the analyses of variance are each decreased by unity for each cell with missing data.

With no interaction, the analysis of variance would be completed as shown in the table. The correction for disproportionate sub-class numbers

TABLE 12.17.2
ESTIMATES MADE FROM FITTED CONSTANTS. INTERACTION ASSUMED ZERO.
MOUSE DATA OF TABLE 12.17.1

Organ-ism	Constants	RI $a_1 = 0.4506$	Z $a_2 = 1.2240$	Ba $a_3 = -1.6746$	Mean
9D	$b_1 + \bar{x} = 3.9490$	4.3996	5.1730	2.2744	3.9490
11C	$b_2 + \bar{x} = 5.8600$	6.3106	7.0840	4.1854	5.8600
DSC 1	$b_3 + \bar{x} = 6.1375$	6.5881	7.3615	4.4629	6.1375
Mean		5.7661	6.5395	3.6409	

Completed Analysis of Variance

Organisms	2	$309.47 - (-73.12)* =$	382.59
Strains	2	$1{,}227.19 - (-73.12) =$	1,300.31
Interaction	4		175.80
Mice	774		43.95
			5.015

*Correction = (combined sum of squares for Organism and Strain) −
  (reduction due to constants)
  = $1{,}536.66 - 1{,}609.78 = -73.12$

is made from the combined main effects in the preliminary analysis (table 12.17.1) and the reduction due to fitting constants. If there were no interaction, the mean squares for Strains and Organisms would be tested for significance as usual.

EXAMPLE 12.17.1—From table 12.16.2 there is no evidence of interaction in the population. The mean squares for Soil and Tenure in that table and those in example 12.16.1 can be compared with the unbiased estimates made by fitting constants. Carry through the computations for the tenancy survey and you will get (approximately, depending on decimals carried):

Soil	Constants	Owner $a_1 = -10.257$	Renter $a_2 = 7.975$	Mixed $a_3 = 2.282$	Mean
I	$b_1 + \bar{x} = 46.356$	36.1	54.3	48.6	46.4
II	$b_2 + \bar{x} = 45.084$	34.8	53.1	47.4	45.1
III	$b_3 + \bar{x} = 29.202$	28.9	47.2	41.5	39.2
Mean		33.3	51.5	45.8	

Soils	2	5,561	2,780*
Tenancy	2	26,293	13,146**
(Interaction)	4	(3,163)	
Error	508		830

Note: The preliminary analysis of variance was:

Sub-classes	8	37,165.20
Soils	2	6,635.39
Tenancy	2	27,367.09
Error	508	830

REFERENCES

1. R. L. ANDERSON. Biometrics (Bulletin), 2:41 (1946).

2. R. L. ANDERSON and T. A. BANCROFT. Statistical Theory in Research. McGraw-Hill Book Co., Inc., New York (1952).

3. E. R. BECKER and PHOEBE R. HALL. Parasitology, 25:397 (1933).

4. M. W. BITTINGER. Iowa Agricultural Experiment Station (1952).

5. A. E. BRANDT. Thesis submitted for the degree, Doctor of Philosophy, Iowa State University (1932).

6. BERNICE BROWN. Proceedings of the Iowa Academy of Science, 38:205 (1932).

7. W. G. COCHRAN. Supplement to the Journal of the Royal Statistical Society 4:102 (1937).

8. W. G. COCHRAN. Biometrics, 7:17 (1951).

9. W. G. COCHRAN. Biometrics, 10:101 (1954).

10. W. G. COCHRAN and GERTRUDE M. COX Experimental Designs. John Wiley and Sons, Inc., New York (1950).

11. JOHN W. GOWEN. American Journal of Human Genetics, 4:285 (1952).

12. E. S. HABER. Journal of Agricultural Research, 45:101 (1932).

13. E. S. HABER and GEORGE W. SNEDECOR. American Society for Horticultural Science, 48:481 (1946).

14. T. N. HOBLYN and R. C. PALMER. Journal of Pomology (and Horticultural Science), 12:36 (1934).

15. PAUL G. HOMEYER and C. A. BLACK. Soil Science Society of America Proceedings, 11:341 (1946).

16. Iowa Agricultural Experiment Station, Animal Husbandry Swine Nutrition Experiment No. 577 (1952).

17. OSCAR KEMPTHORNE. The Design and Analysis of Experiments. John Wiley and Sons, Inc., New York (1952).

18. ERNST MAYR and TH. DOBZHANSKY. Proceedings of the National Academy of Science, 31:75 (1945).

19. R. H. PORTER. Cooperative Soybean Seed Treatment Trials, Iowa State University Seed Laboratory (1943).

20. D. RICHARDSON *et al.* See reference 26, Chapter 10.

21. F. E. SATTERTHWAITE. Biometrics (Bulletin), 2:110 (1946).

22. A. R. SAUNDERS. Union of South Africa Department of Agriculture and Forestry Science Bulletin No. 200 (1939).

23. E. F. SCHULTZ, JR. Biometrics, 11:123 (1955).

24. H. FAIRFIELD SMITH. Biometrics, 7:70 (1951).

25. GEORGE W. SNEDECOR. Proceedings of the International Statistical Conferences, 3:440 (1947).

26. GEORGE W. SNEDECOR and W. R. BRENEMAN. Iowa State Journal of Science, 19:333 (1945).

27. GEORGE W. SNEDECOR and E. S. HABER. Biometrics (Bulletin), 2:61 (1946).

28. Southern Cooperative Series Bulletin No. 10, page 114 (1951).

29. NORMAN STRAND and RAYMOND J. JESSEN. Iowa Agricultrual Experiment Station Research Bulletin 315 (1943).

30. M. B. WILK and O. KEMPTHORNE. Iowa State University Statistical Laboratory (1954).

31. C. P. WILSIE. Iowa State University Agricultural Experiment Station (1944)

32. F. YATES. Journal of Agricultural Science, 23:108 (1933).

33. F. YATES and W. G. COCHRAN. Journal of Agricultural Science, 28:556 (1938);

34. F. YATES. Imperial Bureau of Soil Science, Technical Communication No. 35 (1937).

CHAPTER 13

Covariance

13.1—Introduction. Uncontrolled environmental conditions may affect both experimental error and estimates of treatment effects. If the conditions can be measured even approximately, some adjustments can be made, often increasing the information in the experiment. An appropriate statistical method is known as *covariance*. It is an extension of the regression methods of chapter 6 to adapt them to the common experimental designs. The measurement on environment is the independent variable X, the dependent variable Y being the observed experimental result. The objectives are to learn the effects of X on Y, to compare treatment effects on Y independent of (or adjusted for) X, or if the treatments have effects on X, to segregate the direct effects of treatments on Y.

13.2—Covariance in a completely randomized experiment with two treatments. In a survey to learn some relations between nutrition

TABLE 13.2.1

AGE AND CONCENTRATION OF CHOLESTEROL (MG./100 ML.) IN THE BLOOD SERUM OF
IOWA AND NEBRASKA WOMEN

Iowa, $n = 11$		Nebraska, $n = 19$			
Age X	Cholesterol Y	Age X	Cholesterol Y	Age X	Cholesterol Y
46	181	18	137	30	140
52	228	44	173	47	196
39	182	33	177	58	262
65	249	78	241	70	261
54	259	51	225	67	356
33	201	43	223	31	159
49	121	44	190	21	191
76	339	58	257	56	197
71	224	63	337		
41	112	19	189		
58	189	42	214		
Sum 584	2,285			873	4,125
$\bar{x}_I = 53.1$	$\bar{y}_I = 207.7$			$\bar{x}_N = 45.9$	$\bar{y}_N = 217.1$

TABLE 13.2.1—(*Continued*)

Iowa

$\Sigma X^2 =$ 32,834	$\Sigma XY =$ 127,235	$\Sigma Y^2 =$ 515,355
$C:$ 31,005	121,313	474,657
$\Sigma x^2 =$ 1,829	$\Sigma xy =$ 5,922	$\Sigma y^2 =$ 40,698

Nebraska

$\Sigma X^2 =$ 45,677	$\Sigma XY =$ 203,559	$\Sigma Y^2 =$ 957,785
$C:$ 40,112	189,533	895,559
$\Sigma x^2 =$ 5,565	$\Sigma xy =$ 14,026	$\Sigma y^2 =$ 62,226

Total, n = 30

$\Sigma X =$ 1,457, $\bar{x}_T =$ 48.6	$\Sigma X^2 =$ 78,511	$\Sigma XY =$ 330,794	$\Sigma Y^2 =$ 1,473,140
$\Sigma Y =$ 6,410, $\bar{y}_T =$ 213.7	$C: =$ 70,762	311,312	1,369,603
	$\Sigma x^2 =$ 7,749	$\Sigma xy =$ 19,482	$\Sigma y^2 =$ 103,537

and health of women in the middle west (10), the concentration of cholesterol in the blood serum was determined on 56 randomly selected subjects
in Iowa and 130 in Nebraska. In table 13.2.1 are subsamples from the
survey data. Figure 13.2.1 shows graphs of the 2 sets of pairs, giving an
impression of linearity of regression and homogeneity of variance; the
former will be assumed in this chapter but the latter will be tested.

The calculations are typical of chapter 6, leading to corrected sums
of squares and products for each sample and for the total (the two combined). For the latter, $\Sigma X^2 =$ 32,834 + 45,677 = 78,511, the sum of ΣX^2
in the separate samples, etc. The corrected sums of squares and products
are entered in table 13.2.2, line 1, 2, and 7.

TABLE 13.2.2
ANALYSIS OF COVARIANCE. CHOLESTEROL DATA

Line	State	f	Σx^2	Σxy	Σy^2	Reg. Coef.	f	Deviations From Regression $\Sigma y^2 - (\Sigma xy)^2/\Sigma x^2$	Mean Square
1	Iowa	10	1,829	5,922	40,698	3.24	9	21,524	2,392
2	Nebraska	18	5,565	14,026	62,226	2.52	17	26,875	1,581
3	Within						26	48,399	1,862
4	Reg. Coef.						1	708	708
5	Common	28	7,394	19,948	102,924	2.70	27	49,107	1,819
6	Adj. Means						1	5,450	5,450
7	Total	29	7,749	19,482	103,537		28	54,557	

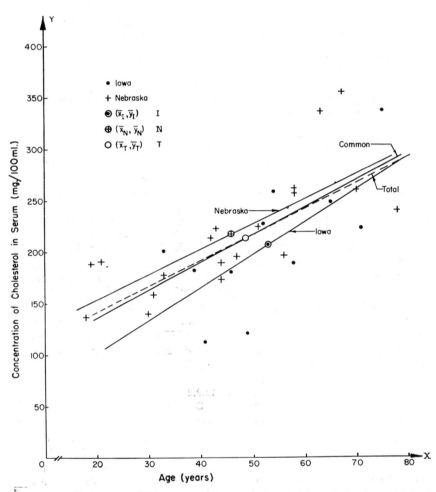

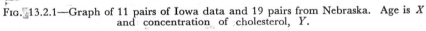

Fɪɢ. 13.2.1—Graph of 11 pairs of Iowa data and 19 pairs from Nebraska. Age is X and concentration of cholesterol, Y.

Before going further, it is well to look at the analyses of variance of X and of Y:

For X:					
Total	29			7,749	
Within	28	1,829 + 5,565 =		7,394	264
Between	1			355	355

For Y:					
Total	29			103,537	
Within	28	40,698 + 62,226 =		102,924	3,676
Between	1			613	613

The means of the two samples of X = age differ little more than would be expected in sampling from a common μ_x. If this were not so, one might suspect that X as well as Y was affected by the treatment (state), in which case the interpretation would be affected.

Similarly, the Y-means are at much the same level above the X-axis. It is the *adjusted means* that will be examined; in the present example, they differ more than the unadjusted, as will become apparent.

Regression coefficients, calculated by the usual formula, $b = \Sigma xy / \Sigma x^2$, together with the corresponding means, are used to draw the regression lines in the figure. The sum of squares of deviations from each regression, $\Sigma d_{y.x}^2$, is entered in table 13.2.2. Available degrees of freedom are decreased by one to compensate for the use of the regression coefficient.

The ultimate purpose is to learn if the linear regressions of cholesterol on age are the same in Iowa and Nebraska. They may differ in several ways; in slope, in elevation, and in $\sigma_{y.x}^2$. The primary interest is usually in elevation; would the cholesterol means be the same if the average age were the same? To get evidence on this question, we shall make the following assumptions:

1. The 2 samples are drawn from normal populations with common σ^2.
2. The slopes of the 2 regressions are the same; that is, the population regression lines are parallel.

In table 13.2.2 there seems to be little evidence against assumption 1; the mean squares in lines 1 and 2 at the right are not greatly different. If desired, the hypothesis of common σ^2 could be tested as in sections 4.8 and 10.20. If heterogeneous variance were evident, this might be the pertinent information in the sample. Otherwise, ways would have to be found for segregating the different variances; or perhaps a transformation would be effective. Homogeneous variance will be assumed unless there is contrary evidence. Consequently, the degrees of freedom and the two $\Sigma d_{y.x}^2$ are pooled in line 3 of the table. The result is the mean square, 1,862, $f = 26$, an estimate of σ^2 got from the combined Within State variation.

As for assumption 2, a look at the regression coefficients and the figure may be convincing. In these small samples the difference in slope may well be attributed to sampling variation. Evidence may be obtained by this device: pool the sums of squares and products in the 2 samples to form a Common Regression, line 5. This regression passes through the Total means, $\bar{x}_T = 48.6$ years, $\bar{y}_T = 213.7$ mg./100 ml., and has the slope 2.70. Its slope is a weighted average of the slopes of the two sample regressions. On the assumption of parallel regressions in the population, this Common Regression and deviations from it furnish estimates of β and σ^2 based on the total sample evidence.

Graphically the device just described implies moving the 2 sample regressions, parallel to their actual positions, until their means $(\bar{x}, \bar{y})$ coincide. All the sample points move with the regressions, the deviations x and y remaining the same. In the new position, $\Sigma d_{y.x}^2$ for the sample regressions are the same as before, the least possible sums of squares of deviations from the separate regressions. But, unless the sample regressions are parallel, $\Sigma d_{y.x}^2$ for the common regression is greater than the sum for the 2 samples as it must be because the sum of the former is the minimum. The difference, $49,107 - 48,399 = 708$ in line 4, measures the *difference between the two sample regression coefficients*. This mean square may be compared with the mean square Within Samples, 1,862. Assumption 2 is justified because the mean square for Regression Coefficients is less than normal sampling variation Within States.

If nonsignificance were not obvious, a test of the hypothesis, $\beta_1 = \beta_2$, would be made by

$$F = \frac{\text{Mean Square for Regression Coefficients}}{\text{Mean Square Within Samples}}, f = 1, 26$$

If the sample regression coefficients were found to differ significantly, this might end the investigation. Interpretation would involve the question, "Why?" The ultimate question about the elevation of the population regression lines has little meaning unless the lines are parallel.

Since assumptions 1 and 2 seem justified, it is in order to test the hypothesis that the population regressions coincide; that is, since they are parallel, that they have the same elevation. This is done by comparing lines 5 and 7 in the table. The difference between the $d_{y.x}^2$, $54,557 - 49,107 = 5,450$, corresponds to the *sample difference in elevation*. $F = 5,450/1,819 = 3.00$, $f = 1, 27$, lacks significance at the 5% point. The conclusion is that the two populations may have the same regression lines; at least, differences are not great enough to be detected by the sampling. In the original survey the differences were less pronounced than those in the two subsamples. The investigators felt justified in combining the two surveys for further examination of their problem.

Under the two assumptions above, the model being used is

$$Y_{ij} = \mu + a_i + \beta x_{ij} + \epsilon_{ij}$$

$i = 1, 2; \Sigma a_i = 0; \epsilon_{ij} = N(0, \sigma)$. β is the slope of the common regression line in the population and x_{ij} is the deviation of any X from the Total mean, $\bar{x}_T = 48.6$ years. The difference, $a_1 - a_2$, is the difference in elevation between the population regression lines for Iowa and Nebraska. The null hypothesis tested above is $a_i = 0$.

The difference, $a_1 - a_2$, is estimated by the difference between the two adjusted means (section 6.5),

For Nebraska: $\bar{y}_N - b(\bar{x}_N - \bar{x}_T) = 217.1 - 2.70\,(45.9 - 48.6) = 224.4$

For Iowa: $\bar{y}_I - b(\bar{x}_I - \bar{x}_T) = 207.7 - 2.70\,(53.1 - 48.6) = \underline{195.5}$

Difference: 28.9

This difference, 28.9 mg./100 ml., was found above to be nonsignificant.

It will be observed that the difference between the adjusted means, 28.9, is greater than that between the original Y-means, $217.1 - 207.7 = 9.4$. In other experiments the opposite might be true. But the error for testing the difference in the covariance analysis is characteristically less than that in the analysis of Y alone.

EXAMPLE 13.2.1—Here are 2 samples designed for easy calculation:

Treatment 1.	X: 29,	20,	14,	21,	6
	Y: 22,	22,	20,	24,	12

Treatment 2.	X: 15,	9,	1,	6,	19
	Y: 30,	32,	26,	25,	37

Plot the data on a single graph. Clearly the 2 regressions are not far from parallel.

EXAMPLE 13.2.2—Calculate the analysis of covariance for the preceding example.

Line	Sample	f	Σx^2	Σxy	Σy^2	b	f	Σd^2	Mean Square
1	1	4	294	134	88	0.456	3	26.93	8.98
2	2	4	204	117	94	0.574	3	26.90	8.97
3	Pooled						6	53.83	8.97
4	Reg. Coef.						1	1.66	1.66
5	Common	8	498	251	182	0.504	7	55.49	7.93
6	Adj. Means						1	372.56	372.56
7	Total	9	658	51	432		8	428.05	

For the difference between adjusted means, $F = 47.0$.

EXAMPLE 13.2.3—Calculate the 2 adjusted means and plot them on the graph along with the 2 sample regressions and the common regression. Ans. 17.98 and 32.02.

EXAMPLE 13.2.4—Write the equation for the Common regression in table 13.2.2. Ans. $\hat{Y} = 2.70X + 82.5$ mg./100 ml.

EXAMPLE 13.2.5—Draw a figure showing that, after a point has been moved to the new origin $(\bar{x}_T, \bar{y}_T)$ the deviation from Common regression is different from the deviation from the translated sample regression (unless the sample regressions are parallel).

EXAMPLE 13.2.6—On the graph of the cholesterol samples, plot points for the adjusted means: for Nebraska, (48.6, 224.4); for Iowa, (48.6, 195.5).

EXAMPLE 13.2.7—In table 13.2.2, subtract line 5 from line 7 to get the sums of squares and products Between Means. Calculate the slope of a line passing through the two sample means. Ans. −1.31. Draw the line on the graph.

EXAMPLE 13.2.8—In the covariance model, let $\mu = 20$, $a_1 = 4$, $a_2 = -4$, $\beta = 1$, $\bar{x}_T = 10$. Calculate $Y_{1j} - e_{1j}$ for $X_{1j} = 12$. Ans. 26. Draw a graph showing the two population regressions.

13.3—Covariance in a completely randomized experiment with more than two treatments. The methods of the preceding section are easily extended to accommodate 3 or more treatments. The data in table 13.3.1 illustrate this type of experiment (7). For the moment, random allotment of the pigs is assumed (see section 13.7). Correction of the

TABLE 13.3.1
INITIAL WEIGHT X AND AVERAGE DAILY GAIN Y IN 4 LOTS OF 10 PIGS EACH,
COMPLETELY RANDOMIZED

Lot	6		7		8		9	
Variable	X	Y	X	Y	X	Y	X	Y
	79	1.96	61	1.40	62	1.22	71	1.15
	65	1.77	59	1.79	73	1.39	60	1.28
	57	1.62	59	1.61	58	1.28	54	1.40
	51	1.76	53	1.47	43	1.28	50	1.37
	57	1.88	56	1.69	50	1.45	60	1.19
	66	1.50	50	1.48	44	1.22	61	1.18
	44	1.60	45	1.40	48	1.31	44	1.20
	41	1.49	39	1.42	51	1.57	53	0.96
	44	1.77	38	1.29	40	1.21	41	1.13
	36	1.27	45	1.26	38	1.06	38	1.12
Sums	540	16.62	505	14.81	507	12.99	532	11.98

ΣX^2	30,770		26,143		26,771		29,248	
ΣY^2		28.0068		22.1917		17.0569		14.4992
ΣXY	913.24		756.65		664.20		638.50	

Experiment Totals: $\Sigma X = 2,084$ $\Sigma Y = 56.40$
$\Sigma X^2 = 112,932$ $\Sigma XY = 2,972.59$ $\Sigma Y^2 = 81.7546$

sums of squares and products at the bottom of the table (as in table 13.2.1) leads to the data in the first 4 lines and line 9 of table 13.3.2.

First, look at the analyses of variance of X and Y separately:

		X		Y	
Total	39	4,356		2.2306	
Within	36	4,262	118	0.9726	0.0270
Between Means	3	94	31	1.2580	0.4193**

The mean initial weights differ less than would ordinarily be expected in random sampling. Section 13.7 affords a clue. In contrast, there are

TABLE 13.3.2
ANALYSIS OF COVARIANCE. FOUR LOTS OF 10 PIGS EACH

Line	Lot	f	Σx^2	Σxy	Σy^2	b	f	$\Sigma d_{y.x}^2$	Mean Square
								Deviations From Regression	
1	6	9	1,610	15.76	0.3844	0.010	8	0.2301	
2	7	9	640	8.75	0.2581	0.014	8	0.1385	
3	8	9	1,066	5.61	0.1829	0.005	8	0.1534	
4	9	9	946	1.16	0.1472	0.001	8	0.1458	
5	Within						32	0.6678	0.0209
6	Reg. Coef.						3	0.0752	0.0251
7	Common	36	4,262	31.28	0 9726	0.0073	35	0.7430	0.02123
8	Adj. Means						3	1.2199	0.4066**
9	Total	39	4,356	34.15	2.2306		38	1.9629	

undoubtedly differences among population means of gain. We are to learn how these are related to differences in initial weight.

Turning to the analysis of covariance, it is clear enough that the test of the adjusted means is warranted; homogeneous variance is indicated by lines 1–4 and parallel population regressions is a reasonable assumption (lines 5 and 6). The test in lines 7 and 8 shows notable differences among the adjusted means, 1.65, 1.49, 1.31, and 1.19. It is to be observed that the adjusted means differ little from the original and that F-tests among means and adjusted means are much the same. In this experiment, covariance has been only moderately effective—how effective will be discussed below.

A planned comparison between two adjusted means is conveniently calculated by

$$\bar{y}_{1A} - \bar{y}_{2A} = \bar{y}_1 - \bar{y}_2 - b(\bar{x}_1 - \bar{x}_2) = D$$

As an example, the rations for lots 6 and 7 differed only by the addition of yeast to the former. For these lots,

$$D = 1.662 - 1.481 - 0.0073 (54.0 - 50.5) = 0.155 \text{ lbs./day}$$

The mean square for D is

$$s_D^2 = s_{y.x}^2 \left[\frac{1}{n_1} + \frac{1}{n_2} + \frac{(\bar{x}_1 - \bar{x}_2)^2}{\Sigma x_E^2} \right]$$

where n_1 and n_2 are the numbers of individuals in the 2 lots and Σx_E^2 is the sum of squares of X in Error, line 7; $s_{y.x}^2$ is the Error mean square. For the difference above,

$$s_D^2 = 0.02123 \left[\frac{2}{10} + \frac{(54.0 - 50.5)^2}{4,262} \right] = 0.00431,$$

whence, $s_D = 0.0657$ lbs./day. The 95% confidence limits are 0.155 $\pm$ (2.030) (0.0657) $= 0.155 \pm 0.133$ lbs./day. Alternatively, the t-test may be made if desired. Evidently the addition of yeast results in increased rate of gain but the population difference could be small.

If there are many planned comparisons, calculation of all the s_D becomes tedious. An average s_D may be used in all comparisons (6, 3). The loss in accuracy is not great, especially if degrees of freedom for Error are adequate—Cochran and Cox (1) suggest 20 or more—and if the variation in X is small (the Treatment Mean Square of X should be nonsignificant). This average is got by calculating an average mean square to replace $s_{y.x}^2$:

$$\overline{s_{y.x}^2} = s_{y.x}^2 \left[1 + \frac{\Sigma x_T^2}{(a - 1) \Sigma x_E^2}\right]$$

where Σx_T^2 is the initial weight sum of squares for Treatments, $4{,}356 - 4{,}262 = 94$ in table 13.3.2. Substituting the other data from that table,

$$\overline{s_{y\ x}^2} = 0.0212 \left[1 + \frac{94}{(3)(4{,}262)}\right] = 0.0214$$

For n_1 and n_2 replications, the average mean square for D is now

$$\overline{s_D^2} = \overline{s_{y.x}^2} \left[\frac{1}{n_1} + \frac{1}{n_2}\right]$$

In the pig nutrition experiment there were 2 planned comparisons involving the 4 means. For the sake of illustration, assume instead that all comparisons were to be made. Under that assumption, let us make the sequential test,

$$\overline{s_{\bar{y}A}^2} = 0.0214/10 = 0.00214, \quad \overline{s_{\bar{y}A}} = 0.046 \text{ lb./day}$$

From table 10.6.1, $\quad Q = 2.87, \quad 3.46, \quad 3.81$

Then $\quad Q s_{\bar{y}A} = 0.13, \quad 0.16, \quad 0.18$

Differences:

Lot	$\bar{y}_A$	$\bar{y}_A - 1.19$	$\bar{y}_A - 1.31$	$\bar{y}_A - 1.49$
6	1.65	0.46*	0.34*	0.16*
7	1.49	0.30*	0.18*	
8	1.31	0.12		
9	1.19			

After completing a covariance analysis, the experimenter is sure to ask, "Is it worth while?" The efficiency of the covariance relative to straight analysis of average daily gain is estimated by the ratio of the corresponding Error mean squares:

$$\frac{s_y^2}{s_{y.x}^2} = \frac{s_y^2}{s_{y.x}^2 \left[1 + \dfrac{\Sigma x_T^2}{(a-1)\ \Sigma x_E^2}\right]},$$

where $s_y{}^2$ is based on the Common estimate of error for Y. For the pigs, $s_y{}^2 = 0.9726/36 = 0.0270$, $s_{y.x}{}^2 = 0.0214$. The *relative efficiency*, then, is $0.0270/0.0214 = 126\%$. Without covariance, 26% more pigs would have been required to achieve the same precision. In most experiments the value of the covariance analysis is far greater than the decreased error. The detailed study of the experimental results is rewarding,. Actually, most of the information can be got from the graphs; the covariance adds exact numerical evaluation.

EXAMPLE 13.3.1—The following data were abstracted from a larger investigation of correlations among F_1 crosses and inbred lines of corn (4, 8).

F_1 Cross		Days After June 30 to First Silks (X) and Pounds of Shelled Corn Per Plot (Y) for Inbred Lines									
Silver King	X:	24	31	26	30						
	Y:	7.7	5.4	5.2	4.0						
Lancaster	X:	33	33	32	36	33	38	30	38	31	32	32
	Y:	9.6	7.8	9.6	7.7	8.2	7.3	11.3	9.5	8.8	8.4	6.8
Osterland	X:	31	33	33	33	27	32	36				
	Y:	4.8	9.2	8.5	8.8	9.2	7.9	5.9				

Analyze the variance of time to first silks and of yield. For days to silks, $F = 6.05$ results from the selection of the F_1 crosses; Silver King was an early white line, Osterland an early yellow, and Lancaster a later yellow. Thus X is definitely related to the "treatments" or crosses. It would be unrealistic to adjust the yields to a common X except to learn this: how did the crosses achieve their differences in yield? Was it by earliness alone or were other genetic or environmental characteristics involved?

EXAMPLE 13.3.2—Calculate the following analysis of covariance:

	F_1 Cross	f	Σx^2	Σxy	Σy^2	f	Deviations From Regression $\Sigma y^2 - (\Sigma xy)^2/\Sigma x^2$	Mean Square
1	Silver King	3	32.75	−11.42	7.17	2	3.19	1.60
2	Lancaster	10	72.73	−12.38	16.71	9	14.60	1.60
3	Osterland	6	44.86	− 8.46	18.02	5	16.42	3.28
4	Within					16	34.21	2.14
5	Reg. Coef.					2	0.77	0.38
6	Common	19	150.34	−32.26	41.90	18	34.98	1.94
7	Adj. Means					2	32.97	16.48**
8	Total	21	246.00	18.90	69.40	20	67.95	

It is evident that variation in earliness among the inbred lines does not account for differences among the yields of the crosses.

EXAMPLE 13.3.3—In line 7, the sum of squares of deviations among Adjusted Means is composed of 2 parts. One part is associated with the deviations of the F_1 means *from their own regression,*

Reg. of Means   2   95.66   51.16   27.50   1   0.14   0.14,

the sums of squares and products being the differences between lines 8 and 6 above. The second part, $32.97 - 0.14 = 32.83$, with *a single degree of freedom,* measures the *difference between the Common Regression and that of Means.* For this difference, F = 32.83/

$1.94 = 16.9, f = 1,18$; far beyond the 0.005 point. This shows: (i) That deviations of means from their own regression are trivial; the means lie almost on a straight line. (ii) That the regression of means is different from the Common Regression, the latter sloping downwards and the former upwards. Earliness among inbred lines is favorable to yield; those that get started early enjoy the benefits of a longer season. But among F_1 crosses, earliness is associated with low yields.

EXAMPLE 13.3.4—Draw a graph of the regressions of the inbred lines in the 3 crosses, including the individual points and the means. Put in the common regression line and that for the regression of means.

13.4—Covariance in completely randomized experiments; alternative method. Experience together with graphical methods often gives reasonable assurance of linear, parallel regressions with homogeneous variance. In such cases the test of significance among adjusted means can be made with much less labor than is required by the complete analysis of covariance. For the pig experiment of table 13.3.1, only the totals and treatment sums need be used. Corrected sums of squares and products for Total are calculated as in line 9 and entered in table 13.4.1.

TABLE 13.4.1

COVARIANCE ANALYSIS IN COMPLETELY RANDOMIZED DESIGN.
PIG NUTRITION EXPERIMENT

Source of Variation	f	Σx^2	Σxy	Σy^2	f	Deviations From Regression Sum of Squares	Mean Square
Total	39	4,356	34.15	2.2306	38	1.9629	
Means	3	94	2.87	1.2580			
Common	36	4,262	31.28	0.9726	35	0.7430	0.0212
Test of Adjusted Means					3	1.2199	0.4066 **

Corresponding calculations Between Means follow the usual pattern,

For X: $(540^2 + 505^2 + 507^2 + 532^2)/10 - (2,084)^2/40 = 94$, etc.

The differences in the third line of the table are the same as those which were calculated directly in line 7 of table 13.3.2. The test is the same in the two tables.

A feature to be noticed is that it is the Total and Common regressions in which Σy^2 is partitioned, not the regression of Means. Variation among actual adjusted means would be unsuitable for testing because such means are correlated through the common regression.

13.5—Covariance in randomized blocks. The theory of the foregoing sections applies to randomized blocks. The model becomes

$$Y_{ij} = \mu + a_i + \rho_i + \beta x_{ij} + \epsilon_{ij},$$

where the ρ_j are parameters for blocks.

It is not easy to test linearity of regression or homogeneity of variance; these will be assumed. In testing, we shall confine ourselves to a method corresponding to that of section 13.4.

The data in table 13.5.1 illustrate the problem (9). There was some variation in stand which may affect the variety means and the estimate of error. It is desirable to assess these means on the basis of equal stands;

TABLE 13.5.1

STAND (X) AND YIELD (Y) (POUNDS FIELD WEIGHT OF EAR CORN) OF 4 VARIETIES OF CORN. COVARIANCE IN RANDOMIZED BLOCKS

| | Block | | | | | | | | Total | |
| | 1 | | 2 | | 3 | | 4 | | | |
Variety	X	Y	X	Y	X	Y	X	Y	X	Y
A	28	202	22	165	27	191	19	134	96	692
B	23	145	26	201	28	203	24	180	101	729
C	27	188	24	185	27	185	28	220	106	778
D	24	201	28	231	30	238	30	261	112	931
E	30	202	26	178	26	198	29	226	111	804
F	30	228	25	221	27	207	24	204	106	860
Total	162	1,166	151	1,181	165	1,222	154	1,225	632	4,794

| Source of Variation | f | Σx^2 | Σxy | Σy^2 | Deviations From Regression | | |
					f	$\Sigma d_{y.x}^2$	Mean Square
Total	23	181.33	1,485.00	18,678.50			
Blocks	3	21.67	8.50	436.17			
Varieties	5	45.83	559.25	9,490.00			
Error	15	113.83	917.25	8,752.33	14	1,361.07	97.22
Variety Plus Error	20	159.66	1,476.50	18,242.33	19	4,587.99	
For testing adjusted means,					5	3,226.92	645.38**

the *adjusted* means furnish appropriate comparisons. Moreover, it increases efficiency to eliminate from error the environmental effects of stand as measured by X.

The analyses of X and Y separately are:

X: Varieties 5 9.17 Y: Varieties 5 1,898.0
Error 15 7.59 Error 15 583.5
$F = 1.21$ $F = 3.25*$

The first analysis assures us that the variations in stand are only random effects; that the seed from the several varieties are equally viable. If the treatment (variety) were found to affect X as well as Y, interpretation of the covariance analysis would be modified. As for the analysis of yields, the questions to be answered are these: Do the adjusted yields differ from those directly calculated; is error affected by varying stands, do the adjusted yields differ significantly?

In the table there is nothing new about calculating the sums of squares and products. The novel feature is the addition of Variety and Error to get a sub-total in the next-to-last line. This sub-total takes the place of Total in table 13.4.1. Otherwise the testing is the same in the two tables. Note the striking decrease in Error mean square. For testing varieties, F has increased from 3.25 to $645.38/97.22 = 6.64$.

The adjusted means are

A, 191.8; B, 191.0; C, 193.1; D, 219.3; E, 189.6; F, 213.6

Using the sequential method for testing all differences, D and F are not significantly different, but they differ significantly from all the others which do not differ significantly among themselves.

The efficiency of covariance, relative to the analysis of yields alone, is 555% (see examples). That is, more than 22 replications would be required to detect the same differences if covariance were not used. The estimates of mean yields were not greatly affected by adjustment. The striking feature of the experiment is the reduction in error; most of the discrepancy in Y was due to differences in stand, not to yield per plant.

EXAMPLE 13.5.1—Calculate the adjusted means in the corn experiment and carry through the test of all differences. $s_{\bar{y} \cdot x} = 5.12$ pounds.

EXAMPLE 13.5.2—Calculate the efficiency of the covariance relative to randomized blocks.

13.6—Comparisons in covariance; factorial experiments. A single comparison between adjusted means was illustrated in section 13.3. There the t-distribution was used. An F-test could have been made as follows:

Lot 6: $\Sigma X = 540$	$\Sigma Y = 16.62$
Lot 7: 505	14.81
Difference: 35	1.81

Using Rule 12.2.2, the sums of squares for X and Y are

$$\frac{(35)^2}{(10)(2)} = 61 \qquad\qquad \frac{(1.81)^2}{(10)(2)} = 0.1638$$

A slight modification of the rule, substituting the product for a square, gives the sum of products,

$$\frac{(35)(1.81)}{(10)(2)} = 3.17$$

By the methods of sections 13.4 and 13.5:

	f	Σx^2	Σxy	Σy^2	f	$\Sigma d_{y.x}^2$	Mean Square
Treatment	1	61	3.17	0.1638			
Error	36	4,262	31.28	0.9726	35	0.7430	0.02123
$T + E$	37	4,323	34.45	1.1364	36	0.8619	
For testing treatment difference					1	0.1189	0.1189

Treatment represents the comparison being made. Error is copied from table 13.3.2. The device of comparing Treatment + Error with Error is a standard one in testing treatment differences.

From above, $F = 0.1189/0.02123 = 5.60$. In confirmation, note that for a single degree of freedom, $\sqrt{F} = \sqrt{5.60} = 2.37$, the value of t in the earlier comparison, $t = 0.155/0.0657 = 2.36$ (the difference is due to rounding). The F-test is sometimes convenient for making sets of orthogonal comparisons such as those in factorial experiments.

To illustrate comparisons in factorial experiments, table 13.6.1 is extracted from one performed on sugar beets in northern Iowa. No analysis is required to demonstrate the pronounced effect of superphosphate on both plant number and yield. So far as the producer is concerned, if this were a typical result he would not hesitate to apply superphosphate.

But this experiment is a curiosity. It is not known how the fertilizer happened to affect stand; perhaps the nutritional status of the plants, or their maturity, carried them through some critical period. This was an unexpected feature of the experiment.

Since treatment obviously affected X, there is no hope of estimating Y *free from the effects of* X; both X and Y are affected by the fertilizer. What may be done is to learn if there is any effect of fertilizer on Y over and above that contributed through X. This is complicated by competition.

The analysis of covariance shows that most of the superphosphate effect was on stand. After removing the effect of the fertilizer through stand, the over-all test of adjusted means lacks significance. But the individual roots were larger on the superphosphate plots. Is the difference significant?

The t-test for the phosphorus comparison is made by use of the treatment sums:

$$\text{Phosphorus: } \bar{x}_1 = (1{,}774+1{,}882)/12 = 304.67$$
$$\bar{y}_1 = (33.78+38.92)/12 = 6.058$$
$$\text{No Phosphorus: } \bar{x}_2 = (1{,}378+1{,}371)/12 = 229.08$$
$$\bar{y}_2 = (20.12+21.38)/12 = 3.458$$

TABLE 13.6.1

NUMBERS OF BEETS PER PLOT AND YIELDS (TONS PER ACRE) IN A RANDOMIZED
BLOCKS EXPERIMENT

Fertilizer Applied	Number and Yields	Block						Treatment Sums
		1	2	3	4	5	6	
None	Number	183	176	291	254	225	249	1,378
	Yield	2.45	2.25	4.38	4.35	3.42	3.27	20.12
Superphosphate, P	Number	356	300	301	271	288	258	1,774
	Yield	6.71	5.44	4.92	5.23	6.74	4.74	33.78
Muriate of potash, K	Number	224	258	244	217	192	236	1,371
	Yield	3.22	4.14	2.32	4.42	3.28	4.00	21.38
$P + K$	Number	329	283	308	326	318	318	1,882
	Yield	6.34	5.44	5.22	8.00	6.96	6.96	38.92
Block Sums	Number	1,092	1,017	1,144	1,068	1,023	1,061	6,405
	Yield	18.72	17.27	16.84	22.00	20.40	18.97	114.20

Source of Variation	f	Σx^2	Σxy	Σy^2	Deviations From Regression		
					f	$\Sigma d_{y.x}^2$	Mean Square
Blocks	5	2,756	−36.33	4.6727			
Treatments	3	35,253	1,224.63	42.8939			
Error	15	16,873	381.27	11.7711	14	3.1558	0.2254
$T + E$	18	52,126	1,605.90	54.6650	17	5.1906	
For Test of Adjusted Means					3	2.0348	0.6783

$$F = 0.6783/0.2254 = 3.01 \qquad F_{.05} = 3.34$$

$$D_{\hat{y}.x} = \bar{y}_1 - \bar{y}_2 - b(\bar{x}_1 - \bar{x}_2) = 6.058 - 3.458 - 0.0226\,(304.67 - 229.08)$$
$$= 0.892 \text{ ton/acre}$$

$$s_D^2 = s_{y.x}^2 \left[\frac{2}{r} + \frac{(\bar{x}_1 - \bar{x}_2)^2}{\Sigma x_E^2} \right] = 0.2254 \left[\frac{2}{12} + \frac{(75.59)^2}{16,873} \right] = 0.1139,$$

$$s_D = 0.338, \quad t = 0.892/0.338 = 2.64, \quad P = 0.02$$

This comparison indicates that individual roots have larger population size with superphosphate plots *despite the greater competition.*

Alternative to the *t*-test, the *F*-test of differences among adjusted means is shown in table 13.6.2. The phosphorus comparison is calculated thus:

$$X: \quad \frac{(1,774 + 1,882 - 1,378 - 1,371)^2}{(6)(4)} = \frac{(3,656 - 2,749)^2}{(12)(2)} = 34,277$$

$$Y: \quad \frac{(72.70 - 41.50)^2}{(12)(2)} = 40.5600$$

$$XY: \quad \frac{(3,652 - 2,749)(72.70 - 41.50)}{(12)(2)} = 1,179.10$$

The Error statistics are copied from table 13.6.1. The test for phosphorus is shown; also the F-values for the tests of potassium and interaction. The identity of the F and t-tests is evidenced by the comparison of $\sqrt{F}$ with the value of t in the t-test above.

TABLE 13.6.2
SUMS OF SQUARES AND PRODUCTS FOR P, K, AND PK. THE F-TEST AND AN
APPROXIMATE F-TEST

Comparisons	$b^2 =$ 0.0005106 Σx^2	$-2b =$ -0.04512 Σxy	Σy^2	M.S.	Approximate Test* F
P	34,277	1,179.10	40.5600	4.7759	21.19
K	425	26.93	1.7067	0.7067	3.14
PK	551	18.59	0.6273	0.0685	0.30
Sum	35,253	1,224.62	42.8940	$\Sigma d_{y.x}^2$	M.S.
Error	16,873	381.27	11.7711	3.1558	0.2254
$P + E$	51,150	1,560.37	52.3311	4.7324	
For Testing Adjusted Mean Difference for Phosphorus,				1.5766	1.5766

$$F = 1.5766/0.2254 = 6.99, \quad t = \sqrt{F} = 2.64$$

For K: $F = 3.06$ For PK: $F = 0.29$

* Not appropriate for this experiment in which $\bar{x}$ varies significantly. See text.

Notice the absence of the adjusted means in making the F-test. They must be calculated separately in order to know what is being tested. This makes the F-test somewhat more tedious than the t unless no estimate is needed.

In experiments where X has a mean square which is small as compared to error, an approximate F-test is available. It is not suitable for the beet experiment because of the large variation in X, but its calculation is illustrated in table 13.6.2. The reduction in sum of squares due to Error regression is calculated for each of the 3 treatment effects. Since their own regressions are not used, but the Common instead, the method of calculating $\Sigma d_{y.x}^2$ is to sum the squares of $y - bx$ in each line. Using $b = 381.27/16,873 = 0.022596$ (in Error), put $b^2 = 0.0005106$ above Σx^2

and $-2b = -0.045192$ over Σxy. Then for each line calculate $\Sigma y^2 - 2b\Sigma xy + b^2\Sigma x^2$. For P,

$40.5600 - (0.045192)(1,179.10) + (0.0005106)(34,277) = 4.7759$

$$F = 4.7759/0.2254 = 21.19$$

In this approximate test, F is always overestimated; not seriously if X varies little. In the beet experiment, with large variation in X, the test is inappropriate, as you can see.

EXAMPLE 13.6.1—To learn about the individual beet weights, the natural method would be to examine the ratio Y/X. This would give correct results if the scale of measurement were linear. As shown in section 6.14, if the regression of Y on X is linear, then the ratio Y/X is non-linear unless the regression line contains the origin.

One way to get evidence on this is to apply the test of additivity to the ratios (section 11.14). I tried this and found no evidence against the hypothesis. Another way to get evidence is to fit the linear model independently to X and to Y in table 13.6.1. One gets 24 pairs of deviations, $X_{ij} - \hat{X}_{ij}$ and $Y_{ij} - \hat{Y}_{ij}$. The graph of these pairs gives some indication of the shape of the regression and of the distribution of the deviations therefrom. For linear regression the line has the slope $b = 0.0226$ as estimated from Error.

EXAMPLE 13.6.2—There is some slight evidence that the regression of yield on beet number is curved so that the ratio Y/X could be linear. Making this assumption, calculate the 24 values of Y/X (code by multiplying each by 10,000), then analyze the variance of these beet weights. Ans. $F = 14.30$. If the assumptions are correct, the evidence in favor of superphosphate accumulates; its use results in substantially larger roots despite increased competition. See also section 15.5.

13.7—A question about design. In experiments where a predictor of outcome is available in advance, the investigator has a choice among designs. He may randomly allot individuals to the treatments, then use covariance as described in sections 13.2 and 13.3. Or he may use the predicting variable to form blocks, one containing individuals with highest predicted outcome, another with the lowest, and others with the intermediate. Here the design would call for the randomized blocks analysis of chapter 11. A third plan, often used, is to *balance* the lots so that the average of the predictor is the same (or nearly so) in every lot. It is expected that the means will be better estimated but that the estimate of error (if calculated as in chapters 4 and 10) will be biased upward.

The randomized blocks design has the advantage of being approximately balanced, every treatment having one individual from each level or block. To compensate for the lack of exact balance, the design may specify the covariance analysis of section 13.5. If the correlation between predictor and outcome is high, an appreciable increase in efficiency may ensue.

Lucas (5) has advanced some evidence that, after balancing, an unbiased (or approximately unbiased) estimate of error may be obtained from a covariance analysis like that of sections 13.2 and 13.3. A recognized argument is that a precise estimate with an approximate test is worth more than an imprecise estimate with an exact test. The balanced lots with covariance appear to be more efficient than random allotment with covariance, the increase in efficiency depending on the size of the lots and on the correlation between predictor and outcome. With small lots (5 or less) the relative efficiency of random allotment is surprisingly small. There are two reasons: (i) The large range in X for every treatment improves the estimate of regression of Y on X. (ii) The small difference, $\bar{x}_1 - \bar{x}_2$, due to the balance on X, decreases s_D^2 by almost or entirely eliminating the inaccuracy due to the error in b.

Either with or without balancing, the assumptions of covariance in lots are somewhat more stringent than those of covariance in randomized blocks and considerably more than those without covariance. The covariance presented in this text assumes linearity of regression and homogeneity of variance. In addition, covariance in lots assumes parallelism of the lot regressions. If these assumptions cannot be met, one would be safer to plan the type of balancing built into randomized blocks despite the fewer degrees of freedom in error.

13.8—Covariance in a Latin square. The foregoing covariance methods are readily applied when two variables are measured in a Latin square experiment. For illustration the data in table 13.8.1 are taken from an experiment on soybeans at Hudson, Iowa, in 1949 (2). The

TABLE 13.8.1

PER CENT STEM CANKER INFECTION X AND YIELD Y (BUSHELS PER ACRE) IN FOUR SOYBEAN LINES A, B, C, D. LATIN SQUARE DESIGN

Row		Column				Total
		1	2	3	4	
1	Line	C	A	B	D	
	X	4.3	19.3	10.1	14.0	47.7
	Y	26.7	21.3	28.3	25.1	101.4
2	Line	A	B	D	C	
	X	29.2	34.7	30.2	48.2	142.3
	Y	19.7	20.7	20.1	14.7	75.2
3	Line	B	D	C	A	
	X	14.0	7.2	6.3	1.0	28.5
	Y	26.0	24.9	29.0	28.7	108.6
4	Line	D	C	A	B	
	X	8.9	6.7	6.4	5.6	27.6
	Y	29.8	29.0	27.3	34.1	120.2
Total	X	56.4	67.9	53.0	68.8	246.1
	Y	102.2	95.9	104.7	102.6	405.4

		ΣX	ΣY	$\bar{x}$	$\bar{y}$
	A	55.9	97.0	13.98	24.25
	B	64.4	109.1	16.10	27.28
	C	65.5	99.4	16.38	24.85
	D	60.3	99.9	15.08	24.98

original design has been altered to make a suitable example but conclusions are unchanged (see example 13.8.1).

The 4 lines were supposed to be equally susceptible to the infection, justifying the assumption that X is unaffected by Line. The analysis of variance of X adduces no contrary evidence.

There is nothing novel in the calculations. The analysis of covariance in table 13.8.2 indicates differences in yielding ability among the 4 lines.

TABLE 13.8.2

COVARIANCE ANALYSIS OF SOYBEAN DATA. LATIN SQUARE

Source of Variation	f	Σx^2	Σxy	Σy^2	Deviations		
					f	$\Sigma d_{y.x}^2$	M.S.
Row	3	2,239.32	−747.97	272.93			
Column	3	48.12	− 14.64	10.80			
Treatment	3	14.30	10.19	21.22			
Error	6	378.88	−131.04	55.23	5	9.91	1.98
$T + E$	9	393.18	−120.85	76.45	8	39.30	
Test of Adjusted Means					3	29.39	9.80*

The adjusted means are:

     A, 23.77; B, 27.53; C, 25.20; D, 24.88 bu./acre

There is only one change in rank from that of the original means.

Application of the sequential test for differences shows that the only significant difference is that between the adjusted means of B and A.

The efficiency of covariance relative to the straight analysis of yield is 460%.

EXAMPLE 13.8.1—The soybean experiment of table 13.8.1 was really laid out in randomized blocks, the blocks corresponding to the rows of the illustration. There were no columns. Revise table 13.8.2 accordingly. For testing treatments you will get $F = 4.79*$.

REFERENCES

1. WILLIAM G. COCHRAN and GERTRUDE M. COX. Experimental Designs. John Wiley and Sons, Inc., New York (1950).

2. JAMES M. CRALL. Iowa Agricultural Experiment Station data (1949).

3. D. J. FINNEY. Biometrics (Bulletin), 2:53 (1946).

4. M. T. JENKINS. Journal of Agricultural Research, 39:677 (1929)

5. H. L. LUCAS. Institute of Statistics Mimeograph Series No. 18. University of North Carolina (1951).

6. K. R. NAIR. Sankhya, 6:167 (1942).

7. GEORGE W. SNEDECOR and C. C. CULBERTSON. Proceedings, American Society of Animal Production, page 25 (1932).

8. GEORGE W. SNEDECOR and GERTRUDE M. COX. Journal of Agricultural Research, 54:449 (1937).

9. G. J. SPRAGUE. Iowa Agricultural Experiment Station data (1952).

10. PEARL P. SWANSON et al. Reference 12 in chapter 14:

Multiple Regression and Covariance

14.1—Introduction. The regression of Y on a single independent variable (chapter 6) is often inadequate to satisfy the researcher's needs. Two or more X may be available to give additional information about Y. These may be utilized in much the same way as was the single X. In addition there is the opportunity to assess the relative contributions of the various X to information about Y.

Drawing together the threads of the foregoing methods, multiple regression completes a fabric of increasingly complex patterns. Starting with a unique sample (chapter 2), the number of groups and the number of variables have been expanded alternately. At present, 3 variables in a single sample will be considered. Next, multiple samples with 3 variables will receive attention. Four and more variables require no new principles, only increasing the extent and intricacy of the computations.

14.2—Two independent variables in a single sample. The increase from one X to two adds a surprising number of new concepts to those developed in chapter 6. Perhaps the most striking is the necessity for 3 dimensions in which to depict the variables graphically. Solid geometry instead of plane is required. If Y depends partly on X_1 and partly on X_2 for its value, 3 mutually perpendicular axes are demanded for graphical representation. X_1 is measured along one, X_2 is laid out parallel to the second, and Y rises from the plane $X_1 X_2$ parallel to the third axis. The points in space, fixed by the triplets of values (X_1, X_2, Y) determine a *regression surface*.

In this chapter a *plane* will be assumed, its equation being

$$\hat{Y} = \bar{y} + b_{Y1.2}\,(X_1 - \bar{x}_1) + b_{Y2.1}\,(X_2 - \bar{x}_2)$$

$b_{Y1.2}$ and $b_{Y2.1}$ being the *partial regression coefficients*. The first is read, "the regression of Y on X_1 independent of X_2." The plane is fitted to the observational points by the method of least squares which specifies that the sum of squares of vertical distances from plane to points shall be a minimum

As in chapters 6 and 7, two models are available. One applies to random samples from a normal *multivariate* population, X_1, X_2, and Y

being three random variables. In the second model, *the* X *are considered fixed*, chosen by the investigator, only Y being a random, normally distributed variable.

The illustration (table 14.2.1) is taken from an investigation of plant-available phosphorus in various Iowa soils (5). The concentrations of inorganic and organic phosphorus in the soils were determined chemically. Plant-available phosphorus was assessed by growing corn plants in the soils. The object was to learn the source of the nutrient utilized by the plant.

The familiar calculations in the table yield the corrected sums of squares and products required. From least squares theory the 2 partial

TABLE 14.2.1

INORGANIC PHOSPHORUS X_1, ORGANIC PHOSPHORUS X_2, AND ESTIMATED PLANT-AVAILABLE PHOSPHORUS Y IN 18 IOWA SOILS AT 20° C. (PARTS PER MILLION)

Soil Sample	X_1	X_2	Y	$\hat{Y}$	$Y - \hat{Y}$
1	0.4	53	64	61.6*	2.4*
2	0.4	23	60	59.0	1.0
3	3.1	19	71	63.4	7.6
4	0.6	34	61	60.3	0.7
5	4.7	24	54	66.7	−12.7
6	1.7	65	77	64.9	12.1
7	9.4	44	81	76.9	4.1
8	10.1	31	93	77.0	16.0
9	11.6	29	93	79.6	13.4
10	12.6	58	51	83.8	−32.8
11	10.9	37	76	79.0	− 3.0
12	23.1	46	96	101.6	− 5.6
13	23.1	50	77	101.9	−24.9
14	21.6	44	93	98.7	− 5.7
15	23.1	56	95	102.4	− 7.4
16	1.9	36	54	62.8	− 8.8
17	26.8	58	168	109.2	58.8
18	29.9	51	99	114.2	−15.2
Sum	215.0	758	1,463	1,463.0	0.0
Mean	11.94	42.11	81.28		

$$\Sigma X_1^2 = 4{,}321.02 \qquad \Sigma X_1 X_2 = 10{,}139.50 \qquad \Sigma X_1 Y = 20{,}706.20$$
$$C = 2{,}568.06 \qquad C = 9{,}053.89 \qquad C = 17{,}474.72$$

$$\Sigma x_1^2 = 1{,}752.96 \qquad \Sigma x_1 x_2 = 1{,}085.61 \qquad \Sigma x_1 y = 3{,}231.48$$

$$\Sigma X_2^2 = 35{,}076.00 \qquad \Sigma X_2 Y = 63{,}825.00 \qquad \Sigma Y^2 = 131{,}299.00$$
$$C = 31{,}920.22 \qquad C = 61{,}608.56 \qquad C = 118{,}909.39$$

$$\Sigma x_2^2 = 3{,}155.78 \qquad \Sigma x_2 y = 2{,}216.44 \qquad \Sigma y^2 = 12{,}389.61$$

* The number of significant digits retained in the preceding calculations will affect these columns by ± 0.1 or ± 0.2.

regression coefficients are given by a pair of simultaneous *normal* equations,

$$\Sigma x_1^2 \; b_{Y1.2} + \Sigma x_1 x_2 \; b_{Y2.1} = \Sigma x_1 y$$

$$\Sigma x_1 x_2 \; b_{Y1.2} + \Sigma x_2^2 \; b_{Y2.1} = \Sigma x_2 y$$

Solution of these equations by the usual algebriac methods leads to the formulas,

$$b_{Y1\,2} = \frac{(\Sigma x_2^2)(\Sigma x_1 y) - (\Sigma x_1 x_2)(\Sigma x_2 y)}{D}$$

$$b_{Y2\,1} = \frac{(\Sigma x_1^2)(\Sigma x_2 y) - (\Sigma x_1 x_2)(\Sigma x_1 y)}{D},$$

where $$D = (\Sigma x_1^2)(\Sigma x_2^2) - (\Sigma x_1 x_2)^2$$

Substituting the phosphorus data,

$$D = (1,752.96)(3,155.78) - (1,085.61)^2 = 4,353,400$$

$$b_{Y1.2} = \frac{(3,155.78)(3,231.48) - (1,085.61)(2,216.44)}{4,353,400} = 1.7898$$

$$b_{Y2\,1} = \frac{(1,752.96)(2,216.44) - (1,085.61)(3,231.48)}{4,353,400} = 0.0866$$

The *multiple regression equation* becomes,

$$\hat{Y} = 81.28 + 1.7898 \,(X_1 - 11.94) + 0.0866 \,(X_2 - 42.11)$$

$$= 56.26 + 1.7898 \, X_1 + 0.0866 \, X_2$$

The meaning is this: The plant-available phosphorus increased an average of 1.7898 ppm. for each part per million of inorganic phosphorus in the soil at the beginning but only 0.0866 ppm. for each ppm. of organic phosphorus. The indication is that, at 20° C. growing temperature, the inorganic phosphorus in the soil was the chief source of plant-available phosphorus. This last deduction goes beyond the arithmetic of multiple regression. The latter does no more then quantify the closeness of the relations between changes in Y and corresponding changes in the two X.

The model that seems more realistic here is that with fixed X. While there was some randomness in the X, nevertheless the soils were selected and were supplied with selected amounts of nutritive additives. Assuming fixed X, the model is,

$$Y = a + \beta_{Y1.2} \,(X_1 - \bar{x}_1) + \beta_{Y2.1} \,(X_2 - \bar{x}_2) + \epsilon,$$

where a and the β are parameters to be estimated and ϵ is $N(0, \sigma)$. Here each Y is made up of a part determined by the parameters (together with the fixed X) plus a random component. The first part is estimated by $\hat{Y}$, a point on the sample regression plane corresponding to X_1 and X_2. The random part will be discussed later.

Two parameters, the β, are required to fix the *orientation* of the regression plane; α determines the *elevation*. In the phosphorus experiment 81.28 estimates α, 1.7898 estimates $\beta_{Y1.2}$, 0.0866 estimates $\beta_{Y2.1}$.

For each soil, $\hat{Y}$ estimates the population regression value corresponding to the X_1 and X_2 of that soil. For example, for soil 1,

$$\hat{Y} = 56\ 26 + 1.7898(0.4) + 0.0866(53) = 61.6 \text{ ppm.}$$

The observed $Y = 64$ ppm. deviates $64 - 61.6 = 2.4$ ppm. from the estimated regression value; that is, the observed ordinate extends 2.4 units above the sample plane. In the model, this is attributed to sampling variation. The 18 values of $\hat{Y}$ are calculated and recorded in table 14.2.1. The deviations $Y - \hat{Y}$ are in the final column; they measure the failure of the X to predict Y.

The investigator now has the opportunity to examine the deviations from regression. In part they might be associated with other variables not included in this study. Or some explanation might be found for certain deviations, especially the large ones. Such explanation might be the most valuable finding of the experiment, or it might lead to the rejection of one or more observations and to a recalculation of the regression. But rejection of aberrant observations is always questionable and should not be done lightly.

Often the purpose of the investigator is to learn the relative strength of the relation between Y and the two independent variables. There is no unique way of doing this but several approaches are available. If the sample standard deviations of X_1 and X_2 were the same, an easy and usually adequate way would be to compare the two regression coefficients. To avoid unequal variation in the X, the *standard partial regression coefficients* may be calculated and compared:

$$b'_{Y1.2} = b_{Y1.2}\sqrt{(\Sigma x_1^2/\Sigma y^2)}, \ b'_{Y2.1} = b_{Y2.1}\sqrt{(\Sigma x_2^2/\Sigma y^2)}$$

For the phosphorus experiment,

$$b'_{Y1.2} = 1.7898\sqrt{(1,752.96/12,389.61)} = 0.67,$$

$$b'_{Y2.1} = 0.0866\sqrt{(3,155.78/12,389.61)} = 0.04$$

There is little doubt that inorganic phosphorus is the more effective predictor of plant-available phosphorus. In succeeding sections you will find methods that lead to more exact statements.

Use of the regression model with fixed X raises the question of possible errors in the measurement of X. If there are such errors, both estimates and tests are biased. The amount of bias depends upon the size of the error relative to the range of X. In addition to references (1) and (14) in chapter 6, see (11).

EXAMPLE 14.2.1—Here is a set of 20 triplets arranged for easy computation:

X_1	X_2	Y	X_1	X_2	Y
29	2	22	21	2	24
1	4	26	12	1	7
5	3	23	24	3	23
31	1	8	16	3	28
25	3	25	6	4	25
16	1	12	20	2	22
26	1	13	35	1	25
15	4	30	9	4	32
6	2	12	19	4	37
10	3	26	14	2	20

Calculate the regression,
$$\hat{Y} = 0.35X_1 + 7.16X_2 - 1.9$$

14.3—Interval estimates and tests of significance. According to the model the ϵ are randomly drawn from $N(0, \sigma)$. σ is estimated from the deviations from sample regression, $Y - \hat{Y} = d_{Y.12}$. Running up the sum of squares in the last column of table 14.2.1, $\Sigma d_{Y.12}^2 = 6{,}414.46$. Using an easier and more accurate method of calculation shown below, $\Sigma d_{Y.12}^2 = 6{,}414.0$. From this, $s_{Y.12}^2 = 6{,}414.0/15 = 427.6$, the degrees of freedom being n minus the number of variables. More particularly, one degree of freedom is assigned to $\bar{y}$ and one to each b.

The remaining sum of squares, $\Sigma y^2 - \Sigma d_{Y.12}^2 = 12{,}389.6 - 6{,}414.0 = 5{,}975.6$, is *due to regression*. It is symbolized by $\Sigma \hat{y}_{12}^2$. The relation among these sums of squares is shown in the table 14.3.1.

TABLE 14.3.1
ANALYSIS OF VARIANCE OF PLANT-AVAILABLE PHOSPHORUS

Source of Variation	Degrees of Freedom	Sum of Squares	Mean Square
Total	17	$\Sigma y^2 = 12{,}389.6$	
Regression	2	$\Sigma \hat{y}_{12}^2 = 5{,}975.6$	2,987.8
Deviations	15	$\Sigma d_{Y.12}^2 = 6{,}414.0$	427.6

$$F = 2{,}987.8/427.6 = 6.99. \quad P < 0.01.$$

The null hypothesis, $\beta_{Y1.2} = \beta_{Y2.1} = 0$, is tested by F. This is an over-all test of the significance of the regression.

In practice, the sum of squares of Y due to regression is calculated thus:

$$\Sigma \hat{y}_{12}^2 = b_{Y1.2}\Sigma x_1 y + b_{Y2.1}\Sigma x_2 y = (1{,}7898)(3{,}231.48) + (0.0866)(2{,}216.44)$$
$$= 5{,}975.6$$

The value of $\Sigma d_{Y.12}^2$ is then

$$\Sigma y^2 - \Sigma \hat{y}_{12}^2 = 12{,}389.6 - 5{,}975.6 = 6{,}414.0$$

This method is less subject to rounding errors than the one used above. The confidence interval for α is

$$\bar{y} \pm t_{.05}s_{Y.12}/\sqrt{n}, \quad f = n - m,$$

where m is the number of variables. Substituting,

$$81.28 \pm (2.131) \sqrt{(427.6)/18}; 70.9 \text{ to } 91.7 \text{ ppm.}$$

Confidence intervals and tests of significance for the regression co-efficients require two *"multipliers,"*

$$c_{11} = \Sigma x_2^2/D = 3{,}155.78/4{,}353{,}400 = 0.0007249$$
$$c_{22} = \Sigma x_1^2/D = 1{,}752.96/4{,}353{,}400 = 0.0004027$$

We now calculate:

$$s_{b_{Y1.2}}{}^2 = s_{Y.12}{}^2 c_{11} = (427.6)(0.0007249) = 0.3100, \; s_{b_{Y1.2}} = 0.557$$
$$s_{b_{Y2.1}}{}^2 = s_{Y.12}{}^2 c_{22} = (427.6)(0.0004027) = 0.1722, \; s_{b_{Y1.2}} = 0.415$$

The quantity, $(b_{Y1.2} - \beta_{Y1.2})/s_{b_{Y1.2}}$, is distributed as t. The hypothesis, $\beta_{Y1.2} = 0$, is tested as usual:

$$t_1 = b_{Y1.2}/s_{b_{Y1.2}} = 1.7898/0.557 = 3.21**$$
$$t_2 = b_{Y2.1}/s_{b_{Y2.1}} = 0.0866/0.415 = 0.21$$

Evidently in the population sampled the fraction of inorganic phosphorus is the better predictor of the plant-available phosphorus. The experiment indicates ". . . that soil organic phosphorus *per se* is not available to plants. Presumably, the organic phosphorus is of appreciable availability to plants only upon mineralization, and in the experiments the rate of miner-alization at 20° C. was too low to be of measurable importance." Com-pare section 14.10.

For further work, it might be decided to measure only the inorganic fraction, ignoring the organic. If so, the regression coefficient of Y on X_1 would be

$$\Sigma x_1 y / \Sigma x_1^2 = 3{,}231.48/1{,}752.96 = 1.843 \text{ instead of } b_{Y1.2} = 1.7898$$

This emphasizes the fact that both estimates and tests depend on the inde-pendent variables included in the regression. In any one regression the estimates and tests are correlated; the whole complex changes if inde-pendent variables are added or deleted. In this sense, statements made about the predictive value of a variable are not unique; they depend upon the other variables being used in the regression.

There is another and more general way of attacking the problem of predictive ability. It is illustrated in table 14.3.2. Start with the sum of squares due to the regression of Y on both X_1 and X_2. First deduct the sum of squares due to Y on X_1, calculated by formula 6.15.4. The remain-der is the sum of squares due to X_2 *after the effect of* X_1 *has been discounted.* In the phosphorus experiment this remainder is trivial. Next, deduct

TABLE 14.3.2

TEST OF EACH X AFTER THE EFFECT OF THE OTHER HAS BEEN REMOVED

Source of Variation	Degrees of Freedom	Sum of Squares	Mean Square
X_1 and X_2	2	$\Sigma \hat{y}_{12}^2 = 5{,}975.6$	
X_1 alone	1	$\Sigma \hat{y}_1^2 = 5{,}957.0$	
X_2 after X_1	1	18 6	18.6
X_1 and X_2	2	5,975.6	
X_2 alone	1	$\Sigma \hat{y}_2^2 = 1{,}556.7$	
X_1 after X_2	1	4,418.9	4,418.9**
Error	15	6,414.0	427.6

from $\Sigma \hat{y}_{12}^2$ the sum of squares due to Y on X_2. The remaining highly significant sum of squares is attributed to X_1 after the effect of X_2 has been taken into account. Non-uniqueness is striking in the comparison of X_2 alone with X_2 after X_1. The fact must be faced that conclusions depend in part on the order in which tests are conducted. The tests are not orthogonal but are interdependent.

The generality of the method just described lies in this: If there are many independent variables, *groups of them* may be discarded if their combined contribution to the sum of squares is small. An illustration will be given in section 14.9.

Where only a single X is eliminated, the F-test of table 14.3.2 is identical with that of t, as shown by comparison of $\sqrt{F} = \sqrt{(4{,}418.9/427.6)} = 3.21$ with the corresponding t_1 calculated above. This throws light on the null hypothesis, $\beta_{Y1.2} = 0$, tested by t_1; it is the same as the hypothesis that there is no remaining sum of squares in Y (aside from error) after the effect of X_2 has been taken into account. The identity of the tests permits alternative methods; it may be more convenient to use the device of table 14.3.2 than to calculate the multipliers required for the t-test. For 3 or more X, don't decide until you have read sections 14.10 and 14.11.

To calculate the confidence interval on the regression value of Y in the population, a third multiplier is needed;

$$c_{12} = -\Sigma x_1 x_2 / D = -1{,}085.61/4{,}353{,}400 = -0.0002494$$

For Y corresponding to (X_1, X_2), the confidence interval is

$$\hat{Y} \pm t_{.05} s_{Y.12} \sqrt{(1/n + c_{11} x_1^2 + c_{22} x_2^2 + 2 c_{12} x_1 x_2)}$$

Example: For the value of Y at the point $X_1 = 4.7$, $X_2 = 24$, soil sample 5, table 14.2.1: $x_1 = 4.7 - 11.9 = -7.2$, $x_2 = 24 - 42 = -18$; so the confidence interval is

$$66.7 \pm (2.131)\sqrt{427.6}\sqrt{[1/18 + (0.0007249)(-7.2)^2}$$
$$+ (0.0004027)(-18)^2 + 2(-0.0002494)(-7.2)(-18)]$$
$$= 66.7 \pm 17.6 \text{ ppm.}$$

Some information about linearity of regression may be got by constructing two scatter diagrams; first, plot $d_{Y.12}$ (last column of table 14.2.1) against X_1, then plot the same deviations against X_2. If regression were not linear, curves instead of horizontal straight lines might be detected in one or both of these graphs. For curved multiple regression, see example 15.5.1

EXAMPLE 14.3.1—Ignoring X_2, analyze the variance of Y in its regression on X_1. You will get the mean squares,

Regression	1	5,957	
Deviations	16	402	$F = 14.82$

Contrast this with table 14.3.1. As compared to X_1, the information furnished by X_2 is so little that F is actually decreased by the inclusion of X_2 in the regression. Trace the mechanism of this decrease.

EXAMPLE 14.3.2—Ignoring X_1, analyze the variance of Y in its regression on X_2.

Regression	1	1,557	
Deviations	16	677	$F = 2.30$

Notice the sizeable sum of squares accounted for by X_2 in the absence of X_1. The seeming contradictions are due to the correlation between X_1 and X_2. In this sense, the contributions of the two variables are not independent. Calculate $r_{12} = 0.46$.

EXAMPLE 14.3.3—Set 95% confidence intervals on $\beta_{Y1.2}$ and $\beta_{Y2.1}$. Ans. 0.60 to 2.98 and -0.79 to 0.97.

EXAMPLE 14.3.4—Compute the correlation between Y and $\hat{Y}$ in table 14.2.1. You will get approximately $R = 0.69$. This is called the *coefficient of multiple correlation*. As you see, it is a measure of the closeness of fit of the regression plane.

EXAMPLE 14.3.5—Calculate R from the formula, $R^2 = \Sigma\hat{y}_{12}^2/\Sigma y^2 = 0.4823$. This shows that, of the total sum of squares of Y, R^2 *is the fraction attributable to regression*. It is in this sense that R^2 measures the goodness of fit of regression.

EXAMPLE 14.3.6—Calculate $1 - R^2 = \Sigma d_{Y.12}^2 /\Sigma y^2 = 0.5177$. This fraction of Σy^2, $1 - R^2$, *measures deviations from regression*, the failure of the regression to account for the variation in Y.

14.4—Multiple covariance in a completely randomized experiment. If there are two or more independent variables in a completely randomized experiment, the methods of covariance in sections 13.2, 13.3, and 13.4 may be expanded to *multiple covariance*. There is no change in the model or in the theory beyond the addition of the extra terms in X. The method is illustrated by the average daily gains of pigs in table 14.4.1. Presumably these are predictable, to some extent, by the ages and weights at which the pigs were started in the experiment. If so, estimates of both treatment effects and error may be improved by covariance. Furthermore, since balancing is evident from the analysis of variance of X_1 and X_2, covariance is expected to yield a reliable estimate of error (section 13.7).

Calculation of the Total sums of squares and products follows the pattern of table 14.2.1, ignoring the separation into lots. The corrected values are entered in the first lines of table 14.4.2.

TABLE 14.4.1

INITIAL AGE (X_1), INITIAL WEIGHT (X_2), AND RATE OF GAIN (Y) OF 40 SWINE. FOUR TREATMENTS IN LOTS OF EQUAL SIZE

Treatment	Initial Age, X_1 (days)	Weight, X_2 (pounds)	Rate of Gain, Y (pounds per day)	Sums ΣX_1	Sums ΣX_2	Sums ΣY	Means $\bar{x}_1$	Means $\bar{x}_2$	Means $\bar{y}$
1	78	61	1.40						
	90	59	1.79						
	94	76	1.72						
	71	50	1.47						
	99	61	1.26						
	80	54	1.28						
	83	57	1.34						
	75	45	1.55						
	62	41	1.57						
	67	40	1.26	799	544	14.64	79.9	54.4	1.46
2	78	74	1.61						
	99	75	1.31						
	80	64	1.12						
	75	48	1.35						
	94	62	1.29						
	91	42	1.24						
	75	52	1.29						
	63	43	1.43						
	62	50	1.29						
	67	40	1.26	784	550	13.19	78.4	55.0	1.32
3	78	80	1.67						
	83	61	1.41						
	79	62	1.73						
	70	47	1.23						
	85	59	1.49						
	83	42	1.22						
	71	47	1.39						
	66	42	1.39						
	67	40	1.56						
	67	40	1.36	749	520	14.45	74.9	52.0	1.44
4	77	62	1.40						
	71	55	1.47						
	78	62	1.37						
	70	43	1.15						
	95	57	1.22						
	96	51	1.48						
	71	41	1.31						
	63	40	1.27						
	62	45	1.22						
	67	39	1.36	750	495	13.25	75.0	49.5	1.35
Total				3,082	2,109	55.53	77.0	52.7	1.39

TABLE 14.4.2

CALCULATION OF SUMS OF SQUARES AND PRODUCTS FOR MULTIPLE COVARIANCE IN A
COMPLETELY RANDOMIZED EXPERIMENT. SWINE DATA OF TABLE 14.4.1

	Σx_1^2	$\Sigma x_1 x_2$	$\Sigma x_1 y$
Total	4,735.90	3,037.55	6.9235
Treatments	187.70	160.15	1.3005
Individuals	4,548.20	2,877.40	5.6230

	Σx_2^2	$\Sigma x_2 y$	Σy^2
Total	5,065.98	27.5408	1.0228
Treatments	189.08	1.3218	0.1776
Individuals	4,876.90	26.2190	0.8452

For treatments, the sums of Y and the two X are handled in the usual
manner. Two examples:

$$\Sigma x_1^2 = \frac{799^2 + 784^2 + 749^2 + 750^2}{10} - \frac{3,082^2}{40} = 187.70$$

$$\Sigma x_1 x_2 = \frac{(799)(544) + \ldots + (750)(495)}{10} - \frac{(3,082)(2,109)}{40} = 160.15$$

One now proceeds to calculate the two b, $\Sigma \hat{y}_{12}^2$ and $\Sigma d_{Y.12}^2$ first for
Total and then for Individuals, using twice in succession the formulas of
sections 14.2 and 14.3. The results are:

Total: $b_{Y1.2} = -0.0032903$, $b_{Y2.1} = 0.0074093$, $\Sigma \hat{y}_{12}^2 = 0.1803$,
$\quad \Sigma d_{Y.12}^2 = 0.8415$

Individuals: $b_{Y1.2} = -0.0034542$, $b_{Y2.1} = 0.0074142$, $\Sigma \hat{y}_{12}^2 = 0.1750$,
$\quad \Sigma d_{Y.12}^2 = 0.6702$

The $\Sigma d_{Y.12}^2$ are entered in table 14.4.3 to complete the analysis of variance
of deviations from regression.

TABLE 14.4.3

ANALYSIS OF COVARIANCE OF PIG GAINS. DEVIATIONS FROM REGRESSION

Source of Variation	Degrees of Freedom	Sum of Squares	Mean Square
Total	37	0.8415	
Error (Individuals)	34	0.6702	0.0197
For Testing Adjusted Treatment Means	3	0.1713	0.0571 *

This analysis is analogous to that in section 13.4. It is assumed that the population regressions are linear and parallel with common σ in a normal and independent distribution of ϵ. One could follow the method of section 13.3, computing the b, $\Sigma \hat{y}_{12}^2$ and $\Sigma d_{Y.12}^2$ for each of the 4 treatments and for the common regression (Error of table 14.4.3). The analysis then would be similar to that of table 13.3.2.

The adjusted treatment means tested in table 14.4.3 are calculated by this formula:

$$\bar{y}_{Ai} = \bar{y}_i - b_{Y1.2}(\bar{x}_{1i} - \bar{x}_{1.}) - b_{Y2.1}(\bar{x}_{2i} - \bar{x}_{2.}),$$

where the subscript i designates the lot and the b are those for Error. For lot 4,

$$\bar{y}_{A4} = 1.35 - (-0.0034543)(75.0 - 77.0) - 0.0074142(49.5 - 52.7)$$
$$= 1.35 - 0.0069 + 0.0237 = 1.37 \text{ pounds per day}$$

In this example there is little change from $\bar{y}_i$ to $\bar{y}_{Ai}$ because the lot means of X_1 and X_2 are close to the corresponding experiment means. The 4 adjusted lot means are

$$1.46, \quad 1.31, \quad 1.44, \quad 1.37 \text{ pounds per day.}$$

Further estimates and tests require the 3 multipliers for Error, calculated as in section 14.3:

$$c_{11} = 0.0003508, \qquad c_{22} = 0.0003272, \qquad c_{12} = -0.0002070$$

The mean square of an adjusted mean Y is

$$s_{\bar{y}_{Ai}}^2 = s_{Y.12}^2 \, [1/r + c_{11}(\bar{x}_{1i}-\bar{x}_{1.})^2 + c_{22}(\bar{x}_{2i}-\bar{x}_{2.})^2 + 2c_{12}(\bar{x}_{1i}-\bar{x}_{1.})(\bar{x}_{2i}-\bar{x}_{2.})]$$

For lot 4,

$$s_{\bar{y}_{A4}}^2 = 0.0197 \, [1/10 + 0.0003508(75.0 - 77.0)^2 + 0.0003272(49.5 - 52.7)^2 + 2(-0.0002070)(75.0 - 77.0)(49.5 - 52.7)]$$
$$= 0.00201. \qquad s_{\bar{y}_{A4}} = 0.045 \text{ pound per day.}$$

This provides the confidence interval on the adjusted mean of lot 4, $1.37 \pm (2.032)(0.045)$; 1.28 to 1.46 pounds per day.

For comparisons planned in advance, the difference between two adjusted means is

$$D = \bar{y}_i - \bar{y}_j - b_{Y1.2}(\bar{x}_{1i} - \bar{x}_{1j}) - b_{Y2\,.1}(\bar{x}_{2i} - \bar{x}_{2j})$$

with the mean square,

$$s_D^2 = s_{Y.12}^2 \, [2/r + c_{11}(\bar{x}_{1i}-\bar{x}_{1j})^2 + c_{22}(\bar{x}_{2i}-\bar{x}_{2j})^2 + 2c_{12}(\bar{x}_{1i}-\bar{x}_{1j})(\bar{x}_{2i}-\bar{x}_{2j})]$$

For illustration, assume that it had been planned to compare the mean gains in lots 1 and 2.

$$D = 1.46 - 1.32 - (-0.003454)(79.9-78.4) - 0.007414(54.4-55.0)$$
$$= 0.15 \text{ lb./day}$$

(which can be got directly from the adjusted means if they are already calculated as above).

$$s_D{}^2 = 0.0197 \ [2/10 + 0.0003508(79.9 - 78.4)^2 + 0.0003272(54.4 - 55.0)^2$$
$$+ \ 2(-0.0002070)(79.9 - 78.4)(54.4 - 55.0)] \ = \ 0.00395$$

From this the 95% confidence interval on the difference is

$$0.15 \ \pm \ (2.032)\sqrt{0.00395}; \ 0.02 \ \text{to} \ 0.28 \ \text{pound/day}.$$

In this experiment individual comparisons were not planned. The correct way to assess all differences requires an average standard error,

$$\overline{s_{\hat{y}.12}{}^2} = \frac{s_{Y.12}{}^2}{n} \left[1 + \frac{c_{11}(\Sigma x_1{}^2)_T + c_{22}(\Sigma x_2{}^2)_T + 2c_{12}(\Sigma x_1 x_2)_T}{a - 1} \right]$$

$$= \frac{0.0197}{10} \left[1 + \frac{(0.0003508)(187.70) + (0.0003272)(189.08)}{4 - 1} \right.$$

$$\left. + \ \frac{2(-0.0002070)(160.15)}{4 - 1} \right]$$

$$= 0.00201; \quad \overline{s_{\hat{y}.12}} = 0.0448$$

The testing of all differences is now carried on as usual:

Lot	$\bar{x}_i$	$\bar{x}_i - \bar{x}_2$	$\bar{x}_i - \bar{x}_4$	$\bar{x}_i - \bar{x}_3$
1	1.46	0.15 (0.13)	0.09 (0.16)	0.02 (0.17)
3	1.44	0.13 (0.16)	0.07 (0.17)	
4	1.37	0.06 (0.17)		
2	1.31			

It is only the largest difference that is significant.

In the pig experiment, the efficiency of covariance relative to the calculation of experimental error from gains alone is

$$s_{\hat{y}}{}^2 / \overline{s_{\hat{y}.12}{}^2} = 0.00235/0.00201 = 117\%$$

Analyses of variance of X_1, X_2, and Y in table 14.4.2 suggest that the pigs were not allotted at random, though this seems to have had little effect on Y. Actually the lots were balanced on initial weight and age. Reverting to section 13.7, one is warranted in thinking that covariance has yielded adequate estimates and tests. Because of the balancing the adjusted means are little changed from the original lot means and the average mean square for mean differences is only slightly larger than $2s_{\bar{y}.12}^2/n$. These are advantages in favor of balancing.

The discriminating user of multiple regression is almost certain to puzzle over this fact: The regression of Y on X_1, either alone or in one set of X, may be quite different from the same regression, Y on X_1, in another set of X—even the signs may be opposite. Consider the regression of Y on X_1 (age) in the pig data. Using Totals (ignoring Lots), the regression coefficient is

$$b_{Y1} = 6.9235/4,735.90 = 0.001462 \text{ lb./day/day of age}$$

Compare this with $b_{Y1.2} = -0.003290$ calculated above, also for Total. Why should average daily gain increase with age in the first case and decrease in the second?

The first regression is an over-all effect, ignoring initial weight. In this sample there was a slight tendency for the initially older pigs to gain faster. But among pigs of the same initial weight (initial weight " held constant") the older pigs gained more slowly. That's the reason the older slow gainers had no more weight than the younger fast gainers.

These facts may be observed in table 14.4.4. The right-hand column shows that both initial age and rate of gain increase with initial weight; they are positively associated because of their common association with

TABLE 14.4.4
DATA ON 40 SWINE (TABLE 14.4.1) CLASSIFIED BY INITIAL WEIGHT

Initial Weight	Number of Swine	Initial Age and Average Daily Gain								Total	Mean
39–44	13	62 1.57	67 1.26	91 1.24	63 1.43	67 1.26	83 1.22	66 1.39	67 1.56		
		67 1.36	70 1.15	71 1.31	63 1.27	67 1.36				904 17.38	69.5 1.34
45–49	5	75 1.55	75 1.35	70 1.23	71 1.39	62 1.22				353 6.74	70.6 1.35
50–54	5	71 1.47	80 1.28	75 1.29	62 1.29	96 1.48				384 6.81	76.8 1.36
55–59	5	90 1.79	83 1.34	85 1.49	71 1.47	95 1.22				424 7.31	84.8 1.46
60–64	8	78 1.40	99 1.26	80 1.12	94 1.29	83 1.41	79 1.73	77 1.40	78 1.37	668 10.98	83.5 1.37
74–80	4	78 1.61	94 1.72	99 1.31	78 1.67					349 6.31	87.2 1.58
Total	40									3,082 55.53	77.05 1.388

initial weight. But within the rows of the table, where initial weight doesn't change much, there is the opposite tendency. The older pigs tend to gain more slowly. A graph of each of the rows will show this in more detail while table 14.4.5 contains exact summaries. In the last line is the *Common Regression*, which is negative. This average differs only slightly

TABLE 14.4.5

ANALYSIS OF COVARIANCE IN WEIGHT CLASSES OF SWINE

Weight Class	Degrees of Freedom	Σx_1^2	$\Sigma x_1 y$	Σy^2	Regression of Y on X_1
		Sums of Squares and Products			
39–44	12	831.2308	−6.1885	0.1917	−0.007445
45–49	4	113.2000	2.0860	0.0729	0.018428
50–54	4	634.8000	2.5720	0.0427	0.004052
55–59	4	324.8000	−0.6480	0.1819	−0.001995
60–64	7	486.0000	−3.6700	0.2140	−0.007551
74–80	3	354.7500	−3.3375	0.1015	−0.009408
Common	34	2,744.7808	−9.1860	0.8047	−0.003347

from the average, $b_{Y1.2} = -0.003290$, estimating the same effect, the regression of average daily gain on initial age in a population of pigs all having the same initial weight.

In the same manner the pigs could be separated into groups each composed of pigs having approximately the same initial age. The common regression within these groups would be about the same as $b_{Y2.1} = 0.007409$ as contrasted with $b_{Y2} = 27.5408/5,065.98 = 0.005436$. By use of multiple regression we segregate in a single equation the independent contributions of X_1 and X_2 to the dependent Y.

14.5—Multiple covariance in two-way table. Two or more covariates may be associated with Y in a 2-way table. In assessing yield, for example, not only number of plants but incidence of some pest may be pertinent information. Except for intricacy of the computations there is nothing new to be added to section 13.5.

As illustration we select data from an experiment (1, 14) carried on in Great Britain from 1932 to 1937. The ultimate object was to learn how to forecast the wheat crop from measurements on a sample of growing plants. In the early stages of the experiment it appeared that most of the available information was contained in the 2 variables, shoot height at ear emergence, X_1, and plant numbers at tillering, X_2. Data on these characters together with yield are set out in table 14.5.1.

TABLE 14.5.1

HEIGHTS OF SHOOTS AT EAR EMERGENCE (X_1), NUMBER OF PLANTS AT TILLERING (X_2), AND YIELD (Y) OF WHEAT IN GREAT BRITAIN
$(X_1,$ inches; $X_2,$ number per foot; $Y,$ cwt. per acre)

Year	Variate	Place						Year Sums
		Seale Hayne	Rotham-sted	New-port	Bog-hall	Sprows-ton	Plump-ton	
1933	X_1	25.6	25.4	30.8	33.0	28.5	28.0	171.3
	X_2	14.9	13.3	4.6	14.7	12.8	7.5	67.8
	Y	19.0	22.2	35.3	32.8	25.3	35.8	170.4
1934	X_1	25.4	28.3	35.3	32.4	25.9	24.2	171.5
	X_2	7.2	9.5	6.8	9.7	9.2	7.5	49.9
	Y	32.4	32.2	43.7	35.7	28.3	35.2	207.5
1935	X_1	27.9	34.4	32.5	27.5	23.7	32.9	178.9
	X_2	18.6	22.2	10.0	17.6	14.4	7.9	90.7
	Y	26.2	34.7	40.0	29.6	20.6	47.2	198.3
Place Sums	X_1	78.9	88.1	98.6	92.9	78.1	85.1	521.7
	X_2	40.7	45.0	21.4	42.0	36.4	22.9	208.4
	Y	77.6	89.1	119.0	98.1	74.2	118.2	576.2

Corrected Sums of Squares and Products:

	Σx_1^2	$\Sigma x_1 x_2$	$\Sigma x_1 y$
Total	230.53	$-$ 0.65	341.25
Place	106.34	$-$47.06	190.83
Season	6.26	26.24	8.41
Error	117.93	20.17	142.01

	Σx_2^2	$\Sigma x_2 y$	Σy^2
Total	385.07	-300.75	982.30
Place	171.46	-257.03	629.22
Season	139.41	$-$ 22.26	124.42
Error	74.20	$-$ 21.46	228.66

For examining relationships, the statistics used should be free of the place and season effects. Assuming fixed X, the model being used, written in terms of sample statistics, is

$$Y_{ij} = \bar{y}.. + S_i + P_j + b_{Y1.2}(X_{1ij} - \bar{x}_1..) + b_{Y2.1}(X_{2ij} - \bar{x}_2..) + e,$$

where S and P represent season and place constants. To eliminate these constants, the linear model,

$$\hat{Y}_{ij} = \bar{y}.. + S_i + P_j$$

might be fitted to the yield data, then a new variable,

$$\hat{Y}_{ij}' = Y_{ij} - \hat{Y}_{ij},$$

used in completing the covariance analysis. The result would be the same as the regression computed from the Error sums of squares and products in table 14.5.1:

$$b_{Y1.2} = 1.3148, \quad b_{Y2.1} = -0.6466, \quad \Sigma \hat{y}_{12}^2 = 200.59, \quad \Sigma d_{Y.12}^2 = 28.07$$

These statistics, with some from the table, lead to the following facts:

1. Freed from the season and place effects, height of shoots and number of plants account for

$$\Sigma \hat{y}_{12}^2 / \Sigma y^2 = 200.59/228.66 = 88\%$$

of the sum of squares for yield.

2. The predictive values of the 2 independent variables are indicated by the following analyses of $\Sigma \hat{y}^2$:

Regression on X_1 and X_2	2	200.59	
Regression on X_1 alone	1	171.01	
	—	————	
X_2 after X_1	1		29.58*
Regression on X_2 alone	1	6.21	
	—	————	
X_1 after X_2	1		194.38**
Error	8	28.07	3.51

While each X accounts for a significant reduction in Σy^2, the height of shoots at ear emergence is the more effective.

3. The mean yield for the experiment, $576.2/18 = 32.0$ cwt./acre, has the confidence interval 31.0 to 33.0 cwt./acre.

4. The Error regression equation is

$$\hat{Y} = 1.393 + 1.3148 \, X_1 - 0.6466 \, X_2$$

Substituting each pair of X, the values of $\hat{Y}$ and $Y - \hat{Y}$ are calculated and entered in table 14.5.2. In this way the season and place effects are estimated. Examples: (i) The mean yield in 1933 was $-19.4/6 = -3.2$ cwt./acre as compared to the average for the entire investigation; (ii) Plumpton averaged $16.9/3 = 5.6$ cwt./acre above the general yield.

TABLE 14.5.2
ACTUAL AND ESTIMATED YIELDS OF WHEAT

Place	1933			1934			1935			Sum
	Y	$\hat{Y}$	$Y - \hat{Y}$	Y	$\hat{Y}$	$Y - \hat{Y}$	Y	$\hat{Y}$	$Y - \hat{Y}$	
Seale Hayne	19.0	25.4	−6.4	32.4	30.1	2.3	26.2	26.0	0.2	−3.9
Rothamsted	22.2	26.2	−4.0	32.2	32.5	−0.3	34.7	32.3	2.4	−1.9
Newport	35.3	38.9	−3.6	43.7	43.4	0.3	40.0	37.7	2.3	−1.0
Boghall	32.8	35.3	−2.5	35.7	37.7	−2.0	29.6	26.2	3.4	−1.1
Sprowston	25.3	30.6	−5.3	28.3	29.5	−1.2	20.6	23.2	−2.6	−9.1
Plumpton	35.8	33.4	2.4	35.2	28.4	6.8	47.2	39.5	7.7	16.9
Sums			−19.4			5.9			13.4	−0.1

If this were a randomized blocks experiment designed to test Places, the F-test would be done in these steps:

1. Add the pairs of sums of squares and products in the rows for Places and Error, table 14.5.1:

$$\Sigma x_1^2 = 224.27, \qquad \Sigma x_1 x_2 = -26.89, \qquad \Sigma x_1 y = 332.84$$

$$\Sigma x_2^2 = 245.66, \qquad \Sigma x_2 y = -278.49, \qquad \Sigma y^2 = 857.88$$

2. For this $P + E$ regression, calculate $\Sigma d_{Y.12}^2 = 129.20$.

3. Enter $P + E$ and E in the following table of deviations from regression:

$P + E$	13	129.20	
E	8	28.08	3.51
	—	——	
For Testing Places	5	101.12	20.22

For testing differences among the adjusted place means, $F = 20.22/3.51 = 5.76$. $P = 0.02$.

EXAMPLE 14.5.1—For the British wheat yields, calculate $c_{11} = 0.008893$ and test the significance of $b_{Y1.2}$. Ans. $t = 7.45^{**} = \sqrt{F} = \sqrt{(194.38/3.51)}$.

EXAMPLE 14.5.2—In the Error regression, calculate $R^2 = 0.8772$.

EXAMPLE 14.5.3—In the Error regression, calculate the standard partial regression coefficients for comparing the predictive abilities of shoot height and plant number. Ans. 0.94 and 0.37.

14.6—Partial correlation. Instead of the fixed X in the foregoing models, all the variables may be random. In a random sample drawn from a *multivariate normal population*, the value of every variable is left to chance. If the sample consists of 18-year-old college freshman men, the random variables might be height, aptitude, economic status, heights of parents, etc. This is an extension of the sampling discussed in chapter 7. The purpose might be to examine the regression of height of sons on heights of the parents. If so, all the regression methods of the preceding sections would apply. But the objective might be to seek for correlations among such variables as height, weight, basal metabolism, etc., among which no variables can be specified as independent or dependent. In that case, *partial correlation* may be used instead of multiple regression as the appropriate method.

If there are 3 variables then there are 3 *simple* or *total* correlations among them, ρ_{12}, ρ_{13}, ρ_{23}. The *partial correlation coefficient*, $\rho_{12.3}$, is the correlation between variables 1 and 2 in a cross section of individuals all having the same value of variable 3; the third variable is *held constant* so that only 1 and 2 are involved in the correlation. In the model, $\rho_{12.3}$ is the same for every value of variable 3.

In samples from a tri-variate population, the estimates of $\rho_{12.3}$ are pretty sure to differ among the various values of variable 3. The over-all estimate of $\rho_{12.3}$ must be an average of these.   This average, the *sample partial correlation*, is given by

$$r_{12.3} = \frac{r_{12} - r_{13}\, r_{23}}{\sqrt{(1 - r_{13}^2)(1 - r_{23}^2)}}$$

The object is to eliminate the effect of variable 3 from the correlation between 1 and 2.

For testing the significance of partial correlations use table 7.6.1, but enter it with $f = n - m$, where n is the number of sets of observations and m is the number of variables.

In Iowa and Nebraska, a random sample of 142 older women was drawn for a study of nutritional status (12).   Three of the variables were Age, Blood pressure, and the Cholesterol concentration in the blood.   The 3 total correlations were

$$r_{AB} = 0.3332, \; r_{AC} = 0.5029, \; r_{BC} = 0.2495$$

Since high blood pressure might be associated with above-average amounts of cholesterol in the walls of blood vessels, it is interesting to examine r_{BC}. But it is evident that both B and C increase with age.   Are they correlated merely because of their common association with age or is there a real relation at every age?   The effect of age is eliminated by calculating

$$r_{BC.A} = \frac{0.2495 - (0.3332)(0.5029)}{\sqrt{(1 - 0.3332^2)(1 - 0.5029^2)}} = 0.1005$$

With $f = 142 - 3 = 139$, this correlation is not significant.   It may be that within the several age groups blood pressure and blood cholesterol are uncorrelated.   At least, the sample is not large enough to detect the correlation if it is present.

Partial correlation is intimately related to regression.   One may consider both blood pressure and blood cholesterol as variables dependent on age but (from the discussion above) otherwise uncorrelated.   Another aspect is illustrated by the consumption of Protein and Fat among part of the older women, the 54 of them from Iowa.   The total correlations were

$$r_{AP} = -0.4865, \; r_{AF} = -0.5296, \; r_{PF} = 0.5784$$

The third correlation shows that protein and fat occur together in all diets while the first two correlations indicate the decreasing quantities of both as age advances; both P and F depend on A.   How closely do they depend on each other at any one age?

$$r_{PF.A} = \frac{0.5784 - (-0.4865)(-0.5296)}{\sqrt{(1 - 0.4865^2)(1 - 0.5296^2)}} = 0.4328$$

So, part of the relationship depends on age but part of it is inherent in the ordinary composition of foods eaten.   Let us examine this further.

One could calculate the regression of P on A then estimate $\hat{P}$ for each

A. The 54 deviations from regression, $P - \hat{P}$, are *freed from the effects of age*. Variation among them must be attributed to other causes, including perhaps the fat content of the diet. Next, the regression of F on A could be handled in the same way. The deviations, $F - \hat{F}$, are independent of age. Finally, the 54 pairs of deviations could be correlated; the correlation would be equal to $r_{PF.A}$, the correlation between protein and fat after the common effect of age is eliminated.

To get a clear notion of the way in which $r_{PF.A}$ is independent of age, consider the 6 women near 70 years of age. Their protein and fat intakes were

P: 56,   47,   33,   39,   42,   38
F: 56,   83,   49,   52,   65,   52 $r_{PF} = 0.4194$

The correlation is close to the average, $r_{PF.A} = 0.4328$. Similar correlations would be found at other ages.

In other situations there might be little or no correlation at any one age. A slight rearrangement of some of the actual data illustrates this:

P: 56,   39,   47,   33,   42,   38
F: 56,   83,   52,   49,   65,   52 $r_{PF} = -0.0621$

But the averages of the 2 variables, unaffected by rearrangements like those above, might change with age as did the averages of P and F:

Age:	30	35	40	45	50	55	60	65	70	75
Average P:	67	62	65	57	54	49	55	64	44	47
Average F:	85	101	130	82	86	81	68	85	59	68

Here the correlation between the averages of protein and fat is 0.7014. This is due only to changing consumption with age; the correlations at the several ages might be any number from -1 to $+1$ depending on the pairing of the observations. This shows how the two effects, age and $r_{PF.A}$, may be independent. Some graphs will help you to understand the relations.

Another connection between partial correlation and multiple regression has utility if many variables are involved. In section 7.4 it was noted that r is the geometric mean of 2 regression coefficients. Similarly,

$$ r_{12.3} = \sqrt{(b_{12.3})(b_{21.3})} $$

Again the fact is emphasized that correlation does not involve the notion of independent and dependent variables. It is a measure of interdependence. The utility with larger numbers of variables lies in the fact that elegant methods are available for calculating the regression coefficients (9) whereas those for higher order correlation coefficients are cumbersome.

EXAMPLE 14.6.1—Brunson and Willier (2) examined the correlations among ear circumference E, cob circumference C, and number of rows of kernels K calculated from measurements of 900 ears of corn:

$\quad\quad\quad r_{EC} = 0.799, \quad\quad r_{EK} = 0.570, \quad\quad r_{CK} = 0.507$

Among ears having the same kernel number, what is the correlation between E and C? Ans. $r_{EC.K} = 0.720$.

EXAMPLE 14.6.2—Among ears of corn having the same circumference, is there any correlation between C and K? Ans. $r_{CK.E} = 0.105$.

EXAMPLE 14.6.3—In a random sample of 54 Iowa women (12), the intake of 2 nutrients was determined together with age and the concentration of cholesterol in the blood. If P symbolizes protein, F fat, A age, and C cholesterol, the correlations are as follows:

	A	P	F
P	−0.4865		
F	−0.5296	0.5784	
C	0.4737	−0.4249	−0.3135

What is the correlation between age and cholesterol independent of the intake of protein and fat? Ans.

$$r_{AC.PF} = \frac{r_{AC.F} - r_{AP.F}\, r_{CP.F}}{\sqrt{(1 - r_{AP.F}^2)(1 - r_{CP.F}^2)}} = \frac{0.3820 - (-0.2604)(-0.3145)}{\sqrt{(1 - 0.2604^2)(1 - 0.3145^2)}} = 0.3274$$

14.7—Solving the normal equations. If the data from table 14.2.1 are substituted in the *normal equations* of that section, they become

$$1{,}752.96\, b_{Y1.2} + 1{,}085.61\, b_{Y2.1} = 3{,}231.48 \tag{1}$$
$$1{,}085.61\, b_{Y1.2} + 3{,}155.78\, b_{Y2.1} = 2{,}216.44 \tag{2}$$

A convenient way to solve these equations is as follows:

(1) ÷ 1,085.61:	**1.61472**$b_{Y1.2} + b_{Y2.1}$	= **2.97665**	(3)
(2) ÷ 3,155.78:	$0.34401 b_{Y1.2} + b_{Y2.1}$	= 0.70234	(4)
(3) − (4):	$1.27071 b_{Y1.2}$	= 2.27431	(5)
(5) ÷ 1.27071:	$b_{Y1.2}$	= **1.78979**	(6)
Substitute (6) in (3)	$b_{Y2.1}$	= **2.97665** − (**1.61472**)(**1.78979**)	
		= 0.08664	(7)

The results are the same as those got by substituting in the formulas.

For future computations, note well this rule for $b_{Y2.1}$, involving bold-face type:

(Number Above) − (Number Left)(Number Below)

Much of the symbolism may well be omitted from the form above. The essential parts are these:

1,752.96	1,085.61	3,231.48
1,085.61	3,155.78	2,216.44
1.61472	1	**2.97665**
0.34401	1	0.70234
1.27071		2.27431
$b_{Y1.2}$		**1.78979**
$b_{Y2.1}$		0.08664

The calculations can all be done on a machine with no side entries. This is a more convenient and more easily remembered device than use of the 2 formulas for the b. Also, it can be extended to the solution of more than 2 normal equations.

Computational note: In the form,

$$(\text{Above}) - (\text{Left})(\text{Below}),$$

the following numbers may be used in an alternative solution,

$$0.70234 - (0.34401)(1.78979) = 0.08663,$$

as before except for a small rounding error. This serves as a check. The final check is to substitute the two b in the original equations:

$$(1{,}752.96)(1.789879) + (1{,}085.61)(0.08664) = 3{,}231.49$$

instead of 3,231.48 in equation (1). Similar substitution in the second equation gives 2,216.43.

Occasionally the Gauss multipliers are needed for setting confidence intervals or making tests. They come from the solution of 2 sets of equations similar to the normal:

First Set	Second Set
$c_{11}\Sigma x_1^2 + c_{12}\Sigma x_1 x_2 = 1$	$c_{21}\Sigma x_1^2 + c_{22}\Sigma x_1 x_2 = 0$
$c_{11}\Sigma x_1 x_2 + c_{12}\Sigma x_2^2 = 0$	$c_{21}\Sigma x_1 x_2 + c_{22}\Sigma x_2^2 = 1$

Both sets of equations are solved by a single series of operations. Using phosphorus data:

		First Set	Second Set
1,752.96	1,085.61	1	0
1,085.61	3,155.78	0	1
1.61472	1	0.000921141	0
0.34401	1	0	0.000316879
1.27071		0.000921141	−0.000316879

$$c_{11} = 0.000724903 \qquad c_{12} = -0.000249372$$
$$c_{21} = -0.000249374 \qquad c_{22} = 0.000402666$$

These are identical with the results in section 14.3.

Computational notes: Calculation by the formula, (Above) − (Left) (Below), is simplified by starting with (Above) = 0 in each case;

$$c_{21} = -(0.34401)(0.000724903) = -0.000249374$$
$$c_{22} = -(1.61472)(-0.000249372) = 0.000402666$$

Both pairs of c should be substituted in one or both of the original equations. Example:

$$(1,752.96)(0.000724903) + (1,085.61)(-0.000249372) = 1.00001$$

After the multipliers are calculated, the regression coefficients may be got by combining them with Σxy as follows:

$$b_{Y1.2} = c_{11}\,\Sigma x_1 y + c_{12}\,\Sigma x_2 y$$
$$b_{Y2.1} = c_{21}\,\Sigma x_1 y + c_{22}\,\Sigma x_2 y$$

Substituting, one gets the coefficients of section 14.2:

$$(0.000724903)(3,231.48) + (-0.000249372)(2,216.44) = 1.7898$$
$$(-0.000249374)(3,231.48) + (0.000402666)(2,216.44) = 0.0866$$

There are advantages in each of the 2 foregoing methods of calculation. The first, using the normal equations, is shorter and yields all the information ordinarily desired (including that about regression coefficients elicited by the b' and a table like 14.3.2). But the second solution, with the multipliers, is required if standard errors are needed for setting confidence intervals on the various parameters. Also it is convenient if there are several sets of Y dependent on a single set of X (section 14.10).

14.8—Four or more variables in a single group.   Computations.
Increasing beyond three the number of measurements on each individual though involving no new principles does introduce increasing complexity into the methods of multiple regression. Only the fundamentals will be presented here. Laboratory methods of calculation, together with more extensive discussions may be found in specialized publications (3, 4, 6, 13).

Amateurs should be cautioned not to rush headlong into regression studies involving many variables. Some people seem to think there is magic in the collection of vast amounts of data—that by some alchemy multiple regression will yield authentic information from careless measurements on heterogeneous material. The fact is that hazards increase with the extent and complexity of the investigation. Danger of the loss of data or failure of techniques, difficulty of finding homogeneous material, perplexities involved in interpretation, these are a few of the obstacles. However, do not be deterred if you have well taken measurements on carefully chosen material, and if you have definite questions whose answers lie in the methods to be used. As compared to the labor of getting the data the calculation of regression statistics is easy.

Should you have four or more variables in several subsamples of individuals, the subsamples being representative of somewhat different but related populations, methods analogous to those of section 14.4 are available.

One should be increasingly cautious of including more variables in small samples. The reason is readily explained by an appeal to the geometry of regression, but we shall have to start with two variables. In a plane, two pairs of observations fix a linear regression, all additional pairs being available not only for improving the regression but for an estimate of error as well. In three-space the required number of triplets of observations to fix a regression plane is three. The analogy may be extended to four and more variables despite the limitations of our three-dimensional world. A regression in six variables would fit perfectly six sets of observations, leaving no information about error. With small samples be meticulous about all tests of significance, then be a bit skeptical besides.

As an example of 4 variables, an additional independent variable X_3, is taken from the original four which were measured in the plant-available phosphorus investigation. For convenience, X_1 and X_2 along with X_3 are copied into table 14.8.1. The Soil Temperature 35° C. will be considered later.

The third X requires the calculation of its sum of squares together with sums of products with each of the other variables:

$$\Sigma x_3{}^2 = 35{,}572; \ \Sigma x_1 x_3 = 1{,}200; \ \Sigma x_2 x_3 = 3{,}364; \ \Sigma x_3 y = 7{,}593$$

TABLE 14.8.1

PHOSPHORUS FRACTIONS IN VARIOUS CALCAREOUS SOILS, AND ESTIMATED PLANT-AVAILABLE PHOSPHORUS AT TWO SOIL TEMPERATURES

Soil Sample No.	Phosphorus Fractions in Soil, ppm. *			Estimated Plant-available Phosphorus in Soil, ppm.	
				Soil Temp. 20° C. Y	Soil Temp. 35° C. Y'
	X_1	X_2	X_3		
1	0.4	53	158	64	93
2	0.4	23	163	60	73
3	3.1	19	37	71	38
4	0.6	34	157	61	109
5	4.7	24	59	54	54
6	1.7	65	123	77	107
7	9.4	44	46	81	99
8	10.1	31	117	93	94
9	11.6	29	173	93	66
10	12.6	58	112	51	126
11	10.9	37	111	76	75
12	23.1	46	114	96	108
13	23.1	50	134	77	90
14	21.6	44	73	93	72
15	23.1	56	168	95	90
16	1.9	36	143	54	82
17	26.8	58	202	168	128
18	29.9	51	124	99	120

*X_1 = inorganic phosphorus by Bray and Kurtz method
X_2 = organic phosphorus soluble in K_2CO_3 and hydrolyzed by hypobromite
X_3 = organic phosphorus soluble in K_2CO_3 and not hydrolyzed by hypobromite

There are now 3 normal equations to be solved for the 3 regression coefficients:

$$\Sigma x_1^2 \, b_{Y1.23} + \Sigma x_1 x_2 \, b_{Y2.13} + \Sigma x_1 x_3 \, b_{Y3.12} = \Sigma x_1 y$$
$$\Sigma x_1 x_2 \, b_{Y1.23} + \Sigma x_2^2 \, b_{Y2.13} + \Sigma x_2 x_3 \, b_{Y3.12} = \Sigma x_2 y$$
$$\Sigma x_1 x_3 \, b_{Y1.23} + \Sigma x_2 x_3 \, b_{Y2.13} + \Sigma x_3^2 \, b_{Y3.12} = \Sigma x_3 y$$

The solution of this set of simultaneous equations is shown in table 14.8.2. The sums of squares and products are taken from table 14.2.1 and from the calculations above. Unnecessary symbols are omitted.

TABLE 14.8.2
SOLUTION OF 3 NORMAL EQUATIONS. PLANT-AVAILABLE PHOSPHORUS

	X_1	X_2	X_3	Y	Line
Sums of Squares X_1	1,752.96	1,085.61	1,200.00	3,231.48	(1)
and Products: X_2	1,085.61	3,155.78	3,364.00	2,216.44	(2)
X_3	1,200.00	3,364.00	35,572.00	7,593.00	(3)
(1) ÷ 1,200.00	*1.460800*	*0.904675*	1	**2.692900**	(4)
(2) ÷ 3,364.00	0.322714	0.938103	1	0.658870	(5)
(3) ÷ 35,572.00	0.033734	0.094569	1	0.213454	(6)
(4) − (6)	1.427066	0.810106		2.479446	(7)
(5) − (6)	0.288980	0.843534		0.445416	(8)
(7) ÷ 0.810106	**1.761579**	1		**3.060644**	(9)
(8) ÷ 0.843534	0.342583	1		0.528036	(10)
(9) − (10)	1.418996			2.532608	(11)
(11) ÷ 1.418996	$b_{Y1.23} =$			**1.784789**	(12)
		$b_{Y2.13} =$		*−0.083403*	(13)
			$b_{Y3.12} =$	0.161133	(14)

$b_{Y2.13} = 3.060644 - (1.761579)(1.784789) = 0.528036 - (0.342583)(1.784789)$
$b_{Y3.12} = 2.692900 - (1.460800)(1.784789) - (0.904675)(-0.083403)$
$\quad\quad = 0.658870 - (0.322714)(1.784789) - (0.938103)(-0.083403),$ etc.

Computational notes: The "back solution" for $b_{Y2.13}$ is like that of the foregoing section, using Above and Left in line 9 or 10, the last block of lines containing 1's. For $b_{Y3.12}$, go to the upper block of 1's, line 4. There are now 2 each of Left and Below, one set in bold face, the second in italics. The form of the calculation in the last 2 lines of the table is

$$(\textbf{Above}) - (\textbf{Left})(\textbf{Below}) - (\textit{Left})(\textit{Below})$$

For verification, this may be repeated in lines (5) and (6).

The above form of calculation is readily extended to more than 3 independent variables. There are dozens, perhaps hundreds of forms for calculating the b in multiple regression (4, 13). Some are a bit shorter than the one shown here but this one has the advantage of following closely the customary method of solving simultaneous equations and so is more easily remembered.

Correctness of the b should be verified by substitution in one or more of the original equations. In (1) for example,

$$(1,752.96)(1.784789) - (1,085.61)(0.083403)$$
$$+ (1,200.00)(0.161133) = 3,231.48,$$

an exact verification.

Meanings and conclusions will be discussed in the next section.

14.9—Four or more variables. Inferences. With the heavy computations behind him, the statistician is ready to consider what has been achieved. His next steps will depend on the purpose of the experiment. "The primary objective of the present investigation was to determine whether there exists an independent effect of soil organic phosphorus on the phosphorus nutrition of plants." That is, the experimenters wished to know if X_2 and X_3 are effective in predicting Y. We shall examine that objective first, then suggest others in the examples.

The "quick and dirty" method is to look at the standard partial regression coefficients, $b_i \sqrt{(\Sigma x_i^2 / \Sigma y^2)}$:

$$b'_{Y1.23} = \quad 1.7848 \sqrt{(1,752.96/12,389.61)} = \quad 0.67$$

$$b'_{Y2.13} = -0.0834 \sqrt{(3,155.78/12,389.61)} = -0.04$$

$$b'_{Y3.12} = \quad 0.1611 \sqrt{(35,572/12,389.61)} \quad = \quad 0.27$$

This leaves little doubt that inorganic phosphorus is the chief contributor and that the organic fraction X_2 is ineffective. Decision about the second organic fraction calls for the more exact methods.

For the first of these, we need the sum of squares of Y due to regression together with the remainder of Σy^2:

$$\Sigma \hat{y}_{123}^2 = (1,7848)(3,231.48) + (-0.0834)(2,216.44) + (0.1611)(7,593.00)$$
$$= 6,806$$
$$\Sigma d_{Y.123}^2 = 12,390 - 6,806 = 5,584$$

Combining this with corresponding $\Sigma \hat{y}_{12}^2$ in table 14.3.1:

Regression on X_1, X_2, X_3	3	6,806	
Regression on X_1, X_2	2	5,976	
	—	———	
X_3 after X_1 and X_2	1	830	830
Error	14	5,584	399

$F = 830/399 = 2.08$ corresponds to a probability in the neighborhood of 0.18. This confirms the earlier finding; the inorganic fraction is the chief, perhaps only, source of phosphorus available to the plant at 20° C.

Some general features of multiple regression may now be observed. First, as noted before, the regression coefficients change with each new grouping of the X. With X_2 only, $b_{Y2} = 2,216.44/3,155.78 = 0.7023$. Adding X_1, $b_{Y2.1} = 0.0866$. With 3 of the X, $b_{Y2.13} = -0.0834$. In any one multiple regression, the coefficients are intercorrelated; either increasing or decreasing the number of X changes all the b.

Second. The value of $\Sigma\hat{y}^2$ never decreases with the addition of new X; ordinarily it increases. Take X_1 alone; $\Sigma\hat{y}_1^2 = (3,231.48)^2/1,752.96 = 5,957$. X_1 and X_2 make $\Sigma\hat{y}_{12}^2 = 5,976$. For all three, $\Sigma\hat{y}_{123}^2 = 6,806$. The increase may be small and nonsignificant, but it represents the new information in the added X.

Third. For checking calculations it is worth noting that $\Sigma\hat{y}^2$ cannot be greater than Σy^2; nearly always it is less. Only if the X predict Y perfectly can $\Sigma\hat{y}^2 = \Sigma y^2$. In that limiting case, $\Sigma d^2 = 0$.

Fourth. High correlation between two of the X can upset calculations. If r_{ij} is above 0.95, even 6 or 8 significant digits may not be sufficient to control rounding errors. If correlation coefficients are used for coded X (example 14.10.7), and if one of them is above 0.95, consider eliminating one of the two X.

Fifth. If $\Sigma\hat{y}^2$ is only a small fraction of Σy^2, that is, if R^2 is small (example 14.3.5), remember that most of the variation in Y is unexplained. It may be random variation or it may be due to other independent variables not considered in the regression. If these other variables were found and brought in, the relations among the X already included might change completely. It is well not to speculate about cause and effect unless R^2 is high; say, above 0.8.

EXAMPLE 14.9.1—Compute the regression of plant-available phosphorus on the 3 fractions. Ans. $\hat{Y} = 1.7848X_1 - 0.0834X_2 + 0.1611X_3 + 43.67$.

EXAMPLE 14.9.2—Estimate the plant-available phosphorus in soil sample 17 and compare it with the observed value. Ans. 119 ppm., $Y - \hat{Y} = 49$ ppm.

EXAMPLE 14.9.3—The experimenter might have information which would lead him to retain X_3 along with X_1 in his predicting equation, dropping X_2. Calculate the new regression. Ans. $\hat{Y} = 1.737X_1 + 0.155X_3 + 41.5$.

EXAMPLE 14.9.4—Calculate the sum of squares due to X_2 after X_1 and X_3. Ans. 16.

EXAMPLE 14.9.5—What is the sum of squares of Y due to X_1 after X_2 and X_3? Ans. 4,394.

EXAMPLE 14.9.6—Calculate $R^2 = \Sigma\hat{y}^2/\Sigma y^2$ with X_1 alone, with X_1 and X_2, and with X_1, X_2, X_3. Ans. $R_{Y.1}^2 = 0.4808$, $R_{Y.12}^2 = 0.4823$, $R_{Y.123}^2 = 0.5493$. Notice that R^2 never decreases with the addition of a new X; ordinarily it increases. Associate this with the corresponding theorem about $\Sigma\hat{y}^2$.

14.10—Four or more variables. Elements of inverse matrix, the Gauss multipliers. Interval estimates and tests of the b, of $\hat{Y}$, etc. require calculation of the c. These are the *elements* of an *inverse matrix*; Gauss called them *multipliers* (8).   Not only are they needed for many tests but are time savers if there are several values of Y corresponding to a single group of independent variables.

As in section 4.7, the elements are conveniently calculated by solving as many sets of simultaneous equations as there are X.   For 3 of the X, they are as follows:

$$\Sigma x_1^2 \; c_{11} + \Sigma x_1 x_2 \, c_{12} + \Sigma x_1 x_3 \, c_{13} = 1, 0, 0$$
$$\Sigma x_2 x_1 \, c_{21} + \Sigma x_2^2 \; c_{22} + \Sigma x_2 x_3 \, c_{23} = 0, 1, 0$$
$$\Sigma x_3 x_1 \, c_{31} + \Sigma x_3 x_2 \, c_{32} + \Sigma x_3^2 \; c_{33} = 0, 0, 1$$

The left sides of the equations are the same as those of the foregoing section with the c replacing the b.   The right members of the first set (1, 0, 0) replace the Σxy, etc.

If you substitute the phosphorus data in the first of the sets of equations then apply the methods of the preceding section, you will divide 1 by 1,200; carried to 6 significant figures this gives 0.000833333.   In the third set you will have $1/35{,}572 = 0.0000281120$.   With 4 or 5 figures to the left of the decimal and 10 to the right, the arithmetic is messy.   Some coding seems worth while.

The best coding I know changes the sums of products into correlation coefficients.   But the coding and decoding are a bit awkward (example 14.10.7).   A substitute which Mrs. Mary Clem of our computing laboratory has found rather uniformly successful is to divide each left member by its Σx^2.   In practice, the reciprocal of Σx^2 is locked into the machine and multiplied successively by the coefficients of the c.   Example from line 1 in table 14.10.1; $1/1{,}752.96 = 0.000570464$, recorded for convenience in line 4.   Multiplying this reciprocal by the 3 terms in this line, you get the first 3 entries in line 4; 1, 0.6193, 0.6846.   To minimize rounding errors, the reciprocals should be carried 2 digits further than the number of digits retained in the body of the table.   The coded numbers become the coefficients of the c.   After they are entered in lines 4, 5, 6, the solution of the equations proceeds as in section 4.7.

You will observe that the coded matrix is not symmetrical; that is, the coefficient of c_{12} is not equal to that of c_{21}, etc.   This does not affect the present method of solving the equations.

The check column at the right could have been introduced in sections 4.7 and 4.8; now it becomes essential.   Simply add the entries in each of lines 4, 5, 6, then treat the sums like any of the other columns.   Example: in line 7, $4.8260 = (1.460707)(3.3039)$.   Verification is done by adding the other entries in line 7:

$$1.4607 + 0.9046 + 1.0000 + 1.4607 = 4.8260$$

as calculated above.   The 2 numbers should be the same except for rounding errors.

The calculated matrix of c is still nonsymmetrical. To decode, divide each *column* by the original Σx^2 in that column. Example, solution 1:

$$(\ \ 1.2707)(0.000570464) = \ \ \ 0.0007249$$
$$(-0.4353)(0.000570464) = -0.0002483$$
$$(-0.0016)(0.000570464) = -0.0000009$$

You may be surprised by the division and by the column. This is an inverse matrix in which elements in the original numerator are now in the denominator and in which rows have become columns. The decoded matrix returns to the original symmetry; this in itself is an excellent check.

As a final verification, substitute the elements of the decoded matrix in the original equations. As an example, substitute the first solution in the first equation:

(18) in (1): $(1,752.96)(0.0007249) - (1,085.61)(0.0002483)$
$$- (1,200.00)(0.0000009) = 1.0001$$

instead of 1.0000, a slight rounding error. Similarly, substituting the second solution in (2),

$$-(1,085.61)(0.0002483) + (3,155.78)(0.0004375)$$
$$-(3,364.00)(0.0000330) = 1.0001$$

The third solution in (3) is not so good, 1.0012. Rounding errors have crept into the decimal third place.

Actually, one cannot be sure of accuracy in the third decimal place if he carries only four significant digits. To show what may be expected, I carried 6 significant digits and a student, 10. A comparison of the more accurate results with those above is indicated this way:

	4 places	6 places	10 places
c_{11}	0.0007249	0.000724929	0.0007249289466
c_{31}	0.0000009	0.000000969	-0.0000009691292
$b_{Y1.23}$	1.7846	1.78479	1.784787539
$b_{Y3.12}$	0.1616	0.161132	0.161132757
$s_{Y.123}^2$	6,809	6,805.9	6,806.13

It is clear that the final results are not much different despite the poor check in equation (3).

Further computations in the table are fairly familiar. Examples:
$$b_{Y2.13} = (-0.0002483)(3,231.48) + (0.0004375)(2,216.44)$$
$$+ (-0.0000330)(7,593.00) = -0.0833$$
$$\Sigma \hat{y}_{123}^2 = (1,7846)(3,231.48) + (-0.0833)(2,216.44)$$
$$+ (0.1616)(7,593.00) = 6,809$$
$$s_{b1} = (20.0)\sqrt{0.0007249} = 0.538$$
$$s_{b2} = (20.0)\sqrt{0.0004375} = 0.418$$
$$t_{b1} = 1.7846/0.538 = 3.32$$

CALCULATION OF ELEMENTS OF INVERSE MATRIX. PLANT-AVAILABLE PHOSPHORUS

	X_1	X_2	X_3	Solution 1	Solution 2	Solution 3	Check	Line
From table 14.8.2: X_1	1,752.96	1,085.61	1,200.00					(1)
X_2	1,085.61	3,155.78	3,364.00					(2)
X_3	1,200.00	3,364.00	35,572.00					(3)
(1)(1/1,752.96).(0.000570464)	1	0.6193	0.6846	1	0	0	3.3039	(4)
(2)(1/3,155.78).(0.000316879)		1	1.0660	0	1	0	3.4100	(5)
(3)(1/35,572.00).(0.0000281120)			1	0	0	1	2.1283	(6)
(4)(1/0.6846).(1.460707)	1.4607	0.9046	1	1.4607	0	0	4.8260	(7)
(5)(1/1.0660).(0.938086)	0.3227	0.9381	1	0	0.9381	0	3.1989	(8)
(6)	0.0337	0.0946	1	0	0	1	2.1283	(9)
(7) − (9)	1.4270	0.8100		1.4607	0.9381	−1	2.6977	(10)
(8) − (9)	0.2890	0.8435		0	0.9381	−1	1.0706	(11)
(10)(1/0.8100).(1.234568)	1.7617	1		1.8033	0	−1.2346	3.3305	(12)
(11)(1/0.8435).(1.185536)	0.3426	1		0	1.1122	−1.1855	1.2692	(13)
(12) − (13)	1.4191			1.8033	−1.1122	−0.0491	2.0613	(14)
(14)(1/1.4191).(0.704672) *Inverse Matrix:*				1.2707	−0.7837	−0.0346	1.4525	(15)
				−0.4353	1.3806	−1.1736		(16)
				−0.0016	−0.1041	1.1122		(17)
Decoded:				0.0007249	−0.0002483	−0.0000010	$\sqrt{c_{11}}$ = 0.0269	(18)
				−0.0002483	0.0004375	−0.0000330	$\sqrt{c_{22}}$ = 0.0209	(19)
				−0.0000009	−0.0000330	0.0000313	$\sqrt{c_{33}}$ = 0.0056	(20)
Σxy (table 14.8.2):				3,231.48	2,216.44	7,593.00		(21)
$b = \Sigma c \Sigma xy$:				1.7846**	−0.0833	0.1616		(22)
$s_b = s_{Y.123}\sqrt{c}$:				0.538	0.418	0.112		(23)
t:				3.32	0.20	1.44		(24)

$$\Sigma y^2 = 12{,}390$$
$$\Sigma \hat{y}^2 = \Sigma b \Sigma xy = 6{,}809$$
$$\Sigma d^2 = 5{,}581$$
$$s^2_{Y.123} = \Sigma d^2/14 = 398.6$$
$$s_{Y.123} = 20.0$$

The identity of the t-test with the F-test of the foregoing section is shown by comparing the results for X_3. For $b_{Y3.12}$, $t = 1.44$. This is $\sqrt{2.08}$, the value of F for X_3 after X_1 and X_2.

The hypothesis that two regression coefficients are equal may now be tested if there is any reason for it. One would scarcely be interested in making the test in the phosphorus experiment because the regressions on the two organic fractions are both nonsignificant. But for illustration, the difference,

$$b_{Y3.12} - b_{Y2.13} = 0.1616 - (-0.0833) = 0.2449,$$

is tested by calculating the mean square,

$$s_D^2 = s_{Y.123}^2 (c_{22} + c_{33} - 2c_{23})$$
$$= 398.6 \, [0.0004375 + 0.0000313 - 2(-0.0000330)] = 0.2132$$

Hence, $s_D^2 = 0.462$, $t = 0.2449/0.462 = 0.53$, $f = 14$.

The confidence interval for Y is got by first calculating the mean square, $s_{\hat{Y}}^2 = s_{Y.123}^2(1/n + c_{11}x_1^2 + c_{22}x_2^2 + c_{33}x_3^2 + 2c_{12}x_1x_2 + 2c_{13}x_1x_3 + 2c_{23}x_2x_3)$, where the x are deviations from means. Substituting the phosphorus data for sample 17 whose regression value was estimated in example 14.9.2,

$x_1 = 26.8 - 11.9 = 14.9$, $x_2 = 58 - 42.1 = 15.9$, $x_3 = 202 - 123 = 79$
$s_{\hat{Y}}^2 = (398.6) \, [1/18 + (0.0007249)(14.9^2) + (0.0004375)(15.9)^2$
$\qquad + \; (0.0000330)(79^2) \; + \; 2(-0.0002483)(14.9)(15.9)$
$\qquad + \; 2(-0.0000010)(14.9)(79) \; + \; 2(-0.0000330)(15.9)(79)$
$\qquad = 123.6$

$s_{\hat{Y}} = 11.1,$ $\qquad t_{.05} = 2.145,$ $\qquad 119 \pm (2.145)(11.1)$; 95 to 143 ppm.

If it is the confidence interval on an individual observation that is wanted, add $s_{Y.123}^2$ to $s_{\hat{Y}}^2$:

$$s_Y^2 = 398.6 + 123.6 = 522.2, \; s_Y = 22.9$$
$$119 \pm (2.145)(22.9); \quad 70 \text{ to } 168 \text{ ppm.}$$

The upper limit happens to fall on the observed Y.

Occasionally there are several sets of Y to be matched with a single set of observations on the independent variables. In the phosphorus experiment, every soil sample was tried at $35°$ C. as well as at $20°$ C. The results are in the last column of table 14.8.1. Since the inverted matrix involves only the X, it can be applied very simply to the second Y series. It is necessary to calculate only the new sums of products,

$$\Sigma x_1 y' = 1{,}720.42, \quad \Sigma x_2 y' = 4{,}337.56, \quad \Sigma x_3 y' = 8{,}324.00$$

Combining these with the c already calculated, the regressions of Y' are

$$b_{Y'1.23} = 0.1618, \quad b_{Y'2.13} = 1.1958, \quad b_{Y'3.12} = 0.1159$$

In this new series, $\Sigma \hat{y}'^2 = 6{,}430$, $\Sigma d^2 = 12{,}390 - 6{,}430 = 5{,}960$, $s_{Y'.123}^2 = 425.7$. From $s_{Y'.123} = 20.6$ ppm., the standard deviations of the 3 regression coefficients are 0.554, 0.431, and 0.115. These lead to the 3 values of t: 0.29, 2.77, and 0.10.

"It is postulated from the results of these two experiments that soil organic phosphorus *per se* is of little or no value in the phosphorus nutrition of plants and that it becomes of value when it is changed to the inorganic form . . . the rate of organic phosphorus mineralization is several times higher at 35° than at 20° C."

EXAMPLE 14.10.1—In studies of the fertilization of red clover by honey bees (10), it was desired to learn the effects of various lengths of the insects' proboscles. The measurement is difficult, so a pilot experiment was performed to determine a more convenient one that might be highly correlated with proboscis length. Three were tried on 44 bees with the results indicated:

$n = 44$	Dry Weight, X_1 (mg.)	Length of Wing, X_2 (mm.)	Width of Wing, X_3 (mm.)	Length of Proboscis, Y (mm.)
Mean	13.10	9.61	3.28	6.59

Sums of Squares and Products

	X_1	X_2	X_3	Y
X_1	16.6840	1.9279	0.8240	1.5057
X_2		0.9924	0.3351	0.5989
X_3			0.2248	0.1848
Y				0.6831

Except for practice, coding is unnecessary. Carrying 4 decimal places, calculate the regression coefficients as in section 14.8. Ans. 0.0291, 0.6152, −0.2017. Note: In calculating b_{Y2}, the 2 results were 0.6156 and 0.6149. For b_{Y3}, the 3 calculations gave −0.2013, −0.2021, −0.2016. I used means. This shows the effects of rounding errors when only 4 decimal places are carried.

EXAMPLE 14.10.2—Make a rough assessment of the relative predictive values of the X. Ans. Standard partial regressions: 0.14, 0.74, and −0.12.

EXAMPLE 14.10.3—Test the significance of the over-all regression. Ans. $F = 16.2, f = 3$ and 40.

EXAMPLE 14.10.4—Test the significance of the joint effect of X_1 and X_3 after X_2. Ans. $F = 0.87$.

EXAMPLE 14.10.5—Calculate the c-matrix, and from it the regression coefficients. Ans. 0.0291, 0.6148, and −0.2009. This gives an idea of the effects of rounding errors with 4 decimals.

EXAMPLE 14.10.6—What are the values of t for testing the 3 regression coefficients? Ans. 1.18, 4.74, 0.76.

EXAMPLE 14.10.7—Code the phosphorus data by calculating correlation coefficients from the sums of squares and products:

	X_1	X_2	X_3
$\Sigma x_1^2, \Sigma x_1 x_j$:	1,752.96	1,085.61	1,200.00
$\sqrt{\Sigma x_1^2}, \sqrt{\Sigma x_1^2}\sqrt{\Sigma x_j^2}$:	41.8684	2,352.01	7,896.61
r_{1j}:	1.0000	0.46156	0.15196
$\Sigma x_2^2, \Sigma x_2 x_3$:		3,155.78	3,364.00
$\sqrt{\Sigma x_2^2}, \sqrt{\Sigma x_2^2}\sqrt{\Sigma x_3^2}$:		56.1763	10,595.15
r_{2j}:		1.0000	0.31750
Σx_3^2:			35,572.00
$\sqrt{\Sigma x_3^2}$:			188.6054

The square roots of the three sums of squares are multiplied in pairs to get the denominators of the correlation coefficients. Example:

$$\sqrt{1,752.96}\sqrt{35,572.00} = (41.8684)(188.6054) = 7,896.61$$

The sums of products are then divided by the corresponding products of square roots to get the r. Example:

$$r_{23} = \frac{\Sigma x_2 x_3}{\sqrt{\Sigma x_2^2}\sqrt{\Sigma x_3^2}} = \frac{3,364.00}{10,595.15} = 0.31750$$

Notice that $r_{11} = r_{22} = r_{33} = 1$.

EXAMPLE 14.10.8—Invert the matrix of correlation coefficients:

1.00000	0.46156	0.15196
0.46156	1.00000	0.31750
0.15196	0.31750	1.00000

Ans.

1.27076	−0.58411	−0.00765
−0.58410	1.38060	−0.34958
−0.00765	−0.34958	1.11215

EXAMPLE 14.10.9—To decode the inverted matrix, divide each element by the same divisor that was used in coding. Examples:

$$-1.27076/1,752.96 = 0.00072492$$
$$-0.58411/2,352.01 = -0.00024834$$
$$1.11215/188.6054 = 0.00003126$$

These elements are more nearly accurate than those in table 14.10.1. At worst, they are off one unit in the last place. Verify your results by calculating the regression coefficients and comparing them with those in table 14.8.2.

14.11—Deletion of an independent variable. After a regression is computed, the utility of a variable may be questioned and its omission proposed. Instead of carrying out the calculations anew, desired information may be got from the statistics in the *reduced regression* by means of the formulas below (7).

In the phosphorus experiment at 20° C., X_2 had practically no predictive value. In examples 14.9.3–4, this variable was deleted by computing 2 regression coefficients and, from them, $\Sigma\hat{y}_{13}^2$, etc. If the inverse matrix is already calculated, the decrease from $\Sigma\hat{y}_{123}^2$ to $\Sigma\hat{y}_{13}^2$ is given by

$$b_{Y2.13}^2/c_{22} = (-0.0833)^2/0.0004375 = 16$$

So $\Sigma\hat{y}_{13}^2 = 6,806 - 16 = 6,790$, a much easier job.

Moreover, the 2 reduced partial regression coefficients are readily calculated:

$$b_{Y1.3} = b_{Y1.32} - c_{12}(b_{Y2.13}/c_{22}) = 1.737$$
$$b_{Y3.1} = b_{Y3.12} - c_{32}(b_{Y2.13}/c_{22}) = 0.155$$

These results agree with those in example 14.9.3.

Instead of the foregoing, one may decide to calculate the elements of the reduced matrix:

$$(c_{11})_R = c_{11} - c_{12}^2/c_{22} = 0.0005840$$
$$(c_{33})_R = c_{33} - c_{32}^2/c_{22} = 0.0000288$$
$$(c_{13})_R = c_{13} - c_{12}c_{32}/c_{22} = -0.0000197$$

From these, all the other required statistics may be calculated. You will see that with only 3 independent variables the method of section 14.2 is easier. With more X, the scheme above is valuable.

Formulas for omitting X_1 or X_3 may be inferred from those given; only keep in mind the subscript of the variable being eliminated and that of the desired statistic. Analogous formulas are easily written for deletion in a regression having more than 4 independent variables. But if more variables than one are to be eliminated, starting from the beginning may well be easier than successive application of the formulas.

EXAMPLE 14.11.1—With the bee data, eliminating wing width, X_3, calculate $\Sigma \hat{y}_{12}^2 = 0.3705$.

EXAMPLE 14.11.2—From the above, test the significance of the over-all regression of Y on X_1 and X_2. Ans. $F = 24.3, f = 2, 41$. Why is this F greater than that of example 14.10.3?

14.12—Summary of formulas.

A. Direct method of calculating the b:
1. $\Sigma \hat{y}^2 = \Sigma b_i \Sigma x_{iy}$
2. $\Sigma d^2 = \Sigma y^2 - \Sigma \hat{y}^2$
3. Fraction of Σy^2 due to regression $= \Sigma \hat{y}^2/\Sigma y^2 = R^2$
4. $s_{Y.12...}^2 = \Sigma d^2/(n - m)$, where $m = $ total number of variables
5. $b'_{Y1.23...} = b_{Y1.23...}\sqrt{\Sigma x_1^2/\Sigma y^2}$

B. After calculating the c-matrix:
1. $b_1 = \Sigma c_{1i}\Sigma x_{iy}$
2. $\Sigma \hat{y}^2 = \Sigma b_i \Sigma x_{iy}$
3. $\Sigma d^2 = \Sigma y^2 - \Sigma \hat{y}^2$
4. $R^2 = \Sigma \hat{y}^2/\Sigma y^2$
5. $s_{Y.12...}^2 = \Sigma d^2/(n - m)$
6. $s_{b_i} = s_{Y.12...}\sqrt{c_{ii}}$
7. $s_{b_1 - b_2} = s_{Y.12...}(\Sigma c_{ii} - 2\Sigma c_{ij}), i < j$
8. $s_{\hat{y}}^2 = s_{Y.12...}^2 (1/n + \Sigma c_{ii}x_i^2 + 2\Sigma c_{ij}x_ix_j), i < j$
9. $s_{Y'}^2 = s_{Y.12...}^2 (1 + 1/n + \Sigma c_{ii}x_i^2 + 2\Sigma c_{ij}x_ix_j), i < j$

REFERENCES

1. M. M. BARNARD. Journal of Agricultural Science, 26:456 (1936).
2. ARTHUR M. BRUNSON and J. G. WILLIER. Journal of the American Society of Agronomy, 21:912 (1929).
3. M. H. DOOLITTLE. United States Coast and Geodetic Survey Report, 1878:115.
4. P. S. DWYER. Linear Computations. John Wiley and Sons, Inc., New York (1951).
5. M. T. EID, C. A. BLACK, O. KEMPTHORNE, and J. A. ZOELLNER. Iowa Agricultural Experiment Station Research Bulletin 406 (1954).
6. MORDECAI EZEKIEL. Methods of Correlation Analysis. John Wiley and Sons, Inc., New York. Revised Edition (1941).

7. R. A. FISHER. Statistical Methods for Research Workers. Oliver and Boyd, Edinburgh (1925).

8. CARL FRIEDRICH GAUSS. Theoria Combinationis Observatorium, Pars Posterior (1821), Werke, 4:31; Supplement (1826), Werke 4:71.

9. CYRIL H. GOULDEN. Methods of Statistical Analysis, page 147. John Wiley and Sons, Inc., New York, 2nd Edition (1952).

10. ROY A. GROUT. Iowa Agricultural Experiment Station Research Bulletin 218 (1937).

11. D. V. LINDLEY. Supplement to the Journal of the Royal Statistical Society, 9:218 (1947).

12. PEARL P. SWANSON, RUTH LEVERTON, MARY R. GRAM, HARRIETT ROBERTS, and ISABEL PESEK. Journal of Gerontology, 10:41 (1955).

13. H. A. WALLACE and GEORGE W. SNEDECOR. Correlation and Machine Calculation. Iowa State University Official Publication 30, No. 4. (1925). Revised (1931).

14. F. YATES. Journal of the Ministry of Agriculture, 43:156 (1936).

CHAPTER 15

Curvilinear Regression

15.1—Introduction. Although linear regression is adequate for many needs, it is a matter of common observation that some variables are not connected by so simple a relation. The discovery of a precise description of the concomitant variation of two or more quantities is one of the problems of *curve fitting*, known as *curvilinear regression*. From this general view the fitting of the straight line is a special case, the simplest and indeed the most useful.

The motives for fitting curves to nonlinear data are various. Sometimes there is the desire to make a good estimate of the dependent variable for any particular value of the independent. This may involve the smoothing of irregular data and the interpolation of estimated Y's for values of X not contained in the observed series. Sometimes the objective is to test or discover a law relating the variables, such as a growth curve. At yet other times, the form of the relationship is of little interest; the end in view is merely the elimination of inaccuracies which nonlinearity of regression may introduce into a correlation coefficient or an experimental error.

The problem of fitting curves to data has been approached from many directions. Except when a law is being tested, the chief difficulty is the selection of a suitable equation. Graphical devices of rectification (12) and more theoretical methods (4, 11, 18) are useful and readily available to one who has some acquaintance with mathematics. In the main, we shall confine our attention to the exponential growth curve and to the polynomial.

15.2—The exponential growth curve. A characteristic of some of the simpler growth phenomena is that the increase at any moment is proportional to the size already attained. This is sometimes called the law of compound interest. During one phase in the growth of a culture of bacteria, the numbers of organisms follow such a law. The relation is nicely illustrated by the dry weights of chick embryos at ages 6 to 16 days (16) recorded in table 15.2.1. The graph of the weights in figure 15.2.1 ascends with greater rapidity as age increases, the regression equation being of the form commonly associated with such growth,

$$W = (A)(B^X),$$

where A and B are constants to be evaluated. Applying logarithms to the equation,

$$\log W = \log A + (\log B)X$$
$$\text{or } Y = a + bX,$$

where $Y = \log W$, $a = \log A$, and $b = \log B$. This means that if $\log W$ instead of W is plotted against X, the graph will be linear. By the device

TABLE 15.2.1

DRY WEIGHTS OF CHICK EMBRYOS FROM AGES 6 TO 16 DAYS,
TOGETHER WITH COMMON LOGARITHMS

Ages in Days X	Dry Weight, W (grams)	Common Logarithm of Weight Y
6	0.029	−1.538*
7	0.052	−1.284
8	0.079	−1.102
9	0.125	−0.903
10	0.181	−0.742
11	0.261	−0.583
12	0.425	−0.372
13	0.738	−0.132
14	1.130	0.053
15	1.882	0.275
16	2.812	0.449

* From the table of logarithms, one reads $\log 0.029 = 8.462 - 10$ or -2.462, which means $-2 + 0.462 = -1.538$.

of using the logarithm instead of the quantity itself, the data are said to be *rectified*.

The values of $Y = \log W$ are set out in the last column of the table and are plotted opposite X in the figure. The regression equation, computed in the familiar manner from the columns X and Y in the table, is

$$Y^* = 0.1959X - 2.689$$

The regression line fits the data points with unusual fidelity, the correlation between Y and X being 0.9992. The conclusion is that the chick embryos, as measured by dry weight, are growing in accord with the exponential law, the logarithm of the dry weight increasing at the estimated uniform rate of 0.1959 per day.

Often there is little interest in the regression equation itself, the objective being merely to learn if the data follow the exponential law. The graph, then, may furnish sufficient information. If so, the use of *semilogarithmic* or *ratio* graph paper obviates the necessity for looking up the

* The distinction between Y and estimated Y is usually obvious. $\hat{Y}$ will be used only when the deviation from regression, $Y - \hat{Y}$, is to be emphasized.

logarithms of Y. The horizontal rulings on the paper are drawn to such a scale that the plotting of the original data results in a straight line if the data follow the exponential growth law. Ratio paper may be purchased at most stationery shops.

It is sometimes considered desirable to write the exponential growth law in the form,

$$W = Ae^{bX},$$

where e is the base of the natural or Naperian system of logarithms, an irrational number whose approximate value is 2.718. If this form is decided upon, the convenient way is to use natural logarithms; then,

$$\log_e W = \log_e A + bX$$

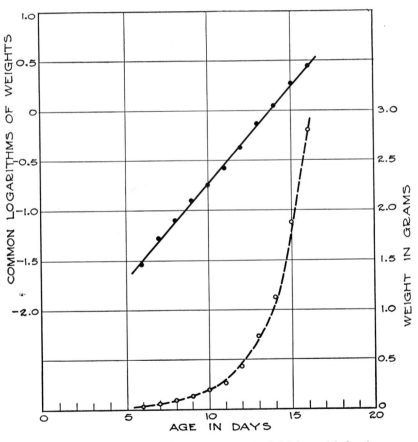

Fig. 15.2.1—Dry weights of chick embryos at ages 6–16 days with fitted curves.
Uniform scale: $W = 0.002046(1.57)^X$
Logarithmic scale: $Y = 0.1959X - 2.689$

It may be shown that the regression coefficient, b, in this equation is the *relative* rate of increase of W; that is, the rate of increase per unit X per unit W. This relative rate is 2.3026 ($= \log_e 10$) times the rate indicated by the slope of the regression line in common logarithms. Thus, for the chick embryos, the relative rate is $(2.3026)(0.1959) = 0.4511$ gram per day per gram. It is clear that the information about relative rate of growth can be deduced from either form of the equation. One may just as well use common logarithms if he finds them more convenient, then get the correct relative rate by multiplication as above. There are no other advantages in the natural logarithms unless tables of natural logarithms are more readily available than those of common logarithms.

If there is a necessity for converting the equation, $\log W = 0.1959X - 2.689$, into the exponential form,*

$$W = (0.002046)(1.57)^X,$$

or the form†

$$W = (0.002046)e^{0.4511X},$$

it must be remembered that the sum of squares of the errors of estimate is not a minimum for the exponential. It is the sum of the squares of $\log W$ — estimated $\log W$ which was minimized. If it is important to reduce to a minimum the sum of squares of deviations from the exponential, methods are available (18, 4, as examples). Ordinarily there is no object in reconverting the equation to the exponential form, or in making the slight improvement in the constants even if it is so converted.

Workers in other lines may wish to test different theoretical regressions. Occasionally the simple inverse proportion is indicated,

$$Y = 1/X$$

Other possibilities are $Y = \log X$, $Y = \sqrt{X}$ and $\log Y = a + b \log X$. The testing of the applicability of the proposed law should first be done graphically. Should the data appear to be rectified by the transformation of one or both the variables, then proceed with the regression computations if desired. For testing the last of the above equations, logarithmic paper is available, both vertical and horizontal rulings being in the logarithmic scale. For directions to the use of graph paper with special scales, see reference (8).

EXAMPLE 15.2.1—J. W. Gowen and W. C. Price counted the number of lesions of Aucuba mosaic virus developing after exposure to X-rays for various times. The following record is from as yet unpublished data made available through courtesy of the investigators.

---

* To get this form, note that $0.1959 = \log 1.57$ and $2.689 = \log 488.65$, hence
$$\log W = (\log 1.57)(X) - \log 488.65 = \log 1.57^X - \log 488.65$$
$$= \log \frac{1.57^X}{488.65} = \log (0.002046)(1.57^X).$$

† This comes from the first form because $\log_e 1.57 = 0.4511$, whence $1.57 = e^{0.4511}$.

Minutes exposure	0	3	7.5	15	30	45	60
Count in hundreds	271	226	209	108	59	29	12

Plot the count as ordinate, then plot its logarithm. Derive the regression, $Y = 2.432 - 0.02227X$, where Y is the logarithm of the count and X is minutes exposure.

EXAMPLE 15.2.2—Repeat the fitting of the last example using natural logarithms. Verify the fact that the rate of decrease of hundreds of lesions per minute per hundred is $(2.3026)(0.02227) = 0.05128$.

EXAMPLE 15.2.3—If the meaning of relative rate isn't quite clear, try this approximate method of computing it. The increase in weight of the chick embryo during the thirteenth day is $1.130 - 0.738 = 0.392$ gram; that is, the average rate during this period is 0.392 gram per day. But the average weight during the same period is $(1.130 + 0.738)/2 = 0.934$ gram. The relative rate, or rate of increase of each gram, is therefore $0.392/0.934 = 0.42$ gram per day per gram. This differs from the average obtained in the whole period from 6 to 16 days, 0.4511, partly because the average weight as well as the increase in weight in the thirteenth day suffered some sampling variation, and partly because the correct relative rate is based on weight and increase in weight at any instant of time, not on day averages.

EXAMPLE 15.2.4—Geddes (10) gives estimates of the baking quality of straight grade flour (Q) after being heated at 170° F. for various numbers of hours (T). Pairs of values (T, Q) are as follows: 0.25, 93; 0.50, 71; 0.75, 63; 1.0, 54; 1.5, 43; 2.0, 38; 3.0, 29; 4.0, 26; 6.0, 22; 8.0, 20. Plot Q on the vertical axis against T on the horizontal. Setting $\log T = X$ and $\log Q = Y$, plot Y against X. Derive the regression, $Y = 1.7116 - 0.4678X$.

EXAMPLE 15.2.5—Placing $Y = 1/Q$ in the last example, plot Y against T. Since the graph is not linear, try $Y = \dfrac{1}{Q-14}$. Compute the regression of the rectified data,

$Y = 0.01996T + 0.00546$, from which $Q = \dfrac{1}{0.01996T + 0.00546} + 14$. Running (14, VI) gives a graphical method for estimating the number that must be subtracted from W in order to get a straight regression. Can you improve on 14? How many degrees of freedom remain for testing with the mean square of errors of estimate?

EXAMPLE 15.2.6—Decker and Andre (3) investigated the mortality of chinch bugs exposed at a temperature of $-12.2°$ C. for various periods:

Hours exposure	0.25	0.5	1	4	12	24	48	72
Percentage mortality	59	63	65	68	70	73	74	75

Let $Y =$ percentage mortality and $X =$ logarithm of hours exposure. Fit the equation, $Y = 6.051X + 64.1$. To plot these data on logarithmic paper, put the logarithmic scale horizontal and plot hours on it.

EXAMPLE 15.2.7—In an experiment on wheat in Australia, fertilizers were applied at various levels with these resulting yields:

Level	X	0	10	20	30	40	60
Yield	y	26.2	34.0	36.3	37.8	38.6	38.9

Fit to these data the Mitscherlich equation (14, 5),
$$Y = a - bX,$$
where $Y = \log (39 - y)$. The yield, 39, is taken as the maximum yield irrespective of the amount of fertilizer. The fitted equation is $Y = 0.01434X - 0.2294$.

15.3—The second degree polynomial. Faced by nonlinear regression, one often has no knowledge of a theoretical equation to use. In many instances the second degree polynomial,

$$Y = a + bX + cX^2,$$

will be found to fit the data satisfactorily. The graph is a parabola whose axis is vertical, but usually only small segments of such a parabola appear in the process of fitting. Instead of rectifying the data a third variate is added, the square of X. This introduces the methods of multiple regression. The calculations proceed exactly as in chapter 14, X and X^2 being the two independent variates. It need only be remarked that $\sqrt{X}$, $\log X$, or $1/X$ might have been added instead of X^2 if the data had required it.

To illustrate the method and some of its applications, we present the data on wheat yield and protein content (13) in table 15.3.1 and figure 15.3.1. The investigator wished to estimate the protein content for various yields. We shall also test the significance of the departure from linearity.

The second column of the table contains the squares of the yields in column 1. The squares are treated in all respects like a third variable in multiple regression. The regression equation, calculated as usual,

$$Y = 17.703 - 0.3415X + 0.004075X^2,$$

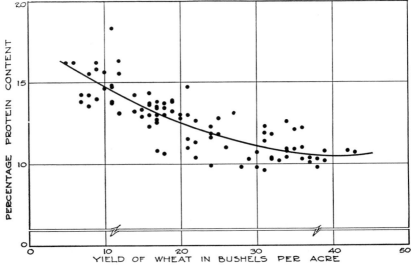

Fɪɢ. 15.3.1—Regression of protein content on yield in wheat, 91 plots.
$$Y = 17.703 - 0.3415X + 0.004075X^2$$

Curvilinear Regression

TABLE 15.3.1

PERCENTAGE PROTEIN CONTENT (Y) AND YIELD (X) OF WHEAT
FROM 91 PLOTS*

Yield, Bushel Per Acre X	Square X^2	Percentage Protein Y	Yield, Bushel Per Acre X	Square X^2	Percentage Protein Y
43	1,849	10.7	19	361	13.9
42	1,764	10.8	19	361	13.2
39	1,521	10.8	19	361	13.8
39	1,521	10.2	18	324	10.6
38	1,444	10.3	18	324	13.0
38	1,444	9.8	18	324	13.4
37	1,369	10.1	18	324	13.7
37	1,369	10.4	18	324	13.0
36	1,296	10.3	17	289	13.4
36	1,296	11.0	17	289	13.5
36	1,296	12.2	17	289	10.8
35	1,225	10.9	17	289	12.5
35	1,225	12.1	17	289	12.7
34	1,156	10.4	17	289	13.0
34	1,156	10.8	17	289	13.8
34	1,156	10.9	16	256	14.3
34	1,156	12.6	16	256	13.6
33	1,089	10.2	16	256	12.3
32	1,024	11.8	16	256	13.0
32	1,024	10.3	16	256	13.7
32	1,024	10.4	15	225	13.3
31	961	12.3	15	225	12.9
31	961	9.6	14	196	14.2
31	961	11.9	14	196	13.2
31	961	11.4	12	144	15.5
30	900	9.8	12	144	13.1
30	900	10.7	12	144	16.3
29	841	10.3	11	121	13.7
28	784	9.8	11	121	18.3
27	729	13.1	11	121	14.7
26	676	11.0	11	121	13.8
26	676	11.0	11	121	14.8
25	625	12.8	10	100	15.6
25	625	11.8	10	100	14.6
24	576	9.9	9	81	14.0
24	576	11.6	9	81	16.2
24	576	11.8	9	81	15.8
24	576	12.3	8	64	15.5
22	484	11.3	8	64	14.2
22	484	10.4	8	64	13.5
22	484	12.6	7	49	13.8
21	441	13.0	7	49	14.2
21	441	14.7	6	36	16.2
21	441	11.5	5	25	16.2
21	441	11.0			
20	400	12.8			
20	400	13.0			

* Read from published graph. This accounts for the slight discrepancy between the correlation we got and that reported by the author.

is plotted in the figure. At small values of yield the second degree term with its small coefficient is scarcely noticeable, the graph falling away almost like a straight line. Toward the right, however, the term in X^2 has bent the curve to practically a horizontal direction.

It is interesting to observe the effect of curvilinearity of regression on the deviations from regression. If linear regression is assumed, $\Sigma d_{y.x}^2 = 110.48$. But when the second degree term is introduced, $\Sigma d_{y.x}^2 = 97.53$. The analysis of variance and test of significance are shown in table 15.3.2.

TABLE 15.3.2
TEST OF SIGNIFICANCE OF DEPARTURE FROM LINEAR REGRESSION

Source of Variation	Degrees of Freedom	Sum of Squares	Mean Square
Deviations from linear regression	89	110.48	
Deviations from curved regression	88	97.53	1.11
Curvilinearity of regression	1	12.95	12.95 **

$$F = 12.95/1.11 = 11.7$$

The reduction in sum of squares, tested against the mean square remaining after curvilinear regression, proves to be significant. The hypothesis of linear regression is abandoned, therefore; there is said to be a significant curvilinearity in the regression.

For any given yield, say 20 bushels per acre, the expected protein content is

$$Y = 17.703 - (0.3415)(20) + (0.004075)(20)^2 = 12.51\%$$

In this way, the regression equation is useful for estimating and interpolating. Confidence statements and tests of hypotheses are made as in chapter 14.

It may be thought that there is a great chasm between the rectification of data in the last section and the treatment of curvilinear regression in this. The distinction, however, is really superficial. If a three-dimensional graph were made, X and X^2 being plotted on separate axes, the regression surface would be a plane. In that sense the data would be rectified as before. It is only the limitations of the two-dimensional graph that make the methods seem different.

As always in regression, either linear or curved, one should be wary of extrapolation. The data may be incompetent to furnish evidence of trend beyond their own range. Looking at figure 15.2.1, one might be tempted by the excellent fit to assume the same growth rate before the sixth day and after the sixteenth. The fact is, however, that there were rather sharp breaks in the rate of growth at both these days. To be useful, extrapolation requires extensive knowledge and keen thinking.

EXAMPLE 15.3.1—Fit a second degree polynomial to the data of example 15.2.1 The result is $Y = 262.245 - 9.851X + 0.09681X^2$, not a very good fit.

EXAMPLE 15.3.2—Decker and Andre (3) exposed eight lots of 500 chinch bugs at −6.6° C. for varying intervals of time. The resulting mortality was as follows:

Days exposure	1	3	3.5	8	13.5	16	21	28
Percentage mortality	0.8	3.6	5.8	11.6	22.8	44.6	67.6	92.0

Fit a second degree polynomial to learn if it reveals a significant deviation from linear regression. $F = 6.09, f = 1$ and 5, shows that the departure from linear regression, as tested by the fitted parabola, is just short of significance.

EXAMPLE 15.3.3—You may think that the parabola is not a suitable equation to fit to the data of the last example. Try putting Y equal to the logarithms of the mortality percentages, then fitting $Y = a + bX$, where X is days of exposure.

How will you compare the fit of this curve with that of the parabola? For the latter, the mean square deviation from second degree regression was 32.2 with $f = 5$. To get a comparable figure from the logarithmic fitting, transform each Y to its antilogarithm P and calculate the deviations from regression. The mean of their squares is 1,270, far greater than the corresponding figure for deviation from second degree regression. Why is this not an exact comparison?

15.4—Test of deviation from linear regression.
In the foregoing section this test was made in table 15.3.2 after the curvilinear regression had been computed. If the data occur in groups, and if it is only deviation from linearity of regression that is interesting, the test can be made rather simply. The method is illustrated by use of the data in table 15.4.1, made

TABLE 15.4.1

LETHAL DOSE (CODED BY SUBTRACTING 50 UNITS) OF UNITED STATES STANDARD OUABAIN, SLOW INTRAVENOUS INJECTION IN CAT TO ENDPOINT OF CARDIAC STOPPAGE

Rate of Injection, $X \dfrac{\text{mg./kg./min.}}{1,000}$				
1.04575	2.0915	4.183	8.366	Total
5	3	34	51	
9	6	34	56	
11	22	38	62	
13	27	40	63	
14	27	46	70	
16	28	58	73	
17	28	60	76	
20	37	60	89	
22	40	65	92	
28	42			
31	50			
31				
ΣY 217	310	435	632	1,594
Number cats 12	11	9	9	41
$\bar{y}$ 18.1	28.2	48.3	70.2	38.9
ΣY^2 4,727	10,788	22,261	45,940	83,716

available through the courtesy of B. J. Vos and W. T. Dawson. Four rates of injection were used, each double the preceding. The particular question under investigation was whether the regression of Y on X is curved. A graph will be quite sufficient to convince most people that there is no evidence of curvilinearity. However, we shall make the test of significance as an illustration of the method.

First, the total sum of squares of the lethal doses is analyzed in the familiar manner of table 15.4.2. It is clear that the chief source of variation is that induced by the rates of injection—the group means differ significantly. We are interested in learning whether the trend of the means departs significantly from linearity.

For regression, Σx^2 and Σxy are required, corresponding to $\Sigma y^2 = 21,744$

TABLE 15.4.2

ANALYSIS OF VARIANCE OF LETHAL DOSES OF OUABAIN AT FOUR RATES OF INJECTION

Source of Variation	Degrees of Freedom	Sum of Squares	Mean Square
Within Rate Groups (Error)	37	5,651	152.7
Rates of Injection	3	16,093	5,364**
Total	40	21,744	

in the table. The calculations differ somewhat from usual because of the occurrence of Y in groups. Thus,

$$\Sigma X = 12(1.04575) + 11(2.0915) + 9(4.183) + 9(8.366) = 148.496,$$

a *weighted* sum. Similarly,

$$\Sigma X^2 = 12(1.04575)^2 + \ldots + 9(8.366)^2 = 848.628$$

From these is computed,

$$\Sigma x^2 = \Sigma X^2 - (\Sigma X)^2/n = 848.628 - 537.831 = 310.797$$

For the sum of products of the observations,

$$\Sigma XY = (1.04575)(217) + (2.0915)(310) + (4.183)(435) + (8.366)(632)$$
$$= 7,982.21$$

Deducting the correction term, $(148.496)(1,594)/41 = 5,773.23$, we have,

$$\Sigma xy = 7,982.21 - 5,773.23 = 2,208.98$$

Finally, the sum of squares for group means is copied from table 15.4.2 into table 15.4.3, then divided into the two parts, one attributed to linear regression and the other to deviations therefrom. The former is, as usual, $(\Sigma xy)^2/(\Sigma x^2) = (2,208.98)^2/310.797 = 15,700$, having one degree of freedom. The remainder, 393, with two degrees of freedom furnishes the mean square corresponding to deviations from linear regression. This mean square is little greater than that for error. No more than random sampling departure from linear regression is indicated.

TABLE 15.4.3

ANALYSIS OF SUM OF SQUARES FOR GROUP MEANS

Source of Variation	Degrees of Freedom	Sum of Squares	Mean Square
Rates of Injection (table 15.4.2)	3	16,093	
Linear Regression, $(\Sigma xy)^2/(\Sigma x^2)$	1	15,700	
Deviations from Linear Regression	2	393	196
Error (table 15.4.2)	37		153

$$F = 196/153 = 1.3$$

EXAMPLE 15.4.1—There is available some additional information about the chinch bugs in example 15.3.2. Each of the eight mortality percentages was an average of five sub-samples of 100 bugs. The mortality percentages in the sub-sample are as shown below.

Sub-sample of 100	Days Exposure							
	1	3	3.5	8	13.5	16	21	28
1	0	3	4	9	21	46	68	93
2	0	4	5	21	23	39	70	100
3	1	2	6	8	27	43	66	92
4	1	5	7	10	25	47	61	86
5	2	4	7	10	18	48	73	89
Total	4	18	29	58	114	223	338	460

Analyze the variance:

Within dates	421.2,	$f = 32$,	Mean square	13.2
Between dates	39,934.4,	$f = 7$,	Mean square	5,704.9

Although some heterogeneity is indicated, the mean square, 13.2, may be taken as the estimate of error against which to test any of the mean squares in example 15.3.2. For example, $F = 32.2/13.2 = 2.44$, $f = 5$ and 32, shows that the departure of these data from second degree regression is not significant.

EXAMPLE 15.4.2—Swanson and Smith (19) determined the total nitrogen content (Y grams per 100 cc. of plasma) of rat blood plasma at nine ages (X days).

Number of Rats	Age								
	25	37	50	60	80	100	130	180	360
1	0.83	0.98	1.07	1.09	0.97	1.14	1.22	1.20	1.16
2	0.77	0.84	1.01	1.03	1.08	1.04	1.07	1.19	1.29
3	0.88	0.99	1.06	1.06	1.16	1.00	1.09	1.33	1.25
4	0.94	0.87	0.96	1.08	1.11	1.08	1.15	1.21	1.43
5	0.89	0.90	0.88	0.94	1.03	0.89	1.14	1.20	1.20
6	0.83	0.82	1.01	1.01	1.17	1.03	1.19	1.07	1.06
7	0.84	0.95	0.93		0.98	1.08	1.19	1.13	1.29
8	0.75	0.92	1.07		0.99	0.98	1.14	1.12	1.25
9	0.67	0.87	1.03			0.98	1.13		1.23
10	0.70		1.13			1.10	1.06		1.22
11	0.77		1.05				1.11		1.17
12	0.76		0.96				1.04		
13	0.75		1.01				1.29		
14	0.78		1.01				1.09		
15	0.76		0.94				1.14		
16	0.86		1.03				1.12		
17	0.78		1.06				1.29		
18	0.84		1.08				1.28		
19	0.85		1.09				1.10		
20	0.83		0.93				1.07		
21	0.85		0.95				1.10		
22	0.85								
23	0.83								
24	0.83								
25	0.70								

Source of Variation	Degrees of Freedom	Sum of Squares	Mean Square
Total	118	2.8686	
Ages	8	2.3076	
Individuals in Age Groups (Error)	110	0.5610	0.0051
Ages	8	2.3076	
Linear Regression	1	1.4851	
Deviations	7	0.8225	0.1175**

15.5—Test of departure from linear regression in covariance analysis. As in any other correlation and regression work, it is necessary in covariance to be assured that regression is linear, else modifications must be made in the methods. In some cases, randomized blocks for example, it is only the error regression that matters. If the error regression is rectified, the adjusted means are appropriate estimates and the test of significance is valid.

For illustration, turn back to the sugar beet data of table 13.6.1. An agronomist, studying the findings of the covariance analysis, expressed surprise that the differences among the adjusted means were not found significant. Two phases of the question were discussed in example 13.6.1. The linearity of regression may be examined by a method similar to that of section 15.3. The squares of the plant numbers are introduced as a second independent variable, X_2. We wish to learn if there is a significant fraction of Σy^2 due to curvilinearity of the error regression.

The squares are expressed in units of 1,000, $(183)^2 = 33,489$ being entered in the data sheet as $X_2 (= X^2) = 33$. The three variables, X_1 = number of beets, $X_2 = X_1^2/1,000$, and Y = tons of beets per acre (in randomized blocks), are handled like those of section 14.5. For Error, the results are

	X_1	X_2	Y
X_1	16,873.13	8,746.25	381.2750
X_2		4,621.00	202.5650
Y			11.7711

Solution of this multiple regression leads to the data in the second line of table 15.5.1. The null hypothesis tested is that $\beta_{Y2.1} = 0$, meaning no

TABLE 15.5.1
TEST OF SIGNIFICANCE OF DEVIATIONS FROM LINEAR ERROR REGRESSION.
SUGAR BEETS OF SECTION 13.6

Source of Variation	Deviations From Regression		
	Degrees of Freedom	Sum of Squares	Mean Square
Linear Regression (table 13.6.1)	14	$\Sigma d_{Y.1}^2 = 3.1558$	
Curved Regression	13	$\Sigma d_{Y.12}^2 = 2.8282$	0.2176
Curvilinearity (X_2)	1	0.3276	0.3276

$$F = 0.3276/0.2176 = 1.51, \quad f = 1, 13$$

curvilinearity of regression. As was found in the earlier discussion, there is little evidence against the hypothesis.

In other 2-way tables the error regression might turn out to be curved. One might then wish to test the significance of differences among means adjusted by the curvilinear regression. From the table of analysis of sums of squares and products, the lines for Treatment and Error would be added and this multiple regression solved for $\Sigma d_{Y.12}{}^2$. Applying the test to the sugar beet data, table 15.5.2 is calculated.

F is little different from the value in table 13.6.1, a consequence of the negligible curvature. If the error regression were decidedly curved, the adjusted means might vary either more or less than the unadjusted.

TABLE 15.5.2

TEST OF SIGNIFICANCE OF DIFFERENCES AMONG MEANS ADJUSTED FOR CURVILINEAR REGRESSION. SUGAR BEETS

Source of Variation	Degrees of Freedom	Deviations From Regression	
		Sum of Squares	Mean Square
Treatment + Error	16	$\Sigma d_{Y.12}{}^2 = 4.8248$	
Error (table 15.5.1)	13	2.8282	0.2176
For Testing Treatments	3	1.9966	0.6655

$$F = 3.06, \quad f = 3, 13$$

EXAMPLE 15.5.1—The test for curvilinearity in multiple regression is similar to those in the last two sections. Emmert (6) measured the nitrogen, N, and phosphorus, P, (parts per million) in the stems of potato plants on June 15, 1935, then recorded the associated yield in pounds, Y, from each of 37 plots. The multiple regression of Y on N and P had $\Sigma d_{Y.12}{}^2 = 2,593$. Since there was some evidence of curvilinearity, the variables N^2 and P^2 were added. The multiple regression of Y on N, P, N^2, and P^2 yielded $\Sigma d_{Y.1234}{}^2 = 2,414$. The decrease indicates some departure from linearity. The t-test showed that this was due to the term in P^2 only, the N^2 term yielding no additional information. The latter term being dropped, therefore, the regression of Y on N, P, and P^2 gave $\Sigma d_{Y.123}{}^2 = 2,414$ as before. The test is as follows:

Source of Variation	Degrees of Freedom	Σd^2	Mean Square
Regression of Y on N and P	34	2,593	
Regression of Y on N, P, and P^2	33	2,414	73.15
Curvilinearity	1	179.4	179.4

$$F = 179.4/73.15 = 2.45, \quad f = 1 \text{ and } 33$$

F being far short of its 5% value, the departure from linearity is attributable to accidents of sampling. The data are on the next page.

N	P	P^2	Y	N	P	P^2	Y
139	195	38	33	330	260	68	46
143	146	21	43	380	134	18	60
147	120	14	40	436	130	17	57
154	178	32	49	436	200	40	64
162	266	71	43	470	134	18	55
182	200	40	27	476	160	26	54
186	260	68	55	555	155	24	37
200	240	58	51	556	188	35	42
208	170	29	45	626	125	16	45
213	195	38	41	700	146	21	63
233	146	21	57	750	178	32	52
257	160	26	38	834	188	35	46
264	146	21	48	834	178	32	56
264	146	21	39	908	105	11	65
264	160	26	40	1125	160	26	46
264	250	62	38	1200	122	15	58
265	175	31	52	1250	140	20	80
286	114	13	49	1625	150	22	70
312	155	24	51				

$$Y = 0.0170N - 0.440P + 1.10P^2 + 82.5$$

15.6—The fitting of orthogonal polynomials. Special methods have been perfected by Fisher (8) for fitting the polynomial,

$$Y = a + bX + cX^2 + dX^3 + \ldots$$

This is a flexible curve, adaptable to fitting a wide assortment of data. It includes the straight line and the parabola as special cases. Fisher's methods are based on the principles of orthogonal polynomials. One is described, and special tables given, in (9). The other, presented below, is more general but involves somewhat heavier calculations.

We shall illustrate only the case in which the values of X are spaced at unit intervals, each accompanied by a single value of Y. If X occurs in equally-spaced intervals different from unity, it may be coded to unit intervals by dividing each value by the common interval. In data having X unequally spaced or having more than one Y for some or all of the X, use the method of section 15.3, extending it to more than two X.

One advantage of orthogonal polynomials is that the fitting can be carried through conveniently in successive stages, the success of fitting terms of higher and higher degree being observed and tested for significance at each stage. The fitting will be terminated with the fourth degree term in the example below. Those who wish formulas for higher degree terms may infer them readily with the assistance of the footnotes. Professor Fisher gives general formulas in his book.

For illustration, the chick embryo data of table 15.2.1 will be used. The dry weights are copied in the first column of table 15.6.1. The sum,

TABLE 15.6.1

SUMS AND DERIVED QUANTITIES FOR FITTING A POLYNOMIAL TO CHICK EMBRYO DATA

Y	2	3	4	5
0.029	0.029	0.029	0.029	0.029
0.052	0.081	0.110	0.139	0.168
0.079	0.160	0.270	0.409	0.577
0.125	0.285	0.555	0.964	1.541
0.181	0.466	1.021	1.985	3.526
0.261	0.727	1.748	3.733	7.259
0.425	1.152	2.900	6.633	13.892
0.738	1.890	4.790	11.423	25.315
1.130	3.020	7.810	19.233	44.548
1.882	4.902	12.712	31.945	76.493
2.812	7.714	20.426	52.371	128.864

$S_1 = 7.714$ $S_2 = 20.426$ $S_3 = 52.371$ $S_4 = 128.864$ $S_5 = 302.212$

$a = 0.701273$ $b = 0.309485$ $c = 0.183115$ $d = 0.128735$ $e = 0.100637$
$a' = 0.701273$ $b' = 0.391788$ $c' = 0.139048$ $d' = 0.031838$ $e' = 0.003066$
$A = 0.701273$ $B = 0.235073$ $C = 0.0463493$ $D = 0.00619072$ $E = 0.00038325$

$S_1 = 7.714$, is divided by $n = 11$, the number of items in the set, to get the mean, $a = 0.701273$, as specified in the first of the following formulas:

$$a = \frac{S_1}{n} = \bar{y}$$

$$b = \frac{(1)(2)}{n(n+1)}(S_2)$$

$$c = \frac{(1)(2)(3)}{n(n+1)(n+2)}(S_3)$$

$$d = \frac{(1)(2)(3)(4)}{n(n+1)(n+2)(n+3)}(S_4)$$

$$e = \frac{(1)(2)(3)(4)(5)}{n(n+1)(n+2)(n+3)(n+4)}(S_5)$$

The remaining formulas will be used later.

The mean, a, is copied in the next line as a', the two being equal according to the first of the next set of formulas:

$$a' = a$$
$$b' = a - b$$
$$c' = a - 3b + 2c$$

$$d' = a - 6b + 10c - 5d$$
$$e' = a - 10b + 30c - 35d + 14e*$$

Again, $A = a' = a$ in the first of the third set:

$$A = a'$$

$$B = \frac{6}{n-1} \ (b')$$

$$C = \frac{30}{(n-1)(n-2)} \ (c')$$

$$D = \frac{140}{(n-1)(n-2)(n-3)} \ (d')$$

$$E = \frac{630\dagger}{(n-1)(n-2)(n-3)(n-4)} \ (e')$$

Finally, the sum of squares of deviations from mean is got by subtracting from $\Sigma Y^2 = 13.577730$ the correction term $nA^2 = (11)(0.701273)^2 = 5.409622$, set down as the first of these quantities:

$$nA^2 = \frac{(\Sigma Y)^2}{n}$$

$$\frac{n(n^2-1)}{12} \ (B^2)$$

$$\frac{n(n^2-1)(n^2-4)}{180} \ (C^2)$$

$$\frac{n(n^2-1)(n^2-4)(n^2-9)}{2,800} \ (D^2)$$

$$\frac{n(n^2-1)(n^2-4)(n^2-9)(n^2-16)}{44,100\ddagger} \ (E^2)$$

---

* The next three of these equations are:
$$f' = a - 15b + 70c - 140d + 126e - 42f$$
$$g' = a - 21b + 140c - 420d + 630e - 462f + 132g$$
$$h' = a - 28b + 252c - 1050d + 2310e - 2772f + 1716g - 429h$$

† The numerators of the next three terms are 2,772, 12,012, 51,480.

‡ The denominators of the next three terms are 698,544, 11,099,088, 176,679,360.

The remainder, $\Sigma y^2 = \Sigma Y^2 - nA^2 = 8.168108$, is the end of the first stage in the fitting. A horizontal straight line, $Y = 0.701273$, has been fitted to the data. The sum of squares of deviations from this line is Σy^2.

The second stage starts with the sums in column 2 of the table. After the first item is copied at the top of the column, the successive sums are:

$$0.029 + 0.052 = 0.081$$
$$0.081 + 0.079 = 0.160$$
$$0.160 + 0.125 = 0.285, \text{ etc.}$$

These are readily run up on an adding machine. The last sum, 7.714, is the same as S_1, a convenient check. The sum of column 2 is $S_2 = 20.426$.

Going through the sets of formulas again, there result:

$$b = \frac{(1)(2)}{(11)(12)} (20.426) = 0.309485$$

$$b' = 0.701273 - 0.309485 = 0.391788$$

$$B = \frac{6}{10} (0.391788) = 0.235073$$

$$\Sigma(Y - \hat{Y})^2 = 8.168108 - \frac{11(11^2 - 1)}{12} (0.235073)^2$$

$$= 8.168108 - 6.078525 = 2.089583$$

The reduction in sum of squares due to fitting the linear regression is 6.078525 with one degree of freedom. This may be tested for significance by comparing it with the remainder, 2.089583, having 9 *d.f.* The mean square for error is, therefore, $2.089583/9 = 0.232$, yielding $F = 6.079 /0.232 = 26.2$, a highly significant value for $f = 1$ and 9.

The third stage involves fitting the second degree term. Starting with $S_3 = 52.371$,

$$c = \frac{(1)(2)(3)}{(11)(12)(13)} (52.371) = 0.183115$$

$$c' = (0.701273) - 3(0.309485) + 2(0.183115) = 0.139048$$

$$C = \frac{30}{(10)(9)} (0.139048) = 0.0463493$$

$$\Sigma(Y - \hat{Y})^2 = 2.089583 - \frac{(11)(11^2 - 1)(11^2 - 4)}{180}(0.0463493)^2$$

$$= 2.089583 - 1.843205 = 0.246378$$

The mean square for testing is now $0.246378/8 = 0.0308$, so that $F = 1.843/0.0309 = 59.8$, which with $f = 1$ and 8 is highly significant.

In the next stage, the third degree term is fitted with this result:

$$\Sigma(Y - \hat{Y})^2 = 0.246378 - 0.236757 = 0.009621$$

This yields $F = 0.237/0.00137$, $f = 1$ and 7, another highly significant reduction.

One would be justified in stopping at this point. The ratio of the remaining sum of squares to Σy^2 is only

$$0.009621/8.1681 = 0.001178$$

However, for two reasons the fitting will be carried one stage further; to illustrate the method, and because the third degree polynomial exhibits certain snakelike curves that make it unsuited to the chick embryo data.

Taking the last of the successive sets of formulas, with $S_5 = 302.212$, one arrives at

$$\Sigma(Y - \hat{Y})^2 = 0.009621 - 0.006049 = 0.003572,$$

so that $F = 0.006049/0.000595 = 10.2$, a significant, but not highly significant, reduction.

For many purposes, the job is complete. Some, though, may wish to plot the curves, and some may require the equations. Those who need the graphs but not the equations should follow the procedure of the next few paragraphs. If equations are necessary, skip to the sixth paragraph below.

In table 15.6.2 are entered some polynomials with corresponding coefficients which enable one to build up the desired values of Y by adding sets of differences to a *terminal value*. The coefficients depend on the size of the sample, while the polynomials are determined by the degree of the last term fitted. As a first illustration of the method we shall calculate points on the best fitting straight line.

Since the last term now to be considered is of degree one, the terminal value is $(a' + 3b') = 0.701273 + 3(0.391788) = 1.8766$. The *first difference* is

$$-\frac{6}{(n - 1)}(b') = -\frac{6}{(11 - 1)}(0.391788) = -0.2351$$

TABLE 15.6.2

COEFFICIENTS AND POLYNOMIALS FOR TERMINAL VALUES AND DIFFERENCES FOR FITTING
TERMS UP TO THE SEVENTH DEGREE

Degree of Poly-nomial	Coefficient Depending on Sample Size	Polynomial Ending With Term of Degree							
		0	1	2	3	4	5	6	7
	Terminal Value →	$a' + 3b' + 5c' + 7d' + 9e' + 11f' + 13g' + 15h'$							
1	$-\dfrac{6}{n-1}$	$b' + 5c' + 14d' + 30e' + 55f' + 91g' + 140h'$							
2	$\dfrac{60}{(n-1)(n-2)}$	$c' + 7d' + 27e' + 77f' + 182g' + 378h'$							
3	$\dfrac{-840}{(n-1)(n-2)(n-3)}$	$d' + 9e' + 44f' + 156g' + 450h'$							
4	$\dfrac{15,120}{(n-1)\ldots(n-4)}$	$e' + 11f' + 65g' + 275h'$							
5	$\dfrac{-332,640}{(n-1)\ldots(n-5)}$	$f' + 13g' + 90h'$							
6	$\dfrac{8,648,640}{(n-1)\ldots(n-6)}$	$g' + 15h'$							
7	$\dfrac{-259,459,200}{(n-1)\ldots(n-7)}$	h'							

By successive additions of this first difference to the terminal value, 1.8766, one gets the successive values of Y, beginning with the largest corresponding to $X = 16$:

$$1.8766 + (-0.2351) = 1.6415$$
$$1.6415 + (-0.2351) = 1.4064, \text{ etc.}$$

X	Polynomial Value, Y	First Difference
6	-0.474	
7	-0.239	
8	-0.004	
9	0.231	
10	0.466	
11	0.701	
12	0.936	
13	1.171	
14	1.406	
15	1.642	
16	Terminal value $= 1.8766$	-0.2351

In the calculating machine all the four decimals are carried, but the last one is deleted in the column of polynomial values. These values are plotted in figure 15.6.1. The straight line is a poor fit, of course, but it does pass through the point $(\bar{x}, \bar{y})$; that is, (11, 0.701).

Next, let us calculate the ordinates for the best fitting parabola. From the table, ending with degree 2:

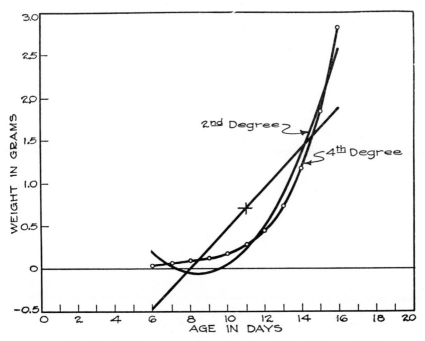

FIG. 15.6.1—Graphs of polynomials of first, second, and fourth degree fitted to chick embryo data of table 15.6.1.

Terminal value $\quad = a' + 3b' + 5c'$

$\qquad\qquad\qquad = 0.701273 + 3(0.391788) + 5(0.139048) = 2.57188$

First difference $\quad = -\dfrac{6}{n-1}\,(b' + 5c')$

$\qquad\qquad\qquad = -\dfrac{6}{10}\,[0.391788 + 5(0.139048)] = -0.65222$

Second difference $= \dfrac{60}{(n-1)(n-2)}\,(c')$

$\qquad\qquad\qquad = \dfrac{60}{(10)(9)}\,(0.139048) = 0.092699$

The calculations are carried through like this:

X	Y	First Difference	Second Difference
6	0.222	0.2748	
7	0.039	0.1821	
8	−0.050	0.0894	
9	−0.047	−0.0033	
10	0.049	−0.0960	
11	0.238	−0.1887	
12	0.519	−0.2814	
13	0.893	−0.3741	
14	1.360	−0.4668	
15	1.920	−0.5595	
16 Terminal value = 2.57188		−0.65222	0.092699

The second difference is added successively to the bottom first difference,

$$0.092699 + (-0.65222) = -0.5595,$$

and to each of the sums above it. Each first difference, starting with the last, is added to a value of Y to get the one next above. Thus,

$$- 0.65222 + 2.57188 = 1.920$$
$$- 0.5595 + 1.920 = 1.360, \text{ etc.}$$

Y is plotted against X to make the graph of the parabola.

Passing to the fourth degree polynomial, the terminal value and differences are:

Terminal value $= a' + 3b' + 5c' + 7d' + 9e' = 2.822337$

First difference $= -\dfrac{6}{n-1}(b' + 5c' + 14d' + 30e') = -0.974844$

Second difference $= \dfrac{60}{(n-1)(n-2)}(c' + 7d' + 27e') = 0.296464$

Third difference $= \dfrac{-840}{(n-1)(n-2)(n-3)}(d' + 9e') = -0.069337$

Fourth difference $= \dfrac{15{,}120}{(n-1)(n-2)(n-3)(n-4)}(e') = 0.009198$

These are entered in the last line of table 15.6.3. The third differences

TABLE 15.6.3

CALCULATION OF THE FOURTH DEGREE POLYNOMIAL VALUES FOR CHICK EMBRYO DATA

X	Y	First Difference	Second Difference	Third Difference	Fourth Difference
6	0.026				
7	0.056	−0.0302			
8	0.086	−0.0295	−0.00069		
9	0.119	−0.0337	0.00426	−0.004951	
10	0.171	−0.0521	0.01841	−0.014149	
11	0.265	−0.0939	0.04176	−0.023347	
12	0.434	−0.1682	0.07430	−0.032545	
13	0.718	−0.2843	0.11605	−0.041743	
14	1.169	−0.4512	0.16699	−0.050941	
15	1.847	−0.6784	0.22713	−0.060139	
16	2.8223	−0.97484	0.296464	−0.069337	0.009198

result from successive additions of 0.009198. The second differences are calculated thus:

$$-0.069337 + 0.296464 = 0.22713$$

$$-0.060139 + 0.22713 = 0.16699, \text{ etc.}$$

All the significant figures are carried in the machine, as before, but one is dropped in copying. The first differences are got in a similar manner, then the polynomial values. These last, plotted on the graph, specify the fourth degree curve. It passes so nearly through the data points that the discrepancies cannot be depicted.

The information now at hand is all that is needed in most cases. The goodness of fit is determined by tests of significance of the reductions in sum squares. The graph not only gives visual representation but serves for interpolation accurately enough for ordinary purposes. There would seem to be little incentive to derive the equation of the curve.

If the equation is desired, omit the computation of the polynomial values in the preceding few paragraphs. After the equation is set up as described below, points on the graph can be computed at will. The equation is of the form,

$$Y = A + BX_1 + CX_2 + \dots$$

where $A, B, C, \dots$ are the quantities last calculated in table 15.6.1 and X_1, X_2, etc., are themselves polynomials in X. It is in this part of the computation that X is assumed to occur at unit intervals. If the actual intervals are equal but not unity, as for example 30 days or 5 years, they may be coded easily by division. Practically, they are simply rewritten as 1, 2, 3, . . . , the new unit being 30 days or 5 years.

One last set of formulas is needed:

$$X_1 = X - \bar{x}$$

$$X_2 = X_1{}^2 - \frac{n^2 - 1}{12}$$

$$X_3 = X_1{}^3 - \frac{3n^2 - 7}{20}(X_1)$$

$$X_4 = X_1{}^4 - \frac{3n^2 - 13}{14}(X_1{}^2) + \frac{3(n^2 - 1)(n^2 - 9)}{560}$$

$$X_5 = X_1{}^5 - \frac{5(n^2 - 7)}{18}(X_1{}^3) + \frac{15n^4 - 230n^2 + 407}{1,008}(X_1)$$

From table 15.2.1, $\bar{x} = 11$ days and $n = 11$. Hence,

$$X_1 = X - 11$$
$$X_2 = (X - 11)^2 - 10 = X^2 - 22X + 111$$
$$X_3 = (X - 11)^3 - 17.8(X - 11) = X^3 - 33X^2 + 345.2X - 1,135.2$$
$$X_4 = (X - 11)^4 - 25(X - 11)^2 + 72$$
$$\quad = X^4 - 44X^3 + 701X^2 - 4,774X + 11,688$$

Any equation up to the fourth degree may be written from the data now before us. As examples, the equation of the best fitting straight line is, $Y = A + BX_1 = 0.701273 + 0.235073(X - 11) = 0.2351X - 1.885$, while that of the fourth degree polynomial is,

$$Y = A + BX_1 + CX_2 + DX_3 + EX_4$$
$$= 0.701273 + 0.235073(X - 11) + 0.046349(X^2 - 22X$$
$$+ 111) + 0.0061907(X^3 - 33X^2 + 345.2X - 1,135.2)$$
$$+ 0.00038325(X^4 - 44X^3 + 701X^2 - 4,774X + 11,688)$$
$$= 0.712 - 0.4772X + 0.11071X^2 - 0.010672X^3 + 0.0003832X^4$$

By substituting the several values of X days in this equation, the polynomial values may be calculated and plotted for the graph.

The student well may question the advisability of fitting curves. A stupendous amount of time has been wasted in ill-advised curve fitting. Only when the end in view is clear should the task be undertaken. Often a graph of the data points is sufficient. Represent them by small circles or heavy dots. If desired, they may be connected by light line segments.

Avoid drawing "eye-fitted" curves. They are highly subjective and are apt to be misleading to both the perpetrator and the victim. Interpolation with these links stands a better chance of being good than does estimating by means of even the most artistic curves. If you know enough about the law to say that there ought to be a curve, then you should be able to write an equation expressing the law and fit it to the data. If you wish to evaluate a correlation when regression is nonlinear, or if you wish to test significance, then suitable curved regressions must be fitted. Occasionally, fitted curves are required for interpolation. In many cases, graphical representation of the data is sufficient.

EXAMPLE 15.6.1—The following five points lie on the parabola, $Y = 9+2X-X^2$: (0, 9), (1, 10), (2, 9), (3, 6), and (4, 1). Using Fisher's method, show that the sum of squares remaining after fitting the second degree term is zero. Calculate the polynomial values. These will be identical with the pairs of values given above. When you plot them, the points will lie exactly on the parabola whose equation is given. Derive this equation by the use of the formulas up to the second degree.

EXAMPLE 15.6.2—Here are some points on the cubic, $Y = 9X - 6X^2 + X^3$: (0, 0), (1, 4), (2, 2), (3, 0), (4, 4), (5, 20). Carry through all the computations by Fisher's method, including the best fitting straight line and parabola. There will be no remaining sum of squares after fitting the third degree term and the polynomial values at that stage of the fitting will be exactly those you start with. Plot the best fitting line and the best fitting parabola and derive their equations.

EXAMPLE 15.6.3—Reed and Holland (17) reported the following average heights of sunflowers:

Week	1	2	3	4	5	6	7	8	9	10	11	12
Height	18	36	68	98	131	170	206	228	247	250	254	254
Polynomial values	15.0	38.9	68.0	100.6	134.6	168.0	198.9	225.5	245.6	257.5	259.1	248.4

The polynomial values are those for the cubic. Verify and plot. The remaining sum of squares after fitting the cubic is 211.03. Calculate the equation of the polynomial, then verify by duplicating the polynomial values given above.

15.7—Biological assay.

Among applications of curve fitting, this has been the topic of greatest interest during the last two decades. The term, *biological assay*, refers to the evaluation of the potency of a stimulus by observing the response it produces in living material. Common examples are the measurements of potency of toxic materials, drugs, hormones, etc., applied to plants or animals.

New impetus in biological assay was supplied by the work of Bliss (2) who developed *probit analysis*. Berkson (1) has adapted the *logistic* curve (15) to the requirements of modern biological assay, coining the phrase *logit analysis*. Finney's book (7) and Berkson's article contain detailed methods and tables with abundant illustrative material.

REFERENCES

1. JOSEPH BERKSON. Journal of the American Statistical Association, 48:565 (1953).

2. C. I. BLISS. Annals of Applied Biology, 22:134 and 22:307 (1935); 24:815 (1937).

3. GEORGE C. DECKER and FLOYD ANDRE. Iowa State Journal of Science, 10:403 (1936).

4. W. EDWARDS DEMING. Statistical Adjustment of Data. John Wiley and Sons, Inc., New York (1943).

5. M. T. EID, C. A. BLACK, O. KEMPTHORNE and J. A. ZOELLNER. Iowa Agricultural Experiment Station Research Bulletin 406 (1954).

6. E. M. EMMERT. Journal of the American Society of Agronomy, 29:213 (1937).

7. D. J. FINNEY. Probit Analysis. Cambridge University Press (1952).

8. R. A. FISHER. Statistical Methods for Research Workers. Oliver and Boyd, Edinburgh (1925), section 27.

9. R. A. FISHER and F. YATES. Statistical Tables. Oliver and Boyd, Edinburgh (1938).

10. W. F. GEDDES. Canadian Journal of Research, 1:528 (1929).

11. A. C. HASKELL. How to Make and Use Graphical Charts. Codex Book Co., Inc., New York (1919).

12. JOSEPH LIPKA. Graphical and Mechanical Computation. John Wiley and Sons, Inc., New York (1918).

13. W. H. METZGER. Journal of the American Society of Agronomy, 27:653 (1935).

14. EILHARD ALFRED MITSCHERLICH. Landw. Jahrb., 38:537 (1909).

15. RAYMOND PEARL. Medical Biometry and Statistics. W. B. Saunders Co., Philadelphia, 2nd Edition (1930).

16. ROBERT PENQUITE. Thesis submitted for the degree Doctor of Philosophy, Iowa State University (1936).

17. H. S. REED and R. H. HOLLAND. Proceedings of the National Academy of Science, 5:140 (1919).

18. T. R. RUNNING. Empirical Formulas. John Wiley and Sons, Inc., New York (1917).

19. PEARL P. SWANSON and A. H. SMITH. The Journal of Biological Chemistry, 97:745 (1932).

CHAPTER 16

Binomial and Poisson Distributions

16.1—Introduction. Small samples from these distributions were dealt with in chapters 1 and 9. We are now ready for the discussion of some features of large samples of enumeration data similar to the large sample methods for measurement data presented in chapter 8. Since in these distributions the mean and the variance are not independent, transformations may be necessary before analysis of variance is applied. Three of these were described in chapter 11.

16.2—The binomial distribution. If the incidence of some event like survival or male sex is observed in *sub-samples* of uniform size, the sub-samples may be classified according to the number of times the event occurs. The resulting frequency distribution may be a sample from a *binomial distribution*, a distribution in which the probability of the occurrence of the event is the same for every individual.

As an example, suppose lots(sub-samples) consisting of four full sister chicks are inoculated with an organism producing equal chances of life or death for every chick. The event of survival in the lots may occur any number of times from none to four. If 96 lots are injected, some such record as this may result:

Number of Surviving Chicks in Sub-sample	Number of Sub-samples With Each Record of Survivals
0	1
1	20
2	41
3	25
4	9
Total	96

Clearly, no survivals in a lot, as well as four survivals, is unlikely. The modal number of living chicks is two.

The two specifications, four individuals in each sub-sample and 50% probability of survival, completely determine a binomial distribution.

Most conveniently, the *relative frequency* of occurrence of 0, 1, 2, 3, and 4 survivors is given by the successive terms of the expansion of the binomial,*

$$\left(\frac{1}{2} + \frac{1}{2}\right)^4$$

$$= \left(\frac{1}{2}\right)^4 + 4\left(\frac{1}{2}\right)^3\left(\frac{1}{2}\right) + 6\left(\frac{1}{2}\right)^2\left(\frac{1}{2}\right)^2 + 4\left(\frac{1}{2}\right)\left(\frac{1}{2}\right)^3 + \left(\frac{1}{2}\right)^4$$

$$= \frac{1}{16} + \frac{1}{4} + \frac{3}{8} + \frac{1}{4} + \frac{1}{16}$$

This means that one-sixteenth of the sub-samples in the population will have no survivals, one quarter will have one, etc. Combining this information with the sample fact of 96 lots, the *hypothetical frequencies* in the classes

are $(96)\left(\dfrac{1}{16}\right) = 6$, etc.; that is, 6, 24, 36, 24, and 6. The discrepancies

between these and the sample frequencies may be due to the vagaries of sampling or to a mistaken assumption about the probability of death among the chicks. These possibilities will be investigated presently.

The general statement of the theory is this: if there is a constant probability, p, in the random sub-samples of k, the relative frequency of 0, 1, 2, ... occurrences is given by successive terms of the binomial

$$(q + p)^k,$$

where $q = 1 - p$ is the probability that the event will not occur; the hypothetical frequencies in the classes of the sample are the products of these relative frequencies by n.

You may find it profitable to verify this theory by sampling a homogeneous population. Selecting a lot of beans of uniform size, shape and texture, color (or otherwise mark) some fraction of them, say one-third, then mix thoroughly. Draw sub-samples of five, for example, by some random method of selecting one bean at a time, noting its color then replacing it among the others. Continue after re-mixing each time. The probability of getting 0, 1, 2, 3, 4, or 5 colored beans is taken from the successive terms of the expansion, $p = 1/3$, $q = 2/3$, $k = 5$:

$$\left(\frac{2}{3} + \frac{1}{3}\right)^5 = \left(\frac{2}{3}\right)^5 + 5\left(\frac{2}{3}\right)^4\left(\frac{1}{3}\right) + 10\left(\frac{2}{3}\right)^3\left(\frac{1}{3}\right)^2 + \cdots$$

$$= \frac{32}{243} + \frac{80}{243} + \frac{80}{243} + \frac{40}{243} + \frac{10}{243} + \frac{1}{243}$$

If you carry on to 243 sub-samples, $n = 243$, the hypothetical frequencies will be the numerators of the six fractions.

---

* Look up the topics, *binomial theorem, probability, sampling, permutations,* and *combinations* in any college algebra.

Instead of beans, the random digits of table 1.5.1 may be used. The digits 3, 6, and 9 take the place of colored beans, while 1, 2, 4, 5, 7, and 8 stand for white: 0 is discarded when drawn. By some such convention, any desired probability may be specified.

The *binomial coefficients*, for the formation of which you will find several rules, are easily remembered by writing them down this way:

Size of Sub-sample k	Binomial Coefficients

k															
1							1		1						
2						1		2		1					
3					1		3		3		1				
4				1		4		6		4		1			
5			1		5		10		10		5		1		
6		1		6		15		20		15		6		1	
7	1		7		21		35		35		21		7		1
8	1	8		28		56		70		56		28		8	1
etc.								etc.							

In this form, called *Pascal's triangle*, each coefficient is the sum of the two just above it to the right and left. The coefficients for $k = 4$ and $k = 5$ verify those used above for the chicks and the beans. You see, the distribution of the coefficients is always symmetrical. If $p = q = 0.5$ the binomial distribution is also symmetrical, the shape approximating more and more closely that of the normal distribution as k gets larger. If the probabilities are unequal, the bimonial distribution is skewed.

In the binomial distribution, as in the normal, the mean and standard deviation are appropriate averages. Setting up the *hypothetical numbers* in the usual manner for calculation (section 8.2):

Number of Living Chicks X	Hypothetical Frequency f	fX	fX^2
0	6	0	0
1	24	24	24
2	36	72	144
3	24	72	216
4	6	24	96
Total	96	192	480

$$\mu = 192/96 = 2 \text{ chicks per lot}$$

$$\sigma = \sqrt{\frac{480 - (192)^2/96}{96}} = 1 \text{ chick per lot}$$

The symbols μ and σ for mean and standard deviation are used to distinguish these population parameters from the sample statistics, $\bar{x}$ and s. The latter, calculated from the *observed* frequencies, are 2.2188 chicks per lot and 0.920 chick per lot: we shall have little use for these statistics. Another point you will notice is that for σ, division was by $n = 96$ instead of by $n - 1 = 95$. Degrees of freedom are appropriate for computing sample statistics but not parameters.

One usually finds these averages expressed as proportions or as percentages rather than as actual numbers per lot. Thus, one reads that the proportion of living chicks expected is $\mu = 2/4 = 0.5$ with $\sigma = 0.25$; or that the percentage is 50% of living chicks with standard deviation 25%. This emancipates the averages from the sub-sample size, making those for lots of four directly comparable with similar ones for lots of any other size.

On account of mathematical relations connected with the binomial distribution, it is unnecessary to go through the calculations shown above. The parameters are got more easily from the formulas,

$$\mu = kp = (4)(0.5) = 2 \text{ chicks per lot}$$
$$\sigma = \sqrt{kpq} = \sqrt{(4)(0.5)(0.5)} = 1 \text{ chick per lot}$$

If the parameters are to be expressed as proportions or percentages, the formulas are

$$\mu = p = 0.5 = 50\%,$$
$$\sigma = \sqrt{pq/k} = \sqrt{(0.5)(0.5)/4} = 0.25 = 25\%$$

Thus, p is not only the probability of occurrence of an event but is also the population mean proportion or percentage of occurrences.

It is worth noticing that, if the sub-sample size were 16 chicks, the expected mean percentage would be the same, $p = 0.5 = 50\%$; whereas the expected standard deviation would be only,

$$\sigma = \sqrt{pq/k} = \sqrt{(0.5)(0.5)/16} = 0.125 = 12.5\%$$

The theoretical standard deviation, then, decreases as the sub-sample size increases. Really, σ is the standard error of the sub-sample mean, varying inversely as the square root of the sub-sample size—a familiar relation in measurement data.

In the whole binomially distributed sample the standard error of the mean is inversely proportional to the square root of the entire number of individuals. That is, if there are n sub-samples of k individuals each,

$$\sigma_{\bar{x}} = \sqrt{\frac{pq}{nk}} = \frac{\sigma}{\sqrt{n}},$$

again a familiar relation. For the entire distribution of chicks, the standard error in percentage is

$$\sigma_{\bar{x}} = \frac{25}{\sqrt{96}} = 2.55\%$$

This question was proposed above: may we attribute to sampling variation the discrepancy between the assumed parameter, $\mu = 50\%$, and the corresponding sample mean, $\bar{x} = 2.2188/4 = 55.74\%$? Naturally, if the sample is from a binomial distribution the test involves chi-square. Rather than use percentages, it is simpler to ask the question directly: is there a significant difference between the hypothetical number of living chicks and the observed number? The former is 50% of the total number of chicks, 50% of 384 being 192 chicks. The latter is the value of ΣfX in the sample,

$$\Sigma fX = (1)(0) + (20)(1) + (41)(2) + (25)(3) + (9)(4) = 213$$

In the usual manner,

$$\chi^2 = \frac{(213 - 192)^2}{192} + \frac{(171 - 192)^2}{192} = 4.59,$$

whose probability of occurrence is about 0.035. The sample number of surviving chicks is, therefore, significantly greater than the proposed 50%.

It is common to find t used instead of χ^2 for the test. In the case under discussion, the tests are identical provided σ is used—s might lead to an erroneous conclusion. To illustrate, we found that the standard error of the mean was

$$\sigma_{\bar{x}} = 25/\sqrt{96} = 2.55\%$$

The difference between the sample mean and the parameter is

$$55.47 - 50 = 5.47\%$$

Then, $t = 5.47/2.55 = 2.15,$

near its 0.035 level, $f = \infty$, just as chi-square was near its 0.035 point. It is interesting to notice that, in these circumstances, $t = \chi$. That is the reason the t-test is valid for this kind of enumeration statistics.

EXAMPLE 16.2.1—In the manner of section 8.2 calculate $\bar{x}$ and s for the sample of surviving chicks.

EXAMPLE 16.2.2—For the proposed sampling of beans, $p = 1/3$, $k = 5$, show that $\mu = 1.667$ and $\sigma = 1.054$ colored beans per sub-sample, or that $\mu = 33.33\%$ with $\sigma = 21.08\%$

EXAMPLE 16.2.3—It is convenient to bear in mind that the total number of individuals in a binomial sample is nk, and that the total number of occurrences of the event is ΣfX. Hence, $\bar{x} = 100(\Sigma fX)/(nk)$ per cent.

EXAMPLE 16.2.4—If 243 sub-samples of the beans ($k = 5, p = 1/3$) were drawn at random with $\bar{x} = 30.37\%$, show that $t^2 = \chi^2 = 4.80$. What conclusion about the sample would you reach?

EXAMPLE 16.2.5—You often see some such statement as this: "As the size of the sample is increased, the sample mean draws nearer and nearer to the population value." This would require chi-square to approach zero. Do you think it would?

As the sample increases in size, the binomial distribution approaches the normal, more rapidly for values of p near 0.5 than for those near 0 or 1. One consequence is that t can be used instead of table 1.3.1 for setting confidence limits. If $n = 100$, for example, and the sample contains 40 individuals with the attribute being observed, then $p = 0.4$, $q = 0.6$, and

$$40 \pm t_{.05}\sqrt{npq} = 40 \pm 1.96\sqrt{(100)(0.4)(0.6)} = 40 \pm 9.6$$

specifies the 95% confidence interval, 30.4 − 49.6. Compare this with the interval, 30 − 50, given in the table.

As another example, suppose 100 individuals having a certain attribute are drawn in a sample of 1,000. Since in the corresponding part of table 1.3.1 ratios are being used, the interval is given by

$$0.1 \pm t_{.05}\sqrt{pq/n} = 0.1 \pm 1.96\sqrt{(0.1)(0.9)/1,000} = 0.1 \pm 0.0186$$

The interval, then, is from 0.0814 to 0.1186; that is, from 8.14% to 11.86%.

16.3—Comparison of a sample distribution with the binomial.

In experimental data there is everpresent sampling variation to be considered. Under the assumption of a binomially distributed population as the source of the sample, we have already tested the significance of the deviation of the sample mean from μ. The question now to be answered is whether the entire distribution of the sample departs from the binomial. The methods are identical with those described in chapter 9.

For illustration we use the data in table 16.3.1 (3). Since these are eight-pig litters, there are nine classes, having respectively 0, 1, . . . 8 males. Let us first set up the hypothesis of equal probability of the sexes. Then

TABLE 16.3.1

Eight-Pig Litters Having Various Numbers of Males. Hypothetical Numbers, and Test of Binomial Distribution

Number Males in Litter X	Number of Litters f	Hypothetical Number	Deviation, Number − Hypothetical	(Deviation)^2	$\dfrac{\text{(Deviation)}^2}{\text{Hypothetical}}$
0	0 ⎫	0.414 ⎫	−0.414 ⎫		
1	5 ⎬14	3.312 ⎬15.320	1.688 ⎬−1.320	1.742	0.114
2	9 ⎭	11.594 ⎭	−2.594 ⎭		
3	22	23.188	−1.188	1.411	0.061
4	25	28.984	−3.984	15.872	0.548
5	26	23.188	2.812	7.907	0.341
6	14 ⎫	11.594 ⎫	2.406 ⎫		
7	4 ⎬19	3.312 ⎬15.320	0.688 ⎬ 3.680	13.542	0.884
8	1 ⎭	0.414 ⎭	0.586 ⎭		
Total	106	106.000	0.000		$\chi^2 = 1.948$

$p = 0.5$, $q = 0.5$, $k = 8$, $n = 106$, and the hypothetical frequencies are given by

$$106\ [(0.5)^8,\ 8(0.5)^7\ (0.5),\ 28(0.5)^6\ (0.5)^2,\ etc.,]$$
$$= (106)(0.5)^8\ [1,\ 8,\ 28,\ 56,\ 70,\ etc.,]$$
$$= 0.414,\ 3.312,\ 11.594,\ etc.$$

The deviations of these hypothetical numbers from actual measure the departure of the sample distribution from the binomial being considered. Is the departure significant? The appropriate test is made by means of chi-square. But since each hypothetical number should be at least as great as five, the first three and last three classes are pooled for the test. The resulting chi-square is moderate for $f = 4$. Actually, there is somewhat less deviation from expected than would be found ordinarily in random sampling.

Why four degrees of freedom? The sum, 106 litters, calculated from the sample and used in the fitting, takes one degree. Effectively, there were only five classes used, leaving four degrees of freedom for the test.

From the results of the comparison, there is no evidence against the hypothesis of a uniform probability of 50% for maleness. This is, of course, not proof that the sex ratio is 1:1. It is merely that there is not a significant departure from that binomial distribution in which $p = q$.

EXAMPLE 16.3.1—Parkes (4) collected information about sex distribution from the National Duroc Jersey Pig Record. Among 402 eight-pig litters he recorded the numbers having 0, 1, 2, ... 8 males as follows: 1, 8, 37, 81, 162, 77, 30, 5, 1. Compute $\chi^2 = 38.7$, $f = 6$. Can you explain the significant deviation from the hypothetical distribution; that is, why the probability of maleness varies significantly among the litters?

EXAMPLE 16.3.2—Ignoring the nonbinomial distribution of the sample, test the significance of the difference between the hypothetical number of males in the foregoing example, 1,608, and the number recorded in the Record, 1,581. Chi-square is 0.90. Does this throw any light on the sample distribution?

EXAMPLE 16.3.3—Test the significance of the deviation of the sample of chicks from the binomial with $p = 50\%$. Chi-square $= 7.07$, $f = 4$. The mean, you may recall, differed significantly from 50%.

EXAMPLE 16.3.4—Test the significance of the deviation of the sample number of males (439) in table 16.3.1 from the number expected (424) under the 50% hypothesis. Chi-square $= 1.06$, $f = 1$.

16.4—The test of homogeneity in a distribution of the binomial form. Often there is no theory upon which to base a hypothesis about the value of p. In that event the question raised and answered in the foregoing section has no meaning. Instead, we may wish to know whether the sample is *homogeneous*; that is, may it be a sample drawn from some binomial distribution, p unspecified? Since there is no theoretical probability, we simply take the sample mean percentage and set up a binomial distribution having that value of p. Naturally we get no test of the value of p, but we do learn if this probability may have been uniformly distributed over all the individuals.

The distribution of surviving chicks furnishes a good illustration. The evidence is strong that the hypothesis of 50% survival was not well founded (section 16.2, example 16.3.3). May the sample be a random drawing from a binomial distribution with $p = 55.47\%$, the sample mean? The successive terms of the binomial,

$$96(0.4453 + 0.5547)^4$$

are the hypothetical frequencies. These are easily calculated:

X	Powers of q	Powers of p	Binomial Coefficients	Relative Frequencies	Hypothetical Frequencies
0	0.0393		1	0.0393	3.77
1	0.0883	0.5547	4	0.1959	18.81
2	0.1983	0.3077	6	0.3661	35.15
3	0.4453	0.1707	4	0.3040	29.18
4		0.0947	1	0.0947	9.09
Total				1.0000	96.00

Place $q = 0.4453$ in the next-to-last row, and in the calculating machine. Multiply repeatedly by q until q^k is reached, recording each power in the table. Repeat for p, entering the successive powers downward in the table beginning with the second row. In the fifth column each relative frequency is the product of the three (or two) numbers to its left. As an example, in the third row,

$$(0.1983)(0.3077)(6) = 0.3661$$

The relative frequencies must add to unity. Multiplication of each of them by $n = 96$ yields the binomially distributed frequencies for $p = 55.47\%$.

The chi-square test is shown in table 16.4.1. The degrees of freedom are now only two—not only does the sample total, $n = 96$, impose a limit on the expected frequencies, but also the sample mean has been made the parameter of the binomial. In this case chi-square exceeds its 50% point but little. There is no evidence against the constancy of

TABLE 16.4.1

TEST OF HOMOGENEITY OF THE CHICK SURVIVALS

X	f	Hypothetical	Deviation	$\dfrac{\text{(Deviation)}^2}{\text{Hypothetical}}$
0	1 ⎱ 21	3.77 ⎱ 22.58	−1.58	0.11
1	20 ⎰	18.81 ⎰		
2	41	35.15	5.85	0.97
3	25	29.18	−4.18	0.60
4	9	9.09	−0.09	0.00
	96	96.00	0.00	$\chi^2 = 1.68$

the probability of survival. The population may be homogeneous, with a uniform probability estimated as 55.47%.

After two samples have been found homogeneous, it is often desired to test the significance of the difference between their means. Assuming a uniform probability in each, do these probabilities differ significantly? In table 16.4.2 are the distributions of males in five- and six-pig litters.

TABLE 16.4.2
NUMBER OF MALES IN LITTERS OF DUROC JERSEY PIGS

	Five-Pig Litters			Six-Pig Litters	
Number Males in Litter	Number Litters	Hypothetical Numbers	Number Males in Litter	Number Litters	Hypothetical Numbers
0	2⎰22	4.08⎰23.54	0	3⎰19	3.62⎰24.99
1	20⎱	19.46⎱	1	16⎱	21.37⎱
2	41	37.07	2	53	52.55
3	35	35.31	3	78	69.08
4	14⎰18	16.84⎰20.05	4	53	50.98
5	4⎱	3.21⎱	5	18⎰18	20.11⎰23.40
			6	0⎱	3.29⎱
Total	116	$\chi^2 = 0.73$		221	$\chi^2 = 3.92$
	$p = 48.79\%$			$p = 49.62\%$	

Each is homogeneous with respect to its own probability. Do these means differ significantly? The test is easily carried out in a 2 × 2 table like this:

Litters	Males	Females	Total
Five-pig	283	297	580
Six-pig	658	668	1,326
Total	941	965	1,906

$$\chi^2 = \frac{[(283)(668) - (297)(658)]^2(1,906)}{(580)(1,326)(941)(965)} = 0.111$$

For $f = 1$, this is a smaller value of chi-square than usual. The small difference between the two percentages,

$$49.62 - 48.79 = 0.83\%,$$

is not significant.

If a pooled value of p, 941/1 906 = 49.3704, is used to compute the standard deviation, $\sqrt{pq(1/n_1 + 1/n_2)} = 0.0249$ this test may be carried through with t in the manner of the last section. That is, χ with one degree of freedom is the same as t with $f = \infty$.

What shall be done with samples that are not homogeneous? If there is no uniform probability of occurrence, and if nothing is known of the laws governing the probability, any conclusions are based on flimsy evidence. There is no assurance that, if the experiment were repeated, the same set of probabilities would be existent. If one doesn't know why the probabilities change or in what manner, he can set up no experimental controls. The first step must be toward improved knowledge of the techniques of selecting and handling the experimental material. Only after the sources of variation are discovered may valid comparisons be made.

Nevertheless, there are times when one wishes to make a test of significance of the difference between means despite heterogeneity. If means differ significantly even in the face of large variation, perhaps the difference represents some population fact. The method used to make the test must be sensitive to the variability present. Probably the best is to calculate the standard deviation of each set in the manner of section 8.2, then test significance as in section 8.8. The assumption of normal distribution there made is more flexible than the assumption of constant p.

You may find interest in contrasting the methods of treating the binomial distribution and the normal. Each has two parameters. A test of significance of sample deviation from theoretical distribution is available in each. But there is a single, basic normal distribution, the relative frequencies being set out in table 8.8.1, whereas there is a separate binomial for each p and k. It follows that tables of the binomial distributions would be clumsy—it is easier to compute each time from the parameters.

EXAMPLE 16.4.1—Calculate chi-square for each of the samples of table 16.4.2.

EXAMPLE 16.4.2—Decker and Andre (1) exposed adult chinch bugs at a temperature of $-8.5°$ C. for 15 minutes, then counted the number dead in 100 sub-samples of 10 bugs. The numbers of sub-samples having 0, 1, 2, . . . 7 dead were 4, 21, 22, 28, 14, 8, 2, 1. No sub-sample had 8 or more dead. Is there a significant lack of homogeneity for probability of death? Chi-square $= 2.89, f = 8$.

EXAMPLE 16.4.3—The sample probability of maleness in example 16.3.1 is 49.160%. Is the sample homogeneous with respect to this percentage? Chi-square $= 38.15, f = 5$.

EXAMPLE 16.4.4—In example 16.3.4 the sample proportion of males in table 16.3.1 was found to be not significantly different from 0.5. Is the sample homogeneous with respect to the probability 0.5177? Chi-square $= 0.73, f = 3$.

EXAMPLE 16.4.5—Using the methods of chapter 8, test the significance of the difference between the mean percentages of males in the samples of table 16.3.1 and example 16.3.1. Since the latter departs significantly from binomial distribution, the use of chi-square in a 2 × 2 table is inappropriate. Ans. $t = 0.88$.

EXAMPLE 16.4.6—Test the significance of the difference between the percentages of males in the five- and six-pig litters of table 16.4.2, using t instead of χ^2. Your result should be $t = \chi = \sqrt{0.111}$.

16.5—The Poisson distribution. Like the binomial, this is the distribution of a *discrete* or *discontinuous* variable arising from enumeration, usually only the integral values occurring. Also, there is the idea of the uniform probability of the occurrence of some event, but this probability, ordinarily small, is somewhat ill defined. In fact, the size of the sub-sample, though supposed to be constant, is usually not known. It is large, however, and must be confined within reasonably narrow limits.

In contrast with both the binomial and the normal, the Poisson distribution is defined by a single parameter, the mean. The variance is equal to the mean.

The Poisson distribution can be shown to be a limiting form of the binomial in which p is very small. The distribution is valuable in its own right, however, quite independent of this relation to the binomial.

If μ is the expected mean frequency of occurrence of some event in the population of sub-samples, and if the frequency follows the Poisson distribution, then the event will occur 0, 1, 2, . . . times in sub-samples with *relative* frequencies equal to the successive terms of this sequence,

$$\frac{1}{e^\mu}, \frac{\mu}{e^\mu}, \frac{\mu^2}{2e^\mu}, \frac{\mu^3}{(2)(3)e^\mu}, \frac{\mu^4}{(2)(3)(4)e^\mu}, \ldots,$$

where e, the base of the natural logarithm, is an irrational number whose value is about 2.718, and whose logarithm (base 10) is 0.434295 very nearly. The hypothetical frequencies are products of these relative frequencies by the number of sub-samples, n.

The fitting of a Poisson distribution to a sample will be illustrated by the data on noxious weed seeds (2) in table 16.5.1. The sub-samples are specified as weighing $\frac{1}{4}$ ounce. Naturally, the number of seeds in the sub-sample varies somewhat, but is large compared with the number of noxious weed seeds. The Poisson distribution, like the binomial, is built

TABLE 16.5.1

DISTRIBUTION OF 98 QUARTER-OUNCE SUB-SAMPLES OF *Phleum pratense* CLASSIFIED BY NUMBER OF NOXIOUS WEED SEEDS. FITTED POISSON DISTRIBUTION. TEST OF SIGNIFICANCE

Numbers of Noxious Weed Seeds	Number of Sub-samples f	Hypothetical Numbers	Deviations From Expected	$\frac{(\text{Deviations})^2}{\text{Hypothetical}}$
0	3	4.78	−1.78	0.663
1	17	14.44	2.56	0.454
2	26	21.81	4.19	0.805
3	16	21.96	−5.96	1.618
4	18	16.58	1.42	0.122
5	9	10.02	−1.02	0.104
6	3 ⎫	5.04 ⎫		
7	5 ⎬ 9	2.18 ⎪		
8	0 ⎪	0.82 ⎪		
9	1 ⎭	0.28 ⎬ 8.41	0.59	0.041
10		0.08 ⎪		
More		0.01 ⎭		
Total	98	98.00	0.00	$\chi^2 = 3.807$

on the assumption that the probability that any seed is that of a noxious weed is constant throughout the population. We shall first fit the theoretical distribution, then test the significance of the deviation of the sample.

The first step is the calculation of the sample mean in the manner of section 8.2:

$$\bar{x} = (\Sigma fX)/(\Sigma f) = 296/98 = 3.02041 \text{ noxious weed seeds per sub-sample}$$

We then set up a Poisson distribution with this mean as its parameter, μ. A distribution with some theoretical mean might be fitted, but that would be unusual. Ordinarily the sample mean is used. We are testing homogeneity only—is there a uniform probability of occurrence of weed seeds throughout the sample?

The remainder of the calculation below is by means of logarithms. The successive steps are rather evident. After the logarithms of the first two hypothetical numbers are reached, those of the successive numbers are got by (i) adding the logarithm of μ, and (ii) subtracting the logarithm of the successive integers beginning with 2. You can see this by writing the hypothetical numbers in this way:

$$\frac{n}{e^{\mu}}, \quad \frac{n\mu}{e^{\mu}}, \quad \left(\frac{n\mu}{e^{\mu}}\right)\left(\frac{\upsilon}{2}\right), \quad \left(\frac{n\mu^2}{2e^{\mu}}\right)\left(\frac{\mu}{3}\right), \cdots$$

The calculations proceed thus:

Symbol	Logarithm	Hypothetical Number
$n = 98$	1.99123	
e^{μ} $(3.02041)(0.434295) =$	1.31175	
n/e^{μ}	0.67948	4.78
$\mu = 3.02041$	0.48007	
$\mu n/e^{\mu}$	$\overline{1}.15955$	14.44
μ	0.48007	
	$\overline{1}.63962$	
2	0.30103	
$\mu^2 n/2e^{\mu}$	$\overline{1}.33859$	21.81
μ	0.48007	
	$\overline{1}.81866$	
3	0.47712	
$\mu^3 n/(2)(3)e^{\mu}$	$\overline{1}.34154$	21.96
μ	0.48007	
	$\overline{1}.82161$	
4	0.60206	
$\mu^4 n/(2)(3)(4)e^{\mu}$	$\overline{1}.21955$	16.58
μ	0.48007	
	$\overline{1}.69962$	
5	0.69897	
	$\overline{1}.00065$	10.02

μ	0.48007	
6	$\overline{1.48072}$	
	0.77815	
	$\overline{0.70257}$	5.04
μ	0.48007	
7	$\overline{1.18264}$	
	0.84510	
	$\overline{0.33754}$	2.18
μ	0.48007	
8	$10\overline{.81761} - 10$	
	0.90309	
	$\overline{9.91452} - 10$	0.82
μ	0.48007	
9	$10\overline{.39459} - 10$	
	0.95424	
	$\overline{9.44035} - 10$	0.28
μ	0.48007	
10	$\overline{9.92042} - 10$	
	1.	
	$\overline{8.92042} - 10$	0.08
Total		$\overline{97.99}$

From the logarithm of 98 is subtracted the logarithm of e^μ which is $\mu\log e = (3.02041)(0.434295)$. The difference is the logarithm of the quotient, the anti-logarithm being the hypothetical number of sub-samples containing no weed seeds. Next is added the logarithm of 3.02041 to get the logarithm of the next hypothetical number, 14.44. Thereafter the logarithm of μ is added each time while the logarithm of the next higher integer is subtracted. The process continues till the hypothetical numbers become smaller than 5. We carried on to illustrate the process, but had to recombine for the test in table 16.5.1.

Chi-square is computed as usual. How many degrees of freedom are there? The sample mean has been set up as the parameter of the distribution, and the sample number of sub-samples, 98, is used to calculate the expected numbers remaining after the fifth (or tenth) class. Hence two degrees of freedom must be deducted from the effective number of classes, leaving $f = 5$ for testing chi-square. Clearly, the sample does not depart significantly from the Poisson distribution. The 98 bags of seeds from which the sub-samples were taken may constitute a population with Poisson distribution. The probability that any randomly selected seed be that of a noxious weed may be uniform throughout.

The variance in the theoretical distribution is the same as the sample mean, 3.0204. Hence $s = \sqrt{3.0204} = 1.738$ seeds per sub-sample. Obviously, the standard deviation has different relations to the Poisson distribution than to the normal. For example, it cannot be said that 68.27% of the individuals in the unsymmetrical Poisson distribution lie within the interval, $\mu \pm \sigma$. However, if the entire sample of 98 quarter ounces is considered as a unit with 296 weed seeds, it may be thought of as a single sample drawn from a population whose mean is estimated as 296 and whose variance is therefore 296. Poisson populations with such large means are distributed almost normally. Hence, for practical purposes this large sample may be treated as though drawn from a normal population whose mean is estimated as $\bar{x} = 296$ with standard error, $s_{\bar{x}} = \sqrt{296} = 17.2$ weed seeds. The numbers of weed seeds in two such samples may then be compared, the difference being tested for significance in the manner of the next section.

EXAMPLE 16.5.1—Leggatt counted various other weed seeds in his 98 sub-samples. Numbers of two genera follow:

Genus	Number of Seeds in Sub-sample								Chi-square	P
	0	1	2	3	4	5	6	7		
Potentilla	37	32	16	9	2	0	1	1	2.931	24%
Carex	36	36	23	2	1				4.476	11%

EXAMPLE 16.5.2—The chinch bug data of example 16.4.2 are well adapted to binomial fitting. It may be interesting to apply the Poisson distribution. Chi-square $= 4.634, f = 5$.

EXAMPLE 16.5.3—If you have the book available, look at table 39 in Biometrika's (5) collection and compare the distribution for $\mu = 3.0$ with that of table 16.5.1. Make a rough check on your work in example 16.5.2 by use of the same table.

EXAMPLE 16.5.4—If μ is large, the Poisson distribution is approximately normal. To verify this, work out the distribution for $\mu = 15$, or take it from Biometrika's table. Group the hypothetical frequencies for $n = 100$ as follows:

Class mark	3	6	9	12	15	18	21	24	27
Frequency	1	1	10	24	30	22	9	2	1

Using the method of section 8.6, show that $g_1 = 0.094 \pm 0.24$ and $g_2 = 0.46 \pm 0.48$.

EXAMPLE 16.5.5—The sample of table 16.5.1 may be looked upon as a single sub-sample of 24.5 ounces drawn from a Poisson population with $\mu = 296$ noxious weed seeds. The variance of this mean is 296. Comparing this with the foregoing example, you see why large means from Poisson populations may be considered as normally distributed.

16.6—Comparison of means in samples from Poisson distributions. A moment's thought will make it clear that means from Poisson distributions cannot be compared like those from the binomial. The records give the number of times the event occurs but not the times it fails. For small samples a chi-square method of testing was explained in section 9.12. But since large sample means drawn from a Poisson population are distributed almost normally, it turns out that the appropriate method of testing differences is that of section 8.8.   An example will recall the method.

"Student" (6) gave two distributions of yeast cells counted in the 400 squares of a haemacytometer, table 16.6.1. The values of chi-square show that they may well be samples from Poisson distributions. The difference between the means is $720 - 529 = 191$ yeast cells per sample. To test

TABLE 16.6.1

Two Samples of Yeast Cells Counted in 400 Squares of a Haemacytometer
Fitted Poisson Distributions

Sample		Number Squares Having Specified Number of Cells										Mean	Chi-square
		0	1	2	3	4	5	6	7	8	9		
1	Observed	103	143	98	42	8	4	2				529	3.177
	Hypothetical	106	141	93	41	14	5						
2	Observed	75	103	121	54	30	13	2	1	0	1	720	7.073
	Hypothetical	66	119	107	64	29			15				

significance, we have the two variances, the same as the means, 720 and 529.   From these, the standard error of the mean difference is

$$\sqrt{(720 + 529)} = 35.3$$

Hence, $t = 191/35.3 = 5.41$, strong evidence that the two samples are not drawn from the same population.

EXAMPLE 16.6.1—Calculate the hypothetical numbers in table 16.6.1, together with the values of chi-square.

EXAMPLE 16.6.2—"Student" recorded one sample of yeast cells with this distribution:

Number of yeast cells	0	1	2	3	4	5
Number of squares	213	128	37	18	3	1

Compute $\chi^2 = 9.683, f = 2$. This departs significantly from Poisson distribution.

EXAMPLE 16.6.3—Using the methods of chapter 8, test the significance of the difference between the means of the two samples in table 16.6.1.   You would be assuming that mean differences are normally distributed, but you would avoid the formula, $\bar{x} = s^2$.   Although this formula is justified in the samples of table 16.6.1, it would not be appropriate if the samples departed significantly from Poisson distribution.   Ans. $t = 5.30$.

EXAMPLE 16.6.4—In table 16.6.1, carry through the test of significance by comparing the mean numbers of yeast cells *per square*, 1.3225 and 1.800.   You should reach the same value of t.

REFERENCES

1. GEORGE C. DECKER and FLOYD ANDRE. Iowa State Journal of Science, 10:403 (1936).

2. C W. LEGGATT. Comptes rendus de l'Association Internationale d'Essais de Semences, 5:27 (1935).

3. HUGH C. McPHEE. Journal of Agricultural Research, 34:715 (1927).

4. A. S. PARKES. Biometrika, 15:373 (1923).

5. E. S. PEARSON and H. O. HARTLEY. Biometrika Tables for Statisticians, Vol. 1. Cambridge University Press, Cambridge, England (1954).

6. "STUDENT." Biometrika, 5:351 (1907).

CHAPTER 17

Design and Analysis of Sampling

by WILLIAM G. COCHRAN

17.1—Populations. In the 1908 paper in which he discovered the *t*-test, "Student" opened with the following words: "Any experiment may be regarded as forming an individual of a *population* of experiments which might be performed under the same conditions. A series of experiments is a sample drawn from this population.

"Now any series of experiments is only of value in so far as it enables us to form a judgment as to the statistical constants of the population to which the experiments belong."

From the previous chapters in this book, this way of looking at data should now be familiar. The data obtained in a biological experiment are subject to variation, so that an estimate made from the data is also subject to variation and is, hence, to some degree uncertain. You can visualize, however, that if you could repeat the experiment many times, putting all the results together, the estimate would ultimately settle down to some unchanging value which may be called the true or definitive result of the experiment. The purpose of the statistical analysis of an experiment is to reveal what the data can tell about this true result. The tests of significance and confidence limits which have appeared throughout this book are tools for making statements about the population of experiments of which your data are a sample.

In such problems the sample is concrete, but the population may appear somewhat hypothetical. It is the population of experiments that might be performed, under the same conditions, if you possessed the necessary resources, time, and interest.

In this chapter we turn to situations in which the population is concrete and definite, and the problem is to obtain some desired information about it. Examples are as follows:

Population	*Information Wanted*
Ears of corn in a field	Average moisture content
Seeds in a large batch	Percentage germination
Water in a reservoir	Concentration of certain bacteria
Third-grade children in a school	Average weight

If the population is small, it is sometimes convenient to obtain the information by collecting the data for the whole of the population. More frequently, time and money can be saved by measuring only a sample drawn from the population. When the measurement is destructive, sampling is of course unavoidable.

This chapter presents some methods for selecting a sample and for estimating population characteristics from the data obtained in the sample. During the past 20 years, sampling has come to be relied upon by a great variety of agencies, including government bureaus, market research organizations, and public opinion polls. Concurrently, much has been learned both about the theory and practice of sampling, and a number of books devoted to sample survey methods have appeared (2, 3, 4, 11, 13). In this chapter we explain the general principles of sampling and show how to handle some of the simpler problems that are common in biological work. For more complex problems, references will be given.

17.2—A simple example.   In the early chapters of this book, you drew samples so as to examine the amount of variation in results from one sample to another and to verify some important results in statistical theory. The same method will illustrate modern ideas about the selection of samples from given populations.

Suppose the population consists of $N = 6$ members, denoted by the letters a to f. The 6 values of the quantity that is being measured are as follows: a 1; b 2; c 4; d 6; e 7; f 16. The total for this population is 36. A sample of 3 members is to be drawn in order to estimate this total.

One procedure already familiar to you is to write the letters a to f on beans or slips of paper, mix them in some container, and draw out 3 letters. In sample survey work, this method of drawing is called *simple random sampling*, or sometimes *random sampling without replacement* (because we do not put a letter back in the receptacle after it has been drawn). Obviously, simple random sampling gives every member an equal chance of being in the sample. It may be shown that the method also gives every combination of three different letters (e.g., *aef* or *cde*) an equal chance of constituting the sample.

How good an estimate of the population total do we obtain by simple random sampling? We are not quite ready to answer this question. Although we know how the sample is to be drawn, we have not yet discussed how the population total is to be estimated from the results of the sample. Since the sample contains 3 members and the population contains 6 members, the simplest procedure is to multiply the sample total by 2, and this is the procedure that will be adopted. You should note that any sampling plan contains two parts—a rule for drawing the sample and a rule for making the estimates from the results of the sample.

We can now write down all possible samples of size 3, make the estimate from each sample, and see how close these estimates lie to the true value of 36. There are 20 possible samples. Their results appear in table

17.2.1, where the successive columns show the composition of the sample, the sample total, the estimated population total, and the error of estimate (estimate *minus* true value).

Some samples, e.g., *abf* and *cde*, do very well, while others like *abc* give poor estimates. Since we do not know in any individual instance whether we will be lucky or unlucky in the choice of a sample, we appraise any sampling plan by looking at its *average* performance.

TABLE 17.2.1

RESULTS FOR ALL POSSIBLE SIMPLE RANDOM SAMPLES OF SIZE 3

Sample	Sample Total	Estimate of Population Total	Error of Estimate	Sample	Sample Total	Estimate of Population Total	Error of Estimate
abc	7	14	−22	*bcd*	12	24	−12
abd	9	18	−18	*bce*	13	26	−10
abe	10	20	−16	*bcf*	22	44	+ 8
abf	19	38	+ 2	*bde*	15	30	− 6
acd	11	22	−14	*bdf*	24	48	+12
ace	12	24	−12	*bef*	25	50	+14
acf	21	42	+ 6	*cde*	17	34	− 2
ade	14	28	− 8	*cdf*	26	52	+16
adf	23	46	+10	*cef*	27	54	+18
aef	24	48	+12	*def*	29	58	+22
				Average	18	36	0

The average of the errors of estimate, taking account of their signs, is called the *bias* of the estimate (or more generally of the sampling plan). A positive bias implies that the sampling plan gives estimates that are on the whole too high; a negative bias, too low. From table 17.2.1 it is evident that this plan gives unbiased estimates, since the average of the 20 estimates is exactly 36 and consequently the errors of estimate add to zero. With simple random sampling this result holds for any population and any size of sample. Estimates that are unbiased are a desirable feature of a sampling plan. On the other hand, a plan that gives a small bias is not ruled out of consideration if it has other attractive features.

As a measure of the accuracy of the sampling plan we use the variance of the estimates taken about the true population value. This variance is

$$\frac{\Sigma(\text{Error of estimate})^2}{20} = \frac{3504}{20} = 175.2$$

The divisor 20 is used, instead of the divisor 19 with which you have become familiar, this being a common convention among writers on sample surveys. To sum up, this plan is unbiased and has a standard error of estimate of $\sqrt{175.2} = 13.2$. This standard error amounts to 37% of the true population total; evidently the plan is not very accurate for this population.

In simple random sampling the selection of the sample is left to the luck of the draw. No use is made of any knowledge that we may possess about the members of the population. Given such knowledge, we should be able to improve upon simple random sampling by using the knowledge to guide us in the selection of the sample. Much of the recent research on sample survey methods has been directed towards taking advantage of available information about the population to be sampled.

By way of illustration, suppose that before planning the sample we expect that f will give a much higher value than any other member in the population. How can we use this information? It is clear that the estimate from the sample will depend to a considerable extent on whether f falls in the sample or not. This statement can be verified from table 17.2.1; every sample containing f gives an overestimate and every sample without f gives an underestimate.

It seems best, then, to make sure that f appears in every sample. We can do this by dividing the population into two parts or *strata*. Stratum I, which consists of f alone, is completely measured. In stratum II, containing a, b, c, d, and e, we take a simple random sample of size 2 in order to keep the total sample size equal to 3.

Some forethought is needed in deciding how to estimate the population total. To use twice the sample total, as was done previously, gives too much weight to f and, as already pointed out, will always produce an overestimate of the true total. We can handle this problem by treating the two strata separately. For stratum I we know the total (16) correctly, since we always measure f. For stratum II, where 2 members are measured out of 5, the natural procedure is to multiply the sample total in that stratum by 5/2, or 2.5. Hence the appropriate estimate of the population total is

$$16 + 2.5(\text{Sample total in stratum II})$$

TABLE 17.2.2
RESULTS FOR ALL POSSIBLE STRATIFIED RANDOM SAMPLES WITH THE UNEQUAL
SAMPLING FRACTIONS DESCRIBED IN TEXT

Sample	Sample Total in Stratum II (T_2)	Estimate $16 + 2.5\,T_2$	Error of Estimate
abf	3	23.5	−12.5
acf	5	28.5	− 7.5
adf	7	33.5	− 2.5
aef	8	36.0	0.0
bcf	6	31.0	− 5.0
bdf	8	36.0	0.0
bef	9	38.5	+ 2.5
cdf	10	41.0	+ 5 0
cef	11	43.5	+ 7.5
def	13	48.5	+12.5
Average		36.0	0.0

These estimates are shown for the 10 possible samples in table 17.2.2. Again we note that the estimate is unbiased. Its variance is

$$\frac{\Sigma(\text{Error of estimate})^2}{10} = \frac{487.50}{10} = 48.75$$

The standard error is 7.0 or 19% of the true total. This is a marked improvement over the standard error of 13.2 that was obtained with simple random sampling.

This sampling plan goes by the name of *stratified random sampling with unequal sampling fractions*. The last part of the title denotes the fact that stratum I is completely sampled, whereas stratum II is sampled at a rate of 2 units out of 5, or 40%. Stratification allows us to divide the population into sub-populations or strata that are less variable than the original population, and to sample different parts of the population at different rates when this seems advisable. It is discussed more fully in sections 17.8 and 17.9.

EXAMPLE 17.2.1—In the preceding example, suppose you expect that both e and f will give high values. You decide that the sample shall consist of e, f, and one member drawn at random from a, b, c, d. Show how to obtain an unbiased estimate of the population total and show that the standard error of this estimate is 7.7. (This sampling plan is not as accurate as the plan in which f alone was placed in a separate stratum, because the actual value for e is not very high.)

EXAMPLE 17.2.2—If previous information suggests that f will be high, d and e moderate, and a, b, and c small, we might try stratified sampling with 3 strata. The sample consists of f, either d or e, and one chosen from a, b, and c. Work out the unbiased estimate of the population total for each of the 6 possible samples and show that its standard error is 3.9.

17.3—Probability sampling. The preceding examples were intended to introduce you to *probability sampling*. This is a general name given to sampling plans in which

(i) every member of the population has a known probability of being included in the sample,

(ii) the sample is drawn by some method of random selection consistent with these probabilities,

(iii) we take account of these probabilities of selection in making the estimates from the sample.

Note that the probability of selection need not be equal for all members of the population: it is sufficient that these probabilities be known. In the first example in the previous section, each member of the population had an equal chance of being in the sample, and each member of the sample received an equal weight in estimating the population total. But in the second example, member f was given a probability 1 of appearing in the sample, as against 2/5 for the rest of the population. This inequality in the probabilities of selection was compensated for by assigning a weight 5/2 to these other members when making the estimate. The use of unequal probabilities produces a substantial gain in precision for some types of population (see section 17.9).

Probability sampling has several advantages. By probability theory it is possible to study the biases and the standard errors of the estimates from different sampling plans. In this way much has been learned about the scope, advantages, and limitations of each plan. This information helps greatly in selecting a suitable plan for a particular sampling job. As will be seen later, most probability sampling plans also enable the standard error of the estimate, and confidence limits for the true population value, to be computed from the results of the sample. Thus, when a probability sample has been taken, we have some idea as to how accurate the estimates are.

Probability sampling is by no means the only way of selecting a sample. An alternative method is to ask someone who has studied the population to point out "average" or "typical" members, and then confine the sample to these members. When the population is highly variable and the sample is small, this method will often give more accurate estimates than probability sampling. Another method is to restrict the sampling to those members that are conveniently accessible. If bales of goods are stacked tightly in a warehouse, it is difficult to get at the inside bales of the pile and one is tempted to confine attention to the outside bales. In many biological problems it is hard to see how a workable probability sample can be devised, as for instance in estimating the number of house flies in a town, or of field mice in a wood, or of plankton in the ocean.

One drawback of these alternative methods is that when the sample has been obtained, there is no way of knowing how accurate the estimate is. Members of the population picked out by an expert as typical may be more or less atypical. Outside bales may or may not be similar to interior bales. Probability sampling formulas for the standard error of the estimate or for confidence limits do not apply to these methods. Consequently, it is wise to use probability sampling unless there is a clear case that this is not feasible or is prohibitively expensive.

17.4—Listing the population. In order to apply probability sampling, we must have some way of subdividing the population into units, called *sampling units*, which form the basis for the selection of the sample. The sampling units must be distinct and non-overlapping, and they must together constitute the whole of the population. Further, in order to make some kind of random selection of sampling units, we must be able to number or *list* all the units. As will be seen, we need not always write down the complete list but we must be in a position to construct it. Listing is easily accomplished when the population consists of 5,000 cards neatly arranged in a file, or 300 ears of corn lying on a bench, or the trees in a small orchard. But the subdivision of a population into sampling units that can be listed sometimes presents a difficult practical problem.

Although we have spoken of the population as being concrete and definite, there may be some vagueness about the population which does not become apparent until a sampling is being planned. Before we can come to grips with a population of farms, or of nursing homes, we must define a farm or a nursing home. The definition may require much study and the final decision may have to be partly arbitrary. Two principles to keep in mind are that the definition should be appropriate to the purpose of the sampling and that it should be usable in the field (i.e., the person collecting the information should be able to tell what is in and what is out of the population as defined).

Sometimes the available listings of farms, creameries, or nursing homes are deficient. The list may be out of date, having some members that no longer belong to our population and omitting some that do belong. The list may be based on a definition different from that which we wish to use for our population. These points should be carefully checked before using any list. It often pays to spend considerable effort in revising a list to make it complete and satisfactory, since this may be more economical than to construct a new list. Where a list covers only part of the population, one procedure is to sample this part by means of the list, and construct a separate method of sampling for the unlisted part of the population. Stratified sampling is useful in this situation: all listed members are assigned to one stratum and unlisted members to another.

Preparing a list where none is available may require ingenuity and hard work. To cite an easy example, suppose that we wish to take a number of crop samples, each 2 ft. $\times$ 2 ft., from a plot 200 ft. $\times$ 100 ft. Divide the length of the plot into 100 sections, each 2 ft., and the breadth into 50 sections, each 2 ft. We thus set up a coordinate system that divides the whole plot into 100 $\times$ 50 or 5,000 quadrats, each 2 ft. $\times$ 2 ft. To select a quadrat by simple random sampling, we draw a random number between 1 and 100 and another random number between 1 and 50. These coordinates locate the corner of the quadrat that is farthest from the origin of our system. However, the problem becomes harder if the plot measures 163 ft. $\times$ 100 ft., and much harder if instead of a plot we have an irregularly shaped field. Further, if we have to select a number of areas each 6 in. $\times$ 6 in. from a large field, giving every area an equal chance of selection, the time spent in selecting and locating the sample areas becomes substantial. Partly for this reason, methods of systematic sampling (section 17.7) have come to be favored in routine soil sampling (8).

Another illustration is a method for sampling (for botanical or chemical analysis) the produce of a small plot that is already cut and bulked. The bulk is separated into two parts and a coin is tossed (or a random number drawn) to decide which part shall contain the sample. This part is then separated into two, and the process continues until a sample of about the desired size is obtained. At any stage it is good practice to make the two parts as alike as possible, provided this is done before the coin is tossed. A quicker method, of course, is to grab a handful of about the desired size; this is sometimes satisfactory but sometimes proves to be biased.

In urban sampling in the United States, the city block is often used as a sampling unit, a listing of the blocks being made from a map of the town. For extensive rural sampling, county maps have been divided into areas with boundaries that can be identified in the field and certain of these areas are selected to constitute the sample. The name *area sampling* has come to be associated with these and other methods in which the sampling unit is an area of land. Frequently the principal advantage of area sampling, although not the only one, is that it solves the problem of providing a listing of the population by sampling units.

In many sampling problems there is more than one type or size of sampling unit into which the population can be divided. For instance, in soil sampling in which borings are taken, the size and shape of the borer can be chosen by the sampler. The same is true of the frame used to mark out the area of land that is cut in crop sampling. In a dental survey of the fifth-grade school children in a city, we might regard the child as the sampling unit and select a sample of children from the combined school registers for the city. It would be administratively simpler, however, to take the school as the sampling unit, drawing a sample of schools and examining every fifth-grade child in the selected schools. This approach, in which the sampling unit consists of some natural group (the school) formed from the smaller units in which we are interested (the children), goes by the name of *cluster sampling*.

If you are faced with a choice between different sampling units, the guiding rule is to try to select the one that returns the greatest prec sion for the available resources. For a fixed size of sample (e.g., 5% of the population), a large sampling unit usually gives less accurate results than a small unit, although there are exceptions. To counterbalance this, it is generally cheaper and easier to take a 5% sample with a large sampling unit than with a small one. A thorough comparison between two units is likely to require a special investigation, in which both sampling errors and costs (or times required) are computed for each unit.

17.5—Simple random sampling. In this and later sections, some of the best-known methods for selecting a probability sample will be presented. The goal is to use a sampling plan that will give the highest precision for the resources to be expended, or, equivalently, that will attain a desired degree of precision with the minimum expenditure of resources. It is worth while to become familiar with the principal plans, since they are designed to take advantage of any information that you may have about the structure of the population and about the costs of taking the sample.

In section 17.2 you have already been introduced to *simple random sampling*. This is a method in which the members of the sample are drawn independently with equal probabilities. In order to illustrate the use of a table of random numbers for drawing a random sample, suppose that the population contains $N = 372$ members and that a sample of size $n = 10$ is wanted. Select a 3-digit starting number from table 1.5.1, say the number is 539 in row 11 of columns 80–82. Read down the column and pick out the first ten 3-digit numbers that do not exceed 372. These are 334, 365, 222, 345, 245, 272, 075, 038, 127, and 112. The sample consists of the sampling units that carry these numbers in your listing of the population. If any number appears more than once, ignore it on subsequent appearances and proceed until ten *different* numbers have been found.

If the first digit in N is 1, 2, or 3, this method requires you to skip many numbers in the table because they are too large. (In the above example we had to cover 27 numbers in order to find 10 for the sample.) This does not matter if there are plenty of random numbers. An alternative method is to use all 3-digit numbers up to $2 \times 372 = 744$. Starting at the same place, the first 10 numbers that do not exceed 744 are 539, 334, 615, 736, 365, 222, 345, 660, 431, and 427. Now subtract 372 from all numbers larger than 372. This gives, for the sample, 167, 334, 243, 364, 365, 222, 345, 288, 59, and 55. With $N = 189$, for instance, we can make use of all numbers up to $5 \times 189 = 945$ by this device, subtracting 189 or 378 or 567 or 756 as the case may be.

As mentioned previously, simple random sampling leaves the selection of the sample entirely to chance. It is often a satisfactory method when the population is not highly variable and, in particular, when estimating proportions that are likely to lie between 20% and 80%. On the other hand, if you have any knowledge of the variability in the population, such as that certain segments of it are likely to give higher responses than others, one of the methods to be described later may be more precise.

If $Y_i (i = 1, 2, \ldots N)$ denotes the variable that is being studied, the standard deviation, σ, of the population is defined as

$$\sigma = \sqrt{\frac{\Sigma (Y_i - \bar{Y})^2}{N - 1}},$$

where $\bar{Y}$ is the population mean of the Y_i and the sum Σ is taken over all sampling units in the population.

The standard error of the mean of a simple random sample of size n is:

$$\sigma_{\bar{y}} = \frac{\sigma}{\sqrt{n}} \sqrt{(1 - \phi)},$$

where $\phi = n/N$ is the *sampling fraction*, i.e., the fraction of the population that is included in the sample. (The sampling fraction is commonly denoted by the symbol f, but ϕ is used here to avoid confusion with our previous use of f for degrees of freedom.)

The term $\sigma/\sqrt{n}$ is already familiar to you: this is the usual formula for the standard error of a sample mean. The second factor, $\sqrt{(1 - \phi)}$, is known as the *finite population correction*. It enters because we are sampling from a population of finite size, N, instead of from an infinite population as is assumed in the usual theory. Note that this term makes the standard error zero when $n = N$, as it should do, since we have then measured every unit in the population. In practical applications the finite population correction is close to 1 and can be omitted when n/N is less than 10%, i.e., when the sample comprises less than 10% of the population.

This result is remarkable. For a large population with a fixed amount of variability (a given value of σ), the standard error of the mean depends mainly on the size of sample and only to a minor extent on the fraction of the population that is sampled. For given σ, a sample of 100 is almost as precise when the population size is 200,000 as when the population size is 20,000 or 2,000. Intuitively, some people feel that one cannot possibly get accurate results from a sample of 100 out of a population of 200,000, because only a tiny fraction of the population has been measured. Actually, whether the sampling plan is accurate or not depends primarily on the size of $\sigma/\sqrt{n}$. This shows why sampling can bring about a great reduction in the amount of measurement needed.

For the *estimated* standard error of the sample mean we have

$$s_{\bar{y}} = \frac{s}{\sqrt{n}} \sqrt{(1 - \phi)},$$

where s is the standard deviation of the sample, calculated in the usual way.

If the sample is used to estimate the population *total* of the variable under study, the estimate is $N\bar{y}$ and its standard error is

$$s_{N\bar{y}} = \frac{Ns}{\sqrt{n}} \sqrt{(1 - \phi)}$$

In simple random sampling for attributes, where every member of the sample is classified into one of two classes, we take

$$s_p = \sqrt{\frac{pq}{n}} \sqrt{(1 - \phi)}$$

where p is the proportion of the sample that lies in one of the classes. Suppose that 50 families are picked at random from a list of 432 families who possess telephones and that 10 of the families report that they are listening to a certain radio program. Then $p = 0.2$, $q = 0.8$ and

$$s_p = \sqrt{\frac{(0.2)(0.8)}{50}} \sqrt{\left(1 - \frac{50}{432}\right)} = 0.053$$

If we ignore the finite population correction, we find $s_p = 0.057$.

Note that the formula for s_p holds only if each unit is classified as a whole into one of the two classes. If you are using cluster sampling and are classifying individual elements within each cluster, a different formula for s_p must be used. For instance, in estimating the percentage of diseased plants in a field from a sample of 360 plants, the formula above holds if the plants were selected independently and at random. To save time in the field, however, we might have chosen 40 areas, each consisting of 3 plants in each of 3 neighboring rows. With this method the area (a cluster of 9 plants) is the sampling unit. If the distribution of disease in the field were extremely patchy, it might happen that every area had either all 9 plants diseased or no plants diseased. In this event the sample of 40 areas would be no more precise than a sample of 40 independently chosen plants, and we would be deceiving ourselves badly if we thought that we had a binomial sample of 360 plants.

The correct procedure for computing s_p is simple. Calculate p separately for each area (or sampling unit) and apply to these p's the previous formula for continuous variates. That is, if p_i is the percentage diseased in the ith area, the sample standard deviation is

$$s = \sqrt{\frac{\Sigma (p_i - p)^2}{(n-1)}},$$

where n is now the number of areas (cluster units). Then

$$s_p = \frac{s}{\sqrt{n}}\sqrt{(1-\phi)}$$

For instance, suppose that the numbers of diseased plants in the 40 areas were as given in table 17.5.1.

TABLE 17.5.1
NUMBERS OF DISEASED PLANTS (OUT OF 9) IN EACH OF 40 AREAS

2	5	1	1	1	7	0	0	3	2	3	0	0	0	7	0	4	1	2	6
0	0	1	4	5	0	1	4	2	6	0	2	4	1	7	3	5	0	3	6

Grand total = 99

The standard deviation of this sample is 2.331. Since the *proportions* of diseased plants in the 40 areas are found by dividing the numbers in table 17.5.1 by 9, the standard deviation of the proportions is

$$s = \frac{2.331}{9} = 0.259$$

Hence, (assuming N large),

$$s_p = \frac{s}{\sqrt{n}} = \frac{0.259}{\sqrt{40}} = 0.041$$

For comparison, the result given by the binomial formula will be worked out. From the total in table 17.5.1, $p = 99/360 = 0.275$. The binomial formula is

$$s_p = \sqrt{\frac{pq}{360}} = \sqrt{\frac{(0.275)(0.725)}{360}} = 0.024,$$

giving an overly optimistic notion of the precision of p.

Frequently, the clusters are not all of the same size. This happens when the sampling units are areas of land that contain different numbers of the plants that are being classified. Let m_i be the number of elements that are classified in the ith unit, and a_i the number that fall into a specified class, so that $p_i = a_i/m_i$. Then p, the over-all proportion in the sample, is $(\Sigma a_i)/(\Sigma m_i)$, where each sum is taken over the n cluster units.

The formula for s, the standard deviation of the p_i, uses the weighted mean square of the m_i:

$$s = \sqrt{\frac{1}{(n-1)} \Sigma \left\{ \left(\frac{m_i}{\bar{m}}\right)^2 (p_i - p)^2 \right\}}$$

where $\bar{m} = \Sigma m_i/n$ is the average size of cluster in the sample. This formula is an approximation, no correct expression for s being known in usable form. As before, we have

$$s_p = \frac{s}{\sqrt{n}}\sqrt{(1 - \phi)}$$

For computing purposes, s is better expressed as

$$s = \frac{1}{\bar{m}}\sqrt{\frac{1}{(n-1)} \left\{ \Sigma a_i^2 - 2p\Sigma a_i m_i + p^2\Sigma m_i^2 \right\}}$$

The sums of squares Σa_i^2, Σm_i^2 and the sum of products $\Sigma a_i m_i$ are calculated without the usual corrections for the mean. The same value of s is obtained whether the corrections for the mean are applied or not, but it saves time not to apply them.

EXAMPLE 17.5.1—If a sample of 4 from the 16 townships of a county has a standard deviation 45, show that the standard error of the mean is 19.5.

EXAMPLE 17.5.2—In the example presented in section 17.2 we had $N = 6$, $n = 3$, and the values for the 6 members of the population were 1, 2, 4, 6, 7, and 16. The formula for the true standard error of the estimated population total is

$$\sigma_{N\hat{y}} = \frac{N\sigma}{\sqrt{n}}\sqrt{\left(1 - \frac{n}{N}\right)}$$

Verify that this formula agrees with the result, 13.2, which we found by writing down all possible samples.

EXAMPLE 17.5.3—A simple random sample of size 100 is taken in order to estimate some proportion (e.g., the proportion of males) whose value in the population is
close to $\frac{1}{2}$. Work out the standard error of the sample proportion p when the size of
the population is (i) 200, (ii) 500, (iii) 1,000, (iv) 10,000, (v) 100,000. Note how little
the standard error changes for N greater than 1,000.

EXAMPLE 17.5.4—Show that the coefficient of variation of the sample mean is
the same as that of the estimated population total.

EXAMPLE 17.5.5—In simple random sampling for attributes, show that the
standard error of p, for given N and n, is greatest when p is 50%, but that the coefficient
of variation of p is largest when p is very small.

17.6—Size of sample. At an early stage in the design of a sample, the
question "How large a sample do I need?" must be considered. Although
a precise answer may not be easy to find, for reasons that will appear,
there is a rational method of attack on the problem.

Clearly, we want to avoid making the sample so small that the estimate is too inaccurate to be useful. Equally, we want to avoid taking a
sample that is too large, in that the estimate is more accurate than we
require. Consequently, the first step is to decide how large an error we
can tolerate in the estimate. This demands careful thinking about the
use to be made of the estimate and about the consequences of a sizeable
error. The figure finally reached may be to some extent arbitrary, yet
after some thought samplers often find themselves less hesitant about
naming a figure than they expected to be.

The next step is to express the allowable error in terms of confidence
limits. Suppose that L is the allowable error in the sample mean, and
that we are willing to take a 5% chance that the error will exceed L. In
other words, we want to be reasonably certain that the error will not exceed L. Remembering that the 95% confidence limits computed from a
sample mean are

$$\bar{y} \pm \frac{2\sigma}{\sqrt{n}},$$

we may put

$$L = \frac{2\sigma}{\sqrt{n}}$$

This gives, for the required sample size,

$$n = \frac{4\sigma^2}{L^2}$$

In order to use this relation, we must have an estimate of the population
standard deviation, σ. Often a good guess can be made from the results
of previous samplings of this population or of other similar populations.
For example, an experimental sample was taken in 1938 to estimate the
yield per acre of wheat in certain districts of North Dakota (7). For a
sample of 222 fields, the variance of the yield per acre from field to
field was $s^2 = 90.3$ (in bushels²). How many fields are indicated if we

wish to estimate the true mean yield within ± 1 bushel, with a 5% risk that the error will exceed 1 bushel? Then

$$n = \frac{4\sigma^2}{L^2} = \frac{4(90.3)}{(1)^2} = 361 \text{ fields}$$

If this estimate were being used to plan a sample in some later year, it would be regarded as tentative, since the variance between fields might change from year to year.

In the absence of data from an earlier sample, we can sometimes estimate σ from a knowledge of the range of variation in the population, using the relation between the range and σ as described in section 2.2. If the range is known in a population of size greater than 500, we may take (range)/6 as a crude estimate of σ.

If the quantity to be estimated is a binomial proportion, the allowable error, L, for 95% confidence probability is

$$L = 2\sqrt{\frac{pq}{n}}$$

The sample size required to attain a given limit of error, L, is therefore

$$n = \frac{4pq}{L^2}$$

In this formula, p, q, and L may be expressed either as proportions or as percentages, provided that they are all expressed in the same units. The result necessitates an advance estimate of p. If p is likely to lie between 35% and 65%, the advance estimate can be quite rough, since the product pq varies little for p lying between these limits. If, however, p is near zero or 100%, accurate determination of n requires a close guess about the value of p.

We have ignored the finite population correction in the formulas presented in this section. This is satisfactory for the majority of applications. If the computed value of n is found to be more than 10% of the population size, N, a revised value n' which takes proper account of the correction is obtained from the relation

$$n' = \frac{n}{1 + \phi}$$

For example, casual inspection of a batch of 480 seedlings indicates that about 15% are diseased. Suppose we wish to know the size of sample needed to determine p, the per cent diseased, to within ± 5%, apart from a 1-in-20 chance. The formula gives

$$n = \frac{4(15)(85)}{(25)} = 204 \text{ seedlings}$$

At this point we might decide that it would be as quick to classify every seedling as to plan a sample that is a substantial part of the whole batch. If we decide on sampling, we make a revised estimate, n', as

$$n' = \frac{n}{1 + \phi} = \frac{204}{1 + \dfrac{204}{480}} = 143$$

The formulas presented in this section are appropriate to simple random sampling. If some other sampling method is to be used, the general principles for the determination of n remain the same, but the formula for the confidence limits, and hence the formula connecting L with n, will change. Formulas applicable to more complex methods of sampling can be obtained in books devoted to the subject, e.g., (2, 4, 11). In practice, the formulas in this section are frequently used to provide a preliminary notion of the value of n, even if simple random sampling is not intended to be used. The values of n may be revised later if the proposed method of sampling is markedly different in precision from simple random sampling.

When more than one variable is to be studied, the value of n is first estimated separately for each of the most important variables. If these values do not differ by much, it may be feasible to use the largest of the n's. If the n's differ greatly, one method is to use the largest n, but to measure certain items on only a sub-sample of the original sample, e.g., on 200 sampling units out of 1,000. In other situations, great disparity in the n's is an indication that the investigation must be split into two or more separate surveys.

EXAMPLE 17.6.1—A simple random sample of houses is to be taken to estimate the percentage of houses that are unoccupied. The estimate is desired to be correct to within ± 1%, with 95% confidence. One advance estimate is that the percentage of unoccupied houses will be about 6%; another is that it will be about 4%. What sizes of sample are required on these two forecasts? What size would you recommend?

EXAMPLE 17.6.2—The total number of rats in the residential part of a large city is to be estimated with an error of not more than 20%, apart from a 1-in-20 chance. In a previous survey, the mean number of rats per city block was 9 and the sample standard deviation was 19 (the distribution is extremely skew). Show that a simple random sample of around 450 blocks should suffice.

EXAMPLE 17.6.3—West (12) quotes the following data for 556 full-time farms in Seneca County, New York.

	Mean	Standard Deviation Per Farm
Acres in corn	8.8	9.0
Acres in small grains	42.0	39.5
Acres in hay	27.9	26.9

If a coefficient of variation of up to 5% can be tolerated, show that a random sample of about 240 farms is required to estimate the total acreage of each crop in the 556 farms with this degree of precision. (Note that the finite population correction must be used.) This example illustrates a result that has been reached by several different investigators; with small farm populations such as counties, a substantial part of the whole population must be sampled in order to obtain accurate estimates.

17.7—Systematic sampling. In order to draw a 10% sample from a list of 730 cards, we might select a random number between 1 and 10, say 3, and pick every 10th card thereafter; i.e., the cards numbered 3, 13, 23, and so on, ending with the card numbered 723. A sample of this kind is known as a *systematic sample*, since the choice of its first member, 3, determines the whole sample.

Systematic sampling has two advantages over simple random sampling. It is easier to draw, since only one random number is required, and it distributes the sample more evenly over the listed population. For this reason systematic sampling often gives more accurate results than simple random sampling. Sometimes the increase in accuracy is large. In routine sampling, systematic selection has become a popular technique.

There are two potential disadvantages. If the population contains a periodic type of variation, and if the interval between successive units in the systematic sample happens to coincide with the wave length (or a multiple of it) we may obtain a sample that is badly biased. To cite extreme instances, a systematic sample of the houses in a city might contain far too many, or too few, corner houses; a systematic sample from a book of names might contain too many, or too few, names listed first on a page, who might be predominantly males, or heads of households, or persons of importance. A systematic sample of the plants in a field might have the selected plants at the same positions along every row. These situations can be avoided by being on the lookout for them and either using some other method of sampling or selecting a new random number frequently. In field sampling, we could select a new random number in each row. Consequently, it is well to know something about the nature of the variability in the population before deciding to use systematic sampling.

The second disadvantage is that from the results of a systematic sample there is no reliable method of estimating the standard error of the sample mean. Textbooks on sampling give various formulas for $s_{\bar{y}}$ that may be tried: each formula is valid for a certain type of population, but a formula can be used with confidence only if we have evidence that the population is of the type to which the formula applies. However, systematic sampling often is a part of a more complex sampling plan in which it is possible to obtain unbiased estimates of the sampling errors.

17.8—Stratified sampling. There are three steps in stratified sampling:

(1) The population is divided into a number of parts, called *strata*.

(2) A sample is drawn independently in each part.

(3) As an estimate of the population mean, we use

$$\bar{y}_{st} = \frac{\Sigma N_h \bar{y}_h}{N},$$

where $\mathcal{N}_h$ is the total number of sampling units in the hth stratum, $\bar{y}_h$ is the sample mean in the hth stratum and $\mathcal{N} = \Sigma\mathcal{N}_h$ is the size of the population. Note that we must know the values of the $\mathcal{N}_h$ (i.e., the sizes of the strata) in order to compute this estimate.

There are several reasons why stratification is commonly employed in sampling plans. It can be shown that differences between the strata means in the population do not contribute to the sampling error of the estimate $\bar{y}_{st}$. In other words, the sampling error of $\bar{y}_{st}$ arises solely from variations among sampling units that are in the same stratum. If we can form strata so that a heterogeneous population is divided into parts each of which is fairly homogeneous, we may expect a gain in precision over simple random sampling. In taking 24 soil or crop samples from a rectangular field, we might divide the field into 12 compact plots, and draw 2 samples at random from each plot. Since a small piece of land is usually more homogeneous than a large piece, this stratification will probably bring about an increase in precision, although experience indicates that in this application the increase will be modest rather than spectacular. To estimate total wheat acreage from a sample of farms, we might stratify by size of farm, using any information available for this purpose. In this type of application the gain in precision is frequently large.

In stratified sampling, we can choose the size of sample that is to be taken from any stratum. This freedom of choice gives us scope to do an efficient job of allocating resources to the sampling within strata. In some applications, this is the principal reason for the gain in precision from stratification. Further, when different parts of the population present different problems of listing and sampling, stratification enables these problems to be handled separately. For this reason, hotels and large apartment houses are frequently placed in a separate stratum in a sample of the inhabitants of a city.

We now consider the estimate from stratified sampling and its standard error. For the population mean, the estimate given above may be written

$$\bar{y}_{st} = \frac{1}{\mathcal{N}}\Sigma\mathcal{N}_h\bar{y}_h = \Sigma W_h\bar{y}_h,$$

where $W_h = \mathcal{N}_h/\mathcal{N}$ is the relative *weight* attached to the stratum. Note that the sample means, $\bar{y}_h$, in the respective strata are weighted by the sizes, $\mathcal{N}_h$, of the strata. The arithmetic mean of the sample observations is no longer the estimate except in one important special case. This occurs with *proportional allocation*, when we sample the same fraction from every stratum. With proportional allocation,

$$\frac{n_1}{\mathcal{N}_1} = \frac{n_2}{\mathcal{N}_2} = \ldots = \frac{n_h}{\mathcal{N}_h} = \frac{n}{\mathcal{N}}$$

It follows that

$$W_h = \frac{N_h}{N} = \frac{n_h}{n}$$

Hence

$$\bar{y}_{st} = \Sigma W_h \bar{y}_h = \frac{\Sigma n_h \bar{y}_h}{n} = \bar{y},$$

since $\Sigma n_h \bar{y}_h$ is the total of all observations in the sample. With proportional allocation, we are saved the trouble of computing a weighted mean: the sample is *self-weighting*.

The standard error of $\bar{y}_{st}$ is

$$s(\bar{y}_{st}) = \sqrt{\Sigma W_h^2 \frac{s_h^2}{n_h}}$$

where s_h^2 is the sample variance in the hth stratum, i.e.,

$$s_h^2 = \frac{\Sigma (Y_{hi} - \bar{y}_h)^2}{n_h - 1},$$

where Y_{hi} is the ith member of the sample from the hth stratum. The formula for the standard error of $\bar{y}_{st}$ assumes that simple random sampling is used within each stratum and does not include the finite population correction. If the sampling fractions ϕ_h exceed 10% in some of the strata, we use the more general formula

$$s(\bar{y}_{st}) = \sqrt{\Sigma \frac{W_h^2 s_h^2}{n_h}(1 - \phi_h)}$$

With proportional allocation the sampling fractions ϕ_h are all equal and the general formula simplifies to

$$s(\bar{y}_{st}) = \sqrt{\frac{\Sigma W_h s_h^2}{n}} \cdot \sqrt{(1 - \phi)}$$

If, further, the population variances are the same in all strata (a reasonable assumption in some agricultural applications), we obtain an additional simplification to

$$s(\bar{y}_{st}) = \frac{s_w}{\sqrt{n}}\sqrt{(1 - \phi)}$$

This result is the same as that for the standard error of the mean with simple random sampling, except that s_w, the pooled standard deviation *within strata*, appears in place of the sample standard deviation, s. In practice, s_w is computed from an analysis of variance of the data.

As an example of proportional allocation, the data in table 17.8.1 come from an early investigation by Clapham (1) of the feasibility of sampling for estimating the yields of small cereal plots. A rectangular plot of barley was divided transversely into 3 equal strata. Ten samples, each

TABLE 17.8.1
ANALYSIS OF VARIANCE OF A STRATIFIED RANDOM SAMPLE
Wheat grain yields — gm. per meter

Source of Variation	Degrees of Freedom	Sum of Squares	Mean Square
Total	29	8,564	295.3
Between strata	2	2,073	1,036.5
Within strata	27	6,491	240.4

a meter length of a single row, were chosen by simple random sampling from each stratum. The problem is to compute the standard error of the estimated mean yield per meter of row.

In this example, $s_w = \sqrt{240.4} = 15.5$, and $n = 30$. Since the sample is only a negligible part of the whole plot, n/N is negligible and

$$s(\bar{y}_{st}) = \frac{s_w}{\sqrt{n}} = \frac{15.5}{\sqrt{30}} = 2.83 \text{ gm.}$$

How effective was the stratification? From the analysis of variance it is seen that the mean square between strata is over four times as large as that within strata. This is an indication of real differences in level of yield from stratum to stratum. It is possible to go further, and estimate what the standard error of the mean would have been if simple random sampling had been used without any stratification. With simple random sampling, the corresponding formula for the standard error of the mean is

$$s(\bar{y}) = \frac{s}{\sqrt{n}},$$

where s is the ordinary sample standard deviation. In the sample under discussion, s is $\sqrt{295.3}$ (from the *total* mean square in table 17.8.1). Hence, as an estimate of the standard error of the mean under simple random sampling, we might take

$$s(\bar{y}) = \frac{\sqrt{295.3}}{\sqrt{30}} = 3.14 \text{ gm.,}$$

as compared with 2.83 gms. for stratified random sampling. Stratification has reduced the standard error by about 10%.

This comparison is not quite correct, for the rather subtle reason that the value of s was calculated from the results of a stratified sample and not, as it should have been, from the results of a simple random sample. Valid methods of making the comparison are described for all types of stratified sampling in (2). The approximate method which we used is close enough when the stratification is proportional and at least 10 sampling units are drawn from every stratum.

17.9—Choice of sample sizes in the individual strata.   It is sometimes thought that in stratified sampling we should sample the same fraction from every stratum; i.e., we should make n_h/N_h the same in all strata, using proportional allocation. A more thorough analysis of the problem shows, however, that the *optimum* allocation is to take n_h proportional to $N_h\sigma_h/\sqrt{c_h}$, where σ_h is the standard deviation of the sampling units in the hth stratum, and c_h is the cost of sampling per unit in the hth stratum. This method of allocation gives the smallest standard error of the estimated mean $\bar{y}_{st}$ for a given total cost of taking the sample. The rule tells us to take a larger sample, as compared with proportional allocation, in a stratum that is unusually variable (σ_h large), and a smaller sample in a stratum where sampling is unusually expensive (c_h large). Looked at in this way, the rule is consistent with common sense, as statistical rules always are if we think about them carefully. The rule reduces to proportional allocation when the standard deviation and the cost per unit are the same in all strata.

In order to apply the rule, advance estimates are needed both of the relative standard deviations and of the relative costs in different strata. These estimates need not be highly accurate; rough estimates often give results satisfactorily near to the optimum allocation. When a population is sampled repeatedly, the estimates can be obtained from the results of previous samplings. Even when a population is sampled for the first time, it is sometimes obvious that some strata are much more accessible to sampling than others. In this event it usually pays to hazard a guess about the differences in costs. In other situations we are unable to predict with any confidence which strata will be more variable or more costly, or we think that any such differences will be small. Proportional allocation is then used.

There is one common situation in which disproportionate sampling pays large dividends. This occurs when the principal variable that is being measured has a highly skewed or asymmetrical distribution. Usually, such populations contain a few sampling units that have large values for this variable and many units that have small values. Variables that are related to the sizes of economic institutions are often of this type, for instance, the total sales of grocery stores, the number of patients per hospital, the amounts of butter produced by creameries, and (for certain types of farming) farm income.

With populations of this type, stratification by size of institution is usually highly effective, and the optimum allocation is likely to be much better than proportional allocation. As an illustration, table 17.9.1 shows data for the number of students per institution in a population consisting of the 1,019 senior colleges and universities in the United States. The data, which apply mostly to the 1952–53 academic year, might be used as background information for planning a sample designed to give a quick estimate of total registration in some future year. The institutions are arranged in 4 strata according to size.

TABLE 17.9.1

DATA FOR TOTAL REGISTRATIONS PER SENIOR COLLEGE OR UNIVERSITY,
ARRANGED IN 4 STRATA

Stratum: Number of Students Per Institution	Number of Institutions N_h	Total Registration for the Stratum	Mean Per Institution $\bar{Y}_h$	Standard Deviation Per Institution σ_h
Less than 1,000	661	292,671	443	236
1,000–3,000	205	345,302	1,684	625
3,000–10,000	122	672,728	5,514	2,008
Over 10,000	31	573,693	18,506	10,023
Total	1,019	1,884,394		

Note that the 31 largest universities, about 3% in number, have 30% of the students, while the smallest group, which contains 65% of the institutions, contributes only 15% of the students. Note also that the within-stratum standard deviation, σ_h, increases rapidly with increasing size of institution.

Table 17.9.2 shows the calculations needed for choosing the optimum sample sizes within strata. We are assuming equal costs per unit within all strata. The products, $N_h\sigma_h$, are formed and added over all strata. Then the relative sample sizes, $N_h\sigma_h/\Sigma N_h\sigma_h$, are computed. These ratios, when multiplied by the intended sample size n, give the sample sizes in the individual strata.

TABLE 17.9.2

CALCULATIONS FOR OBTAINING THE OPTIMUM SAMPLE SIZES IN INDIVIDUAL STRATA

Stratum: Number of Students	Number of Institutions N_h	$N_h\sigma_h$	Relative Sample Sizes $N_h\sigma_h/\Sigma N_h\sigma_h$	Actual Sample Sizes	Sampling Rate (%)
Less than 1,000	661	155,996	.1857	65	10
1,000–3,000	205	128,125	.1526	53	26
3,000–10,000	122	244,976	.2917	101	83
Over 10,000	31	310,713	.3700	31	100
Total	1,019	839,810	1.0000	250	

As a consequence of the large standard deviation in the stratum with the largest universities, the rule requires 37% of the sample to be taken from this stratum. Suppose we are aiming at a total sample size of 250. The rule then calls for (.3700)(250) or 92 universities from this stratum although the stratum contains only 31 universities in all!. With highly skewed populations, as here, it is sometimes found that the optimum allocation demands 100% sampling, or even more than this, of the largest institutions. When this situation occurs, the best procedure is to take 100% of the "large" stratum, and employ the rule to distribute the remainder of the sample over the other strata. Following this procedure, we include in the sample all 31 largest institutions, leaving 219 to be distributed among the first 3 strata. In the first stratum, the size of sample is

$$219 \left\{ \frac{.1858}{.1858 + .1526 + .2917} \right\} = 65$$

The allocations, shown in the second column from the right of table 17.9.2, call for over 80% sampling in the second largest group of institutions (101 out of 122), but only a 10% sample of the small colleges. In practice we might decide, for administrative convenience, to take a 100% sample in the second largest group.

It is worth while to ask: Is the optimun allocation much superior to proportional allocation? If not, there is little value in going to the extra trouble of calculating and using the optimun allocation. We cannot, of course, answer this question for a future sample that is not yet taken, but we can compare the two methods of allocation for the 1952–53 registrations for which we have data. To do this, we use the data in tables 17.9.1 and 17.9.2 and the standard error formulas in section 17.8 to compute the standard errors of the estimated population totals by the two methods. These standard errors are found to be 26,000 for the optimum allocation, as against 107,000 for proportional allocation. If simple random sampling had been used, with no stratification, a similar calculation shows that the corresponding standard error would have been 216,000. The reduction in the standard error due to stratification, and the additional reduction due to the optimum allocation, are both striking. In an actual future sampling based on this stratification, the gains in precision would presumably be slightly less than these figures indicate.

17.10—Stratified sampling for attributes. If an attribute is being sampled, the estimate appropriate to stratified sampling is

$$p_{st} = \Sigma W_h p_h$$

where p_h is the sample proportion in stratum h and $W_h = N_h/N$ is the stratum weight. To find the standard error of p_{st} we substitute $p_h q_h$ for s_h^2 in the formulas previously given in section 17.8.

As an example, consider a sample of 692 families in Iowa to determine, among other things, how many had vegetable gardens in 1943. The families were arranged in 3 strata—urban, rural non-farm, and farm—because it was anticipated that the three groups might show differences in the frequency and size of vegetable gardens. The data are given in table 17.10.1.

TABLE 17.10.1
NUMBERS OF VEGETABLE GARDENS AMONG IOWA FAMILIES, ARRANGED IN 3 STRATA

Stratum	Number of Families N_h	Weight W_h	Number in Sample n_h	Number With Gardens	Percentage With Gardens
Urban	312,393	0.445	300	218	72.7
Rural non-farm	161,077	0.230	155	147	94.8
Farm	228,354	0.325	237	229	96.6
	701,824	1.000	692	594	

The numbers of families were taken from the 1940 census. The sample was allotted roughly in proportion to the number of families per stratum, a sample of 1 per 1,000 being aimed at.

The weighted mean percentage of Iowa families having gardens was estimated as

$$\Sigma W_h p_h = (0.445)(72.7) + (0.230)(94.8) + (0.325)(96.6) = 85.6\%$$

This is practically the same as the sample mean percentage, 594/692 or 85.8%, because allocation was so close to proportional.

For the variance of the estimated mean, we have

$$\Sigma W_h^2 p_h q_h / n_h = (0.445)^2 (72.7)(27.3)/300 + \text{etc.} = 1.62$$

The standard error, then, is 1.27%.

With a sample of this size, the estimated mean will be approximately normally distributed: the confidence limits may be set as

$$85.6 \pm (2)(1.27) : 83.1\% \text{ and } 88.1\%$$

For the optimum choice of the sample sizes within strata, we should take n_h proportional to $N_h \sqrt{p_h q_h / c_h}$. If the cost of sampling is about the same in all strata, as is true in many surveys, this implies that the fraction sampled, n_h/N_h, should be proportional to $\sqrt{p_h q_h}$. Now the quantity $\sqrt{pq}$ changes relatively little as p ranges from 25% to 75%. Consequently, proportional allocation is often highly efficient in stratified sampling for attributes. The optimum allocation will produce a substantial reduction in the standard error, as compared with proportional allocation, only when some of the p_h are close to zero or 100%, or when there are differential costs.

The example on vegetable gardens departs from the strict principles of stratified sampling in that the strata sizes and weights were not known exactly, being obtained from census data three years previously. Errors in the strata weights reduce the gain in precision from stratification and make the standard formulas inapplicable. It is believed that in this

example these disturbances are of negligible importance.   Discussions of
stratification when there are errors in the weights are given in (2) and (10).

EXAMPLE 17.10.1—The purpose of this example is to compare simple random
sampling and systematic sampling of a small population.   The following data are the
weights of maize (in 10-gm. units) for 40 successive hills lying in a single row: 104, 38,
105, 86, 63, 32, 47, 0, 80, 42, 37, 48, 85, 66, 110, 0, 73, 65, 101, 47, 0, 36, 16, 33, 22,
32, 33, 0, 35, 82, 37, 45, 30, 76, 45, 70, 70, 63, 83, 34.   To save you time, the population standard deviation is given as 30.1.   Compute the standard deviation of the mean
of a simple random sample of 4 hills.   A systematic sample of 4 hills can be taken by
choosing a random number between 1 and 10 and taking every 10th hill thereafter.
Find the mean $\bar{y}_{sv}$ for each of the 10 possible systematic samples and compute the
standard deviation of these means about the true mean $\bar{Y}$ of the population.   Note
that the formula is

$$\sigma(\bar{y}_{sv}) = \sqrt{\frac{\Sigma(\bar{y}_{sv} - \bar{Y})^2}{10}}$$

Verify that the standard deviation of the estimate is about 8% lower with systematic
sampling.   To what do you think this difference is due?

EXAMPLE 17.10.2—In the example of stratified sampling given in section 17.2
show that the estimate which we used for the population total was $N\bar{y}_{st}$.   From the
general formula for the variance of $\bar{y}_{st}$, verify that the variance of the estimated population total is 48.75, as found directly in section 17.2.   (Note that stratum I makes no
contribution to this variance because $n_h = N_h$ in that stratum.)

EXAMPLE 17.10.3—In stratified sampling for attributes, the optimum sample
distribution, with equal costs per unit in all strata, follows from taking n_h proportional to $N_h\sqrt{p_hq_h}$.   It follows that the actual value of n_h is

$$n_h = n\left\{\frac{N_h\sqrt{p_hq_h}}{\Sigma N_h\sqrt{p_hq_h}}\right\}$$

In the Iowa vegetable garden survey, suppose that the p_h values found in the sample
can be assumed to be the same as those in the population.   Show that the optimum
sample distribution gives sample sizes of 445, 115, and 132 in the respective strata, and
that the standard error of the estimated percentage with gardens would then be 1.17%,
as compared with 1.27% in the sample itself.

EXAMPLE 17.10.4—For the population of colleges and universities discussed in
section 17.9 it was stated that a stratified sample of 250 institutions, with proportional
allocation, would have a standard error of 107,000 for the estimated total registration
in all 1,019 institutions.   Verify this statement from the data in table 17.9.1.   Note that
the standard error of the estimated population total, with proportional allocation, is

$$N\sqrt{\frac{\Sigma W_h\sigma_h^2}{n}}\sqrt{\left(1 - \frac{n}{N}\right)}$$

17.11—Sampling in two stages.   Consider the following miscellaneous group of sampling problems: (1) a study of the vitamin A content of
butter produced by creameries, (2) a study of the protein content of wheat
in the wheat fields in an area, (3) a study of red blood cell counts in a
population of men aged 20–30, (4) a study of insect infestation of the leaves
of the trees in an orchard, and (5) a study of the number of defective
teeth in third-grade children in the schools of a large city.   What do these
investigations have in common?   First, in each study an appropriate sampling unit suggests itself naturally—the creamery, the field of wheat, the
individual man, the tree, and the school.   Secondly, and this is the important point, in each study the chosen sampling units can be *sub-sampled*
instead of being measured completely. Indeed, sub-sampling is essential

in the first three studies.   No one is going to allow us to take *all* the butter produced by a creamery in order to determine vitamin A content, or all the wheat in a field for the protein determination, or all the blood in a man in order to make a complete count of his red cells.   In the insect infestation study, it might be feasible, although tedious, to examine *all* leaves on any selected tree.   If the insect distribution is spotty, however, we would probably decide to take only a small sample of leaves from any selected tree in order to include more trees.   In the dental study we could take all the third-grade children in any selected school or we could cover a larger sample of schools by examining only a sample of children from the third grade in each selected school.

This type of sampling is called *sampling in two stages,* or sometimes *sub-sampling.*   The first stage is the selection of a sample of *primary sampling units*—the creameries, wheat fields, and so on.   The second stage is the taking of a *sub-sample* of *second-stage units,* or *sub-units,* from each selected primary unit.

As illustrated by these examples, the two-stage method is sometimes the only practicable way in which the sampling can be done.   Even when there is a choice between sub-sampling the units and measuring them completely, two-stage sampling gives the sampler greater scope, since he can choose both the size of the sample of primary units and the size of the sample that is taken from a primary unit.   In some applications an important advantage of two-stage sampling is that it facilitates the problem of listing the population.   Often it is relatively easy to obtain a list of the primary units, but difficult or expensive to list all the sub-units.   To list the trees in an orchard and draw a sample of them is usually simple, but the problem of making a random selection of the leaves on a tree may be very troublesome.   With two-stage sampling this problem is faced only for those trees that are in the sample.   No complete listing of all leaves in the orchard is required.

In the discussion of two-stage sampling we shall assume that the primary units are of approximately the same size.   A simple random sample of n_1 primary units is drawn, and the same number n_2 of sub-units is selected from each primary unit in the sample.   The estimated standard error of the sample mean $\bar{y}$ *per sub-unit* is then given by the formula

$$s_{\bar{y}} = \frac{1}{\sqrt{n_1}} \sqrt{\frac{\Sigma(\bar{y}_i - \bar{y})^2}{n_1 - 1}},$$

where $\bar{y}_i$ is the mean per sub-unit in the ith primary unit.   This formula does not include the finite population correction, but is reliable enough provided that the sample contains less than 10% of all primary units.   Note that the formula makes no use of the individual observations on the sub-units, but only of the primary unit means $\bar{y}_i$.   If the sub-samples are taken for a chemical analysis, a common practice is to composite the sub-sample and make one chemical determination for each primary unit.   With data of this kind we can still calculate $s_{\bar{y}}$.

In section 10.12 you learned about the "components of variance" technique, and applied it to a problem in two-stage sampling. The data were concentrations of calcium in turnip greens, 4 determinations being made for each of 3 leaves. The leaf can be regarded as the primary sampling unit, and the individual determination as the sub-unit. By applying the components of variance technique, you were able to see how the variance of the sample mean was affected by variation between determinations on the same leaf and by variation from leaf to leaf. You could also predict how the variance of the sample mean would change with different numbers of leaves and of determinations per leaf in the experiment.

Since this technique is of wide utility in two-stage sampling, we shall repeat some of the results. The observation on any sub-unit is considered to be the sum of two independent terms. One term, associated with the primary unit, has the same value for all second-stage units in the primary unit, and varies from one primary unit to another with variance σ_1^2. The second term, which serves to measure differences between second-stage units, varies independently from one sub-unit to another with variance σ_2^2. Suppose that a sample consists of n_1 primary units, from each of which n_2 sub-units are drawn. Then the sample as a whole contains n_1 independent values of the first term, whereas it contains $n_1 n_2$ independent values of the second term. Hence the variance of the sample mean $\bar{y}$ per sub-unit is

$$\sigma_{\bar{y}}^2 = \frac{\sigma_1^2}{n_1} + \frac{\sigma_2^2}{n_1 n_2}$$

The two components of variance, σ_1^2 and σ_2^2, can be estimated from the analysis of variance of a two-stage sample that has been taken. Table 17.11.1 gives the analysis of variance for a study by Immer (6), whose object was to develop a sampling technique for the determination of the sugar percentage in field experiments on sugar beets. Ten beets were chosen from each of 100 plots in a uniformity trial, the plots being the primary units. The sugar percentage was obtained separately for each beet. In order to simulate conditions in field experiments, the Between Plots mean square was computed as the mean square between plots within blocks of 5 plots. This mean square gives the experimental error variance that would apply in a randomized blocks experiment with 5 treatments.

TABLE 17.11.1

ANALYSIS OF VARIANCE OF SUGAR PERCENTAGE OF BEETS (ON A SINGLE-BEET BASIS)

Source of Variation	Degrees of Freedom	Mean Square	Parameters Estimated
Between plots (primary units)	80	2.9254	$\sigma_2^2 + 10\,\sigma_1^2$
Between beets (sub-units) within plots	900	2.1374	σ_2^2

The estimate of σ_1^2, the Between Plots component of variance, is

$$s_1^2 = \frac{2.9254 - 2.1374}{10} = 0.0788,$$

the divisor 10 being the number of beets (sub-units) taken per plot. As an estimate of σ_2^2, the within-plots component, we have

$$s_2^2 = 2.1374$$

Hence, if a new experiment is to consist of n_1 replications, with n_2 beets sampled from each plot, the predicted variance of a treatment mean is

$$s_{\bar{y}}^2 = \frac{0.0788}{n_1} + \frac{2.1374}{n_1 n_2}$$

We shall illustrate a few of the questions that can be answered from these data. How accurate are the treatment means in an experiment with 6 replications and 5 beets per plot? For this experiment we would expect

$$s_{\bar{y}} = \sqrt{\left(\frac{0.0788}{6} + \frac{2.1374}{30}\right)} = 0.29\%$$

Since the sample is large, the sugar percentage figure for a treatment mean would be correct to within $\pm$ (2) (0.29) or 0.58%, with 95% confidence.

If the standard error of a treatment mean is not to exceed 0.2%, what combinations of n_1 and n_2 are allowable? We must have

$$\frac{0.0788}{n_1} + \frac{2.1374}{n_1 n_2} = (0.2)^2 = 0.04$$

Since n_1 and n_2 are whole numbers, they will not satisfy this equation exactly: we must make sure that the left side of the equation does not exceed 0.04. You can verify that with 4 replications ($n_1 = 4$), there must be 27 beets per plot; with 8 replications, 9 beets per plot are sufficient; and with 10 replications, 7 beets per plot. As one would expect, the intensity of sub-sampling decreases as the intensity of sampling is increased. The total size of sample also decreases from 108 beets when $n_1 = 4$ to 70 beets when $n_1 = 10$.

17.12—The allocation of resources in two-stage sampling. The last example illustrates a general property of two-stage samples. The same standard error can be attained for the sample mean by using various combinations of values of n_1 and n_2. Which of these choices is the best? The answer depends, naturally, on the cost of adding an extra primary unit to the sample (in this case an extra replication) relative to that of adding an extra sub-unit in each primary unit (in this case an extra beet in each plot). Similarly, in the turnip greens example (section 10.12) the best sampling plan depends on the relative costs of taking an extra leaf and of making an extra determination per leaf. Obviously, if it is cheap to add primary units to the sample but expensive to add sub-units, the most economical plan will be to have many primary units and few (perhaps only one) sub-units per primary unit. For a general solution to this problem, however, we require a more exact formulation of the costs of various alternative plans.

The nature of the costs will vary from one application to another. In many sub-sampling studies the cost of the sample (apart from fixed overhead costs) can be approximated by a relation of the form

$$\text{cost} = c_1 n_1 + c_2 n_1 n_2$$

The factor c_1 is the average cost per primary unit of those elements of cost that depend solely on the number of primary units and not on the amount of sub-sampling. Thus in the sugar beet example c_1 includes the average cost of land and field operations required to produce one plot. If it were intended in actual experiments to composite all beets from a plot and make a *single* sugar determination for each plot, c_1 would also include the cost of making this determination. The factor c_2, on the other hand, is the average cost per sub-unit of those constituents of cost that are directly proportional to the total number of sub-units. This includes the average cost per beet of locating and picking the sample of beets. The cost of grinding and mixing the beets prior to the sugar analysis is also assigned to c_2, assuming that this cost is roughly proportional to the number of beets taken.

If advance estimates of these constituents of cost are made from some preliminary study, an efficient job of selecting the best amounts of sampling and sub-sampling can be done. The problem may be posed in two different ways. In some studies we specify the desired variance V for the sample mean, and would like to attain this as cheaply as possible. In other applications the total cost C that must not be exceeded is imposed upon us, and we want to get as small a value of V as we can for this outlay. These two problems have basically the same solution. In either case we want to minimize the product

$$VC = \left(\frac{s_1^2}{n_1} + \frac{s_2^2}{n_1 n_2} \right) (c_1 n_1 + c_2 n_1 n_2)$$

Upon expansion, this becomes

$$VC = (s_1^2 c_1 + s_2^2 c_2) + n_2 s_1^2 c_2 + \frac{s_2^2 c_1}{n_2}$$

It can be shown that this expression has its smallest value when

$$n_2 = \sqrt{\frac{c_1 s_2^2}{c_2 s_1^2}}$$

This result gives an estimate of the best number of sub-units (beets) per primary unit (plot). The value of n_1 is found by solving either the cost equation or the variance equation for n_1, depending on whether cost or variance has been preassigned.

In the sugar beet example we had $s_1{}^2 = 0.0788$, $s_2{}^2 = 2.1374$, from which

$$n_2 = \sqrt{\frac{2.1374}{0.0788}}\sqrt{\frac{c_1}{c_2}} = 5.2\sqrt{\frac{c_1}{c_2}}$$

In this study, cost data were not reported, although it is likely that c_1, the cost per plot, would be much greater than c_2. Evidently a fairly large number of beets per plot would be advisable. In practice, factors other than the sugar percentage determinations must also be taken into account in deciding on the number of replications in sugar beet experiments.

In the turnip greens example (section 10.12), n_1 is the number of leaves and n_2 the number of determinations of calcium concentration per leaf. Also, in the present notation,

$$s_1{}^2 = s_t{}^2 = 0.0724$$
$$s_2{}^2 = s^2 = 0.0066$$

Hence the most economical number of determinations per leaf is estimated to be

$$n_2 = \sqrt{\frac{c_1 s_2{}^2}{c_2 s_1{}^2}} = \sqrt{\frac{0.0066}{0.0724}}\sqrt{\frac{c_1}{c_2}} = 0.30\sqrt{\frac{c_1}{c_2}}$$

In practice, n_2 must be a whole number, and the smallest value it can have is 1. This equation shows that $n_2 = 1$, i.e., one determination per leaf, unless c_1 is many times greater than c_2. Actually, since c_2 includes the cost of the chemical determinations, it is likely to be greater than c_1. The relatively large variation among leaves and the cost considerations both point to the choice of one determination per leaf. This example also illustrates that a choice of n_2 can often be made from the equation even when information about relative costs is not too definite. This is because the equation often leads to the same value of n_2 for a wide range of ratios of c_1 to c_2. The values of n_2 are subject to sampling errors; for a discussion, see (2).

In section 10.14 you studied an example of *three-stage sampling* of turnip green plants The first stage was represented by plants, the second by leaves within plants, and the third by determinations within a leaf. In the notation of the present section, the variance of the sample mean is

$$s_{\bar{y}}{}^2 = \frac{s_1{}^2}{n_1} + \frac{s_2{}^2}{n_1 n_2} + \frac{s_3{}^2}{n_1 n_2 n_3}$$

Copying the equation given in section 10.14, we have

$$s_{\bar{y}}{}^2 = \frac{0.3652}{n_1} + \frac{0.1610}{n_1 n_2} + \frac{0.0067}{n_1 n_2 n_3}$$

To find the most economical values of n_1, n_2, and n_3, we set up a cost equation of the form

$$\text{cost} = c_1 n_1 + c_2 n_1 n_2 + c_3 n_1 n_2 n_3$$

and proceed to minimize the product of the variance and the cost as before. The solutions are

$$n_2 = \sqrt{\frac{c_1 s_2^2}{c_2 s_1^2}}. \qquad\qquad n_3 = \sqrt{\frac{c_2 s_3^2}{c_3 s_2^2}},$$

while n_1 is found by solving either the cost or the variance equation. Note that the formula for n_2 is the same in three-stage as in two-stage sampling, and that the formula for n_3 is the natural extension of that for n_2. Putting in the numerical values of the variance components, we obtain

$$n_2 = \sqrt{\frac{c_1(0.1610)}{c_2(0.3652)}} = 0.66\sqrt{\frac{c_1}{c_2}}, \quad n_3 = \sqrt{\frac{c_2(0.0067)}{c_3(0.1610)}} = 0.20\sqrt{\frac{c_2}{c_3}}$$

Since the computed value of n_3 would be less than 1 for any likely value of c_2/c_3, more than one determination per leaf is uneconomical. The optimum number n_2 of leaves per plant depends on the ratio c_1/c_2. This will vary with the conditions of experimentation. If many plants are being grown for some other purpose, so that there are always ample numbers available for sampling, c_1 includes only the extra costs involved in collecting a sample from many plants instead of a few plants. In this event the optimum n_2 might also turn out to be 1. If the cost of growing extra plants is to be included in c_1, the optimum n_2 might be higher than 1.

The device of sub-sampling is widely used in crop, soil, and ecological studies which cover an extensive geographic area; in field experiments where chemical determinations or estimates of soil and crop insects are made; and in laboratory investigations. Research workers who have not previously taken stock of the components of variation and the cost factors that apply to their data may find it rewarding to do so, particularly when some steps in the process are expensive.

If the primary units differ substantially in size from one another, some modification is advisable in the methods discussed here. One technique that has proved efficient is to select primary units with probabilities proportional to their sizes, and to select the same number of sub-sampling units from each primary unit in the sample. For a discussion of the various available methods, see (4, 11, 13).

EXAMPLE 17.12.1—This is the analysis of variance, on a single sub-sample basis, for wheat yield and percentage of protein from data collected in a wheat sampling survey in Kansas in 1939.

Source of Variation	Yield (bushels per acre)		Protein (%)	
	Degrees of Freedom	Mean Square	Degrees of Freedom	Mean Square
Fields	659	434.52	659	21.388
Samples within fields	660	67.54	609	2.870

Two sub-samples were taken at random from each of 660 fields. Calculate the components of variance for yield. Ans. $s_1^2 = 183.49$, $s_2^2 = 67.54$.

EXAMPLE 17.12.2—For yield, estimate the variance of the sample mean for samples consisting of (i) 1 sub-sample from each of 800 fields, (ii) 2 sub-samples from each of 400 fields, (iii) 8 samples from each of 100 fields. Ans. (i) 0.313, (ii) 0.543, (iii) 1.919.

EXAMPLE 17.12.3—With 2 sub-samples per field, it is desired to take enough fields so that the standard error of the mean yield will be not more than $\frac{1}{2}$ bushel, and at the same time the standard error of the mean protein percentage will be not more than $\frac{1}{8}$%. How many fields are required? Ans. About 870.

EXAMPLE 17.12.4—Suppose that it takes on the average 1 man-hour to locate and pace a field that is to be sampled. A single protein determination is to be made on the bulked sub-samples from any field. The cost of a determination is equivalent to 1 man-hour. It takes 15 minutes to locate, cut, and tie a sub-sample. From these data and the analysis of variance for protein percentage (example 17.12.1), compute the variance-cost product, VC, for each value of n_2 from 1 to 5. What is the most economical number of sub-samples per field? Ans. 2. How much more does it cost, for the same V, if 4 sub-samples per field are used? Ans. 12%.

17.13—Ratio and regression estimates. The *ratio estimate* is a different way of estimating population totals (or means) that is useful in a number of sampling problems. Suppose that you have taken a sample in order to estimate the population total of a variable, Y, and that a complete count of the population was made on some previous occasion. Let X denote the value of the variable on the previous occasion. You might then compute the ratio

$$R = \frac{\Sigma Y}{\Sigma X},$$

where the sums are taken over the sample. This ratio is an estimate of the present level of the variate relative to that on the previous occasion. On multiplying the ratio by the known population total on the previous occasion (i.e., by the population total of X), you obtain the ratio estimate of the population total of Y. Clearly, if the relative change is about the same on all sampling units, the ratio R will be accurate and the estimate of the population total will be a good one.

The ratio estimate can also be used when X is some other kind of supplementary variable. The conditions for a successful application of this estimate are that the ratio Y/X should be relatively constant over the population and that the population total of X should be known. Consider an estimate of the total amount of a crop, just after harvest, made from a sample of farms in some region. For each farm in the sample we record the total yield, Y, and the total acreage, X, of that crop. In this case the ratio, $R = \Sigma Y/\Sigma X$, is the sample estimate of the mean yield per acre. This is multiplied by the total acreage of the crop in the region, which would have to be known accurately from some other source. This estimate will be precise if the mean yield per acre varies little from farm to farm.

The estimated standard error of the ratio estimate $\hat{Y}_R$ of the population total from a simple random sample of size n is, approximately,

$$s(\hat{Y}_R) = N\sqrt{\frac{\Sigma(Y - RX)^2}{n(n-1)}}$$

The ratio estimate is not always more precise than the simpler estimate $N\bar{y}$ (number of units in population times sample mean). It has been shown that the ratio estimate is more precise only if ρ, the correlation coefficient between Y and X, exceeds $C_X/2C_Y$, where the C's are the coefficients of variation. Consequently, ratio estimates must not be used indiscriminately, although in appropriate circumstances they produce large gains in precision.

Sometimes the purpose of the sampling is to estimate a ratio, e.g., ratio of dry weight to total weight or ratio of clean wool to total wool. The estimated standard error of the estimate is then

$$s(R) = \frac{1}{\bar{X}}\sqrt{\frac{\Sigma(Y - RX)^2}{n(n-1)}}$$

This formula has already been given (in a different notation) at the end of section 17.5, where the estimation of proportions from cluster sampling was discussed.

In chapter 6 the linear regression,

$$\hat{Y} = a + bx,$$

was discussed. With an auxiliary variable, X, you may find that when you plot Y against X from the sample data, the points appear to lie close to a straight line, but the line does not go through the origin. This implies that the ratio Y/X is not constant over the sample. As pointed out in section 6.14, it is then advisable to use a linear regression estimate instead of the ratio estimate. For the population total of Y, the linear regression estimate is

$$N\hat{Y} = N\{\bar{y} + b(\bar{X} - \bar{x})\},$$

where $\bar{X}$ is the population mean of X. The term inside the brackets is the sample mean, $\bar{y}$, adjusted for regression. To see this, suppose that you have taken a sample in which $\bar{y} = 2.35$, $\bar{x} = 1.70$, $\bar{X} = 1.92$, $b = +0.4$. Your first estimate of the population mean would be $\bar{y} = 2.35$. But in the sample the mean value of X is too low by an amount $(1.92 - 1.70) = 0.22$. Further, the value of b tells you that unit increase in X is accompanied, on the average, by $+0.4$ unit increase in Y. Hence, to correct for the low value of the mean of X, you adjust the sample mean for the regression on x, i.e.,

$$2.35 + (+0.4)(0.22) = 2.44 = \bar{y} + b(\bar{X} - \bar{x})$$

To estimate the population total, this value is multiplied by N, the number of sampling units in the population.

The standard error of the estimated population total is, approximately,

$$s_{N\hat{y}} = N s_{y \cdot x} \sqrt{\left(\frac{1}{n} + \frac{(\bar{X} - \bar{x})^2}{\Sigma x^2} \right)}$$

If a finite population correction is required in the standard error formulas presented in this section, insert the factor $\sqrt{(1 - \phi)}$. In finite populations the ratio and regression estimates are both slightly biased, but the bias is seldom important in practice.

17.14—Sampling methods in biology. The purpose of this section is to indicate the types of sampling plan currently used in a few of the important applications of sampling in biology.

In making crop and livestock estimates and in studies of farm management or farm economics, we have to deal with a population of farms. In the United States, reliable lists of farms are seldom available. As we have mentioned, a common practice is to take as the sampling unit an area of land, demarcated by easily recognizable boundaries, and containing on the average about 6 farms. Before sampling begins, these areas are marked out on large-scale maps. For national agricultural surveys, maps of this kind have been prepared covering the whole of the country, in what is known as the Master Sample of Agriculture. The areas can be classified into strata in various ways, depending on the purpose of the survey. In some surveys it pays to assemble also a special list of large farms, which are placed in a separate stratum.

For surveys of a region that is not too large, such as a state, the sampling plan involves a stratified sample of these areas. Within a stratum, areas may be selected at random, although frequently a systematic sample is used for convenience. In any area so drawn, the data are obtained for all farms that lie in this area. For national surveys the plan is more complex, multi-stage sampling being employed so as to cut down travel costs and facilitate supervision.

In forestry surveys to estimate the volume of timber of the principal types and age-classes, the first step is to delineate the forest land, either from maps or from aerial photographs. The forest region is then divided into strata according to the type of trees and the density and size of the trees.   This can be done fairly successfully by a careful stereoscopic inspection of recent aerial photographs; results from older photographs tend to be disappointing.   Within each stratum, sample plots are marked out and are measured in detail on the ground by field crews.   Some problems on which research has been done concern the amount of resources that should be devoted to the construction of the strata, relative to that devoted to measurement of sample plots, the best size and shape of plot, and the advantages of optimum versus proportional allocation of the numbers of sample plots per stratum (5).

Studies of wildlife present many complexities, because the members of the population—fish, birds, beavers, field mice—do not stay in the same place and are sometimes difficult to find at all.   Generally speaking, strata can be set up if there is some information about the distribution and habitat of the species in question.   Area sampling units that constitute a random or systematic sample of each stratum can be marked out.

The difficulty is to count the numbers in these areas.   In certain cases a reasonably complete count can be made.   With deer, a field crew may search each sample area thoroughly; fish can be caught by nets or by giving them an electric shock.   Very large animals such as buffalo or antelope can be counted from an airplane in some types of terrain.   One method, used for game birds, is to traverse certain routes by car at the same time of day and the same time of year in successive years, recording the numbers of birds seen.   This approach does not pretend to take a random sample of a stratum, but relies on an assumption that the numbers of birds seen in successive years will be roughly proportional to the total abundances of birds in those years.

With species that cannot be seen easily, various trapping methods are in use.   Sometimes it is possible to catch over 50% of all the animals in a sample area by repeated trapping.   By noting the rate of decline in the catch per trap on successive occasions, one can attempt to estimate the number of animals that have escaped capture and thus make a correction for them.   Where only a relatively small proportion of a large population can be caught, specimens that are caught may be identified by a mark or tag and then released.   An estimate of the size of the population can then be made from the proportion of recaptures found in the traps on a subsequent occasion.   Both of these methods depend on various assumptions about the population—in particular, the assumption that all animals are equally likely to be caught.   There is good reason to believe that this is not so, but little is known at present about the extent of the biases that these methods involve.   Finally, in cases where any visual count is extremely difficult, biologists have tried to construct indices of abundance from indirect signs, such as nests, dens, tracks, or droppings. A general account of methods for wildlife estimation has been given by Scattergood (9).

For the sake of conciseness, some of the difficult practical problems in biological applications of sampling have been omitted. Moreover, sampling methods are subject to continuous evolution, since biologists are working steadily towards improved techniques. The methods described here will doubtless be modified as knowledge accumulates and new aids to sampling are discovered.

REFERENCES

1. A. R. Clapham. Journal of Agricultural Science, 19:214 (1929).

2. W. G. Cochran. Sampling Techniques. John Wiley & Sons, New York (1953)

3. W. Edwards Deming. Some Theory of Sampling. John Wiley & Sons, New York (1950).

4. M. H. Hansen, W. N. Hurwitz, and W. G. Madow. Sample Survey Methods and Theory. John Wiley & Sons, New York (1953).

5. A. A. Hasel Chapter 19 in Statistics in Mathematics and Biology. Iowa State University Press (1954).

6. F. R. Immer. Journal of Agricultural Research, 44:633 (1932).

7. A. J. King, D. E. McCarty, and M. McPeak. U. S. Department of Agriculture Technical Bulletin 814 (1942).

8. J. A. Rigney and J. Fielding Reed. Journal of the American Society of Agronomy' 39:26 (1947).

9. L. W. Scattergood. Chapter 20 in Statistics in Mathematics and Biology. Iowa State University Press (1954).

10. F. F. Stephan. Journal of Marketing, 6:38 (1941).

11. P. V. Sukhatme. Sampling Theory of Surveys With Applications. Iowa State University Press (1954).

12. Q. M. West. Mimeographed Report, Cornell University Agricultural Experiment Station (1951).

13. F. Yates. Sampling Methods for Censuses and Surveys. Charles Griffin, London (1954).

Index of Mathematical Tables

(All entries are by page numbers)

General Index
and Index of Symbols

THE AUTHOR

As author, teacher, and researcher, Dr. George W. Snedecor has high stature in the field of statistics and experimental research. His writings have been numerous and helpful in making statistical methods usable, and his professional honors have been wide and varied.

He holds an honorary Doctor of Science Degree from Iowa State University, also one from North Carolina State College. He is a Fellow and past President of the American Statistical Association; a Fellow, AAAS, and Institute of Mathematical Statistics, and is an Honorary Fellow, British Royal Statistical Society.

At the Journal's inception in 1945, Dr. Snedecor became editor of the Queries Section of *Biometrics*.

He initiated the first formal courses in biological statistics at Iowa State University, and founded and directed the Statistical Laboratory there for 14 years. Under his direction, the study of statistics grew until it was established as a separate university department in 1947. Dr. Snedecor retired from his administrative duties in that year, but continued his teaching contributions unabated. A portion of each year since has been spent as professor of statistics at Iowa State. He has also held visiting professorships and consultantships at other colleges and universities under assignments arranged by the North Carolina Institute of Statistics. Under Rockefeller Foundation sponsorship, he spent five months as consultant in agricultural statistics in Sao Paulo, Brazil. He has served as consultant, Human Factors Division, U. S. Navy Electronics Laboratory, San Diego.

Besides this book, which is now in complete translation in at least three foreign languages, he wrote CORRELATION AND MACHINE CALCULATION, with Henry A. Wallace (1925); ANALYSIS OF VARIANCE AND COVARIANCE (1934) and EVERYDAY STATISTICS, FACTS AND FALLACIES (1950), as well as numerous research bulletins and scientific journal articles.